◎Harden's

in association with

RÉMY MARTIN
FINE CHAMPAGNE COGNAC

UK
Restaurants
2005

D0418642

RÉMY MARTIN
FINE CHAMPAGNE COGNAC

A TASTE FOR THE FINEST

Founded in 1724, Rémy Martin is renowned for producing Fine Champagne Cognacs of the highest quality. Whether you are enjoying a cocktail or long drink based on Rémy Martin Grand Cru, a glass of the world's favourite VSOP, the smooth and spicy XO Excellence, the elegant Extra or the ultimate cognac, Louis XIII de Rémy Martin, each cognac in the range reflects the brand's philosophy of excellence.

Rémy Martin has a passion for creating exceptional taste experiences. The very best grapes are selected from the finest growing areas of Cognac and expensive traditional methods of production are still used to ensure that Rémy Martin cognacs remain the finest in the world.

In the same way, talent, passion, good judgement of taste and a dedication to creating excellence are the characteristics of a truly outstanding chef. These are the qualities that we reward in the third year of the Restaurant Rémy awards.

PAYING TRIBUTE TO EXCELLENCE

Rémy Martin launched the Restaurant Rémy awards in 2003
to recognise the emerging talent of the UK restaurant
scene – those restaurants that were receiving consistently
excellent reviews from British diners and setting new
exacting standards for the whole industry.

These awards are won not through the ratings of restaurant
critics or panels of judges but through the reviews of ordinary
people who love dining out and understand what it takes to
make that experience a real pleasure.

In our third year we are once more delighted to announce that
twenty establishments from all over the UK have achieved an
outstanding level of excellence and have been awarded a
2005 Restaurant Rémy award.

The diversity of cuisine amongst this year's winners provides an
insight into the rapidly changing landscape of the UK restaurant
scene and demonstrates the exciting and vibrant choice on
offer. In each and every winner we are witness to a commitment
to delivering excellence and new taste experiences to our tables.

WINNER OF THE 2005 EXCELLENCE AWARD

ANTHONY'S – LEEDS

For some diners, roast duck served with olive oil chocolate bonbons followed by peanut ice cream with artichoke caramel might seem like a daunting prospect for the tastebuds. However, at Anthony's, culinary conventions are being overturned and an exciting illustration of the future of fine dining for foodies in the North is starting to emerge. For this reason, Anthony's has earned this year's Excellence Award in the 2005 Restaurant Rémy Awards.

Anthony Flinn builds on the 'molecular gastronomy' philosophy of Heston Blumenthal (a Restaurant Rémy Award winner in 2003) of The Fat Duck and the legendary Ferran Adria of El Bulli in Montjoi, near Barcelona (possibly the most talked-about restaurant in the world) by combining kitchen traditions with scientific principles. Savoury and sweet are unexpectedly paired, experimented with and new dining experiences are enjoyed.

Molecular gastronomy may sound like an inaccessible and high-brow concept for food snobs – but here, you will be pleasantly surprised. The restaurant is a relaxed and elegant family affair and the cuisine is simple, uncluttered, expertly executed and unpretentious.

At just 24 years of age, Anthony has a wisdom and imagination beyond his years. Since leaving Huddersfield Catering College eight years ago, he has worked his way up a ladder of Michelin-starred restaurants in Britain and Spain. In fact he is the only English chef ever to have been on the payroll at El Bulli – and his experience shows. Despite earning numerous plaudits for his gastronomic wizardry, Flinn has a more modest interpretation of fine dining. In his opinion, a good meal is quite simply something that makes diners smile.

REMY MARTIN
FINE CHAMPAGNE COGNAC

2005 RESTAURANT RÉMY AWARDS
REGIONAL WINNERS

THE EBB – PADSTOW

A sleek and smart family-run seafood restaurant, The Ebb combines eclectic cooking with a true sense of hospitality. Peter and Karen Scott's delicious menu and commitment to local and seasonal produce mark the restaurant out amongst locals and critics alike.

THAI TERRACE – GUILDFORD, SURREY

The hot ticket for sophisticated business lunches and packed every weekend since it opened in late 2003, the Thai Terrace is a chic, sophisticated restaurant renowned for its attention to detail and great-value food and wine list. With terrace views over Guildford, this is the perfect restaurant for summertime eating.

THE SEAFOOD RESTAURANT
ST. ANDREWS, SCOTLAND

"A heart-stopping piece of modern architecture", this cubic restaurant sits in an idyllic location with panoramic views of the bay at St. Andrews. The setting is matched with imaginative and decadent dishes created by accomplished chef, Craig Millar.

2005 Restaurant Rémy Awards
Regional Winners

Due South – Brighton

Due South is located in one of the Brighton arches cut below the promenade road, a delightful site right down at beach level. With a devotion to locally sourced, seasonal and organic raw materials, guests can enjoy a delicious breakfast, lunch or dinner accompanied by uninterrupted sea views, whether inside the restaurant or on the open-air terrace.

The London Carriage Works
Liverpool

Opened in December 2003, The London Carriage Works already looks likely to set a new benchmark for Liverpool dining. With a theme very loosely based on New York's Gramercy Tavern, it melds friendly service and fine dining with food best described as 'modern international', taking its influences from all over the world.

Cedar Tree – Manchester

Chef patron Hassan Chahine comes from a long line of Lebanese cooks and it's his simple, understated cooking that has started to make serious waves around Manchester. Guests are treated to an intimate and relaxed dining experience, with a fantastically good value and authentic menu that changes seasonally.

RÉMY MARTIN
FINE CHAMPAGNE COGNAC

2005 RESTAURANT RÉMY AWARDS
REGIONAL WINNERS

THE FALCON
POULTON, GLOUCESTERSHIRE

Owners Robin Couling and Jeremy Lockley set out to "inject a bit of city style into the often dull traditional country pub". Within a year, The Falcon has started to win praise for its simple, full-flavoured and hearty dishes presented in a traditional English pub setting.

THE CRAB – CHIEVELEY, BERKSHIRE

David Barnard made quite a name for the Crab & Lobster at Asenby in North Yorkshire, and – after an unsuccessful attempt at early retirement – has popped up again at this intriguingly revamped inn in the heart of racing country. As ever, seafood is a key characteristic of the menu, which is presided over – as it was up North – by chef David Moss.

JESSICA'S – EDGBASTON, BIRMINGHAM

Since opening, Jessica's has – at last! – put Birmingham on the map for fine dining in the UK. Co-proprietor and chef Glynn Purnell combines strong yet complementary flavours, to create a menu that fuses classical French cuisine with the best of modern British food.

2005 Restaurant Rémy Awards
London Winners

Patterson's – Mayfair

"Immune to fads and fashion", Patterson's is a family-run Mayfair restaurant which, intentionally or not, celebrates the Auld Alliance: former Garrick Club head chef Raymond Patterson sources many of his ingredients from this native Scotland, but the cuisine is essentially traditional French.

1880 – South Kensington

Tucked away in an opulent new hotel in a quiet corner of South Kensington, this decadent restaurant offers head chef Andrew Turner's grazing menu concept. Diners – who often find it difficult to choose from the tantalising à la carte selection – are offered the menu in miniature, allowing them to enjoy between five and ten courses.

Morgan M – Islington

Morgan Meunier's creative touch is evident in everything – from his modern French menu to the paintings on the wall – at this Islington eatery. Formerly chef at the Admiralty and the celebrated Monsieur Max, Morgan prides himself on the delicate flavours he creates from luxury French ingredients.

2005 Restaurant Rémy Awards
London Winners

Yauatcha – Soho

The latest brainchild of Alan Yau – founder of Wagamama, Hakkasan and Busaba Eathai – this is London's first specialist dim sum restaurant, serving some two dozen varieties of these delicious Chinese snacks in the basement restaurant, whose exotic décor (by Christian Liaigre) includes a tropical fish tank bar.

Lanes – City of London

A much-appreciated addition to the local dining scene, tucked away near Liverpool Street station. Marco Pierre White-trained owners James Robertson and Hamish Smith and chef Hayden Smith serve a City-sensible lunching menu, spiced up with flashes of New Zealand influence. "Simple things done well" is the motto here.

Frontline Club – Paddington

This club restaurant (also open to the public) aims to provide "unobtrusive but exceptional hospitality, and fine food at affordable prices", with service overseen by ex-Ivy maître d' Fernando Peire. The cuisine is essentially contemporary British, but dishes from North Africa and the Middle East add a touch of spice.

The Coach & Horses – Clerkenwell

Friendly service and good-value food and wine menus have already made this buzzing gastropub popular with locals. What's perhaps so appealing is that it offers all the basic 'pub' virtues, but adds a sprinkling of totally contemporary finesse.

2005 RESTAURANT RÉMY AWARDS
LONDON WINNERS

LATIUM – FITZROVIA

Maurizio Morelli and Antonio Cerilli have married their respective talents in Italian cookery and wine to create this already celebrated addition to the Fitzrovia restaurant scene. The kitchen combines perfectly balanced flavours with beautiful presentation, in a simple modern setting. Reasonably priced set menus help diners control their budgets too.

LE CERCLE – CHELSEA

Combining the culinary sophistication of its famous sister restaurant Club Gascon with an intriguing and glamorous modern setting, Le Cercle has been an immediate hit with the Chelsea beau monde. The kitchen, headed by Thierry Beyris, offers a grazing menu with dishes from all the regions of France.

NOTTING HILL BRASSERIE
NOTTING HILL

The team behind the Notting Hill Brasserie pride themselves on having created a real neighbourhood restaurant, which offers modern French cuisine from ingredients in season. Live jazz and blues nightly adds a mellow twist.

THE SECRETS OF EXCELLENCE

At Rémy Martin we insist on an adherence to the most exacting production methods in our pursuit of the finest taste.

Cognac, as distinct from any other brandy, can only be produced in the specified area surrounding the town of Cognac, consisting of six crus (growing areas). At Rémy Martin we select only grapes from the two finest crus of the Cognac region – Grande Champagne and Petite Champagne – to ensure the aromatic richness of our cognacs. The combination of grapes from these two prestigious areas leads to the name Fine Champagne Cognac.

Our wines undergo a double distillation on the lees in small copper stills to impart a wonderful texture and rich complexity of flavour.

Rémy Martin uses only the highest quality Limousin oak barrels for the long ageing of its eaux-de-vie, ensuring the natural, warm amber colour and delicious aromas and flavours that characterise Rémy Martin cognacs.

The skill of the Cellar Master is central to the crafting of our sublime spirit. The Cellar Master's art lies in combining selected eaux-de-vie to create the perfect combination of aromas and flavours in each of our cognacs.

Our passion for excellence ensures that you can enjoy the quality of Rémy Martin however you choose to drink your cognac – served neat, over ice, mixed in a long drink or savoured with food.

RÉMY MARTIN
FINE CHAMPAGNE COGNAC

DISCOVER PERFECT TASTE
MATCHES WITH RÉMY MARTIN

While you sample the diversity of cuisine represented by the twenty Restaurant Rémy award winners, why not embark on a journey of new taste discoveries with Rémy Martin Fine Champagne Cognacs?

Cognac has an incredible flexibility beyond traditional digestifs and the smooth texture and richness of flavours and aromas found in the Rémy Martin range can create some stunning partnerships with food. Instead of waiting for a glass to cap the end of a great meal, why not enjoy a serving as you dine?

FROZEN RÉMY MARTIN VSOP
WITH SMOKED SALMON

When served frozen, Rémy Martin takes on a wonderful viscosity and intensity of flavours, which complement the oily texture and gentle acidity of smoked fish. Enjoy Rémy Martin VSOP's spicy vanilla flavours and aromatic hints of violet and apricot – a perfect match for smoked salmon.

DISCOVER PERFECT TASTE MATCHES WITH RÉMY MARTIN

RÉMY MARTIN XO EXCELLENCE WITH DARK CHOCOLATE

Indulge yourself by partnering a glass of Rémy Martin XO Excellence with your favourite chocolate dessert. The cognac's rich velvet texture and aromatic notes of candied fruit, fig and juicy prunes marry beautifully with the bitter-sweet flavours of rich, dark chocolate.

RÉMY MARTIN VSOP WITH ROQUEFORT CHEESE

Strongly flavoured and aromatic cheeses like Roquefort can overwhelm a wine, but the depth of flavour and texture found in Rémy Martin VSOP make this the ideal accompaniment. A glass served at room temperature can really enhance Roquefort's indulgent creamy texture and intense flavours.

Publisher's announcements

Harden's on your PDA

Harden's London Restaurants and *Harden's UK Restaurants* are now available for use on your PDA (both Pocket PC and Palm OS).

Other Harden's titles

Hotel Guide
London Restaurants
London Party & Corporate Event Guide
Theatregoers' Handbook
Good Cheap Eats in London
London Bars & Pubs
London Baby Book
UK Baby Book – NEW
London for Free

The ideal corporate gift

Harden's London Restaurants, Harden's UK Restaurants, Harden's Hotel Guide and *Harden's London Bars & Pubs* are available in a range of specially customised corporate gift formats.
For further information on any of the above, please call (020) 7839 4763 or visit www.hardens.com.

© Harden's Limited 2004

ISBN 1-873721-68-4

British Library Cataloguing-in-Publication data:
a catalogue record for this book is available from the British Library.

Printed and bound in Italy by Legoprint

Research Manager: Frances Gill

Harden's Limited
14 Buckingham Street
London WC2N 6DF

The views expressed in the editorial section of this guide are exclusively those of Harden's Limited.

The contents of this book are believed correct at the time of printing. Nevertheless, the publisher can accept no responsibility for errors or changes in or omissions from the details given.

CONTENTS

RATINGS & PRICES

We see little point in traditional rating systems, which generally tell you nothing more than that expensive restaurants are 'better' than cheap ones because they use costlier ingredients and attempt more ambitious dishes. You probably knew that already. Our system assumes that, as prices rise, so do diners' expectations.

Prices and ratings are shown as follows:

£ Price
The cost of a three-course *dinner* for one person.
We include half a bottle of house wine, coffee and service (or a 10% tip if there is no service charge).

Food
The following symbols indicate that, ***in comparison with other restaurants in the same price-bracket***, the cooking at the establishment is:

★★ **Exceptional**
★   **Very good**

We also have a category for places which attract a notably high proportion of adverse comment:

X   **Disappointing**

Ambience
Restaurants which provide a setting which is very charming, stylish or 'buzzy' are indicated as follows:

 𝔸 **Particularly atmospheric**

Restaurant Rémy awards

 A bold Restaurant Rémy symbol signifies this year's winners – see front colour section

 A faded Restaurant Rémy symbol signifies a former year's winner

Small print

Telephone number – *All numbers in the London section are (020) numbers. Dublin numbers are shown for dialling within the Republic (the international code for which is + 353).*

Sample dishes – *these dishes exemplify the style of cooking at a particular establishment. They are merely samples - it is unlikeley that these specific dishes will be available at the time of your visit.*

Details – *the following information is given where relevant:*

Directions – *to help you find the establishment.*

Website – *if applicable.*

Last orders time – *at dinner (Sun may be up to 90 mins earlier).*

Opening hours – *unless otherwise stated, restaurants are open for lunch and dinner seven days a week.*

Credit and debit cards – *unless otherwise stated, Mastercard, Visa, Amex and Switch are accepted.*

Dress – *where appropriate, the management's preferences concerning patrons' dress are given.*

Smoking – *cigarette smoking restrictions are noted. Pipe or cigar smokers should always check ahead.*

Children – *if we know of a specified minimum age for children, we note this.*

Accommodation – *if an establishment has rooms, we list how many and the minimum price for a double.*

FROM THE EDITORS

To an extent we believe to be unique, this guide is written 'from the bottom up'. That is to say, its composition reflects the restaurants, pubs and cafés which people across the country – as represented by our diverse reporter base – talk about. It does not, therefore, concentrate on hotel restaurants (as does one of the major 'independent' guides whose publisher also does big business in paid-for hotel inspections). Nor does it 'overweight' European cuisines. Most restaurants in this country fall in the category usually called 'ethnic', but most guidebooks would lead you to think that such places are generally unworthy of serious commentary. It seems to us that this approach is positively wrong-headed in a country where the diversity of restaurant types is one of the most notable (and positive) features.

The effects of London's restaurant revolution of the '90s are now becoming apparent across the whole of the UK. Most major conurbations, for example, now have several ambitious restaurants good enough to be of note to visitors. The areas that are still truly 'culinary deserts' are becoming both smaller and more dispersed. Much as this is to be applauded, it does not make our task any easier, and we are keenly aware – as any honest publisher must acknowledge – that all guide books are imperfect. There will be deserving places missing, and opinions will be repeated that the passing of time has rendered redundant. However, we believe that our system – involving the careful processing of tens of thousands of reports – is the best available.

We are very grateful to each of our thousands of reporters, without whose input this guide could simply not have been written. Many of our reporters express views about a number of restaurants at some length, knowing full well that – given the concise format of the guide – we can seemingly never 'do justice' to their observations. We must assume that they do so in the confidence that the short – and we hope snappy – summaries we produce are as fair and as well-informed as possible. You, the reader, must judge – restaurant guides are not works of literature, and should be assessed on the basis of utility. This is a case where the proof of the pudding really is in the eating.

Given the growing scale of our task, we are particularly grateful for the continuing support we have received from Rémy Martin Fine Champagne Cognac in the publication of this guide. With their help, this is now well on the way to becoming the most comprehensive – as well as the most democratic and diverse – guide available to the restaurants of the UK.

All restaurant guides are the subject of continual revision. This is especially true when the restaurant scene is undergoing a period of rapid change, as at present. **Please help us to make the next edition even more comprehensive and accurate: sign up to join the survey by following the instructions overleaf.**

Richard Harden   **Peter Harden**

HOW THIS BOOK IS ORGANISED

This guide begins in *London*, which, in recognition of the scale and diversity of its restaurant scene, has an extensive introduction and indexes, as well as its own maps. Thereafter, the guide is organised strictly alphabetically, without regard to national divisions – Ballater, Beaumaris, Belfast and Birmingham appear together under 'B'.

For *cities and larger towns*, you should therefore be able to turn straight to the relevant section. Cities which have significant numbers of restaurants also have a brief introductory overview, as well as entries for the restaurants themselves.

In *less densely populated areas*, you will generally find it easiest to start with the map of the relevant area at the back of the book, which will guide you to the appropriate place names.

HOW THIS BOOK IS RESEARCHED

This book is the result of a research effort involving thousands of 'reporters'. These are 'ordinary' members of the public who share with us summary reviews of the best and the worst of their annual dining experiences. This year, some 7,000 people gave us approximately 80,000 reviews in total.

The density of the feedback on London (where many of the top places attract several hundred reviews each) is such that the ratings for the restaurants in the capital included in this edition are almost exclusively statistical in derivation. We have, as it happens, visited almost all the restaurants in the London section, anonymously, and at our own expense, but we use our personal experiences only to inform the standpoint from which to interpret the consensus opinion.

In the case of the more commented-upon restaurants away from the capital, we have adopted an approach very similar to London. In the case of less-visited provincial establishments, however, the interpretation of survey results owes as much to art as it does to science.

In our experience, smaller establishments are – for better or worse – generally quite consistent, and we have therefore felt able to place a relatively high level of confidence in a lower level of commentary. Conservatism on our part, however, may have led to some smaller places being underrated compared to their more visited peers.

HOW YOU CAN JOIN THE SURVEY

Register on our mailing list at www.hardens.com and you will be invited, in the spring of 2005, to participate in our next survey. **If you take part you will, on publication, receive a complimentary copy of *Harden's UK Restaurants 2006*.**

LONDON
INTRODUCTION
& SURVEY RESULTS

LONDON INTRODUCTION

How does London compare internationally?

London is not Paris, Rome or Madrid. As the capital of a country which, for at least two centuries, has had no particular reputation for its gastronomy, its attractions are rarely indigenous. By-and-large, only tourists look for 'English' restaurants.

Where London does score – and score magnificently – is in the range and quality it offers of everyone else's national styles of cooking. Always an entrepot, London is now a culinary melting pot, too: in terms of scale *and* variety, its only obvious competitor is New York.

Which is London's best restaurant?

However much we may speak of melting pots and diversity, when people talk about the very best cooking, they tend – rightly or wrongly – to mean the best French cooking. The capital's best Gallic restaurant is undoubtedly Chelsea's *Gordon Ramsay*, perhaps the only London restaurant whose cooking can be said to be notable on an international scale.

There is a very solid second tier. At the top of this, traditionalists would put *Le Gavroche* – London's longest-established grand French restaurant. Other contenders include two new kids on the block – *Tom Aikens* and *1880*. Perennials which perhaps attract less attention than their cooking deserves include the *Capital* (being given a new, fashionably retro look as we go to press) and *Aubergine*.

Stepping down a level, *Roussillon* – hidden away, but accessible, in Pimlico – is central London's 'secret' top-class French restaurant. For Gallic fish dishes, *Restaurant One-O-One* remains the capital's top place.

What's 'in' at the moment?

Rather unusually, the past year has seen not one but two would-be entrants to the 'in' hall of fame. *The Wolseley* certainly offers affordable glamour, but does its prominent location make it just too 'obvious'? Time will tell. Although it received much less advance hype, Mayfair's discreetly-located *Cipriani* – which had the advantages of siblings both in Venice and NYC – has immediately put itself on the map as *the* destination for those who aspire to join the private-jet set.

Some restaurants are always 'in'. *The Ivy* (if you can get a booking) and siblings *Le Caprice* and (more recently) *J Sheekey* are perennial 'can't-go-wrong' choices for pretty much any occasion.

For the fashion crowd, *Momo* is something of a Mecca. The same owner's year-old *Sketch*, however – a brave venture, verging on folly – may well have already enjoyed its 15 minutes of fame. Recent years have seen a welcome number of restaurants that are both fashionable *and* good, and which have achieved a consistently trendy status. It was *Nobu* which set the trend, but it now has a host of imitators, such as *Hakkasan*, *Zuma* and, more recently, *Taman gang* and *Roka*.

I'm not really fussed about fashionable scenes - where can I find a really good meal without spending the earth?

The Ivy, J Sheekey and *Le Caprice* are not that expensive, and if you want a bit of glamour plus a decent meal in the heart of town, this trio of establishments is hard to beat.

In Knightsbridge, *Racine* is now well-established. Though more remote, three places owned by Nigel Platts-Martin are top choices – *Chez Bruce* in Wandsworth, *La Trompette* in Chiswick and *The Glasshouse* in Kew. Do not be fooled by their suburban locations – these are serious restaurants! For sheer consistency, few restaurants match the amazing performance over the years of *Clarke's* in Kensington.

What if I want the best of British tradition?

Because Britain is a 'pub culture', there are very few traditional restaurants of note (and fewer which can be recommended). *The Dorchester Grill* is currently the grandest of the native flag bearers. The venerable *Rules* combines generally good cooking with charming period style. Nearby, the famous *Simpsons-in-the-Strand* has been too variable to recommend in recent years, but is now improving. The City preserves some extraordinary olde-worlde places such as *Sweetings* and *Simpson's Tavern*.

For foodies, Smithfield's *St John* has made quite a name for its exploration of traditional British cooking, including lots of offal: uncompromising food in an uncompromising setting. A new South Bank gastropub, the *Anchor & Hope* has instantly created a huge reputation by offering similar (but perhaps less 'threatening') fare, in a rather similar vein.

For afternoon tea, *The Wolseley* or *The Ritz* are best. Any light meal at *Fortnum's Fountain* is pleasant. For good old fish 'n' chips, the best chippies are *Toff's, Two Brothers* and *Faulkners* (none of which has a particularly convenient location).

Isn't London supposed to be a top place for curry?

London is the world's leading Indian restaurant city: curry is just part of a panoply of interest. At the top end, establishments such as *Chutney Mary, Vama, Zaika, Tamarind, The Cinnamon Club* and the new *Rasoi Vineet Bhatia* are 'pushing back the frontiers'.

To eat well on a budget, the capital's inexpensive Indians offer a great deal of choice in almost all areas. Such names as *New Tayaab* and the *Lahore Kebab House* stand out, but the number of interesting places is large. The very best Indian restaurants – except at the top price-level – are invariably not to be found in the West End. *Veeraswamy*, a smart modern establishment whose origins make it the UK's oldest 'curry house', is a handily-placed exception to the rule worth knowing about.

What are gastropubs?

In the past ten years, many pubs have re-invented themselves as informal restaurants. *The Eagle* was the original (1991), and is still often credited as the best. This year, however, has seen a stand-out newcomer in the form of the Rémy Award-winning *Anchor & Hope*. The trend goes from strength to strength. There are now almost no affluent suburbs which lack pubs serving food of a quality that even five years ago would have been inconceivable. Outlying examples include *The Ealing Park Tavern, The Earl Spencer* and *St Johns*. (As of last year, incidentally, even that most important London suburb, New York City, boasts an English gastropub!)

Generally the pub tradition of ordering at the bar is kept, but some of the grander establishments offer full table service and have really become restaurants in all but name (usually with a bar attached). Whether these are really pubs any more becomes a question of semantics. Examples include *The Drapers Arms and The Ebury*.

You said diverse: what about other cuisines?

London has good representations of most major cuisines (with the possible exception of Latin American ones, although, even here, there are some signs of life).

Italian cooking has long been a popular choice for relaxed neighbourhood dining, especially in the more affluent parts of town, and there is an enormous variety of trattorias and pizzerias. In recent years, some excellent high-level Italians have emerged and the idea of the generic 'Italian' restaurant will soon seem as passé as the '50s idea that olive oil was something you bought at the chemist.

Of the many traditional Chinese restaurants, the very best – with the exception of *Yming* and *Fung Shing* – are not in or near Chinatown. The biggest concentration of very good restaurants is, in fact, in Bayswater – including *Royal China* and *Mandarin Kitchen*. In the West End, *Hakkasan*, and its new sibling *Yauatcha,* are at long last bringing a revolutionary degree of style to the quality Chinese dining experience.

The capital was historically weak in other oriental cuisines, but there has been much activity in recent years, often combining quality Japanese (or Japanese fusion) cooking with innovative design. *Zuma,* its new offshoot *Roka* and *Sumosan* are good examples.

Thai cooking is also widespread but strongest in west London. Fulham's grand *Blue Elephant* has been amazingly consistent over the years, as has Notting Hill's *Churchill Arms* – an example of that curious London creation: Thai in a pub.

A major hit of recent years has been the cuisines of North Africa and the Eastern Mediterranean. These cuisines lend themselves well to good budget experiences – the *Tas* chain and *Haz* are among the good, less expensive places.

See the lists on pages 26 and 27 for the top exponents of each type of cuisine by nationality.

SURVEY – MOST MENTIONED

These are the restaurants which were most frequently mentioned by reporters. (Last year's position is given in brackets.) An asterisk* indicates the first appearance in the list of a recently-opened restaurant.

1   J Sheekey (1)
2   The Ivy (2)
3   Gordon Ramsay (3)
4   Hakkasan (6)
5   Nobu (4)
6   Oxo Tower (10)
7   Bleeding Heart (14)
8   Chez Bruce (5)
9   Gordon Ramsay at Claridge's (11)
10 Andrew Edmunds (12)

11   The Wolseley*
12   La Poule au Pot (7)
13   Locanda Locatelli (9)
14   Le Caprice (16)
15   Club Gascon (20)
16   Mirabelle (8)
17   Le Gavroche (22)
18   Sketch (39)
19= The Square (15)
19= The Cinnamon Club (17)

21   Pétrus (13)
22   La Trompette (19)
23   Blue Elephant (18)
24   Tom Aikens*
25   Coq d'Argent (27=)
26   Zuma (30=)
27   The River Café (23)
28= Savoy Grill (-)
28= Le Pont de la Tour (21)
30   Moro (26)

31   Racine (25)
32   Zafferano (27=)
33   Zaika (-)
34   Chutney Mary (34)
35   Connaught (Angela Hartnett) (29)
36   Busaba Eathai (35)
37   Café du Marché (30=)
38   Orrery (30=)
39   1 Lombard Street (33)
40   Bank (-)

LONDON – HIGHEST RATINGS

These are the restaurants which received the best average food ratings.

Where the most common types of cuisine are concerned, we present the results in two price-brackets. For less common cuisines, we list the top three, regardless of price.

The rankings presented below are calculated purely on the basis of average marks for food quality awarded in the survey. No adjustment is made for price (in contrast to the calculation of food (F) ratings which do take price into account). Consequently, a higher position in the rankings below, will not invariably be reflected by a higher food (F) grade.

British, Modern

£40 and over	*Under £40*
1 Chez Bruce	1 Earl Spencer
2 1880	2 The Havelock Tavern
3 Clarke's	3 The Anglesea Arms
4 Notting Hill Brasserie	4 Cotto
5 The Glasshouse	5 Lamberts

French

£40 and over	*Under £40*
1 Gordon Ramsay	1 Le Cercle
2 Capital Hotel	2 Les Associés
3 Aubergine	3 Lou Pescadou
4 Roussillon	4 Paul
5 Pied à Terre	5 Emile's

Italian/Mediterranean

£40 and over	*Under £40*
1 Assaggi	1 Pappa e Ciccia
2 Zafferano	2 Il Bordello
3 Quirinale	3 Aglio e Olio
4 Passione	4 The Red Pepper
5 Alloro	5 Latium

Indian

£40 and over	*Under £40*
1 Chutney Mary	1 Mirch Masala
2 Vama	2 New Tayyab
3 Zaika	3 Lahore Kebab House
4 Tamarind	4 Sarkhel's
5 The Cinnamon Club	5 Vijay

Chinese

£40 and over
1 Hakkasan
2 Ken Lo's Memories
3 Kai
4 Ken Lo's Memories W8
5 Mr Wing

Under £40
1 Hunan
2 Mandarin Kitchen
3 Yauatcha
4 Royal China
5 Jenny Lo's

Japanese

£40 and over
1 Tatsuso
2 Sumosan
3 Nobu
4 Zuma
5 Ubon

Under £40
1 Tsunami
2 Jin Kichi
3 Café Japan
4 Itsu
5 K10

British, Traditional
1 The Anchor & Hope
2 Savoy Grill
3 Connaught

Vegetarian
1 Blah! Blah! Blah!
2 The Gate
3 Manna

Burgers, etc
1 Fine Burger Co.
2 Gourmet Burger K'n
3 Hamburger Union

Pizza
1 Pappa e Ciccia
2 Pizza Metro
3 Eco

Fish & Chips
1 Toff's
2 Two Brothers
3 Faulkner's

Thai
1 Patara
2 Amaranth
3 Churchill Arms

Fusion
1 Nobu
2 Zuma
3 Ubon

Fish & Seafood
1 Rest. One-O-One
2 J Sheekey
3 Mandarin Kitchen

Greek
1 Vrisaki
2 The Real Greek
3 Lemonia

Spanish
1 Moro
2 Fino
3 Rebato's

Turkish
1 Haz
2 Gallipoli
3 Tas

Lebanese
1 Fairuz
2 Noura
2 Maroush

SURVEY – NOMINATIONS

Ranked by the number of reporters' votes.

Top gastronomic experience

1 Gordon Ramsay (1)
2 Chez Bruce (2)
3 Gordon Ramsay at Claridge's (3)
4 Tom Aikens*
5 Le Gavroche (10)
6 Nobu (4)
7 Club Gascon (-)
8 The Ivy (6)
9 La Trompette (9)
10 Locanda Locatelli (5)

Favourite

1 The Ivy (1)
2 Chez Bruce (2)
3 J Sheekey (5)
4 Le Caprice (4)
5 Gordon Ramsay (3)
6 La Trompette (10)
7 Hakkasan (8)
8 The Wolseley*
9 Andrew Edmunds (7)
10 Zuma (-)

Best for business

1 Coq d'Argent (3)
2 The Square (1)
3 Bleeding Heart (4)
4 1 Lombard Street (2)
5 The Don (5)
6 Savoy Grill (-)
7 The Ivy (9)
8 Oxo Tower (6)
9 Bank Aldwych (7)
10 J Sheekey (-)

Best for romance

1 La Poule au Pot (1)
2 Andrew Edmunds (2)
3 Bleeding Heart (3)
4 Chez Bruce (6=)
5 Le Caprice (-)
6 The Ivy (4)
7 Julie's (8)
8 Oxo Tower (6=)
9 Blue Elephant (5)
10 Odette's (7)

OPENINGS AND CLOSURES

Restaurants in **bold** are included in the London section of this guide – for the full selection, see *Harden's London Restaurants 2005* (£9.99), available in all good bookshops.

OPENINGS

About Thyme
Absolute Thai
Amano Café
Amaya
Amici
Anchor & Hope
Aperitivo, *NW1*
Ashbell's
Atlantic 66
Aubaine
Baker & Spice, *SW1, SW3*
Base, *W1*
Bevis Marks
Bistrothèque
Blue Kangaroo
Blue Pumpkin, *SW17*
Bluebird Club &
  Dining Rooms
Bodean's, *SW4*
Brunello
Burlington
Café Arabica
Café Crêperie
  de Hampstead, *SW6*
Camerino
Castle
Cat & Mutton
Cây Tre
Le Cercle
Chai Pani
The Chancery
Chez Kristof
Cipriani
Club Mangia
Coach & Horses
Cocoon
Crazy Bear
Cristini, *Sussex Pl*
Curryleaf
Darbar
Destino
Deya
$
Drunken Monkey
East@West
1880
Eriki
Esenza
Exmouth Grill
Fabbrica

Fig
Fine Burger Company
Fishworks, *W1*
Floridita
The Food Room
1492
La Fromagerie Café
The Frontline Club
Fuel
Fuzzy's Grub
Gallipoli, *107 Upper St*
Garrison
Greyhound
The Gunmakers
Hamburger Union
Harlem
Harry Ramsden's
The Hartley
Hide
Hoxton Apprentice
Inc.
India EC1
Inn the Park
Isis
Island
Kew Grill
Lanes, *E1*
Latium
Levantine
Loco
Lucio
Ma Cuisine, *TW1*
Made in Brasil
Malmaison
Manicomio
Marechiaro
Medcalf
Mediterranean Kitchen, *N1*
Mehek
Meza
Mirto
Morgan M
Nama
Nathalie
Nimmo's
Novelli in the City
number10
Osteria dell' Arancio
The Painted Heron, *SE11*
The Palmerston

OPENINGS (cont'd)

Papageno
Paternoster Chop House
Patterson's
Pearl
Petit Max
Phene Arms
Pomodorino
Rasoi Vineet Bhatia
Real Greek Souvlaki, *SE1*
Refettorio
Rocket, *SW15*
Rocket, *W3*
Roka
Rosemary Lane
The Rôtisserie, *HA5*
RV2
Sardo Canale
Sarracino
Sax

Sea Cow
Seraphin
Silka
06 St Chad's Place
SoChina
Taman gang
Tas Pide, *EC1*
Thyme, *WC2*
Umu
Vacherin
Vivat Bacchus
White Swan
  Pub & Dining Room
Whits
Winkles
Yi-Ban
The Zetter

CLOSURES

Aaura
Anda
Bar Japan
Bar Mezé, *EC1*
Bibo
Blu
Bonchurch Brasserie
Byron's
Café Flo *all branches exc SW7*
Café 206
Cafeteria
Caffé Uno
Cedar Lounge
Chez Max
Chintamani
La Contenta
The Crescent
Dakota
Dexter's Grill, *SW11 & SW15*
Dining Room
Dish Dash
Ditto Grill
Don Pedro
Down Mexico Way
1837
East One
English Garden
Enigma
fish!, *Belvedere Rd SE1*
Fleur

Foxtrot Oscar, *EC3*
Front Page
The Gate, *NW3*
Gaudi
Gili Gulu, *W2*
Glaisters, *SW11*
Golborne House
Goolies
Goya
Granita
House on Rosslyn Hill
It's, *all branches*
Jason's
Kennington Lane
Khew
King's Road Café
Konditor & Cook, *The Cut*
Lan Na Thai
Manor
Matriciano
Mezzo
Monkeys
Le Muscadet
192
Ophim
Orange, Lemon & Lime
Paolo

Pharmacy
Pollo
Poons in the City
prospectGrill
Pucci Pizza
QC
Red Cube
Riso
River Walk
Rôtisserie *W12*
The Salt House
Samphire
Sandrini
Savoy River Restaurant
Soulard
Soup Opera (all branches)
The Stepping Stone
The Sugar Club
Tartuf
Thai on the River
Thyme, *SW4*
West Street Restaurant
Wharf
White's
Zaika Bazaar
Zilli *(W11)*

LONDON DIRECTORY

A Cena TWI £40
418 Richmond Rd   8288 0108
*With its "civilised" style and "high standard of cooking" ("especially for the area"), this smart Italian two-year-old, south of Richmond Bridge, is big news locally. / **Value tip:** set weekday L £22(FP). **Details:** 10.30 pm; closed Mon & Sun D; booking: max 6, Fri & Sat.*

The Abbeville SW4 £27   Ⓐ
67-69 Abbeville Rd   8675 2201   6–2D
*A "very welcoming" Clapham "local" – like a gastropub, but not quite – praised for its "original" food and "imaginative" interior. / **Details:** www.theabbeville.co.uk; 10.45 pm; no booking.*

The Abingdon W8 £37   Ⓐ
54 Abingdon Rd   7937 3339   4–2A
*"Good for dates or mates" – this "stylish" Kensington bar/restaurant is a "friendly" and "buzzing" neighbourhood hang-out, where "tasty" food comes at prices "that aren't beyond the pale"; the booths are "particularly nice". / **Details:** 11 pm.*

Abu Zaad WI2 £16   Ⓐ★
29 Uxbridge Rd   8749 5107
*"For a fast and unusual meal (with all sorts of strange things on the menu)", it's hard to beat this "authentic" and "excellent-value" Syrian, near Shepherd's Bush Market; no alcohol. / **Details:** 11 pm; no smoking area.*

L'Accento Italiano W2 £35   Ⓐ★
16 Garway Rd   7243 2201
*"No-frills" Bayswater Italian that's again showing signs of the cracking form that briefly made it a 'vogue' destination in the '90s; locals agree that its "delicious" and "reasonably-priced" cooking, and "great" service make it "a gem". / **Details:** 11.15 pm; closed Sun.*

Adams Café WI2 £24   Ⓐ
77 Askew Rd   8743 0572
*This "quirky" Shepherd's Bush greasy spoon makes a good breakfast stop, but it "transforms in the evenings" into a BYO Tunisian café (majoring in couscous); "friendly" owners and "reasonable" prices help make it a hardy "perennial". / **Details:** 11 pm; D only, closed Sun.*

Admiral Codrington SW3 £40
17 Mossop St   7581 0005   4–2C
*With "loads of bustly atmosphere", this "staunch regular haunt" for Brompton Cross types "has no pretentions to great cuisine"; the dining room is especially nice in summer "when the glass roof opens". / **Details:** 10.30 pm.*

Aglio e Olio SW10 £29   ★
194 Fulham Rd   7351 0070   4–3B
*"It's getting more and more difficult to hear anything", at this "packed" and "friendly" Chelsea Italian, where "fresh-tasting" pasta and so on comes at "great prices". / **Details:** 11.30 pm.*

Alloro WI £46   ★
19-20 Dover St   7495 4768   2–3C
*"If there were a category for 'Best Mayfair Restaurant for Business that does not Charge Stupid Prices', Alloro would win hands-down", says one of the many fans of this "professional" Italian, whose cooking is almost always "well executed", and sometimes "superb". / **Details:** 10.30 pm; closed Sat L & Sun.*

The Almeida N1 £41
30 Almeida St 7354 4777
"Excellent, mainly French staff" and "high-quality" cuisine – featuring an "awesome charcuterie trolley" – make this vaguely '70s-style Conran establishment in Islington one of that group's best; it's especially handy for the nearby Almeida Theatre. / Details: www.almeida-restaurant.co.uk; 11 pm.

Amano Café SE1 £22 ★★
Victor Whf, Clink St 7234 0000 5–3C
"Incredibly fresh" dishes makes it worth knowing of this new South Bank café/sandwich bar (by the Clink); "the queue moves quickly", and the stylish setting is surprisingly "relaxing". / Details: www.amanocafe.com; 10.30 pm; no smoking; no booking.

Amaranth SW18 £22 A★★
346 Garratt Ln 8871 3466 6–2B
"It's always full, so you need to book", for this "incredibly friendly" Earlsfield Thai, which serves "good, simple, spicy scoff", at "great-value" prices; BYO. / Details: 10.30 pm; D only, closed Sun; no Amex; no smoking area.

The Anchor & Hope SE1 £36 ★
36 The Cut 7928 9898 5–4A
With its "down-to-earth" style and "hearty but imaginative" cooking, this "proper English gastropub" on the South Bank is widely – in its first year! – voted "top of its class"; "arrive early", as it already gets "impossibly busy". / Details: 10.30 pm; closed Mon L & Sun; no Amex; no booking.

Andrew Edmunds W1 £30 A★
46 Lexington St 7437 5708 2–2D
"Quirky" but phenomenally popular, this Soho townhouse is an "abiding" favourite, especially for romance; "genuinely helpful" staff serve "simple but good-quality" food and an "unbelievable-value" wine list in "quaint" but "cramped", candlelit quarters. / Details: 10.30 pm; no Amex; booking: max 6.

The Anglesea Arms W6 £30 A★★
35 Wingate Rd 8749 1291
"Amazingly tasty" cooking at "unbeatable prices" has long made this "basic" but characterful pub – "on a pretty corner", near Ravenscourt Park – one of London's best; its service is infamously "shambolic", but seems to be "improving". / Details: 10.45 pm; no Amex; no booking.

Anglo Asian Tandoori N16 £21 A★
60-62 Stoke Newington Church St 7254 9298
"Obliging service" and "tasty and interesting" food maintain the consistent allure of this slightly 'different' Stoke Newington curry house. / Details: www.angloasian.co.uk; 11.30 pm; no smoking area.

Antipasto & Pasta SW11 £28 A
511 Battersea Park Rd 7223 9765 6–1C
With its "excellent value on half-price nights (now four a week – Mon, Thu, Sat & Sun)", this "friendly neighbourhood trattoria" certainly knows how to pack 'em in! / Details: 11.30 pm; no Amex; need 4+ to book.

Aperitivo £30 A
41 Beak St, W1 7287 2057
30 Hawley Cr, NW1 7267 7755
With its "charming" service and its "tasty" Italian tapas menu, this "cool but unpretentious" Soho spot makes a "handy" rendezvous; there's now also a branch in Camden Town. / Details: www.aperitivo-camden.com; 10 pm; W1 closed Sun; NW1 no Amex; no smoking area, NW1.

Arancia SE16   £ 25   A
52 Southwark Park Rd   7394 1751
"A gem in an area you'd least expect it" – this *"shabby-chic"*
Bermondsey *"treasure"* serves up *"well put-together"* rustic Italian
dishes at *"amazing"* prices; unsurprisingly, it enjoys quite a local
following. / **Details:** www.arancia-london.co.uk; 11 pm; closed Mon & Sun.

Archipelago W1   £ 55   A
110 Whitfield St   7383 3346   1–1B
"Madcap" décor and an *"outlandish"* but *"successful"* menu (featuring
the likes of ants, zebra and crocodile) combine to create a *"fantastical"*
effect at this *"super-friendly"* little place, near the Telecom Tower;
it's *"perfect for a date"*. / **Value tip:** set weekday L
£37(FP). **Details:** 10.30 pm; closed Sat L & Sun; no smoking area.

Armadillo E8   £ 35   A★★
41 Broadway Mkt   7249 3633
"Who would have thought 'Latin' food could be so creative?" –
the cooking *"may look strange, but it always tastes great"*, at this *"hip"*
and *"happening"* Hackney venue. / **Details:** www.armadillorestaurant.co.uk;
10.30 pm; closed Mon.

**Asia de Cuba
St Martin's Lane WC2**   £ 62   A
45 St Martin's Ln   7300 5500   3–4C
Sometimes *"inspiring"* fusion cuisine (based around *"a sharing
concept"*) makes this *"faintly futuristic"* (going on *"pretentious"*) design-
hotel dining room near Covent Garden more than just a 'beautiful
people' rendezvous; naturally, though, it's *"way overpriced"*. /
Details: www.asiadecuba-restaurant.com; midnight, Sat 1 am; no smoking area.

Assaggi W2   £ 51   ★★
39 Chepstow Pl   7792 5501
"Simple" but *"sensuous"* dishes, using *"fabulous ingredients"*, make this
"unexpected" dining room – over an *"unassuming"* Bayswater boozer –
simply *"the best Italian in London"*, for many reporters; the interior may
feel *"a bit exposed and noisy"*, but it's still *"stupidly hard to get
a table"*. / **Details:** 11 pm; closed Sun; no Amex.

Les Associés N8   £ 33   ★
172 Park Rd   8348 8944
This *"charming little place"* in Crouch End has long had a reputation for
"wonderful" Gallic cooking and *"really nice"* service; its ambience
is *"like eating in someone's front room"*. / **Details:** 10 pm; closed Mon,
Tue–Sat D only, closed Sun D; no Amex; no smoking area.

The Atlas SW6   £ 29   A★
16 Seagrave Rd   7385 9129   4–3A
"A real winner"; this *"unspoilt"* boozer can seem a surprise discovery
near Earl's Court 2, but it's *"always buzzing"*, thanks to its *"fresh and
imaginative"* Mediterranean grub; there's a small courtyard garden
(*"now with an awning and heaters"*). / **Details:** www.theatlaspub.co.uk;
10.30 pm; no Amex; no booking.

Aubergine SW10   £ 72   A★★
11 Park Walk   7352 3449   4–3B
"Powerful flavours, expertly woven together" put William Drabble's
cooking in the premier league of London cuisine, yet this *"obliging"* and
"classy" Chelsea restaurant rarely gets much press – perhaps its
"discreet" style is just too understated? / **Value tip:** set weekday L
£49(FP). **Details:** 11 pm; closed Sat L & Sun; jacket required.

Aurora W1   £ 34   A
49 Lexington St   7494 0514   2–2D
"Small, cosy, and perfect for a romantic meal", this "Soho gem" serves "tasty" modern bistro fare, and boasts the summer boon of a "secluded little garden"; it's a bit "cramped", though, service is "casual", and much of the point is lost if you sit in the basement. /
Details: 10.30 pm; closed Sun; no Amex.

L'Aventure NW8   £ 51   A★
3 Blenheim Ter   7624 6232
*"The best summer terrace in London" helps create "a superb romantic atmosphere", at this "intimate" St John's Wood "gem", where "charming" staff are overseen by the patronne of 25 years' standing; it serves "very good", "proper French" cooking. / **Value tip:** set weekday L £32(FP). **Details:** 11 pm; closed Sat L & Sun.*

Back to Basics W1   £ 41   ★★
21a Foley St   7436 2181   1–1B
*"Nothing but stunning fish dishes" fill the blackboard menu at this "simple", "packed" and "buzzing" Fitzrovia backstreet bistro; "go early – food goes quickly". / **Details:** www.backtobasics.uk.com; 10.30 pm; closed Sun.*

Balans   £ 32
60 Old Compton St, W1   7439 2183
239 Old Brompton Rd, SW5   7244 8838
187 Kensington High St, W8   7376 0115
*There's "plenty of people-watching", at these "always-busy", gay-friendly diners, particularly known as top tips for brunch; standards are waning, though – "even the waiters aren't as cute as they used to be". / **Details:** www.balans.co.uk; midnight; SW5 Sun-Thu 1 am, Fri & Sat 2am; W1 Mon-Sat 5 am, Sun 2 am; no smoking area; W1 Fri & Sat no booking, SW5 Sun L no booking, W8 weekend brunch no booking.*

Baltic SE1   £ 25   A
74 Blackfriars Rd   7928 1111   5–4A
*"A brilliant hip setting" and "many speciality vodkas" have helped establish this "minimalist" bar/restaurant as Borough's coolest rendezvous; its "hearty" and "firmly-flavoured" Polish fare is surprisingly "inventive", too. / **Details:** www.balticrestaurant.co.uk; 11 pm; closed Sat L.*

Bam-Bou W1   £ 39   A★
1 Percy St   7323 9130   1–1C
*"Sensual" décor and "superb" cocktails help create an "enchanting" ambience at this darkly-decorated Fitzrovia townhouse-oriental; the "delicious" Vietnamese-inspired food and "efficient" service are "much better nowadays than when it first opened". / **Details:** www.bam-bou.co.uk; 11.30 pm; closed Sat L & Sun.*

Bank Aldwych WC2   £ 46
1 Kingsway   7379 9797   1–2D
*"Location is the great virtue" which has made this "big and brassy" Covent Garden brasserie a 'natural' for business lunches (and "a top power breakfast haunt"); let's hope the revamp concluded as we went to press boosts its "tired" standards. / **Value tip:** set weekday L £27(FP). **Details:** www.bankrestaurants.com; 11 pm.*

Banners   £ 30   A
83 Hazelville Rd, N19   7686 2944
21 Park Rd, N8   8348 2930
*This "old favourite" in Crouch End (with an offshoot in Upper Holloway) is "atmospheric at all times of day" – it kicks off with "the best brunch" ("mobbed by families at weekends"), thereafter serving "good but not amazing" dishes, plus some "excellent cocktails". / **Details:** 10.30 pm; no Amex.*

Bar Italia W1   £11   A
22 Frith St   7437 4520   3–2A
*"Without doubt the best coffee in London", "more poseurs than you
could shake a panettone at" and "Italian football on TV" means the
story's the same as ever at this "grotty" but "efficient" 24/7 Soho pit
stop. / Details: Mon-Sat open 24 hours, Sun 3 am; no booking.*

Barcelona Tapas   £26
481 Lordship Ln, SE22   8693 5111
1a Bell Ln, E1   7247 7014
1 Beaufort Hs, St Botolph St, EC3   7377 5111
13 Well Ct, EC4   7329 5111
*"Tasty" tapas and a "good, relaxed" atmosphere is a formula that
works surprisingly consistently across the disparate branches of this
"genuine" Spanish chain – from a "hidden-away bunker" in EC4, to a
family-friendly branch near Dulwich. / Details: 10 pm; City branches closed
Sat & Sun.*

The Barnsbury N1   £32
209-211 Liverpool Rd   7607 5519
*A small and "civilised" Islington gastropub, praised for its "courteous"
service and "consistent" cooking. / Details: www.thebarnsbury.co.uk; 10 pm;
no smoking area.*

Beirut Express W2   £18   ★★
112-114 Edgware Rd   7724 2700
*For a "fast-paced, highly entertaining" bite, check out this aptly-named
Maroush-group outlet; it serves "great Lebanese food at reasonable
prices", and "beautiful fresh juices". / Details: www.maroush.com; 1.45 am;
no credit cards.*

The Belsize NW3   £32   A
29 Belsize Ln   7794 4910
*"Impressive" décor ups the tone at this "very popular" and "relaxing"
Belsize Park gastropub, where the food is "usually very good". /
Details: 11 pm.*

Belvedere W8   £50   A
Holland Park, off Abbotsbury Rd   7602 1238
*With its "calm, beautiful and classy" design, few venues are
as "romantic" as this "high-ceilinged" Art Deco gem, "gorgeously"
located in Holland Park; many reporters find the school-of-MPW cuisine
"irresistible", too, but "uninspiring" meals are also by no means
unknown. / Value tip: set weekday L £33(FP). Details: www.whitestarline.org.uk;
10.30 pm; closed Sun D; no jeans or trainers.*

Ben's Thai W9   £24
93 Warrington Cr   7266 3134
*The (truly) impressive setting is the special feature of this "enjoyable"
Thai fixture on the first floor of an enormous Maida Vale pub; the food
is "reliably decent", and "good value". / Details: 10 pm; D only; no Amex;
no smoking area.*

Benares W1   £50
12 Berkeley Hs, Berkeley Sq   7629 8886   2–3B
*Can Atul Kochhar's "upmarket" Mayfair yearling make a go of this first-
floor "graveyard site"?; the interior design is "good" ("for a tricky
space"), and his "complex" modern Indian cuisine can impress… but
it's not as good as when he was at nearby Tamarind. /
Details: www.benaresrestaurant.com; 10.30 pm; closed Sat L & Sun L; no smoking.*

Bengal Clipper SE1   £31
Shad Thames   7357 9001   5–4D
*"It's worth the taxi-ride", say supporters of this "light, airy and open"
South Bank Indian, where often "interesting" dishes are served at "well-
spaced" tables; this year's reports, though, were a little more up-and-
down than usual. / Details: www.bengalclipper.co.uk; 11.30 pm.*

Bermondsey Kitchen SE1   £31

194 Bermondsey St   7407 5719   5–4D

This "simple" venture "in an unpromising area" strikes some reporters as "an ideal local" (even if the food is "not very special"); its relaxed charms are most apparent for brunch – "midweek, it can be quiet". / **Details:** *www.bermondseykitchen.co.uk; 10.30 pm; no Amex; no smoking area.*

Bersagliera SW3   £26   𝔸

372 King's Rd   7352 5993   4–3B

"Polite but fun" (and "child-friendly") service contributes to an atmosphere "as close as you'll get to Naples", at this veteran Chelsea Italian; it's especially praised for its "good pizzas". / **Details:** *11.30 pm; closed weekday L; no Amex.*

Bevis Marks EC3   £43   𝔸★

4 Heneage Ln   7283 2220   5–2D

"The City's new kosher restaurant" – "beautifully situated" adjacent to the eponymous synagogue – is "a real treat" for all who comment on it; "the menu is excellent, even for the non-kosher-minded". / **Value tip:** *pre-th. £23(FP).* **Details:** *www.BevisMarksTheRestaurant.com; 7.15 pm; closed Fri D, Sat & Sun; no Amex; no smoking.*

Bibendum SW3   £61   𝔸

81 Fulham Rd   7581 5817   4–2C

"Still resting rather on its laurels, but there's no room like it in London"; this "sophisticated" Brompton Cross veteran (over the Conran Shop) is undoubtedly a "wonderful and airy" venue – unfortunately, however, the food is sometimes "indifferent", but the "incredible" wine list offers some consolation. / **Details:** *www.bibendum.co.uk; 11 pm.*

Big Easy SW3   £41   𝔸

332-334 King's Rd   7352 4071   4–3C

"There's lots of getting fingers messy", at this long-established Chelsea American, which serves "top-notch ribs, wings and burgers", and so on; thanks to its "happy vibe", it's "always crowded". / **Value tip:** *set weekday L £24(FP).* **Details:** *www.bigeasy.uk.com; 11.20 pm, Fri & Sat 12.20 am; no smoking area.*

Bistro Aix N8   £38

54 Topsfield Pde   8340 6346

It can seem "expensive for Crouch End", but this Gallic yearling has proved "a great addition" to the area, thanks to its "classic" cuisine and its "genuinely concerned" service. / **Details:** *www.bistroaix.co.uk; 11 pm; closed Mon; no smoking area.*

Bistrothèque E2   £34

23-27 Wadeson St   8983 7900

"Buzzing and packed, despite the location" – this brave new Bethnal Green venture has found an instant following; its simple Gallic fare may not always hit the heights, but it's generally "well executed". / **Details:** *10.30 pm.*

Black & Blue   £36

90-92 Wigmore St, W1   7486 1912
105 Gloucester Rd, SW7   7244 7466
215-217 Kensington Church St, W8   7727 0004
205-207 Haverstock Hill, NW3   7443 7744

"They don't skimp on portions", at this growing chain, where "friendly" staff serve up "fantastic meat" (steak and burgers) in "simple" surroundings – "exactly what you want from this kind of place". / **Details:** *11 pm; no Amex; no smoking area; no booking.*

Blah! Blah! Blah! W12   £25   ★★

78 Goldhawk Rd   8746 1337

The "sparkling" scoff of this "friendly" veteran veggie can come as a bit of a surprise on a grungy stretch of highway, near Goldhawk Road tube; if the conversation palls, "you can doodle on the tablecloths". / **Details:** *11 pm; closed Sun; no credit cards.*

Blakes Hotel SW7   £ 96   A
33 Roland Gdns   7370 6701   4–2B
It's "undeniably sexy", and the "naughty" charms of this "dimly-lit"
South Kensington basement have long made it an "intoxicating"
destination – why else would anyone shell out the "silly money"
demanded for its eclectic but unremarkable cooking? /
Details: www.blakeshotels.com; 11.30 pm.

Bleeding Heart EC1   £ 43   A★
Bleeding Heart Yd, Greville St   7242 8238   5–2A
"Authentic Gallic staff" serve up "delicious" traditional dishes (and "a
fantastic choice of wine") at this "buzzy" "rabbit warren" of a place,
"tucked away" near Holborn; "the tavern, the bistro and the restaurant
are all good", and much praised for both business and romance. /
Details: www.bleedingheart.co.uk; 10.30 pm; closed Sat & Sun.

Blue Elephant SW6   £ 46   A★
3-6 Fulham Broadway   7385 6595   4–4A
It may be "like stepping into Disney's version of Thailand", but this
"romantic" Fulham fantasy has always – to a surprising extent – served
"seriously good food"; this year's reports, though – while still impressive
– were fractionally less ecstatic than usual. / **Value tip:** set weekday L
£28(FP). **Details:** www.blueelephant.com; midnight; closed Sat L.

Bluebird SW3   £ 51   X
350 King's Rd   7559 1000   4–3C
"A total rip-off" – Conran's cavernous, first-floor Chelsea landmark
dining room is pasted by reporters for its "lack of character", its "slow"
and "arrogant" service and its "utterly disappointing" cooking. /
Details: www.conran.com; 11 pm.

Bohème Kitchen & Bar W1   £ 38   A
19 Old Compton St   7734 5656   3–2A
"Cool for eats or just drinks"; this "buzzy" Soho joint (adjacent to Café
Bohème) serves surprisingly "good" nosh – "fantastic burgers" are
particularly praised. / **Details:** www.bohemekitchen.co.uk; 11.45 pm.

Boiled Egg & Soldiers SW11   £ 20   A★
63 Northcote Rd   7223 4894   6–2C
"Between-the-Commons types, complete with hangovers or babies"
form most of the clientèle of this "old-faithful" Battersea café;
the "great weekend brunch" is a highlight. / **Details:** 6 pm; L & afternoon
tea only; only Switch; no booking.

Boisdale SW1   £ 44   A
13-15 Eccleston St   7730 6922   1–4B
"The panelled setting and jazz make for a great night out", at this
"cosy and decadent" Belgravia Caledonian; with its "traditional" (steak,
game and haggis) menu, its "great wine" and its "fantastic array
of malts", it's "just the place to take a manly man". /
Details: www.boisdale.co.uk; 10.30 pm; closed Sat L & Sun.

Bombay Bicycle Club SW12   £ 35   ★
95 Nightingale Ln   8673 6217   6–2C
This Wandsworth institution – known for Its "light and elegant" food –
has long been "the best upmarket Indian south of the river" (and also
runs some successful take-aways); let's hope that the group which
recently bought it – with explicit chain-intentions – doesn't wreck it. /
Details: 11 pm; D only, closed Sun.

Bombay Brasserie SW7   £ 52   A
Courtfield Close, Gloucester Rd   7370 4040   4–2B
"Redolent of the Raj", this grand South Kensington Indian is, for its
many admirers, a "reliable" performer that's "still great after all these
years" (especially if you bag a seat in the "lovely" conservatory);
it's "not cheap", though, and even fans say it "can disappoint". /
Details: www.bombaybrasserielondon.com; 11.30 pm; no smoking area.

Bombay Palace W2   £ 38   ★★
50 Connaught St   7723 8855
*"You really can't go wrong at this top Indian" – that's the invariable
theme of feedback on this "understated" (and too little-known)
establishment, just north of Hyde Park. /*
Details: *www.bombay-palace.co.uk; 11.30 pm; no smoking area.*

Il Bordello E1   £ 36   A★
75-81 Wapping High St   7481 9950
*"Noisy", "busy" and "tightly packed", this Wapping Italian is "big on
value", serving "ridiculous-sized" thin-base pizzas (and so on),
with "unfailing" smiles. /* **Details:** *www.ilbordello.com; 11 pm; closed Sat L.*

Boudin Blanc W1   £ 40   A
5 Trebeck St   7499 3292   2–4B
*"Really French (including a touch of arrogance)" – this "cosy" (going
on "squashed") and rustic Shepherd Market fixture is an ever-popular
West End rendezvous, especially for romantics. /* **Value tip:** *set weekday L
£26(FP).* **Details:** *www.boudinblanc.co.uk; 11 pm.*

Boulevard WC2   £ 31
40 Wellington St   7240 2992   3–3D
*With its "accommodating" staff, "honest" brasserie fare and "cheerful"
atmosphere, this "trusty old friend" in Covent Garden is "a good stand-
by"; it's "not too pricey", either. /* **Details:** *www.boulevardbrasserie.co.uk;
midnight; no smoking area.*

Boxwood Café
The Berkeley SW1   £ 52
Wilton Pl   7235 1010   4–1D
*'Café' is "a bit of a misnomer" for this "grand" Gordon Ramsay-
managed Knightsbridge basement (once Vong, RIP); fans hail its
"informal but slick NYC-style ambience" and its "superb" and
"luxurious" dishes, but critics just find it "pretentious" and "too pricey".
/* **Details:** *www.gordonramsay.com; 11 pm; no smoking.*

The Brackenbury W6   £ 36   A★
129-131 Brackenbury Rd   8748 0107
*A new owner is "cutting a dash" at this "cosy but stylish" fixture, in "a
pretty Hammersmith side street" (which has a "lovely summer
terrace"); both "unhurried and friendly" service and "reasonably-priced
food of a high standard" scored particularly well this year. /* **Value
tip:** *set weekday L £25(FP).* **Details:** *10.45 pm; closed Sat L & Sun D; no smoking.*

Brady's SW18   £ 21
513 Old York Rd   8877 9599   6–2B
*"Sensibly-priced fresh fish served in plain but pleasant café-like
surroundings" has made Mr Brady's "very friendly" chippie into
"a veritable institution", down Wandsworth way. /* **Details:** *10.30 pm;
D only, closed Sun; no credit cards; no booking.*

Brick Lane Beigel Bake E1   £ 4   ★★
159 Brick Ln   7729 0616
*"THE place for a midnight – or any time – east-London snack";
this famous bakery boasts an almost-permanent "ludicrous" queue,
thanks to its "top-class" bagels – not least the "vast and terrific" salt
beef ones – that are "as cheap as can be". /* **Details:** *open 24 hours;
no credit cards; no smoking; no booking.*

La Brocca NW6   £ 29   A
273 West End Ln   7433 1989
*The "atmospheric and cosy" setting, plus "good and massive" pizzas,
win acclaim for this West Hampstead basement "neighbourhood
Italian"; "you need to book" – "the place shows no sign of fading in the
face of more recent nearby competition". /* **Details:** *11 pm; booking:
max 8.*

The Builder's Arms SW3   £ 29   A
13 Britten St   7349 9040   4–2C
"Hands-down the best place for a relaxing meal" – regulars
"just adore" the *"comfortable and convivial"* vibe at this *"lovely"*
younger-scene Chelsea gastropub, where the grub is reliably *"good"* and
"solid". / **Details:** www.geronimo-inns.co.uk; 9.45 pm; no Amex; no booking.

Busaba Eathai   £ 23   A
106-110 Wardour St, W1   7255 8686
22 Store St, WC1   7299 7900
Dark wood fittings lend "a classy feel" to this "hip" communal-table
Thai (from the creator of Wagamama); the food "isn't as exciting as it
once was, but still a good bargain for the West End" and there can
be quite a queue; (a new branch is set to open near St Christopher's
Place, at 8-13 Bird Street, in early 2005). / **Details:** 11 pm, Fri & Sat
11.30 pm; no smoking; no booking W1.

Café 209 SW6   £ 18   A
209 Munster Rd   7385 3625   6–1B
"Hilarious", "motor-mouth" owner Joy "rules the roost", at this small
and (very) "crowded" Fulham café, creating a "brilliant" atmosphere for
the consumption of her "cheap" and "simple" Thai scoff; BYO. /
Details: 10.30 pm; D only, closed Sun; no credit cards.

Café du Marché EC1   £ 39   A ★
22 Charterhouse Sq   7608 1609   5–1B
"A slice of old France in a dark corner near Smithfield Market" –
this "fantastically atmospheric" warehouse-conversion has long been
a favourite, not only for "unstuffy" business lunches, but also for
"cosy and romantic" dinners. / **Details:** 10 pm; closed Sat L & Sun; no Amex.

Café Japan NW11   £ 27   ★
626 Finchley Rd   8455 6854
"Ultra-fresh sushi" at "very affordable prices" – and *"charming"*
service, too – justify the trip to this *"Spartan"* Golders Green café. /
Value tip: set weekday L £13(FP). **Details:** 10 pm; closed Mon & Tue; no Amex;
no smoking.

Café Lazeez   £ 36
21 Dean St, W1   7434 9393
93-95 Old Brompton Rd, SW7   7581 9993
88 St John St, EC1   7253 2224
"Great Indian food" has long been the mainstay of these "modern",
"trendy"-ish joints, where you can get anything from a drink and
a snack to a full meal. / **Details:** www.cafelazeez.com; EC1 10.30 pm,
W1 10.45 pm, Fri & Sat 11.30 pm, SW7 midnight; EC1 closed Sun; no smoking
area.

Café Pacifico WC2   £ 30
5 Langley St   7379 7728   3–2C
After a recent refurb, this Covent Garden cantina has got closer to living
up to its (undemanding) reputation as "the best Mexican in town";
"indulgent" margaritas and a "cattle-market" ambience are all part
of the fun. / **Details:** www.cafepacifico.com; 11.45 pm; no booking, except
Thu-Sat.

Café Portugal SW8   £ 26
5a-6a Victoria Hs, South Lambeth Rd   7587 1962   6–1D
Touted by one or two devotees as "the best place in Vauxhall's 'Little
Portugal'", this (recently refurbished) ultra-authentic café – smaller and
less well-known than nearby Bar Estrela – *certainly offers cheap and*
tasty scoff. / **Value tip:** set weekday L £14(FP). **Details:** www.cafeportugal.com;
11 pm; no smoking area.

Café Spice Namaste E1 £ 35 ★
16 Prescot St   7488 9242
*Cyrus Todiwala's "innovative" Parsi cooking "is in a different world from most curry menus", and his "cavernous" east-London HQ remains a popular destination; its bright "Changing Rooms" décor wins more mixed praise (but in summer you can now eat out in the new 'Ginger Garden'). / **Details:** www.cafespice.co.uk; 10.30 pm; closed Sat L & Sun.*

Cambio de Tercio SW5 £ 45 Ⓐ
163 Old Brompton Rd   7244 8970   4–2B
*Fans still acclaim this South Kensington favourite as "the best Spaniard in town", fêting the "excellent twists" in its cuisine and its "funky" setting; it's seen as increasingly "over-rated", though. / **Value tip:** set weekday L £25(FP). **Details:** www.cambiodetercio.com; 11.30 pm.*

Capital Hotel SW3 £ 79 ★★
22-24 Basil St   7589 5171   4–1D
*Eric Chavot's Gallic cuisine is truly "inspired", but it's often "overlooked" at this hotel dining room near Harrods – perhaps this will be put to rights by a major refurbishment, in '40s French style, underway as this guide went to press. / **Value tip:** set weekday L £47(FP). **Details:** www.capitalhotel.co.uk; 11 pm.*

Le Caprice SW1 £ 48 Ⓐ★
Arlington Hs, Arlington St   7629 2239   2–1C
*"All-round professionalism" – including "first-rate" cooking and "effortless" service – maintains reporters' intense affection for this "urbane" and ever-"glamorous" brasserie, behind the Ritz; its décor may seem a bit "dated", but "it seems to work". / **Details:** midnight.*

Caraffini SW1 £ 37 Ⓐ★
61-63 Lower Sloane St   7259 0235   4–2D
*"Genuinely friendly" staff help "put a smile on everyone's face", at this "exemplary neighbourhood Italian" in Chelsea, where "very dependable" food is served in a "noisy", "cramped" and "fun" setting. / **Details:** www.caraffini.co.uk; 11.30 pm; closed Sun.*

Carpaccio's SW3 £ 45
4 Sydney St   7352 3433   4–2C
*A "bustling" and "fashionable" destination with "authentic" food, or a "raucous" place that's simply "over-rated"? – though many reporters still count this Chelsea Italian as a "favourite", it came in for much more flak than usual this year. / **Value tip:** set weekday L £28(FP). **Details:** www.carpaccio.uk.com; 11.30 pm; closed Sun.*

Casale Franco N1 £ 37 Ⓐ
rear of 134-137 Upper St   7226 8994
*For "the best pizza and pasta on Upper Street", many Islington cognoscenti seek out this "rustic" Italian, hidden away down an alley by a car showroom; dining outside can be "very romantic". / **Details:** 11 pm, Sun 9 pm; closed Mon, Tue-Fri D only, Sat & Sun open L & D; no smoking area; need 6+ to book.*

Cat & Mutton E8 £ 28
76 Broadway Mkt   7254 5599
*This "hip" new gastropub may only offer a "limited" menu, "simply cooked", but it's still something of a beacon, down Hackney way, and "beginning to get very busy". / **Details:** 10 pm; closed Mon L & Sun D; no Amex.*

Cecconi's W1 £ 60 Ⓐ
5a Burlington Gdns   7434 1500   2–3C
*Under new management, this "upscale" Mayfair Italian is emerging as something of an "under-rated gem"; its "sleek" décor and "professional" service are its prime attractions, but the cooking can be "very good", too. / **Details:** 11 pm; booking: max 6.*

Le Cercle SW1 £ 32 A★★
1 Wilbraham Pl
7901 9999 4–2D
The "creative culinary genius" of the Club Gascon team – twinned with
"beautiful", "floaty curtains" décor that just about manages to disguise
the fact that you're in a basement – has made an instant smash hit
of this new "Gallic tapas" venture, just north of Sloane Square. /
Details: 11.30 pm; closed Mon & Sun; no smoking.

Champor-Champor SE1 £ 37 A★★
62 Weston St
7403 4600 5–4C
"A total find!"; with its "psychedelic" south east Asian fusion menu,
its "charming and attentive" service and its "enchanting" décor,
this "jewel" near London Bridge attracts a paean of praise; "recently
expanded to twice the size, it's just as unusual as ever". /
Details: www.champor-champor.com; 10.15 pm; closed L (unless receive a booking
for 6+), closed Sun; booking: max 12.

Chapter Two SE3 £ 29
43-45 Montpelier Vale 8333 2666
Blackheath folk applaud their local brasserie for its "superb" service
and "buzz", and for "cooking that rivals the West End"; its ratings
slipped a little this year, though – maybe the new chef from its
celebrated Kent sibling will pep things up. /
Details: www.chaptersrestaurant.co.uk; 10.30 pm, Fri & Sat 11.30 pm; no smoking
in dining room; booking: max 10.

Chelsea Bun Diner £ 22
9a Lamont Rd, SW10 7352 3635
70 Battersea Bridge Rd, SW11 7738 9009
"Find your hangover cure", at this "efficient and friendly" World's End
diner; "always packed at weekends", it offers an "enormous" menu,
which stretches all the way from "lower-fat options" to "cholesterol
heaven". / **Details:** SW10 11 pm, SW11 L only; SW10 closed Sun D; no Amex;
SW10 no brunch bookings.

Chez Bruce SW17 £ 45 A★★
2 Bellevue Rd 8672 0114 6–2C
It has the "cramped" feel of a "neighbourhood favourite", but "people
flock from far and wide" to Bruce Poole's Wandsworth Common-side
dining room, thanks to his "top-notch" cooking that "delivers time and
again"; "down-to-earth" service and a "cracking" wine list play noble
supporting roles. / **Details:** 10.30 pm; no smoking; booking: max 6 at D.

Chez Liline N4 £ 33 ★★
101 Stroud Green Rd 7263 6550
"The best kept seafood secret in north London" – this Finsbury Park
institution serves "superb" Mauritian-influenced cuisine that has long
defied its grungy location; perhaps a recent refurbishment will even
boost its customary rock-bottom ambience rating! / **Details:** 10.30 pm;
closed Mon & Sun L.

Chez Lindsay TW10 £ 32 A
11 Hill Rise 8948 7473
An "uncomplicated" bistro, near Richmond Bridge, popular for its
"extremely relaxed" and "friendly" style and its "decently-priced"
Breton cooking – "great crêpes" are, of course, a feature, as is a range
of ciders. / **Value tip:** set weekday L £18(FP). **Details:** 10.45 pm; no Amex.

Chor Bizarre W1 £ 45 A
16 Albemarle St 7629 9802 2–3C
"Unexpected and delightful" junk-shop décor is the hallmark of this
Mayfair subcontinental; sceptics, as ever, find it "average", but it does
have ardent fans who extol its "very traditional" north Indian food;
(in the basement, it now serves "a range of teas and tiffin"). /
Details: www.chorbizarre.com; 11 pm; closed Sun L; no smoking area.

Churchill Arms W8   £ 17   A★
119 Kensington Church St   7792 1246
"Delicious Thai food at amazingly low prices" has long made a big
name for the *"greenhousy"* annexe of this Kensington boozer;
even when *"horribly busy"* (often), it remains a *"happy and bustling"*
place, despite somewhat *"perfunctory"* service. / **Details:** 9.30 pm; closed
Sun D; no smoking area; no booking at L.

Chutney Mary SW10   £ 50   A★
535 King's Rd   7351 3113   4–4B
Since it *"shed its colonial past"*, with an *"elegant"* modern refit a couple
of years ago, this distant-Chelsea Indian has gone from strength
to strength; *"wonderful"* contemporary cuisine and *"helpful and
knowledgeable"* staff make it now the best all-round *"upmarket"*
subcontinental in town. / **Details:** www.realindianfood.com; 11 pm; closed
weekday L; no smoking area.

Cicada EC1   £ 36   A★
132-136 St John St   7608 1550   5–1B
"Going from strength to strength", this *"vibrant"* Clerkenwell
bar/restaurant offers *"great and eclectic Asian-inspired food"*, in a *"fun"*
setting. / **Details:** www.cicada.nu; 10.45 pm; closed Sat L & Sun; no smoking
area.

Cinnamon Cay SW11   £ 34   A★
87 Lavender Hill   7801 0932   6–1C
"Imaginative" Antipodean fare and *"always-cheerful"* service have won
a more-than-local following for this *"small"* and *"cosy"* Battersea outfit.
/ **Details:** www.cinnamoncay.co.uk; 10.30 pm; closed Sun.

The Cinnamon Club SW1   £ 62   ★
Great Smith St   7222 2555   1–4C
"Spectacular but pricey 'New Age' Indian food" maintains a huge
following for this *"sophisticated"* conversion of a former Westminster
library. / **Details:** www.cinnamonclub.com; 11 pm; closed Sat L & Sun;
no smoking area; booking: max 8.

Cipriani W1   £ 62   A
25 Davies Street   7399 0500   2–2B
The *"jet set"* is fighting for tables at Mayfair's *"elegant"* new sibling
to Venice's Harry's Bar; it certainly looks the part, but its menu
of *"rich people's Italian comfort food"* and its sometimes *"terrible"*
service can make it seem a very *"smug"* operation indeed. / **Value
tip:** set weekday L £35(FP). **Details:** www.cipriani.com; 11 pm; booking: max 6.

Circus W1   £ 42
1 Upper James St   7534 4000   2–2D
This *"stylish"*, if *"slightly sterile"*, Soho space is a popular media lunch
spot, and can be quite *"hip"* in the evenings, too; ratings for its *"light
and fresh"* cuisine and (especially) its *"efficient and informed"* service
improved this year. / **Value tip:** set weekday L
£28(FP). **Details:** www.egami.co.uk; midnight; closed Sat L & Sun.

City Miyama EC4   £ 40   ★★
17 Godliman St   7489 1937   5–3B
"You don't go for the ambience", to this *"anodyne"* City Japanese
basement – you do go, though, for *"unsurpassed"* sushi (and there's
also a *"great teppan-yaki"*). / **Details:** 9.30 pm; closed Sat D & Sun.

Clarke's W8   £ 62   A★★
124 Kensington Church St   7221 9225
"Sally Clarke's formula never fails", say fans of her *"sophisticated but
unpretentious"* Californian-influenced Kensington dining room, where
"beautifully-sourced" ingredients are *"simply"* cooked to *"sublime"*
effect; (NB part of that formula is zero choice at dinner). /
Details: www.sallyclarke.com; 10 pm; closed Mon D, Sat D & Sun; no smoking.

Club Gascon EC1   £ 45   A★★
57 West Smithfield   7796 0600   5–2B
*"A foie gras explosion" – with "fantastic wines from SW France" –
can make for an "extravagant" foodie experience at this "intimate"
City-fringe fixture, whose "amazing" tapas-style dishes have helped
it win a huge following. / **Details:** 10 pm, Fri & Sat 10.30 pm; closed Sat L &
Sun.*

Club Mangia
The Punch Tavern EC4   £ 17   A
99 Fleet St   7353 6658   5–2A
*"Good staff" and a vaguely Boho vibe helps create an un-City-like
ambience at this genial historic tavern; representing "the acceptable
face of buffets", the place offers an array of tasty dishes, plus superior
coffee and cakes. / **Details:** 11 pm; closed Sat & Sun; no smoking area at L.*

Coach & Horses EC1   £ 34   ★
26-28 Ray St
7278 8990   5–1A
*"More-refined-than-usual" gastropub cooking – with a "creative" wine
list, too – and notably "welcoming" service are immediately making
a name for this relaunched boozer, behind The Guardian. /
Details: 9.30 pm; closed Sat L & Sun D; no Amex.*

Le Colombier SW3   £ 42   A
145 Dovehouse St   7351 1155   4–2C
*In a quiet Chelsea backwater, this "very traditional Gallic brasserie" is a
super-"safe" destination, with an "excellent" wine list, "charming"
service and a terrace that's "pleasant winter and summer"; the cooking,
though, is so "classic bourgeois" as to avoid anything approaching
excitement. / **Details:** 10.30 pm.*

(Angela Hartnett's Menu)
The Connaught W1   £ 74
Carlos Pl   7592 1222   2–3B
*"Pre-Ramsay", it was a "splendid" (and unique) experience to dine
at this "luxurious" Mayfair hotel, and – perhaps inevitably – it now
"lacks the character of yesteryear"; some "top-notch" meals are still
to be had, but, overall, AH's cooking is judged only "moderate, for the
money", and the once-magical service likewise. / **Value tip:** set weekday L
£48(FP). **Details:** www.the-connaught.co.uk; 11 pm; jacket required; no smoking;
booking: max 10.*

Coopers Arms SW3   £ 28
87 Flood St   7376 3120   4–3C
*"Bare" but "characterful", this Chelsea backstreet boozer serves
a "good choice" of dishes that are "not too generically gastro-pubby". /
Details: www.drinkatthecoopers.co.uk; 9.30 pm; closed Sun D; no booking, Sun.*

Coq d'Argent EC3   £ 51
1 Poultry   7395 5000   5–2C
*"An idyllic setting in the heart of the City" (complete with
a "spectacular roof garden" and "great views") helped win Conran's
Bank-side eyrie this year's top place in nominations 'For Business';
its food, service and prices, however, remain as "ordinary",
"unimpressive" and "inflated" as ever. / **Details:** www.conran.com; 10 pm;
closed Sat L & Sun D.*

Cotto W14   £ 30   ★
44 Blythe Rd   7602 9333
*"I can't believe it's not in your guide!" (actually it was, but got left out
last year by accident) – "fantastic, classy" modern British cuisine and
"accommodating" service win rave reviews for this rather "austere"
venture; its "in-the-shadow-of-Olympia" location, though, can leave
it undeservedly "half empty". / **Details:** 10.30 pm; closed Sat L & Sun.*

The Cow W2   £ 35   𝔸 ★
89 Westbourne Park Rd   7221 0021
"If you can squeeze past the trustafarians", and find a table at Tom
Conran's "cramped" Bayswater boozer, you'll enjoy "excellent oysters,
fish and seafood platters" (plus a good pint of Guinness); staff attitude,
*though, can be "poor". / **Details:** 10.30 pm; no Amex.*

Crazy Bear W1   £ 45   𝔸
26 Whitfield St   7631 0088   1–1C
A pile of cash has been sunk into the lavish and "eccentric" look of this
Fitzrovia newcomer (sibling to a well-known Oxfordshire venture) whose
"very cool" basement bar – and particularly loos – are not to be
missed; the surprise is that the oriental nosh, if pricey, is "seriously
*good". / **Details:** 10.45 pm; closed Sat L & Sun D.*

The Criterion Grill W1   £ 41   𝔸X
224 Piccadilly Circus   7930 0488   2–3D
"Really second-rate food" and some of "the most arrogant and ill-
mannered service in town" make this potentially great West End dining
room one to avoid – even the "Byzantine delight" of its interior
*is insufficient compensation. / **Details:** www.whitestarline.org.uk; 11 pm;*
closed Sun.

Delfina Studio Café SE1   £ 36   𝔸★★
50 Bermondsey St   7357 0244   5–4D
"An exceptional venue for lunch, and terrific value" is the theme
of practically all reports on this "spacious and buzzing" dining space
in a Bermondsey art gallery, acclaimed for its "inventive" menu and
"consistently excellent" service; now also open Friday night. /
***Details:** www.delfina.org.uk; 10 pm; L only, except Fri when L&D, closed Sat & Sun;*
no smoking area.

La Delizia SW3   £ 25   𝔸
63-65 Chelsea Manor St   7376 4111   4–3C
"Proper thin-base pizzas" maintain a small but dedicated following for
this pint-sized and "intimate" spot, "hidden away in a Chelsea
*backwater". / **Details:** midnight; no Amex.*

Deya W1   £ 39   ★★
34 Portman Sq   7224 0028   1–2A
Backed by Sir Michael Caine, this new 'nouvelle' Indian (attached to an
anonymous hotel, off Oxford Street) is a surprise 'miss' on the glamour
front; an early visit, however, found eager-to-please staff and
wonderfully deft and moderately-priced cooking. /
***Details:** www.deya-restaurant.co.uk; 10.45 pm; closed Sat L & Sun.*

The Don EC4   £ 45   𝔸★
20 St Swithin's Ln   7626 2606   5–3C
With its "cosy" brasserie in "character-filled old port cellars" and
a "more formal" upstairs restaurant, this "classy" three-year-old has
rapidly become a top City business rendezvous; it marries "fine" food
with "faultless" service and a "superb" wine list. /
***Details:** www.thedonrestaurant.com; 10 pm; closed Sat & Sun.*

don Fernando's TW9   £ 29   𝔸
27f The Quadrant   8948 6447
"Good for groups, and convenient for the station" – this "lively"
Richmond tapas bar benefits from "prompt and cheerful" staff, plus a
*dependable selection of dishes. / **Details:** www.donfernando.co.uk; 11 pm;*
no smoking area; no booking.

Don Pepe NW8   £ 28   𝔸
99 Frampton St   7262 3834
This "real local tapas bar (and Spanish restaurant)", just around the
corner from Lord's, is the UK's oldest place of its type, and still delivers
*some "top-quality" dishes in a characterful setting. / **Details:** 11.45 pm;*
closed Sun.

(Grill Room)
Dorchester Hotel W1   £62   A
53 Park Ln   7629 8888   2–3A
This "wonderful" Spanish Baronial-style Mayfair dining room is one
of the last bastions of "faultless" service in ancien régime style;
the food's pretty "classic", too – "good, but not good enough to get
*in the way of business". / **Value tip:** set weekday L*
*£38(FP). **Details:** www.dorchesterhotel.com; 11 pm.*

Dove W6   £26   A
19 Upper Mall   8748 5405
A tranquil riverside setting and a "great Sunday lunch" are the twin
highlights at this cosy Dickensian tavern, which can get very crowded;
*no kids. / **Details:** 9 pm; closed Sun D; no booking.*

The Drapers Arms N1   £35   A
44 Barnsbury St
7619 0348
"Decent food in the bar, the restaurant or the beautiful garden" makes
this "light and airy" Georgian tavern a key Barnsbury destination;
the cooking, though, has slightly slipped since its heady early days. /
***Details:** 10.30 pm; closed Sun D.*

Drunken Monkey E1   £22   A
222 Shoreditch High St   7392 9606   5–1D
"A fun place to eat dim sum and drink beer" – everything you need
to know about this Shoreditch boozer, recently revamped in striking
*oriental style. / **Details:** www.thedrunkenmonkey.info; 10.45 pm; closed Sat L.*

E&O W11   £37   A★★
14 Blenheim Cr
7229 5454
A "hip bar" helps power the "fun" and "buzzy" vibe that's won fame
for Will Ricker's "star-studded" Notting Hill oriental; of equal note,
though, are the "light" dishes of "truly imaginative" fusion fare, which
*reporters say are "a joy". / **Details:** www.eando.nu; 10.30 pm; booking:*
max 6.

The Eagle EC1   £24   A★
159 Farringdon Rd   7837 1353   5–1A
"The original London gastropub, and still the best" – a "noisy" and
"scruffy" Farringdon institution, where mainly Mediterranean dishes are
cooked "with commitment, passion and flair"; service, however,
*can come "with attitude". / **Details:** 10.30 pm; closed Sun D; no Amex;*
no booking.

Eagle Bar Diner W1   £25   A
3-5 Rathbone Pl   7637 1418   3–1A
"Chunky burgers" and "fabulous cocktails" are a popular mix at this
"trendy" and "laid-back" American bar/restaurant, just north of Oxford
*Street. / **Details:** www.eaglebardiner.com; 10.45 pm; closed Sun D; no Amex;*
need 6+ to book.

Ealing Park Tavern W5   £29   A★
222 South Ealing Rd
8758 1879
Even if you don't agree that this is "Ealing's best eating place" – which
it may well be – this "first-rate" gastropub is well worth knowing about
for its "chilled" and "spacious" feel, its "friendly" service and its "great
*comfort food". / **Details:** 10.15 pm; closed Mon L; no smoking in dining room;*
booking: max 10.

Earl Spencer SW18   £ 29   ★★

260-262 Merton Rd   8870 9244   6–2B

*"It deserves all the accolades it gets", say fans of this year-old
Southfields gastropub cousin of the fabled Havelock Tavern; it wins all-
round endorsements for its "unbeatable" cooking, its "very friendly"
service ("particularly to children") and its "lively" (if slightly "barn-like")
setting. / Details: www.theearlspencer.co.uk; 10 pm; no Amex; no booking.*

East@West WC2   £ 56   ★★

13-15 West St   7010 8600   3–2B

*Star Aussie chef Christine Mansfield's "fabulous little pots" of "really
precise" Asian fusion cuisine create a "memorable" experience at this
Covent Garden newcomer; it's "expensive", though, and the décor –
little changed since the days of West Street (RIP) – can seem "a tad too
cool". / Details: www.egami.co.uk; 11.30 pm; D only.*

The Ebury SW1   £ 39   𝔸

11 Pimlico Rd   7730 6784   4–2D

*"Is it a pub, a brasserie or a restaurant?" – in the Pimlico void, it hardly
matters, and Tom Etridge's "great" newcomer (which in fact combines
all three) has been a huge hit with trendier locals; "super seafood" is a
highlight. / Details: www.theebury.co.uk, 10.15, Fri & Sat 10.45 pm.*

Eco   £ 29   ★

162 Clapham High St, SW4   7978 1108
4 Market Row, Brixton Mkt, SW9   7738 3021

*Only the "zingy" thin-base pizzas really unite this odd couple –
a "buzzing" Clapham hang-out that gets "crowded" and "too noisy",
and (lunch only) "a tiny bustling place in the heart of Brixton market,
with quirky service and bizarre passers-by". / Details: SW4 11 pm, Fri &
Sat 11.30 pm; SW9 L only, closed Wed & Sun; SW9 no booking.*

Ed's Easy Diner   £ 23   𝔸

12 Moor St, W1   7439 1955
Trocadero, W1   7287 1951
362 King's Rd, SW3   7352 1956
O2 Centre, 255 Finchley Rd, NW3   7431 1958

*"The Fonz would be at home", at these "fabulous" retro diners, which
offer "yummy burgers", "killer milkshakes" and "even better
atmosphere"; service is "refreshingly pleasant", too. / Details: W1
midnight, 11 pm Sat & Sun, SW3 & NW3 10.30 pm; no smoking area, except
O2 Centre; no booking.*

Eight Over Eight SW3   £ 40   𝔸★

392 King's Rd   7349 9934   4–3B

*"For Chelsea's trendier elements", Will Ricker's "always buzzing" hang-
out near World's End is proving a worthy spin-off from Notting Hill's
E&O, offering "mouth-watering" fusion dishes (and "minor celeb-
watching, too"). / Details: www.eightovereight.nu; 11 pm; closed Sun L.*

1802
Museum In Docklands E14   £ 36

1 West India Quay, Hertsmere Rd   0870 444 3886

*"Better than most of the lacklustre restaurants in E14", this Canary
Wharf waterside wine bar offers an all-round "pleasant" experience,
especially at the outside tables. / Details: www.searcys.co.uk; 10 pm;
no smoking area; no booking at D.*

1880
The Bentley Hotel SW7

£ 65   A★

27-33 Harrington Gdns
7244 5555   4–2B
"OTT", "marbled" décor provides an "opulent" and "spacious" setting
at this new South Kensington Hotel dining room; it offers a "traditional",
"fine dining" experience, in which the star turn is ex-1837 chef, Andrew
Turner's "stunning" multi-course grazing menus (matched by "a
magnificent wine list"). / Details: www.thebentley-hotel.com; 10 pm; D only,
closed Sun; no smoking.

Ekachai EC2   £ 25
9-10 The Arcade, Liverpool St   7626 1155   5–2D
"Long queues at lunchtime" attest to the popularity of this "reasonably-
priced" Malaysian/Thai "noodle, rice and soup bar", near Liverpool
Street. / Details: 10 pm; closed Sat & Sun; no smoking at L; book only at D.

El Rincón Latino SW4   £ 28   A
148 Clapham Manor St   7622 0599   6–2D
"Like stepping into a bodega in Madrid" – this "superb", "busy"
Clapham bar is "full of life" and offers "fresh-tasting" tapas,
with "cheap" wine. / Details: 11.30 pm.

Electric Brasserie W11   £ 42
191 Portobello Rd   7908 9696
For a "top Sunday brunch", this "funky" and "buzzy" Notting Hill
brasserie is one of the hottest tickets in town; its general appeal as a
"cool" hang-out, though, is hampered by its "average" food and
"lacklustre" service. / Details: www.the-electric.co.uk; 10.45 pm.

Elena's L'Etoile W1   £ 49   A
30 Charlotte St   7636 7189   1–1C
This Fitzrovia "period piece" is an "enjoyably dated" destination where
famed octogenarian front-of-house Elena Salvoni greets her many long-
time regulars, who come in search of "no-gimmicks" Gallic fare. /
Details: www.simplyrestaurants.com; 10.30 pm; closed Sat L & Sun.

Elephant Royale
Locke's Wharf E14   £ 37   A
Westferry Rd   7987 7999
"The lovely outdoor setting", with many tables "overlooking the
Thames", is the special reason to seek out this OTT Thai cocktail
bar/restaurant at the south end of the Isle of Dogs; that said, the food,
if "pricey", is "surprisingly good". / Details: www.elephantroyale.com;
10.30 pm; no smoking area.

Elistano SW3   £ 35   A
25-27 Elystan St   7584 5248   4–2C
"If you don't mind the noise", this simple Chelsea Italian has a lot going
for it – "a lively buzz", "personalised" service and "good prices for the
area"; esteem for the "authentic" cooking, however, continues
to dwindle. / Details: 10.45 pm.

Emile's SW15   £ 29   ★
96-98 Felsham Rd   8789 3323   6–2B
"If anything, prices are too low!", say regulars at Putney's "secret
favourite" – a rambling and "rather old-fashioned" bistro, praised for its
"good, honest food", and for a wine list which is "small, but well-priced
and interesting". / Details: emiles-restaurant.co.uk; 11 pm; D only, closed Sun;
no Amex.

The Engineer NW1   £ 38   A
65 Gloucester Ave   7722 0950
The "wonderful" atmosphere (boosted by an "unbeatable" garden)
helps secure a perennially "trendy" following for this "seminal Primrose
Hill gastropub"; the food is "of a high standard", but "pricey" for what
it is. / Details: www.the-engineer.com; 11 pm; no Amex.

L'Escargot W1   **£ 45**

48 Greek St   7437 2679   3–2A

On a good day, you get "top-class" cooking to complement the
"amazing" wine list at this Soho institution – either in the "romantic"
bistro, or in the "pleasant" (and pricey) Picasso Room; sagging ratings,
though, support those who say it's becoming "inconsistent" and
"unimpressive". / Value tip: set weekday L
£31(FP). **Details:** www.whitestarline.org.uk; 11.30 pm; closed Sat L & Sun (Picasso
Room also closed Mon).

Esenza W11   **£ 40**   ★

210 Kensington Park Rd   7792 1066

New from the Osteria Basilico stable, this "closely-packed" Notting Hill
Italian is already attracting raves for its "extremely tasty" food; "service
is good, if occasionally scatty". / Details: 11.30 pm; no Amex.

Fairuz   **£ 34**   ★

3 Blandford St, W1   7486 8108
27 Westbourne Grove, W2   7243 8444

"Lush" Lebanese dishes delivered "with real pride" make this "basic
and unpretentious" mini-chain – in Marylebone and Bayswater –
very popular. / Details: W1 11.30 pm, W2 midnight.

Fakhreldine W1   **£ 45**   Ⓐ

85 Piccadilly   7493 3424   2–4C

The recent make-over of this "oddly-located" Mayfair Lebanese
"has certainly been for the better" – it's much more tasteful nowadays,
and the food's "good" going on "interesting"; daylight visitors still get
"nice views over Green Park". / Details: www.fakhreldine.co.uk; midnight.

La Famiglia SW10   **£ 42**

7 Langton St   7351 0761   4–3B

"This old favourite's still going strong", say fans of this ever-fashionable
World's End Italian, who applaud its cooking "like Mama makes",
its "top garden" and its "winning way with families"; doubters, though,
find the food "tired" and the attitude "self-satisfied". /
Details: www.lafamiglialondon.com; 11.45 pm.

Faulkner's E8   **£ 22**   ★

424-426 Kingsland Rd   7254 6152

"Easily the best chippie in town", say its fans, but this esteemed
Dalston institution also managed a few "average" meals this year –
perhaps it was the strain of bracing for a total refit in the late summer
of 2004. / Details: 10 pm; no smoking area; need 8+ to book.

Ffiona's W8   **£ 35**   Ⓐ

51 Kensington Church St   7937 4152   4–1A

"Ffiona induces a relaxed, casual and extremely romantic atmosphere",
says one of the many fans of this "straightforward" English bistro
in Kensington, where the patronne is usually very much in evidence. /
Details: 11 pm; D only, closed Mon.

Fifteen N1   **£ 70**   X

15 Westland Pl   7251 1515   5–1C

"Jamie Oliver is seriously taking the p***", at his "amateurish", made-
for-TV Hoxton venture, where "average" food comes "at Gordon
Ramsay prices" – "just because it's a charity doesn't give them the right
to rip people off". / Details: www.fifteenrestaurant.com; 10 pm; closed Sun;
no smoking.

Fig N1   **£ 35**

169 Hemingford Rd   7609 3009

"Very cosy and intimate", this charmingly-located, pocket-sized
Islingtonian has picked up where the Dining Room (RIP) left off, offering
a "short, fresh and varied" menu attracting almost unanimous praise. /

Fine Burger Company £22 ★★
256 Muswell Hill Broadway, N10   8815 9292
37 Bedford Hill, SW12   8772 0266
"Beautifully cooked, freshly made burgers, with unusual toppings" have
made an instant smash-hit of this new chain; their still-small fan club
rates them *"the best in London by far"* – move over Gourmet Burger
Co? / **Details:** *www.homebar.co.uk/fbc; 11 pm; no smoking before 7 pm.*

Fino W1 £40 ★
33 Charlotte St
7813 8010   1–1C
"Fabulous" dishes (*"a modern upmarket take on traditional tapas"*) –
with *"warm and helpful"* service, too – have made a big hit of this
Fitzrovia basement yearling; we've always thought the décor surprisingly
un-Spanish – perhaps this will be put to rights by a late-2004 refurb'. /
Value tip: *pre-th. £25(FP).* **Details:** *www.finorestaurant.com; 10.30 pm; closed
Sat L & Sun.*

Fish Hoek W4 £40 ★★
6-8 Elliott Rd   8742 0766
"I'm hoeked!" – *"an amazing array"* of *"bizarrely-named"* fish help
make the menu at this *"very cramped"* South African bistro in Chiswick
"one of the most interesting in London"; the way they cook them
is *"wonderful"*, too. / **Details:** *10.30 pm; closed Mon (except Aug-Dec);
no Amex; no smoking area.*

Flâneur EC1 £39
41 Farringdon Rd   7404 4422   5–1A
"Delicious organic food" makes this *"chic"* Farringdon *"deli-diner"* very
popular with some reporters; *"excellent breakfasts"* win particular
praise. / **Details:** *10 pm; closed Sun D; no smoking.*

Floriana SW3 £45
15 Beauchamp Pl   7838 1500   4–1C
This *"discreet"* Knightsbridge Italian may be *"a quiet and stylish
retreat"*, but (for such a prominent location) it continues to inspire
surprisingly few – and rather mixed – reports, especially regarding its
ambitious cuisine. / **Details:** *www.floriana.co.uk; 11 pm; closed Sun; no smoking
area.*

Florians N8 £30
4 Topsfield Pde   8348 8348
This *"friendly"* Italian fixture in Crouch End seems to be back on more
consistent form; the bar may be *"a crush"*, but its *"unbeatable value"*
means it's still usually preferred to the quieter rear restaurant. /
Details: *www.floriansrestaurant.co.uk; 11 pm; no Amex.*

Foliage
Mandarin Oriental SW1 £67
66 Knightsbridge   7201 3723   4–1D
"Flamboyantly-presented" cooking and a *"fabulous"* wine list make this
"sophisticated" Knightsbridge dining room a top choice for some
reporters (especially for lunch, and particularly if you can get a park
view); satisfaction, though, is drifting down across the board. /
Details: *www.mandarinoriental.com; 10.30 pm; no smoking area; booking: max 6.*

Formosa Dining Room
The Prince Alfred W9 £36 Ⓐ
5a Formosa St   7286 3287
"Full of character", this converted Victorian boozer in Maida Vale had
a *"stylish and clean-lined"* dining extension added a couple of years
ago; staff *"try hard"* and the food, if a *"bit pricey"*, is *"consistently
correct"*. / **Details:** *10.45 pm; no Amex.*

(The Fountain)
Fortnum & Mason W1   £ 38
181 Piccadilly   7734 8040   2–3D
*St James's "quintessentially English" grocery and department store
makes a good spot for a "classy" breakfast, lunch, or pre-theatre bite;
for "the classic afternoon tea", head for the St James's Restaurant
(4th floor). / **Details:** www.fortnumandmason.co.uk; 7.45 pm; closed Sun;
no smoking area; no booking at L.*

Frantoio SW10   £ 37   A
397 King's Rd   7352 4146   4–3B
*This World's End fixture is "building up a strong local following" –
at last! – thanks to its "friendly" staff, its "roomy" quarters and its
Italian menu that's "consistently good and reasonably priced". /
Details: 11.30 pm.*

Frederick's N1   £ 44   A
106 Camden Pas   7359 2888
*"Tucked away from the bustle of Upper Street", this "professional"
Islington "classic" – with its impressive and charming conservatory –
has long been known as a "solid performer"; all aspects of the
operation, however, are "slipping". / **Value tip:** set weekday L
£29(FP). **Details:** www.fredericks.co.uk; 11.30 pm; closed Sun; no smoking area.*

French House W1   £ 37   A
49 Dean St   7437 2477   3–3A
*"Something special about the place, especially for a date" wins
a disproportionate fan club for this small and "easy-going" dining room
above an historic Soho boozer; the "straightforward" cooking can seem
"too plain", but most find it "sufficient for its purpose". / **Value
tip:** pre-th. £23(FP). **Details:** 11 pm; closed Sun D; booking: max 8.*

The Frontline Club W2   £ 34   A
13 Norfolk Pl
7479 8960
*"Huge windows" and "arresting photography" add drama to this
"classy" new venue (named after its ties with a war reporters' club),
which has been a "welcome arrival" in the grim area near St Mary's
Paddington; early feedback heaps praise on its "sympathetic" service
and "interesting" (if not ambitious) cooking. /
Details: www.frontlinerestaurant.com; 10.15 pm; closed Sun D; no smoking area.*

Fujiyama SW9   £ 19
7 Vining St   7737 2369   6–2D
*"It puts Wagamama in its place", say fans of this "friendly" and
"darkly-decorated" Brixton noodle bar, which serves "fast and simple"
noodles and bento boxes, at "dirt-cheap" prices. /
Details: www.newfujiyama.com; 10.45 pm, Sat & Sun midnight; no Amex;
no smoking area.*

Fung Shing WC2   £ 35   ★★
15 Lisle St   7437 1539   3–3A
*After a blip last year, this "down-at-heel" Chinatown veteran has
regained its traditional pre-eminence, offering Chinese cooking which
is "among the best, if not the best, in town" (especially the "unusual
specialities" and seafood dishes). / **Details:** www.fungshing.co.uk; 11.30 pm.*

Fuzzy's Grub SW1   £ 9   ★★
6 Crown Pas   7925 2791   2–4D
*"A brilliant concept" is hailed by fans of this superior British caff, which
serves "delicious" roasted meats – in "amazing sarnies", or served with
roasters and veg' – as well as "devastatingly good" breakfasts. /
Details: L only, closed Sat & Sun.*

Gallipoli   £21   Ⓐ
102 Upper St, N1   7359 0630
107 Upper St, N1   7226 5333
120 Upper St, N1   7226 8099
*The "frenetically busy" but "chilled" vibe – boosted by "staff who are
reliably friendly, even under pressure" – underpins the huge success
of this "burgeoning Islington mini-empire" of Turkish bistros; "tasty" and
"good-value" mezze also play their part. / Details: www.gallipolicafe.com;
11 pm, Fri & Sat midnight; no Amex.*

The Gate W6   £31   ★★
51 Queen Caroline St   8748 6932
*Thanks to "some of the best veggie cooking in the UK", you can take
carnivores – "without any whingeing" – to this "converted church hall",
five minutes' walk from Hammersmith Broadway; (the NW3 branch
is no more). / Details: www.gateveg.co.uk; 10.45 pm; closed Sat L & Sun.*

Le Gavroche W1   £91   Ⓐ★
43 Upper Brook St   7408 0881   2–2A
*For traditionalists, Michel Roux Jr's "luxurious" and "old-fashioned"
Mayfair basement – with its "impeccable" classic French cuisine, and a
wine list "like War & Peace" – is a destination which "never
disappoints"; prices, though, can seem "OTT". / Value tip: set weekday L
£62(FP). Details: www.le-gavroche.co.uk; 11 pm; closed Sat L & Sun; jacket
required at D.*

Gay Hussar W1   £39   Ⓐ
2 Greek St   7437 0973   3–2A
*"Old Labour still comes in droves", to this "cosy" and "delightfully old-
fashioned" Soho bastion of champagne socialism; the Hungarian
cooking may be a bit beside the point, but – having improved again
after a recent 'dip' – it's "still enjoyable". / Details: www.trpplc.com;
10.45 pm; closed Sun.*

Geeta NW6   £15   ★★
57-59 Willesden Ln   7624 1713
*"The décor's a nightmare", but "nothing matches" this Kilburn
subcontinental "for consistency, for warmth of welcome or for prices" –
make sure you choose from "the 'specials' and the south Indian dishes";
licensed, or you can BYO. / Details: 10.30 pm, Fri & Sat 11.30 pm; no Switch.*

Ghillies   £37   Ⓐ
271 New King's Rd, SW6   7371 0434
94 Point Pleasant, SW18   8871 9267
*"Dependable" and "unfussy" fish dishes win consistent approval for
these "cosy" bistros; the Wandsworth branch is notable for its "perfect"
summer setting – between a park and the Thames. / Details: SW6
10.30 pm, SW18 10 pm; SW6 closed Sun D.*

Giraffe   £29
6-8 Blandford St, W1   7935 2333
270 Chiswick High Rd, W4   8995 2100
7 Kensington High St, W8   7938 1221
29-31 Essex Rd, N1   7359 5999
46 Rosslyn Hill, NW3   7435 0343
27 Battersea Rise, SW11   7223 0933
*"Great for pancakes, fresh fruit smoothies or just an old-fashioned fry-
up" – this "bright and buzzy" chain was again the survey's 'No 1 for
breakfast'; weekend brunches – the highlight – are, however, "only truly
great if you love kids". / Details: 11 pm; no smoking.*

The Glasshouse TW9   £ 45   A★★
14 Station Pde   8940 6777
"Cracking" modern British cooking and "friendly and unpretentious" staff help make this "classy" Kew fixture "one of London's best local restaurants"; "pricing is fair", too, and the only gripe is that the premises can seem "noisy" and "cramped". / **Value tip:** *set weekday L £28(FP).* **Details:** *10.30 pm; no smoking.*

Globe Restaurant NW3   £ 38
100 Avenue Rd   7722 7200
"Always new ideas on the menu" and service which makes "plenty of effort" win loyal support for this Swiss Cottage spot, which is especially handy for the Hampstead Theatre; a regular cabaret is a feature. / **Value tip:** *pre-th. £26(FP).* **Details:** *www.globerestaurant.co.uk; 11 pm; closed Sat L & Sun; no Amex; no smoking area.*

Gordon Ramsay SW3   £ 91   A★★
68-69 Royal Hospital Rd   7352 4441   4–3D
Despite groans that "he should spend less time on TV", GR's "intimate" Chelsea flagship maintains the "world-class" form which makes it unique in London; "exhilaratingly good" modern French cuisine (overseen during the great man's absences by Mark Askew) is delivered by "Jean-Claude and the other staff, who treat you like royalty". / **Value tip:** *set weekday L £53(FP).* **Details:** *www.gordonramsay.com; 10.30 pm; closed Sat & Sun; jacket required; no smoking; booking: max 8.*

Gordon Ramsay at Claridge's
Claridge's Hotel W1   £ 72
55 Brook St   7499 0099   2–2B
The cooking (under Mark Sargeant) is "good, but not what you'd expect, given Gordon's reputation", at the "beautiful" Art Deco dining room of this famed Mayfair hotel; service is improving, though, as is the rather "hit-and-miss" ambience. / **Value tip:** *set weekday L £44(FP).* **Details:** *www.gordonramsay.com; 11 pm; jacket required; no smoking; booking: max 8.*

Gordon's Wine Bar WC2   £ 20   AX
47 Villiers St   7930 1408   3–4D
With its "murky" décor, its setting in "dark and beautiful" vaults (near Embankment) and its "great wine and sherry list", London's oldest wine bar "keeps you hooked, and the hours fly by"; the food (cheese platters, salads, simple dishes) is sometimes "terrible", but few seem to notice; great terrace in summer. / **Details:** *www.gordonswinebar.com; 11 pm; no Amex; no booking.*

Goring Hotel SW1   £ 59   A
15 Beeston Pl   7396 9000   1–4B
For "traditional English atmosphere", you can't beat this family-owned Victoria "time warp" hotel, where "attentive" staff serve "conservative" (but "beautifully-presented") fare to "well-spaced" tables; breakfast, naturally, is "the best in town". / **Details:** *www.goringhotel.co.uk; 10 pm; closed Sat L; no smoking area; booking: max 12.*

Gourmet Burger Kitchen   £ 21   ★
49 Fulham Broadway, SW6   7381 4242
50 Westbourne Grove, W2   7243 4344
131 Chiswick High Rd, W4   8995 4548
331 West End Ln, NW6   7794 5455
44 Northcote Rd, SW11   7228 3309
333 Putney Bridge Rd, SW15   8789 1199
"Great patties, dripping with gorgeous sauces" and "crisp, chunky chips" have quickly established this Kiwi-run chain as the source of London's "benchmark burger"; "can we have more of these places, please?" / **Details:** *www.gbkinfo.co.uk; 11 pm; no Amex; no smoking; no booking.*

The Grapes E14 £ 38 𝔸★
76 Narrow St 7987 4396
"Undiscovered by the Canary Wharf crowd", this ancient pub dining
room overlooking the Thames is a "timeless" place unanimously hailed
by reporters for "real ale and real food"; fish, the speciality, is "great"
(and "remember to book your oysters before you go"). /
Details: 9.15 pm; closed Sun D.

Great Eastern Dining Room EC2 £ 34 𝔸★
54 Great Eastern St 7613 4545 5–1D
"Fantastic tastes" – from an "excellent Thai fusion menu" – combine
with "helpful" staff and a "relaxed" vibe to create all-round satisfaction
with Will Ricker's reviving venture, once the epicentre of Shoreditch
cool. / **Details:** www.greateasterndining.co.uk; 10.45 pm; closed Sat L & Sun.

Green's SW1 £ 55 𝔸
36 Duke St 7930 4566 2–3D
"Understated, but infallibly classy", this clubland fixture's unchanging
virtues make it – for its "heavily-suited" following – some sort
of nirvana; the cooking is "pricey", of course, but it's "highly
professional", with "superb fish" a highlight; to ensure booth seating,
book ahead. / **Details:** www.greens.org.uk; 11 pm; closed Sun, May-Sep.

The Greenhouse W1 £ 80 𝔸
27a Hays Mews 7499 3331 2–3B
Early reports on Marlon Abela's new régime at this Mayfair mews old-
timer extol its "enormous" wine list and its "terrific" food; prices are
"scary", though, service can be "slow", and the new look – at least
in our personal view – is horribly corporate. / **Value tip:** set weekday L
£48(FP). **Details:** www.greenhouserestaurant.co.uk; 11 pm; closed Sat L & Sun;
booking: max 16.

The Greyhound NW10 £ 33 𝔸★
64-66 Chamberlayne Rd 8969 8080
"A great new asset for north west London", this Queens Park newcomer
(from the owners of the Highgate) is unanimously hailed by early
reporters as "a model gastropub". / **Details:** 10.30 pm; closed Mon L;
no Amex.

Gung-Ho NW6 £ 29 𝔸★
328-332 West End Ln 7794 1444
Back on its usual form, this "superior" West Hampstead Chinese
veteran consistently wins the thumbs up for its "terrific" service,
its "attractive" interior and its "clean-tasting" food. / **Details:** 11.30 pm;
no Amex.

The Gunmakers EC1 £ 27
13 Eyre Street Hill 7278 1022 5–1A
This "tucked-away" Farringdon boozer, newly revamped, already draws
praise for its "relaxed" setting, its "great" staff and its "well-prepared"
scoff. / **Details:** 10 pm; closed Sat & Sun D.

Hakkasan W1 £ 66 𝔸
8 Hanway Pl 7927 7000 3–1A
With its "outstanding" Chinese dishes, (not least "wonderful" dim sum),
Alan Yau's "sleek", "funky" and "clubby" basement, just north of Soho,
still delivers a "wow" experience; service can be "slow" and "annoying",
though, and the prices can seem plain "crazy". / **Details:** 11 pm;
no smoking area.

Hamburger Union   £ 20
25 Dean St, W1   7437 6004
4-6 Garrick St, WC2   7379 0412
*If you're looking for a "five-star McDonalds", this Covent Garden
newcomer – accompanied by a larger Soho site from late-2004 – is just
the place; almost all reports say it offers "first-class burgers, efficiently
served".* / **Details:** *www.hamburgerunion.com; 10.30 pm; no Amex; no smoking;
no booking.*

Harbour City W1   £ 25
46 Gerrard St   7439 7859   3–3B
*"Refurbishment has lifted the atmosphere" – and pepped up the
"courteous" service, too – at this Chinatown fixture; it's for "very good
dim sum" that it's most popular.* / **Details:** *11.30 pm.*

Hardy's W1   £ 38
53 Dorset St   7935 5929   1–1A
*A "reliable" bistro/wine bar "in a quiet Marylebone street" that makes
"a good haunt for a quick meal"; it's "useful for business as well
as pleasure".* / **Details:** *10.30 pm; closed Sat L & Sun; no smoking area.*

The Havelock Tavern W14   £ 29   A★★
57 Masbro Rd   7603 5374
*"The hardest part is getting a table", at this "outstanding" Olympia
gastropub, which delivers "gorgeous" cooking in a "buzzy" setting; if it
weren't for the "dreadful arrogance of the staff" – "as though they
trained for it!" – it would be pretty much perfect.* /
Details: *www.thehavelocktavern.co.uk; 10 pm; no credit cards; no booking.*

The Haven N20   £ 31   A★
1363 High Rd   8445 7419
*"What on earth is it doing in Whetstone? – this place is great"; reports
on all aspects of this "polished" neighbourhood restaurant suggest
it lives up to its name in this thin area: "it would be twice the price
in the West End".* / **Details:** *www.haven-bistro.co.uk; 11 pm; no smoking.*

Haz E1   £ 27   ★
9 Cutler St   7929 7923   5–2D
*This "bustling" Turkish yearling, "tucked away near Liverpool Street",
serves "simple and expert grills" and "great mezze", in "crowded"
conditions; it's "fantastic for a group of friends", or for an informal
business lunch.* / **Details:** *www.hazrestaurant.com; 11.30 pm; no smoking area.*

Hunan SW1   £ 37   ★★
51 Pimlico Rd   7730 5712   4–2D
*"Leave the ordering to Mr Peng and the results will be superb", at this
"uninspiring"-looking Pimlico fixture, whose "exceptional" and "fresh"
Chinese cuisine is among the best in town.* / **Details:** *11 pm; closed Sun;
no smoking area.*

The Ifield SW10   £ 31   A
59 Ifield Rd   7351 4900   4–3A
*Hidden away in the backwoods of Chelsea, this louche hang-out is still
tipped by some as the "ideal gastropub"; it doesn't attract nearly the
volume of rave reviews it once did, though.* / **Details:** *11 pm;
Mon-Thu D only, Fri-Sun open L & D.*

Imperial City EC3   £ 38   A★
Royal Exchange, Cornhill   7626 3437   5–2C
*"Above-par" Chinese cooking and "swift" service make this heart-of-the-
City basement an ever-"reliable" business lunching destination; given all
these advantages, its prices are surprisingly "reasonable", too!* /
Details: *www.imperial-city.co.uk; 9.30 pm; closed Sat & Sun.*

Inaho W2 £ 27 ★★
4 Hereford Rd   7221 8495
"The best, certainly the best-value traditional Japanese food in London"
(with sushi that's "second to none") is to be found at this odd
Bayswater shack; service, though, is "often frustratingly slow". /
Details: 11 pm; closed Sat L & Sun; no Amex or Switch; no smoking.

L'Incontro SW1 £ 50 𝔸★
87 Pimlico Rd   7730 6327   4–2D
Now run by one of the founder's daughters, this "comfortable" and
"understated" Pimlico Italian is much improved; some still say it's
"too expensive", but the soaring ratings support those who say it's
becoming a "very good" all-rounder. / **Details:** www.lincontro-restaurant.com;
11.30 pm; closed Sun.

Indigo
One Aldwych WC2 £ 49 ★
1 Aldwych   7300 0400   1–2D
"Overlooking a cool and buzzy bar", this "comfy" and "understated"
boutique-hotel mezzanine offers a "tranquil" setting whose appeal for
business is boosted by its "brisk" service; the menu – "from casual
to surprisingly complex" – is "consistently well done". /
Details: www.onealdwych.com; 11.15 pm; no smoking at breakfast.

Inn the Park SW1 £ 40 𝔸
St James's Pk   7451 9999   1–3C
A "great terrace" adds to the "unique" charms of this "wonderfully
exciting" new building, by the St James's Park lake; with Oliver Peyton
in charge, though, it's no surprise that the straightforward British food
is pricey for what it is, or that service is "disorganised", but brunch (or a
self-service sandwich in the adjacent café) is a safe bet. /
Details: 9.45 pm; no smoking.

Inside SE10 £ 34
19 Greenwich South St   8265 5060
"Worth a visit, if in Greenwich" – this "pleasant" neighbourhood
restaurant wins praise for its "interesting" fare, with a "superb"
weekend brunch a highlight. / **Details:** www.insiderestaurant.co.uk; 11 pm;
closed Mon, Tue L & Sun D; no Amex; no smoking area.

Itsu £ 24 𝔸★
103 Wardour St, W1   7479 4790
118 Draycott Ave, SW3   7590 2400
Level 2, Cabot Place East, E14   7512 5790
"Miles better than Yo! Sushi" – these "buzzy" conveyor-joints offer
"a great modern take on sushi" (plus some "innovative", "fusion"
dishes), in a "fun and stylish" setting. / **Details:** www.itsu.co.uk; 11 pm,
W1 Fri & Sat midnight; E14 closed Sat & Sun; no smoking; no booking.

The Ivy WC2 £ 50 𝔸
1 West St   7836 4751   3–3B
It's hard to shake off the feeling that this "glamorous" Theatrelander –
for an amazing ninth year, the survey's No. 1 favourite – may be
nearing the end of its reign; the "upmarket comfort food" has never
been the main point, but it's been more "forgettable" of late,
and "disappointments" generally are on the up. / **Value tip:** set weekday L
£32(FP). **Details:** midnight; booking: max 6.

Jenny Lo's Tea House SW1 £ 21 ★★
14 Eccleston St   7259 0399   1–4B
"Fast but amazing-quality food" is on offer at this "friendly" Belgravia
noodle-canteen – no wonder it "seems to be getting busier". /
Details: 10 pm; closed Sun; no credit cards; no booking.

Jin Kichi NW3   £33   ★★
73 Heath St   7794 6158
*"Authentic" and "cramped", this Hampstead Japanese, is "always
mobbed" (less so downstairs), thanks to its "great-value" food and its
"always-polite" service; the "different" menu features "great yakitori"
(grilled skewers) as well as "very good sushi". /* **Details:** www.jinkichi.com;
11 pm; closed Mon, Tue-Fri D only, Sat & Sun open L & D.

Joe Allen WC2   £39   A
13 Exeter St   7836 0651   3–3D
*It may be "trading on its history", but this famous Covent Garden
basement's "vibrant" late-night ambience can still make it a good
Theatreland "hide-away"; the menu is "stale", though, and its
realisation "hit-and-miss" (with the off-menu burger the star turn). /*
Details: www.joeallen.co.uk; 12.45 am; no smoking area.

Julie's W11   £45   A
135 Portland Rd   7229 8331
*"Character spills out of every inch" of this "unique" Holland Park
labyrinth, whose "intimate and seductive" nooks and crannies are
famed for their "incredibly romantic" charm; the food, however,
is perennially "lazy". /* **Details:** www.juliesrestaurant.com; 10.45 pm.

Just Oriental SW1   £33   A
19 King St   7976 2222   2–4D
*A "stylish" St James's basement bar whose "interesting" oriental menu
makes it a surprisingly good place for "a quiet lunch"; a late licence has
been applied for – look out for a loungier style and the arrival
of regular DJs. /* **Value tip:** set weekday L
£21(FP). **Details:** www.juststjames.com/joabout.htm; 11 pm; closed Sat L & Sun.

K10 EC2   £25   ★
20 Copthall Ave   7562 8510   5–2C
*"Look beyond the gimmicky conveyor belt" – this "subterranean City
hang-out" serves "top-quality Japanese food, hot and cold"; its ratings
are not as starry as they were, though – perhaps the strain of opening
a new take-away branch in Fleet Street. /* **Details:** www.k10.net; 9.45 pm;
closed Sat & Sun; no smoking; no booking.

Kai W1   £53   ★
65 South Audley Street   7493 8507   2–3A
*A "very classy" Mayfair Chinese that reliably dishes up "pricey but very
good" food in a "civilised" and "comfortable" (if slightly "corporate")
environment. /* **Details:** www.kaimayfair.com; 10.45 pm.

Kastoori SW17   £21   ★★
188 Upper Tooting Rd   8767 7027   6–2C
*"The flavours just explode in your mouth", at this "slightly dingy" but
"very friendly" shop-conversion on Tooting's main drag – its "unusual
African-influenced, Indian vegetarian food" is among the best in town. /*
Details: 10.30 pm; closed Mon L & Tue L; no Amex or Switch; booking: max 12.

Kazan SW1   £28
93-94 Wilton Rd   7233 7100   1–4B
*"An oasis in a culinary desert", this "good local Turk" has quickly
gathered a following among Pimlico folk; it's also quite handy for those
passing through Victoria, five minutes' walk away. /* **Details:** 11 pm;
no Amex; no smoking area.

Ken Lo's Memories SW1   £52   ★
67-69 Ebury St   7730 7734   1–4B
*The food is "wonderful" ("which it should be for the price"), at this
veteran Chinese near Victoria, "which deserves a medal for
consistency"; the setting is "smart", too, though the ambience
is "slightly indifferent". /* **Details:** 11.15 pm; closed Sun L.

Ken Lo's Memories of China W8 £ 47 ★
353 Kensington High St   7603 6951
*"Very refined" cooking makes this "reliable" but anodyne-looking
Chinese, on the way to Olympia, an "an all-time favourite" for some
reporters. / Value tip: set weekday L
£29(FP). Details: www.atozrestaurants.com; 11.15 pm.*

Kew Grill TW9 £ 43
10b, Kew Grn   8948 4433
*The locals "must be pleased" by the arrival of TV-chef Antony Worrall
Thompson's "relaxing" but small and "tightly-packed" newcomer,
off Kew Green, where "good steaks" are a highlight of a simple grills
menu; it can seem rather "pricey", though, for what it is. /
Details: www.awtonline.co.uk; 10.30 pm; no smoking.*

Lahore Kebab House E1 £ 19 ★★
2 Umberston St   7488 2551
*"OK it ain't pretty, but the food's amazing" and "brilliant value for
money", at this famously "back-to-basics", BYO East End diner;
the kebabs, in particular, are "sublime". / Details: 11.30 pm; no Amex;
need 12+ to book.*

Lamberts SW12 £ 36 ★
2 Station Pde   8675 2233   6–2C
*"The best food in Balham" is proclaimed by the many supporters
of this "really strong" yearling, which has "improved in leaps and
bounds since it opened"; an "excellent Sunday lunch" is a highlight. /
Details: www.lambertsrestaurant.com; 10.30 pm; closed Mon, Tue-Fri D only, Sat &
Sun open L & D; no Amex; no smoking area.*

Lanes
East India House E1 £ 40 ★
109-117 Middlesex St
7247 5050   5–2D
*"Top-notch food, served in an unpretentious atmosphere that's unusual
in the City" has made this late-2003 newcomer an immediate hit;
service – from the "young and talented" (ex-MPW) proprietors –
is "delightful", too. / Details: www.lanesrestaurant.co.uk; 10 pm; closed Sat &
Sun.*

Langan's Bar & Grill SW5 £ 35
254-260 Old Brompton Rd   7259 2599   4–3A
*With its "old-fashioned Gallic fare", its "notably friendly" service and its
pleasant front terrace, this Earl's Court brasserie ought to be a useful
stand-by; it has never found much of a following in recent times, though,
and supporters insist it's "under-valued". /
Details: www.langansrestaurants.co.uk; 11 pm.*

Langan's Brasserie W1 £ 46 Ⓐ
Stratton St   7491 8822   2–3C
*"Always buzzy, and full of entertaining characters", this "really lively"
Mayfair institution remains a popular Big Night Out destination
(especially for out-of-towners); its formula has looked "dated" in recent
times, but ratings began to stage a recovery this year. /
Details: www.langansrestaurants.co.uk; 11.45 pm; closed Sat L & Sun.*

Lansdowne NW1 £ 36 Ⓐ★
90 Gloucester Ave   7483 0409
*This "unpretentious" Primrose Hill gastropub consistently draws
a "young and trendy" crowd, thanks not least to its "sophisticated"
cuisine; there is a ground-floor bar or a posher upstairs (for which you
can book) – fans divide over which is better. / Details: 10 pm; closed
Mon L; no Amex; no smoking area.*

La Lanterna SE1   **£ 30**   Ⓐ★

6-8 Mill St   7252 2420

This "fun" and "lively" Italian, near Butlers Wharf, wins nothing but praise for its "friendly" style, its "good pizzas and pasta" and its "great outdoor summer dining" – and all at "good-value" prices! /
Details: *www.millstreetcafe.co.uk; 11 pm; closed Sat L; no smoking area.*

Latium W1   **£ 39**   ★

21 Berners St

7323 9123   1–1C

"Cracking" cooking and "impeccable" service have made this new north-Italian "a real success"; despite the "warm" welcome, though, the atmosphere of its premises, just north of Oxford Street, can seem a little "stark" – surely growing popularity will soon jazz it up? /
Details: *www.latiumrestaurant.com; 10.30 pm; closed Sat L & Sun.*

Laughing Gravy SE1   **£ 39**

154 Blackfriars Rd   7721 7055   5–4A

"A great find in a wasteland"; "friendly proprietors" add to the ambience at this "quirky" Southwark venture, where "hearty" meat and fish dishes are a highlight; some tip the "second-to-none" bar menu over that in the restaurant; (NB, as we go to press, sale is mooted). /
Details: *10 pm; closed Sat L & Sun; no Amex.*

Launceston Place W8   **£ 46**   Ⓐ

1a Launceston Pl   7937 6912   4–1B

"Tucked away in a Kensington backwater", this "calm" and "charming" English fixture – which often offers "delicious" cooking – remains "a great place to take your best squeeze or your mum"; some reporters do fear, though, that "middle-aged complacency" may be setting in. /
Details: *www.egami.co.uk; 11.30 pm; closed Sat L & Sun D.*

Lemonia NW1   **£ 27**   Ⓐ

89 Regent's Park Rd   7586 7454

This "astonishingly successful" Primrose Hill Greek is "always full", and emanates "a wonderful joie de vivre"; the taverna fare is "nothing clever", though, but it is "cheap" and "consistent", and the staff "look after you so well". / **Value tip:** *set weekday L £18(FP).* **Details:** *11.30 pm; closed Sat L & Sun D; no Amex.*

Levantine W2   **£ 32**   Ⓐ★

26 London St   7262 1111

Early reports, though few, have been very 'up' on this new venture, which certainly looks surprisingly "authentic" and "ornate" for somewhere a stone's throw from Paddington station; the "delicious mezze menu" wins particular praise. / **Details:** *midnight.*

Lightship E1   **£ 40**   Ⓐ

5a Katharine's Way, St Kath's Dock   7481 3123   5–3D

"To impress your date", this "cosy" and "intimate" former lightship, moored near Tower Bridge, certainly offers a "unique" and "original" setting; its modern Scandinavian fare is fine, too, but is unlikely to distract from the magic of the moment. / **Details:** *www.lightshipx.com; 10 pm; closed Sat L & Sun D.*

Lindsay House W1   **£ 73**

21 Romilly St   7439 0450   3–3A

Richard Corrigan's "quirky old Soho townhouse" is putting in an ever more mixed performance; at times the cooking is still "absolutely fantastic", but "quality has fallen" in recent years, service verges on "shambolic", and the place's "romantic" ambience is suffering. / **Value tip:** *set weekday L £48(FP).* **Details:** *www.lindsayhouse.co.uk; 11 pm; closed Sat L & Sun.*

Lisboa Patisserie W10   £ 5   ★★

57 Golborne Rd   8968 5242

*"Great... if you can get in", this "real North Kensington hang-out"
serves "coffee how it should be"; "unbeatable pasteis de nata" (custard
tarts) are the highlight among the "excellent sweet and savoury
pastries".* / **Details:** *8 pm; L & early evening only; no Amex; no booking.*

Little Basil NW3   £ 27   🅐★

82 Hampstead High St   7794 6238

*"Hampstead's only Thai", handily located in the heart of village, offers
"great-value" fare in a "simple but imaginative" setting – it's no great
surprise that it's quickly acquired "local-favourite" status.* /
Details: *11 pm; no Amex; no smoking area.*

Little Bay   £ 23   🅐

228 Belsize Rd, NW6   7372 4699
228 York Rd, SW11   7223 4080
171 Farringdon Rd, EC1   7278 1234

*"Unbelievable value for money" is the theme of all commentary on this
small chain of "bargain bistros", where the food is "far better than
it has any right to be, given the prices".* / **Details:** *11.30 pm;
NW6 no credit cards, no Amex; no smoking area, NW6; NW6 need 4+ to book.*

LMNT E8   £ 25   🅐

316 Queensbridge Rd   7249 6727

*With its "wacky", "funky" and "fabulous" Egyptian-style décor,
this Dalston "oasis" is a "see-it-to-believe-it" destination; surprisingly,
it also offers "truly decent food at seriously low prices".* /
Details: *www.lmnt.co.uk; 11 pm; no Amex.*

Lobster Pot SE11   £ 38   🅐★★

3 Kennington Ln   7582 5556

*"Neither the name nor the location prepares you" for this "kitsch"
("almost comical") seafood parlour, where the recorded cries of Breton
sea-gulls drown out the Kennington traffic; "very French" staff deliver
"outstanding", "traditional" Gallic fish dishes.* / **Value tip:** *set weekday L
£25(FP).* **Details:** *www.lobsterpotrestaurant.co.uk; 10.30 pm; closed Mon & Sun;
no smoking area; booking: max 8.*

**Locanda Locatelli
Churchill InterCont'l W1**   £ 49   🅐★

8 Seymour St
7935 9088   1–2A

*"A great interpretation of modern Italian food" is hailed by fans
of Giorgio Locatelli's "sophisticated" (and "moody") Portman Square
two-year-old; there's no denying, though, that for a vocal minority
of reporters the place is just "overhyped" and "overpriced".* /
Details: *www.locandalocatelli.com; 11 pm; closed Sun; booking: max 6.*

Lots Road SW10   £ 32

114 Lots Rd   7352 6645   4–4B

*"Fantastic burgers" are the sort of "better-than-average pub food"
which draw people to this "out-of-the-way" gastropub –
an "atmospheric" hang-out, by the entrance to Chelsea Harbour.* /
Details: *10 pm.*

Lou Pescadou SW5   £ 38   ★

241 Old Brompton Rd   7370 1057   4–3A

*This "very French" Earl's Court "stalwart" has such a reputation as a
"friendly", "neighbourhood" place that it's easy to overlook the fact that
– for "classic, unadulterated seafood" – it is now one of the top places
in town.* / **Value tip:** *set weekday L £22(FP).* **Details:** *midnight.*

Lowiczanka
Polish Social & Cultural Assoc'n W6   £ 25
238-246 King St   8741 3225
A "good-value" café attached to a Hammersmith cultural centre,
to which ethnic dishes and émigré-regulars add interest. / **Value tip:** set
weekday L £15(FP). **Details:** 10 pm.

Luc's Brasserie EC3   £ 38
17-22 Leadenhall Mkt   7621 0666   5–2D
"Still enjoyable, despite the change of ownership"; this "great French
restaurant", with "genuine Gallic waiters", still does what it does very
well, and it remains "a top place for an informal City lunch". /
Details: L only, closed Sat & Sun.

Lucio SW3   £ 42   A
257 Fulham Rd   7823 3007   4–3B
Judging by its already-"bustling" ambience, this elegant latest occupant
of an ever-changing Chelsea site may exorcise the many ghosts which
haunt it; service is exemplary and the Italian cooking is consistently
enjoyable. / **Details:** 10.30 pm; no Amex.

Lucky Seven W11   £ 30   A
127 Westbourne Park Rd   7727 6771
Tom Conran's "beautiful re-creation of an American diner" – complete
with "fun, shared booths" – serves "damn fine" burgers and
"awesome" shakes to a hip Notting Hillbilly crowd; service is "beautiful
but rude". / **Details:** 11 pm; closed Mon L; no credit cards; no booking.

Lundum's SW7   £ 40   A ★
119 Old Brompton Rd   7373 7774   4–2B
"An unsung haven of continental civilisation"; this "brilliant" South
Kensington Scandinavian "gem" (recently doubled in size) is a "unique
and enjoyable" destination, whose "attentive" staff serve up "authentic"
food in a "quiet" and "romantic" setting. / **Value tip:** set weekday L
£27(FP). **Details:** www.lundums.com; 11 pm; closed Sun D.

Ma Cuisine   £ 26   ★
6 Whitton Rd, TW1
8607 9849
"Well-executed French classic dishes" at "excellent" prices plus "keen"
staff have won an instant stellar reputation for this "cramped"
Twickenham bistro ("a spin-off from neighbouring McClements"). /
Details: 11 pm; no Amex; no smoking area.

Madhu's UB1   £ 28   ★★
39 South Rd   8574 1897
"It's a pity Southall's not easier to get to, or I'd be a regular", says a
(Clapham) fan of this recently revamped curry house; its "excellent and
authentic Indian cooking" draws reporters from all over town. /
Details: www.madhusonline.com; 11.30 pm; closed Tue, Sat L & Sun L.

Maggie Jones's W8   £ 46   A ★
6 Old Court Pl   7937 6462   4–1A
"Particularly on a chilly winter night", it's a joy to visit this rustic-style
fixture, near Kensington Palace, where many "cosy crannies" make for
a "wonderfully seductive" atmosphere; its "hearty" Anglo/French fare
put in a stronger-than-usual showing this year. / **Details:** 10.30 pm.

Maggiore's WC2   £ 46   A
33 King St   7379 9696   3–3C
"A surprise in the heart of Covent Garden", this "cosy" and "untouristy"
fixture is "perfect for impressing a date", thanks to its "magical" setting
(complete with cute inner courtyard); its "simple" cooking generally
"hits the spot", too, and is supported by a "stunning wine cellar". /
Value tip: pre-th. £32(FP). **Details:** www.maggiores.co.uk; 11 pm.

Maison Bertaux W1   £ 9   A★
28 Greek St   7437 6007   3–2A
This "precious" coffee house (est. 1871) remains a "ritual of Soho life"
– even those who say it's a "dingy" place with "exalted prices" often
adore its "eccentric" service and its "outstanding pastries and coffee". /
Details: 9 pm; no credit cards; no smoking area; no booking.

Malabar W8   £ 28   ★
27 Uxbridge St   7727 8800
It's "hard to fault" this incredibly dependable, long-established Notting
Hill curry house – "the food is fresh and inventive", the setting
is "minimal and cool" ("if rather poky downstairs"), and the service
is "charming". / **Details:** www.malabar-restaurant.co.uk; 11.15 pm; no Amex.

Malabar Junction WC1   £ 34
107 Gt Russell St   7580 5230   1–1C
This almost "stately" Bloomsbury Indian offers "more interesting cuisine
than is usual in its price range", plus "friendly" service; the occasional
misfire, however, is not unknown. / **Value tip:** set weekday L
£13(FP). **Details:** 11.30 pm; no smoking area.

Malmaison EC1   £ 39   A
18-21 Charterhouse St   7012 3700   5–1B
This national boutique-hotel chain – never before present in the capital
– has made a solid London debut with this "calm" and "chic" Smithfield
dining room; it's immediately been applauded as "a great all-rounder",
where the food is "unadventurous" but "well-executed". /
Details: www.malmaison.com; 10.30 pm; no smoking area.

Mandalay W2   £ 18   ★★
444 Edgware Rd   7258 3696
You get "a feast of flavours" at an "incredibly low" price, at this simple
Burmese (Chinese-meets-Indian), north of Edgware Road tube;
its premises don't win any prizes for interior design, but "great personal
service" is ample compensation. / **Value tip:** set weekday L
£12(FP). **Details:** 10.30 pm; closed Sun; no smoking.

Mandarin Kitchen W2   £ 33   ★★
14-16 Queensway   7727 9012
"The best seafood in town" ensures a constant crush at this "chaotic"
Bayswater Chinese (which "claims to serve more lobsters than
anywhere else in the UK!"); "book, but even so you may have to wait".
/ **Details:** 11.15 pm.

Mangal E8   £ 15   ★★
10 Arcola St   7275 8981
It's "mangy-looking from the street", but "crowded", "busy" and "really
atmospheric" within at this Dalston Turk, where "there's no menu –
the waiter shows you what's available"; the kebabs are arguably
"the best in London" and they are so so "cheap"; BYO. /
Details: midnight; no credit cards; need 10+ to book.

Mango Room NW1   £ 30   A★
10 Kentish Town Rd   7482 5065
This "fantastically atmospheric" Camden Town Caribbean "favourite"
is "always full", thanks to its "interesting" cooking and its "reasonable"
prices; the rum punch is "fab", too. / **Details:** www.mangoroom.co.uk;
10.45 pm; closed Mon L; no Amex.

Manicomio SW3   £ 38
85 Duke of York Sq   7730 3366   4–2D
"Italian deli-style food", using "delicious fresh ingredients", wins many
fans for this "traffic-free" spot – with many alfresco tables – in the new
development near Sloane Square; critics find it "characterless", though,
and rather "overpriced". / **Details:** 10.30 pm; no smoking area.

Manna NW3   £ 34   ★
4 Erskine Rd   7722 8028
"Very inventive and tasty vegetarian food" is again making a bigger name for this "veteran" Primrose Hill veggie (the UK's oldest); it can still seem a bit "drab", though. / **Details:** *www.manna-veg.com; 10.45 pm; D only, ex Sun open L & D; no Amex; no smoking.*

Marine Ices NW3   £ 26
8 Haverstock Hill   7482 9003
Children of all ages love the Mansi family's north London institution – a Chalk Farm fixture of over 50 years' standing – which serves pizza and pasta of "consistent" quality, as well, of course, as "yummy" ice cream. / **Details:** *11 pm; no Amex; no smoking area.*

Maroush   £ 40   ★
I) 21 Edgware Rd, W2   7723 0773
II) 38 Beauchamp Pl, SW3   7581 5434
III) 62 Seymour St, W1   7724 5024
IV) 68 Edgware Rd, W2   7724 9337
V) 3-4 Vere St, W1   7493 3030
"Garden") 1 Connaught St, W2   7262 0222
"Where else can you eat well at 3am?" – these "busy", "brightly-lit" kebab cafés (at I, II and V) generate a "cheerful babble", and serve "lovely kebabs" and "delicious" juices into the early hours; the more sedate restaurant sections (all branches) attract less attention from reporters. / **Details:** *1 am, SW3 2.30 am.*

Masala Zone   £ 22
9 Marshall St, W1   7287 9966
80 Upper St, N1   7359 3399
Critics find them too "loud and brash", and say that realisation is "hit-and-miss", but most reporters hail this "funky" small chain for its "great-value Indian street food" (and "excellent thalis"). / **Details:** *www.realindianfood.com; 11 pm; no smoking; no booking.*

McClements TW1   £ 52
2 Whitton Road   8744 9610
The new Michelin gong seems to have gone to the head of John McClement's ambitious Twickenham restaurant – yes, it still attracts mainly "superb-as-ever" reviews, but a visit now strikes some reporters as "outrageously expensive" or "overblown". / **Details:** *www.mcclementsrestaurant.com; 10.30 pm; closed Sun D; no smoking area.*

Mediterraneo W11   £ 37
37 Kensington Park Rd   7792 3131
"Cramped and always buzzing", this Notting Hill Italian is thought of by some reporters as "an upmarket version of Osteria Basilico" (nearby, same owners); recently, however, the place has "lost soul" – perhaps it's something to do with the strain of opening Esenza? / **Details:** *11.30 pm; booking: max 8.*

Le Metro SW3   £ 31
28 Basil St   7591 1213   4–1D
"A very good and reasonably-priced wine list" adds to the appeal of this "relaxed" bar/bistro, hidden away under an hotel near Harrods; for the area, it offers "good VFM". / **Details:** *www.capitalgrp.co.uk; 9.45 pm; closed Sun L & D; no smoking area.*

Mildred's W1   £ 26
45 Lexington St   7494 1634   2–2D
"Central London's best veggie" (in the backwoods of Soho) is a "relaxed" and "buzzy" sort of place – "if you need health, this hits the spot". / **Details:** *www.mildreds.co.uk; 11 pm; closed Sun; only Switch; no smoking; no booking.*

Mint Leaf SW1   £ 48   🅐

1 Suffolk Pl   7930 9020   1–2C

*With its "very cool bar" and stylish, partitioned décor, it's easy
to dismiss this "chic" basement yearling, near Trafalgar Square, as a
"Hakkasan wannabe"; its "quality" Indian "fusion" cooking, however,
is part of a consistently good overall performance. /
Details: www.mintleafrestaurant.com; 11 pm; closed Sat L & Sun; no smoking area.*

Mirabelle W1   £ 60   🅐

56 Curzon St   7499 4636   2–4B

*"Even the mirror ball looks classy", at this "glamorous" Mayfair
favourite, which numbers "stunning" Art Deco décor, "attentive" service
and a "fantastic" wine list among its attractions; MPW's "timeless
catalogue" of Gallic gastronomy generally pleases, too, but reports also
recorded quite a few "uninspired" results this year. / **Value tip:** set
weekday L £40(FP). **Details:** www.whitestarline.org.uk; 11.15 pm; no smoking area.*

Mirch Masala   £ 16   ★★

1416 London Road, SW16   8679 1828
213 Upper Tooting Rd, SW17   8672 7500
171-173 The Broadway, UB1   8867 9222

*"Fantastic food on Formica tables" is the deal at these "no-frills"
Pakistani canteens in Norbury and Tooting (and now since May 2004
in Southall), which serve some of "the best subcontinental cuisine
in London". / **Value tip:** set weekday L £9(FP). **Details:** midnight; no Amex;
no smoking, SW17.*

Mirto SW6   £ 34   ★

839 Fulham Rd   7736 3217   6–1B

*"Personable" service helps make up for the lack of pizazz at this small
and difficult Fulham site; it's well worth a try, though, as the "light"
Sardinian cooking can be "fantastic". / **Details:** 10.30 pm.*

Miyabi
Great Eastern Hotel EC2   £ 36   ★★

Liverpool St   7618 7100   5–2D

*"Get there early or book", if you want to enjoy the "very good sushi and
sashimi" at this "small but perfectly formed" Conran group outlet,
by Liverpool Street station. / **Details:** www.miyabi.co.uk; 10.30 pm; closed
Sat & Sun; booking: max 6.*

Mohsen W14   £ 19   ★★

152 Warwick Rd   7602 9888

*"The greatest cheap Persian food" (not least, "flatbread to die for")
is served by the "open and friendly" proprietors of this simple Olympia
café (which enjoys a grandstand view of 'Homebase', opposite); BYO. /
Details: 11.30 pm; no credit cards.*

Momo W1   £ 47   🅐

25 Heddon St   7434 4040   2–2C

*"A Eurotrash clientèle" laps up the "intoxicating atmosphere" of this
"sexy-as-hell" party-Moroccan (which also has a "fantastic" basement
bar); perennial gripes about service were less in evidence, this year,
and the grub seems to be improving, too. / **Details:** www.momoresto.com;
11.30 pm; closed Sun L.*

Mon Plaisir WC2   £ 46   🅐

19-21 Monmouth St   7836 7243   3–2B

*This "real French bistro" in Covent Garden is a "romantic", "warren-
like" veteran of half a century's standing, and has long been
appreciated for its "fail-safe" virtues (not least "the best value pre-
theatre deal in town"); those who say it's "really slipped", however,
are becoming ever-harder to ignore. / **Value tip:** set weekday L
£28(FP). **Details:** www.monplaisir.co.uk; 11.15 pm; closed Sat L & Sun.*

Monmouth Coffee Company WC2   £ 9   ★★
27 Monmouth St   7379 3516   3–2B
The air is "thick with caffeine", at this café near Borough Market; as a
gourmet coffee experience, it is simply without equal – "you may have
to wait for a seat, particularly at weekends". /
Details: www.monmouthcoffee.co.uk; no smoking.

Monsieur Max TW12   £ 52   ★★
133 High St   8979 5546
"A distillation of everything French, but without the snobbery" –
this Hampton Hill "hidden treasure" remains simply "top-notch" all-
round, and is consistently praised for its "wonderful" cuisine. / **Value**
tip: *set weekday L £36(FP).* **Details:** *9.30 pm; closed Sat L.*

Morgan M N7   £ 42   ★★
489 Liverpool Road
7609 3560

"Simply outstanding" Gallic cooking has made an instant gastronomic
hit of ex-Admiralty chef M. Meunier's "rather serious" newcomer,
notwithstanding its "odd" (ex-pub) location, at the top end of Islington;
a "divine" chocolate pudding featured in a number of reports. /
Details: *10 pm; closed Mon, Tue L, Sat L & Sun D; no Amex; booking: max 6.*

Moro EC1   £ 41   Ⓐ★★
34-36 Exmouth Mkt   7833 8336   5–1A
"A lovely Spanish/North African fusion" – that's "simple, but well
realised" – has long made this "vibrant" Clerkenwell linchpin "a sure-
fire hit"; the setting is "a bit cheek-by-jowl", though, and staff risk
becoming "a bit blasé". / **Details:** *www.moro.co.uk; 10.30 pm; closed Sat L &*
Sun; some booking restrictions apply.

Mr Wing SW5   £ 45   ★
242-244 Old Brompton Rd   7370 4450   4–2A
Since they did away with the amazing jungle décor – in favour of a
more "serious", "contemporary" look – this Earl's Court Chinese has
lost some of its unique charm; the place is "still on good form", though,
offering "great, if costly" cooking and "helpful" service. / **Value tip:** *set*
weekday L £23(FP). **Details:** *www.mrwing.com; 11.30 pm.*

Murano TW9   £ 38
110 Kew Rd   8948 8330
Regulars approve the move from central Richmond to these new
ground-floor premises "on a busy road"; they say "this is a good Italian
that could use more support". / **Details:** *www.muranorestaurant.co.uk;*
11 pm; no smoking area.

Nahm
Halkin Hotel SW1   £ 60   ★
5 Halkin St   7333 1234   1–3A
David Thompson offers "the best Thai food in Britain", according
to fans of this stark Belgravia boutique-hotel dining room; there are
many sceptics, though, to whom the place is "ridiculously overpriced",
and even supporters concede that there's "zero" ambience. / **Value**
tip: *set weekday L £39(FP).* **Details:** *www.halkin.co.uk; 11 pm; closed Sat L &*
Sun L.

New Tayyab E1   £ 15   ★★
83 Fieldgate St   7247 9543   5–2D
"If you thought the Lahore Kebab House was London's ultimate curry,
you were wrong" – the food at this "noisy" and "jam-packed" East
Ender is simply "excellent"; BYO, and prepare to queue. /
Details: *www.tayyabs.co.uk; 11.30 pm; closed for Ramadan; no booking at L.*

Niksons SW11   **£ 42**
172-174 Northcote Rd   7228 2285   6–2C
*The "light and airy" rear dining room of this "convivial" Battersea local
(entered "through a lively bar") is generally a reliable destination;
some reports, though, suggest it's becoming "fairly average" in all
respects. / Details: www.niksons.co.uk; 10.30 pm; Mon-Thu D only, Fri-Sun open
L & D; no smoking area.*

**Nobu
Metropolitan Hotel W1**   **£ 75**   ★
Old Park Lane   7447 4747   2–4A
*"Divine" food, "astronomical" prices and "the chance to spot a celeb"
remain key themes in reports on this "much-imitated" Mayfair
Japanese; service is rather "up itself", though, and – compared
to sexier recent competitors – its interior seems ever more "bland". /
Details: www.noburestaurants.com; 10.15 pm, Fri & Sat 11 pm; no smoking area;
booking: max 12.*

Notting Hill Brasserie W11   **£ 48**   A★★
92 Kensington Park Rd
7229 4481
*Since a 2003 relaunch, "fabulous food every time" – with "friendly"
and "efficient" service, too – has made this "soothing" and "intimate"
Notting Hill townhouse something of a surprise 'hidden gem'. / Value
tip: set weekday L £32(FP). Details: 11 pm; closed Sun; no smoking area.*

Noura SW1   **£ 39**   A★
16 Hobart Pl   7235 9444   1–4B
*"Professional" cooking and "efficient and charming" service win this
large and "classy" Belgravian numerous votes as "the best Lebanese
in town". / Details: www.noura-brasseries.co.uk; 11.30 pm.*

The Oak W2   **£ 37**   A★
137 Westbourne Park Rd
7221 3355
*"Delicious wood-fired pizzas" win consistent praise for this "tarted-up
pub", on the fringe of Notting Hill; it draws a "beautiful" crowd with its
"relaxed" but "buzzing" style; (its first-floor dining room is now a
members-only club). / Details: 10.30 pm; closed Mon L; no booking..*

Odette's NW1   **£ 48**   A★
130 Regent's Park Rd   7586 5486
*Simone Greene may have gone, but the "fabulous" eclectic cuisine she
cherished at this "old-faithful" North London fixture lives on; with its
"mirrored walls, candle-light and plush seating", it remains "one of the
most romantic and intimate spots in town". / Details: 11 pm; closed
Sat L & Sun D.*

Odin's W1   **£ 41**   A
27 Devonshire St   7935 7296   1–1A
*"Fabulous" pictures on the walls and "faultless" service lend a very
"refined" air to this "convivial" and "old-fashioned" Marylebone fixture;
its "classic" (but slightly "boring") English cooking is the only
"unexceptional" part of the package. /
Details: www.langansrestaurants.co.uk; 11 pm; closed Sat & Sun; no smoking area.*

1 Lombard Street EC3   **£ 62**
1 Lombard St   7929 6611   5–3C
*"In the heart of the City", this former banking hall – with its "decent,
if not spectacular" food – remains, for many reporters, a "perfect"
business rendezvous; some prefer the "buzzy" brasserie to the pricier
(and quieter) restaurant proper. / Details: www.1lombardstreet.com; 10 pm;
closed Sat & Sun.*

One-O-One
Sheraton Park Tower SW1   £ 70   ★
William St, 101 Knightsbridge
7290 7101   4–1D
Pascal Proyart's "out-of-this-world" fish cookery is, for many fans, simply
"the best in town"; it's a shame, then, that this Knightsbridge showcase
for his talents is getting so "pricey", and that its décor "looks so much
like a bog-standard hotel restaurant". / *Value tip:* set weekday L
£44(FP). **Details:** 10.15 pm; no smoking area.

Opera NW3   £ 28
68 Heath St   7794 6666
"Inexpensive and different", this Hampstead pub-conversion has quite
a local name for its "great dim sum" – the bar area is "cramped" and
can get "very busy", so it may be worth seeking out the quieter
restaurant behind. / **Details:** 10 pm.

L'Oranger SW1   £ 68   𝔸
5 St James's St   7839 3774   2–4D
"A great feeling of contentment" envelops most visitors to this
"dignified" and "clubby" St James's dining room – it's "perfect for
business" but can also be quite "romantic"; the modern French cuisine
is "always of a high standard", if short on fireworks. / **Details:** 10.45 pm;
closed Sat L & Sun; no smoking area; booking: max 8.

Orrery W1   £ 68
55 Marylebone High St   7616 8000   1–1A
A name as "the best of the Conran places" precedes this Marylebone
dining room, and many reports are indeed of a "jewel" of an
experience; "OTT prices" and a rather "dull" ambience, have, however,
always been concerns, and those who find the cuisine "nothing special"
have become more vocal this year. / *Value tip:* set weekday L
£38(FP). **Details:** www.orrery.co.uk; 10.30 pm.

Osia SW1   £ 53   ★
11 Haymarket   7976 1313   3–4A
After a slow start, some "spectacular" and "refreshingly creative"
cooking is helping this little-known West End Antipodean to greater
prominence; invisible from the street, there's also an unusual and
"extremely pleasant" bar, well worth seeking out in its own right. /
Details: www.osiarestaurant.com; 10.45 pm; closed Sat L & Sun.

Oslo Court NW8   £ 45   ★★
Charlbert St, off Prince Albert Rd   7722 8795
"Waiters fall over themselves to help you", at this fabulous St John's
Wood institution, whose "dated" but comfortable '70s décor only adds
to its "special occasion" credentials (in particular for its core, silver-
haired following); the cooking is "old-school, but always a treat". /
Details: 11 pm; closed Sun.

Osteria Basilico W11   £ 37   𝔸★
29 Kensington Park Rd   7727 9957
"Homely", "hectic" and "fun", this "crowded" trattoria remains
a linchpin of the Notting Hill whirl (though its standards wobbled
fractionally this year); "tasty and thin pizza" is a highlight of its
"good classic Italian country cooking". / **Details:** 11 pm; no booking, Sat L.

(Brasserie)
Oxo Tower SE1   £ 43   𝔸X
Barge House St   7803 3888   5–3A
"Only go for the spectacular views"; this "crazily expensive" venue
on the eighth floor of a South Bank landmark again tops survey
nominations for 'disappointment' – "miserable" service and "terrible"
food mean it's too often "a real let-down". /
Details: www.harveynichols.com; 11 pm.

(Restaurant)
Oxo Tower SE1 £ 63 AX
Barge House St   7803 3888   5–3A
*"A waste of the best restaurant views in London" – though no-one
expects the grander section of this top-floor landmark dining room
to be a bargain, does it have to deliver "cynical rubbish" that's
so "massively overpriced"? / **Value tip:** set weekday L
£42(FP). **Details:** www.harveynichols.com; 11 pm; booking: max 8.*

Page in Pimlico SW1 £ 27
11 Warwick Way   7834 3313   1–4B
*Especially in these parts, it's worth knowing about the "generous" and
"fairly-priced" Thai dining options at this "friendly" pub. /
Details: www.frontpagepubs.com; 10 pm; closed Sat L & Sun L.*

The Painted Heron £ 39 ★★
112 Cheyne Walk, SW10
7351 5232
205-209 Kennington Ln, SE11
7793 8313
*A "fabulous find" – after a slow start, the "cracking" Chelsea original
of this Indian duo is receiving the acclaim its "stunning" cuisine
deserves; its new branch (on the site of Kennington Lane, RIP) also
started "quiet", but early reporters say the food is "brilliant" there, too.
/ **Details:** www.thepaintedheron.com; SE11 10.30 pm, SW10 11 pm;
SW10 closed Sat L & Sun; no smoking area, SE11.*

Le Palais du Jardin WC2 £ 44
136 Long Acre   7379 5353   3–3C
*With its "reliable" menu (featuring "great seafood platters") and its
"buzzy" feel, this very large Covent Garden brasserie makes
a "convenient" location for "after-show eating" (or for business on a
budget); service, though, can be "surly". / **Details:** 11.45 pm.*

Pappa e Ciccia £ 25 A★
105-107 Munster Rd, SW6   7384 1884
41 Fulham High St, SW6   7736 0900
90 Lower Richmond Rd, SW15   8789 9040
*Staff who "couldn't be friendlier" help win high south west London
popularity for this "fun", family-run, Italian mini-chain, whose "genuine"
pizza is "the best"; "you need to squash to get in to the Munster Road
original" which "has the bonus of being BYO" (as does Fulham High
St). / **Details:** www.pappaciccia.com; 11 pm.*

Pappagallo W1 £ 39
54-55 Curzon St   7629 2742   2–4B
*A contemporary re-launch of the old Mayfair stand-by, Ristorante
Italiano (RIP), which early reporters say offers "good" Italian fare
at "reasonable" prices; there's a "cosy" bar upstairs, too. /
Details: 11 pm; closed Sat L & Sun L.*

Parco's E1 £ 30
1 Whitechapel High St   7488 2817   5–2D
*A pleasant Italian – cheap and cheerful in the basement, grander above
– which makes a "good lunch venue" for those with business where the
East End meets the City. / **Details:** L only, closed Sat & Sun.*

Pasha SW7 £ 43 A
1 Gloucester Rd   7589 7969   4–1B
*"Dark, cosy, scented, mysterious" – this "exotic" South Kensington
Moroccan evokes "the best of Marrakesh"; more reporters judged the
cooking "well prepared" this year, but service can still be "haughty". /
Value tip: set weekday L £15(FP). **Details:** www.pasha-restaurant.co.uk; 11 pm;
closed Sun L; booking: max 10 at weekends.*

Pasha N1 £29 𝔸

301 Upper St 7226 1454

"A bit posher than Gallipoli" (all things are relative), this "crowded" Turk offers "good food at good prices" to "well-heeled Islingtonians". / **Details:** *11.30 pm, Fri & Sat midnight.*

Passione W1 £51 ★

10 Charlotte St 7636 2833 1–1C

An "intimate" Fitzrovian that's often "crowded", thanks to the quality of Geraldo Contaldo's "authentic" and "truly delicious" Italian cooking. / **Details:** *www.passione.co.uk; 10.15 pm; closed Sat L & Sun.*

Patara £42 ★★

3&7 Maddox St, W1 7499 6008
181 Fulham Rd, SW3 7351 5692
9 Beauchamp Pl, SW3 7581 8820

"Superb Thai cooking" wins the highest praise for this well-established and "friendly" group – considering its consistent quality, it keeps a very low profile. / **Details:** *10.30 pm; no smoking area.*

Patterson's W1 £48 ★

4 Mill St
7499 1308 2–2C

The "interesting" cooking is "really getting into its stride", at this "enthusiastic", family-run newcomer, on the former Mayfair site of Pizzeria Condotti (RIP); for value in the heart of the West End, this place is hard to beat. / **Value tip:** *set weekday L £33(FP).* **Details:** *www.pattersonsrestaurant.com; 11 pm; closed Sun.*

Paul £14 ★

115 Marylebone High St, W1 7224 5615
29-30 Bedford St, WC2 7836 3304

"Pastries to die for" help "transport you to France" from the Covent Garden and Marylebone branches of these "brilliant" boulangeries/pâtisseries/tea-rooms; the "terrible" service, though – "surly" and "slow" – can be a bit too authentique. / **Details:** *8.30 pm; no smoking; no booking.*

The Pepper Tree £18 𝔸

537-539 Garratt Ln, SW18 8879 3599
19 Clapham Common S'side, SW4 7622 1758

"Perfect for a quick, very tasty, cheap meal"; these "canteen-style" Clapham and Earlsfield Thais – where you sit on long benches at shared tables – make ever-"dependable" and "efficient" stand-bys. / **Details:** *11 pm, Mon & Sun 10.30 pm; no Amex; no smoking area; no booking at D.*

Pétrus
Berkeley Hotel SW1 £82 ★

Wilton Pl 7235 1200 4–1D

"The best wine list in town" is a stand-out attraction at this "formal" and "well oiled" gastro-temple, which moved, in late-2003, from St James's to the former Knightsbridge site of Tante Claire (RIP); Marcus Wareing's cuisine is rated a notch lower in this bigger room, but it can still be "spectacular". / **Value tip:** *set weekday L £48(FP).* **Details:** *www.marcuswareing.com; 10.45 pm; closed Sat L & Sun; jacket required; no smoking; booking: max 8.*

Pied à Terre W1 £70 ★

34 Charlotte St 7636 1178 1–1C

It perennially lacks 'profile', but, under chef Shane Osborne, this "outstanding" Fitzrovia foodie temple delivers "exquisite" cuisine with "impressive consistency"; the "understated" setting strikes some as "sombre", but fans prefer the adjectives "discreet" and "intimate". / **Details:** *www.pied.a.terre.co.uk; 11 pm; closed Sat L & Sun; no smoking area; booking: max 8.*

La Piragua N1 £ 23
176 Upper St 7354 2843
*A "mustachioed owner" helps create a "relaxed cantina ambience",
at this "cheap and cheerful" Islington south American, which serves
"nice, big steaks". / **Details:** www.lapiragua.co.uk; midnight; no Amex.*

Pizza Metro SW11 £ 28 𝔸★★
64 Battersea Rise 7228 3812 6–2C
*"Awesome pizzas by the metre", "the best antipasti" and "a bustling
and exciting party atmosphere" create "a real slice of Neapolitan life",
at this 'destination' Battersea Italian (little affected by a management
change-over this year). / **Details:** 11 pm; closed weekday L; no Amex.*

Ciro's Pizza Pomodoro £ 32 𝔸
51 Beauchamp Pl, SW3 7589 1278
7-8 Bishopsgate Churchyard, EC2 7920 9207
*"Live music, most nights" contributes to the "fantastic buzz" –
in particular at the sleazy Knightsbridge basement original – which has
long underpinned the appeal of these "cheerful" pizzerias. /
Details: SW3 1 am, EC2 midnight; EC2 closed Sat & Sun, SW3 D only; no smoking
area at L.*

Plateau E14 £ 55
Canada Pl 7715 7100
*For "Canary Wharf financiers", this "Bladerunner-esque" fourth-floor
newcomer makes a "great" business rendezvous; in "typical Conran"
style, however, the prices are justified by the "fantastic" view, not by the
"average" cooking or service. / **Details:** www.conran.com; 10 pm; closed
Sat L & Sun D.*

Le Pont de la Tour SE1 £ 63 𝔸
36d Shad Thames 7403 8403 5–4D
*"Brilliant views" of Tower Bridge help make the grandest of Conran's
riverside eateries a "sure place to impress" a client or a date; prices
can seem plain "stupid", though, given the "run-of-the-mill" cooking and
the "inefficient" service. / **Details:** www.conran.com; 11 pm; closed Sat L.*

Le Pont de la Tour Bar & Grill SE1 £ 48 𝔸
36d Shad Thames 7403 8403 5–4D
*As at the adjoining restaurant, it's the "superb location" (in particular
the outside tables) which makes this riverside brasserie of interest;
those who do not avail themselves of the "surprisingly good-value lunch
menu", however, may find it "overpriced" and "disappointing". / **Value
tip:** set weekday L £31(FP). **Details:** www.conran.com; 11 pm; no booking.*

Porchetta Pizzeria £ 23
33 Boswell St, WC1 7242 2434
141-142 Upper St, N1 7288 2488
147 Stroud Green Rd, N4 7281 2892
84-86 Rosebery Ave, EC1 7837 6060
*"There is no other pizza" ("especially for the price"), say fans of these
"cheap" and "no-nonsense" – and slightly "mad" – north-London
Italians (which also offer a wide menu of other "good solid fare");
"Stroud Green Road is the original and the best". / **Details:** midnight,
WC1 10.30 pm; WC1 closed Sat L & Sun, N1 Mon-Fri closed L, N4 Mon-Thu
closed L, EC1 closed Sat L; no Amex; need 5+ to book.*

La Porte des Indes W1 £ 49 𝔸★
32 Bryanston St 7224 0055 1–2A
*"Huge, kitschy and fun", this "OTT" subcontinental in a "luxurious"
basement near Marble Arch makes visitors "feel like Indian royalty";
even with all these competing distractions, though, the cuisine
(with French colonial influences) "does not disappoint". /
Details: www.pilondon.net; 11.30 pm; closed Sat L.*

Potemkin EC1   **£ 35**
144 Clerkenwell Road   7278 6661   5–1A
"An incomparable vodka list" is the key attraction of this slightly odd,
but "trendy" Clerkenwell Russian bar (plus "white-walled" basement
restaurant); the "plain" cooking is "reasonably authentic" and "tasty"
(but portions are "not over-large"). / Details: www.potemkin.co.uk;
10.30 pm; closed Sat L & Sun; no smoking area.

La Poule au Pot SW1   **£ 43**   𝔸
231 Ebury St   7730 7763   4–2D
Few places have the "enduring allure" of this "rustic", "dark" and
"intimate" Pimlico bistro – for ten consecutive years, reporters' top
nomination for romance; appropriately for a place that feels "just like
France", the staff are "masters of the Gallic put-down". / Value tip: set
weekday L £30(FP). Details: 11 pm.

The Providores W1   **£ 50**
109 Marylebone High St   7935 6175   1–1A
Peter Gordon's "cramped" Marylebone dining room has never won him
the following he had in his Sugar Club days, and whereas some
reporters hail his fusion combos as "astonishing", others just find the
place "hyped" and "pretentious"; weekend brunch, though, has quite
a following. / Details: www.theprovidores.co.uk; 10.30 pm; no smoking; booking:
max 12.

Quaglino's SW1   **£ 51**   X
16 Bury St   7930 6767   2–3D
Conran Restaurants "continues to charge top dollar" for the
"very average" product on offer at this "brash" St James's mega-
brasserie – how long before it follows its stable-mate Mezzo into
oblivion? / Value tip: set weekday L £32(FP). Details: www.conran.com;
midnight, Fri & Sat 1 am.

Quirinale SW1   **£ 46**   ★★
North Ct, 1 Great Peter St   7222 7080   1–4C
"Everything just glides along", at this "understated" Westminster
basement, where the "outstanding" cooking and "immaculate" service
are beginning to win quite a following (not least of "grandees and
famous faces"); the setting is "cool", too – though arguably to excess. /
Details: 10.30 pm; closed Sat L & Sun.

Racine SW3   **£ 46**   ★
239 Brompton Rd
7584 4477   4–2C
"Close your eyes and you're in Paris", at this phenomenally popular
Knightsbridge brasserie; it offers "classic" cuisine at "sensible prices",
"impeccably" served, in a "cramped" and "buzzy" setting. / Value
tip: set weekday L £31(FP). Details: 10.30 pm.

Randall & Aubin   **£ 35**   𝔸
16 Brewer St, W1   7287 4447
329-331 Fulham Rd, SW10   7823 3515
"Fun staff", "a fabulous clientèle" and "the underworld passing by the
window" make the Soho original ex-deli branch the more interesting
member of this odd duo; the more standard Chelsea brasserie is quite
OK, though, and both locations serve "quality" simple fare – oysters,
crustacea, grills and so on. / Details: www.randallandaubin.co.uk; 11 pm;
W1 no booking.

Ransome's Dock SW11   **£ 44**
35 Parkgate Rd   7223 1611   4–4C
The cooking is "consistent"-enough, but it's the "smasher" of a wine list
("reasonably priced" and "full of treats and curiosities") that draws
regulars from far and wide to Martin Lam's "good neighbourhood
place", in Battersea. / Details: www.ransomesdock.co.uk; 11 pm, Sat midnight;
closed Sun D; no smoking in dining room.

Rasa   **£ 32**   ★★
6 Dering St, W1   7629 1346
55 Stoke Newington Church St, N16   7249 0344
The "mouthwatering" dishes at this "magical" veggie duo – with their
"astonishing tastes, textures and colours" – help "blow away
preconceptions" about Indian cuisine; the Stoke Newington original
"outshines" Mayfair, and it's "slightly cheaper", too. /
Details: www.rasarestaurants.com; 10.45 pm; N16 Mon-Thu closed L, W1 closed
Sun L; no smoking area, N16.

Rasa Travancore N15   **£ 26**   ★★
56 Stoke Newington Church St   7249 1340
"Definitely worth a trip to Stokie" – "the meat-eater's version of Rasa"
provides "an excellent alternative" to the more famous veggie original,
across the road; it also serves "superb fish curries". /
Details: www.rasarestaurants.com; 10.45 pm; D only, ex Sun open L &
D; no smoking.

Rasoi Vineet Bhatia SW3   **£ 66**   ★
10 Lincoln St   7225 1881   4–2D
Vineet Bhatia is arguably London's top Indian chef, and a June 2004
visit to his new solo venture found accomplished cuisine (and charming
service, too); prices are very high, though, and the décor at this Chelsea
townhouse even harsher than it was in the dying days of the former
régime (The English Garden, RIP). / **Details:** 10.15 pm; D only, closed Sun;
no smoking.

The Real Greek Souvlaki   **£ 27**
1-2 Riverside House,
The Queen's Walk, SE1
7620 0162
140-142 St John St, EC1   7253 7234
Many reports from this "humming and buzzing" Smithfield bar/café are
still of "melt-in-the-mouth" souvlaki and other "well-crafted" dishes;
crashing ratings, though, don't bode well for its bold expansion plans
(already on the South Bank, with more planned).
/**Details:** www.therealgreek.co.uk; 11 pm; EC1 closed Sun; no Amex.

Rebato's SW8   **£ 26**   𝔸★
169 South Lambeth Rd   7735 6388   6–1D
"You feel like you're in Spain", at this "winning" Vauxhall tapas bar,
which is praised for its "sturdy" dishes, "attentive" service and
"authentic" atmosphere; there's a cheesy restaurant adjoining,
too, which some reporters say is "better than it's cracked up to be". /
Details: www.rebatos.com; 10.45 pm; closed Sat L & Sun.

Red Fort W1   **£ 50**
77 Dean St   7437 2525   3–2A
This Soho veteran has long been hailed as a "different" Indian, whose
"consistent" and superior performance put it in London' front rank;
even fans say it's "on the pricey side", though, and – despite its "stylish"
refit a year or so ago – it is rated "a notch below" some newer arrivals.
/ **Details:** 11.15 pm; closed Sat L & Sun L.

The Red Pepper W9   **£ 32**   ★
8 Formosa St   7266 2708
"High-standard pizza" (in particular) has made this "hard-to-beat
local" a Maida Vale institution; service can be "surly", though,
and conditions – especially in the basement – are "totally cramped". /
Details: www.theredpeppergroup.com; 11 pm; closed weekday L; no Amex.

Redmond's SW14   **£ 43**   ★★
170 Upper R'mond Rd West   8878 1922   6–1A
"Pippa runs a tight and friendly ship", at this family-run East Sheen
venture, where "skilfully-executed" cooking is twinned with a relatively
"affordable" wine list. / **Details:** www.redmonds.org.uk; 10 pm; D only,
ex Sun L only; no Amex; no smoking.

Refettorio
The Crowne Plaza Hotel EC4   £ 47
19 New Bridge St   7438 8052   5–3A
"Fantastic cheeses, cured meats and breads" are highlights at this
"spacious" new City Italian, off an hotel foyer; it's pricey (and gives little
hint of Giorgio Locatelli's involvement), but – as an *"informal"*
rendezvous *"with an interesting twist"* – it already has a fair following. /
Details: www.london-city.crowneplaza.com; 10.30 pm; closed Sat L & Sun.

Rhodes 24 EC2   £ 51   A★
25 Old Broad St   7877 7703   5–2C
"The panorama is impressive, and the food matches it" – that's the
general view on Gary R's new 24th-floor City operation, which makes
"a great place for business"; its *"new British classic"* dishes may not yet
be quite up to the standard of City Rhodes (RIP), but they are still done
"with precision and flair". / **Details:** www.rhodes24.co.uk; 8.30 pm; closed
Sat & Sun; booking essential.

Riccardo's SW3   £ 33   A
126 Fulham Rd   7370 6656   4–3B
An *"Italian tapas"* formula that's *"perfect for a quick bite or a group
dinner"* ensures continuing popularity for this *"fun and buzzy"* Chelsea
spot. / **Details:** 11.30 pm.

Rick's Café SW17   £ 29   A★
122 Mitcham Rd   8767 5219   6–2C
"Real food at very fair prices" makes this *"friendly"* open-kitchen
Tooting dining room extremely popular; no one really seems to care that
it's *"squashed"* and *"crowded"*. / **Details:** 11 pm; no Amex.

The Ritz W1   £ 80   AX
150 Piccadilly   7493 8181   2–4C
"The most romantic dining room in the world", it may be, but this Louis
XVI chamber shamelessly exploits its *"opulent"* charms – *"judged
on their own merits, the food and service do not begin to justify the
prices"*. / **Details:** www.theritzlondon.com; 11 pm; no jeans or trainers.

The River Café W6   £ 60
Thames Whf, Rainville Rd   7386 4200
"Crazily pricey", world-famous Italian that occupies an obscure
backstreet Hammersmith location (with the benefit of *"a perfect
riverside terrace in summer"*); reporters divide roughly 50/50 between
those praising its *"terrific freshness and food quality"*, and those who
feel it's simply a *"rip-off"*. / **Details:** www.rivercafe.co.uk; 9.30 pm; closed
Sun D.

The Rivington Grill Bar Deli EC2   £ 42
28-30 Rivington St   7729 7053   5–1C
This Shoreditch corner bistro is *"a nice chilled place"*, which attracts
"loads of interesting people – from City types to arty locals"; foodwise,
it's *"like being back in a (good) school canteen"*. /
Details: www.rivingtongrill.co.uk; 11 pm.

Rocket   £ 30   A
4-6 Lancashire Ct, W1   7629 2889
Brewhouse St, SW15   8789 7875
This *"vibrant"* chain is acclaimed by fans for *"phenomenal pizza"* –
both at the *"refuge-from-Bond-Street"* original and the spin-off in a new
Putney riverside development; the occasional sceptic finds it *"totally
overhyped"*, however. / **Details:** www.freedombrewery.com; SW15 11 pm,
W1 11.30 pm; W1 closed Sun.

Roka W1 £ 45 ★

37 Charlotte St   7580 6464   1–1C

*A central 'robata grill' dominates both the room – and the menu –
at this svelte Fitzrovia 'restaurant row' newcomer; on an early visit,
the precise cooking (also including sushi and other dishes) and excellent
service lived up to its sibling Zuma – its 'goldfish bowl' setting is as slick,
but less discreet.* / **Details:** *10.45 pm; no smoking.*

Rosmarino NW8 £ 42

1 Blenheim Terrace   7328 5014

*"A sunny-day lunch on the terrace can be splendid", at this "friendly"
St John's Wood spot; even if standards here do not approach those
of its legendary sibling, Zafferano, it's still "one of the best Italians
in NW London".* / **Details:** *10.30 pm; no smoking area.*

Roussillon SW1 £ 61 ★★

16 St Barnabas St   7730 5550   4–2D

*Perhaps "London's most un-sung fine dining" – Alexis Gauthier creates
"outstanding" Gallic dishes at this "unknown" Pimlico backstreet
"delight", and the service is "attentive" and "unpretentious", too; some
think the place is "held back by its uncosy ambience", but others find
it "romantic".* / **Details:** *www.roussillon.co.uk; 10.30 pm; closed Mon L, Sat L &
Sun; no smoking area.*

Royal China £ 34 ★★

40 Baker St, W1   7487 4688
13 Queensway, W2   7221 2535
68 Queen's Grove, NW8   7586 4280
30 Westferry Circus, E14   7719 0888

*"Brilliant dim sum" is a highlight at this 'benchmark' chain, regularly
hailed for offering "London's best Chinese food"; its deliciously tacky
black 'n' gold interiors, however, are "hardly the place if you're trying
to impress".* / **Details:** *10.45 pm, Fri & Sat 11.15 pm; E14 no bookings Sat &
Sun L.*

Royal China SW15 £ 31 ★★

3 Chelverton Rd   8788 0907   6–2B

*The "original" Putney 'outpost' of the famous Chinese chain has not,
in fact, been part of it for years; if you didn't know, though, you'd never
spot the difference, and it serves similarly "excellent dim sum".* /
Details: *11 pm; only Amex.*

RSJ SE1 £ 37

33 Coin St   7928 4554   5–4A

*It's a shame about the perennially "sterile" atmosphere of this "quiet"
South Bank fixture – it offers "reliable" British cooking, accompanied
by "an amazing selection of Loire wines".* / **Details:** *www.rsj.uk.com;
11 pm; closed Sat L & Sun.*

La Rueda £ 30 Ⓐ

102 Wigmore St, W1   7486 1718
642 King's Rd, SW6   7381 2684
66-68 Clapham High St, SW4   7627 2173

*"You get a good night out" at these "lively" bars, where "good-quality
tapas come at reasonable prices"; the Clapham branch is the original
and the best.* / **Details:** *11.30 pm.*

Rules WC2 £ 50 Ⓐ

35 Maiden Ln   7836 5314   3–3D

*"The oldest, and still the best" – London's most venerable restaurant
(est. 1798) is, naturally, "a bit touristy", but its "polished" Covent
Garden premises help make it a "classic" and, it can still serve up some
"delicious game and steak" (plus "puddings to die for"); service, though,
can be "patchy".* / **Details:** *www.rules.co.uk; 11.30 pm; no smoking.*

Running Horse W1   £24
50 Davies St   7493 1275   2–2A
*Tom Etridge apparently has plans for a posh re-launch of this modestly
trendified Mayfair boozer in Spring 2005; perhaps that's a shame,
as its understated charms already attract pretty consistent praise
(if from only a small fan club).* / **Details:** www.therunninghorselondon.co.uk;
10.45 pm; closed Fri D, Sat D & Sun; need 8+ to book.

Sabras NW10   £26   ★★
263 High Rd   8459 0340
*The décor "could use an update", but who cares? – this Willesden
Green veteran serves "a wonderful range" of "first-class veggie food
at reasonable prices".* / **Details:** www.sabras.co.uk; 10.30 pm; D only, closed
Mon; no Amex; no smoking area.

Sagar W6   £21   ★★
157 King St   8741 8563
*You'd easily miss this year-old South Indian veggie café
on Hammersmith's grotty main drag; that would be a shame, as its
"different" menu delivers "marvellous tastes at incredibly low prices"
and its staff are "charming and effective", too.* / **Details:** 10.45 pm;
no smoking area.

St John EC1   £42   ★
26 St John St   7251 0848   5–1B
*Fergus Henderson is both a "true pioneer" and an "offally good" chef
(ho ho), and his "esoteric" British dishes (in which no part of an animal
is wasted) remain very popular with reporters; service at his Spartan
Smithfield premises is "assured" and "well-informed", too.* /
Details: www.stjohnrestaurant.com; 11 pm; closed Sat L & Sun.

St John Bread & Wine E1   £37
94-96 Commercial St   7247 8724   5–1D
*This "more relaxed", "spit-and-sawdust" Spitalfields counterpart
to Smithfield's famous nose-to-tail eatery "can be variable, but is usually
good"; it offers "honest, plainly served food" – including, of course,
"offal presented every which way" – and a range of "superb fresh
bread".* / **Details:** www.stjohnbreadandwine.com; 10 pm; need 10+ to book.

St Johns N19   £33   A★
91 Junction Rd   7272 1587
*The "charming faded grandeur" of "the spectacular ballroom setting"
provides the icing on the cake of a visit to this "friendly" Archway
"gastropub par excellence"; the food is "well cooked", too.* /
Details: 11 pm; closed Mon L; booking: max 12.

St Moritz W1   £38   A
161 Wardour St   7734 3324   2–1D
*It's "especially fun for fondue in deepest winter", but – "if genuine Swiss
food and wine is your thing" – this "chalet-cliché-style" Soho
"institution" can be enjoyable at any time of year.* /
Details: www.stmoritz-restaurant.co.uk; 11.30 pm; closed Sat L & Sun.

Sale e Pepe SW1   £45
9-15 Pavilion Rd   7235 0098   4–1D
*"Expect entertaining service" – as well as "wholesome" traditional
dishes – at this "fun" and "noisy" trattoria, a short walk from Harrods;
you can, however, feel "on top of the next table".* / **Details:** 11.30 pm;
closed Sun.

Salloos SW1   £42   ★★
62-64 Kinnerton St   7235 4444   4–1D
*"The food speaks for itself", at this "authentic" Pakistani veteran in a
Belgravia mews, where lamb chops are the signature dish; ambience,
however, "is not a priority".* / **Details:** 11.15 pm; closed Sun.

San Daniele del Friuli N5 £28

72 Highbury Park   7226 1609
*This "dependable and characterful local", near Highbury Park,
is rumoured to be "the favourite of the Arsenal Team on match days";
supporters say it serves "classic Italian food as it ought to be". /*
Details: *10.45 pm; closed Mon L, Tue L, Sat L & Sun; no Amex; no smoking area.*

Sapori WC2 £26

43 Drury Ln   7836 8296   3–2D
*"Excellent pizzas" are a highlight of the "good-value" fare at this "fun"
Italian – well worth knowing about, two minutes' walk from the Royal
Opera House. /* **Details:** *11.30 pm.*

Sarastro WC2 £35   AX

126 Drury Ln   7836 0101   1–2D
*Everyone agrees that this Theatreland spectacle is "ludicrously OTT",
that "you have to see it to believe it", and that its Turkish food is "dire"
– whether this makes for an "awesome and romantic" occasion, or one
which is "dreadful, phoney and tatty" is a matter of personal taste. /*
Details: *www.sarastro-restaurant.com; 11.30 pm.*

Sardo Canale NW1 £40

42 Gloucester Ave   7722 2800
*This "friendly" new Primrose Hill Sardinian has been a bit of a 'rave'
among the newspaper critics; early reporters, however, tended to share
our up-and-down initial experience (and have noted, as we did,
the absence of any view of the 'canale' or anything else). /*
Details: *www.sardocanale.com; 10 pm; closed Mon; no smoking area.*

Sarkhel's SW18 £28   ★★

199 Replingham Rd   8870 1483   6–2B
*"It looks like an average Indian", but Udit Sarkhel's "mould-breaking"
Southfields venture is a culinary "education", featuring "some of the
best subcontinental cooking in town"; staff are "friendly", too –
"whether it's your first visit or your 50th". /* **Details:** *www.sarkhels.com;
10.30 pm, Fri & Sat 11 pm; no Amex; no smoking area.*

Savoy Grill
Savoy Hotel WC2 £61   A

Strand   7592 1600   3–3D
*Marcus Wareing has, in his first year, "breathed life" into this "elegant"
traditional favourite of captains of industry; while the feel is "fresher",
the place "still has that power lunch ambience", service is "smooth and
unobtrusive" and its "mix of traditional and interesting" dishes
is realised with a "light touch". /* **Value tip:** *set weekday L
£39(FP).* **Details:** *www.marcuswareing.com; 11 pm; jacket & tie required; booking:
max 10.*

Scalini SW3 £54   A

1-3 Walton St   7225 2301   4–2C
*This "hopping", "buzzy" and "crowded" Knightsbridge scene is a firm
"favourite" Italian for many reporters; sceptics can find it a bit
"pretentious". /* **Details:** *midnight.*

The Scarsdale W8 £32   A

23a Edwardes Sq   7937 1811
*This "hidden gem" of a pub is "a perennial favourite", "cosy in winter"
and with a "lovely front garden for summer" (on a picturesque
Kensington square); the food is "back-to-basics" pub grub. /*
Details: *9.45 pm.*

Sea Cow SE22 £16   ★★

37 Lordship Ln   8693 3111
*"Spankingly-good fried and grilled fish" wins adulatory reviews for this
"modern twist on a chippie" – a "basic" ("no puds and few starters")
new fish canteen in East Dulwich, with seating at "long communal
tables"; more branches are planned. /*

sign up for the survey at www.hardens.com

J Sheekey WC2 £ 53 𝔸★★
28-32 St Martin's Ct   7240 2565   3–3B
"Classy" but surprisingly "unpretentious", this Theatreland star-magnet is – for the second year – the survey's most talked-about place; "five-star fish" is the culinary draw, served by "impeccable" staff, in a series of "intimate" parlours. / **Value tip:** *set weekday L £32(FP).* **Details:** *midnight.*

Shogun W1 £ 50 ★★
Adam's Row   7493 1255   2–3A
"Japanese food of the highest quality" (not least "wonderful sushi") and "impeccable" service "dispel any reservations" about the dated décor of this "secluded" Mayfair hotel basement. / **Details:** *11 pm; D only, closed Mon.*

Signor Sassi SW1 £ 50 𝔸
14 Knightsbridge Grn   7584 2277   4–1D
If you like 'em "noisy", "buzzy" and "cramped", you'll "always have a wonderful time" at this Knightsbridge trattoria; "there are lots of laughs to be had with the waiters", and the food is "good, but expensive". / **Details:** *11.30 pm; closed Sun.*

Simpson's Tavern EC3 £ 23 𝔸
38 1/2 Ball Ct, Cornhill   7626 9985   5–2C
With its "simple", "honest" food and "quintessentially English" atmosphere, this (literally) Dickensian institution remains "a good informal lunch place" (and, for some, "an essential part of City life"). / **Details:** *L only, closed Sat & Sun.*

Simpsons-in-the-Strand WC2 £ 56 𝔸
100 Strand   7836 9112   3–3D
"Vastly improved" – this legendary "old-school" Covent Garden temple to Roast Beef took on a new lease of life in the final days of its former ownership; let's hope the new (Irish) proprietors keep up the good work – the famously "sinful" breakfasts must surely be safe in their hands? / **Details:** *www.simpsons-in-the-strand.com; 10.45 pm, Sun 8.30 pm; no jeans or trainers.*

Singapura £ 35 𝔸
31 Broadgate Circle, EC2   7256 5045
78-79 Leadenhall St, EC3   7929 0089
1-2 Limeburner Ln, EC4   7329 1133
"Decent" and "reasonably-priced" cooking maintains the reliable 'stand-by' status of these "efficient" and "spacious" City orientals. / **Details:** *www.singapuras.co.uk; 10.30 pm; closed Sat & Sun, EC3 L only; no smoking area.*

06 St Chad's Place WC1 £ 29 𝔸★
6 St Chad's Pl   7278 3355
Improbably – in an ex-shed by a railway line among the backstreets of King's Cross (behind the Travelodge) – you now find one of London's nicer spaces for lunch (or an evening drink); it offers simple but tasty Mediterranean fare, and pleasant service, too. / **Details:** *www.6stchadsplace.com; 11 pm; closed Sat & Sun; no Amex.*

(Gallery) Sketch W1 £ 53 X
9 Conduit St   0870 777 4488   2–2C
"Shockingly arrogant" staff serve up food that's often just "pretentious rubbish", in the "madly pricey", '70s sci-fi-style brasserie at Momo Mourad's Mayfair folly; "as a temple of design it's stunning", but it's "the most ridiculous excuse for a dining experience". / **Details:** *www.sketch.uk.com; 11 pm; D only, closed Sun.*

(Lecture Room)
Sketch W1   **£125**   X
9 Conduit St   0870 777 4488   2–2C
"Obscenely OTT" prices for *"weird but not wonderful"* cooking risk
making a *"white elephant"* of Momo Mourad's *"glamorous"* but
"absurd" Mayfair dining room; some 'cheaper' menus have been
introduced, but this is still the UK's most expensive place to eat! /
Details: www.sketch.uk.com; 10.30 pm; closed Mon, Sat L & Sun; no smoking area.

(Ground Floor)
Smiths of Smithfield EC1   **£22**   A
67-77 Charterhouse St   7251 7997   5–1A
"For a light bite in young and fashionable surroundings", this Smithfield
bar is a key *"cool hang-out"*, not least for its *"classic"* Sunday brunch
(*"expect to wait for a table"*); the fish finger sandwich is *"a must"*. /
Details: www.smithsofsmithfield.co.uk; 10.30 pm; no booking.

(Dining Room)
Smiths of Smithfield EC1   **£33**   A
67-77 Charterhouse St   7251 7997   5–1A
An *"interesting and convenient location"* (the second floor of an
impressive Smithfield warehouse) and *"simple, well-executed"* food
make this *"noisy"* and *"frenetic"* venue a useful, if *"functional"*,
rendezvous, equally suited to (informal) business or pleasure. /
Details: www.smithsofsmithfield.co.uk; 10.45 pm; closed Sat L & Sun.

(Top Floor)
Smiths of Smithfield EC1   **£52**   A
67-77 Charterhouse St   7251 7950   5–1A
"Great steaks and great views" help create a *"perfect environment for
business"*, at this *"slick"* steakhouse, on the top floor of a Smithfield
warehouse; service can be *"a let-down"*, though – more grist to the mill
for those saying, *"you could expect better for this sort of money"*. /
Details: www.smithsofsmithfield.co.uk; 11 pm; closed Sat L (café open all day);
booking: max 10.

Snows on the Green W6   **£31**   ★
166 Shepherd's Bush Rd   7603 2142
"Imaginative" cooking and *"charming"* service are re-establishing
Sebastian Snow's Brook Green fixture as the *"top gastronomic choice
in the area"*. / **Details:** www.snowsonthegreen.co.uk; 11 pm; closed Sat L &
Sun D; no smoking area.

Sông Quê E2   **£19**   ★★
134 Kingsland Rd   7613 3222
"London's best Vietnamese food", say supporters, is on offer at this
"canteen-like" Shoreditch fixture; it offers *"ridiculously good value"*. /
Details: 11 pm; no smoking area.

Sonny's SW13   **£38**   A★
94 Church Rd   8748 0393   6–1A
It this London's *"best 'neighbourhood' restaurant"*?; with its *"reliably
good"* food, its *"personal"* service, and its *"bustling"* and *"enjoyable"*
atmosphere, this long-standing Barnes institution has a better claim
than most. / **Details:** 10.45 pm; closed Sun D.

Sophie's Steakhouse SW10   **£32**   A★
311-313 Fulham Rd   7352 0088   4–3B
"A great place for burgers and steaks", this *"buzzing"* Chelsea grill
is finally starting to live up to the hype that's always surrounded it –
it's a *"fun"* place, and *"the no-bookings policy means you can turn
up on a whim"*. / **Details:** www.sophiessteakhouse.com; 11.45 pm; no booking.

sign up for the survey at www.hardens.com

Sotheby's Café W1 £ 38 A ★
34 New Bond St 7293 5077 2–2C
*"One of the best lunches in the West End" is to be had at this
"interesting" rendezvous, off the auction house's foyer; it offers a "short
but imaginative" menu, "great" service and a "relaxed" style –
"good people-watching" is thrown in free.* / **Details:** *L only, closed Sat &
Sun; no smoking.*

Spiga £ 39
84-86 Wardour St, W1 7734 3444
312-314 King's Rd, SW3 7351 0101
*Branches of this "stylish" Italian mini-group – where "thin and
authentic" pizzas are the menu stars – are "always buzzing"; it's been
on more "reliable" form of late.* / **Details:** *11.30 pm.*

The Square W1 £ 76
6-10 Bruton St 7495 7100 2–2C
*"Perfect for impressing clients" – this "so professional", if slightly
"soulless", Mayfair dining room showcases Phil Howard's "gutsy and
individual" cuisine; for much of its besuited clientèle, though,
the "incredible selection of wines at fair prices" is much of the appeal.* /
Value tip: *set weekday L £48(FP).* **Details:** *www.squarerestaurant.com; 10.45 pm;
closed Sat L & Sun L.*

Sree Krishna SW17 £ 17 ★★
192-194 Tooting High St 8672 4250 6–2C
*This Tooting south-Indian "institution" – back on top form –
is unanimously hailed by reporters for its "consistent quality and value";
vegetarian dishes are "prolific", but there are also meaty options.* /
Details: *10.45 pm, Fri & Sat midnight; no smoking area.*

Star Café W1 £ 22
22 Gt Chapel St 7437 8778 2–1D
*"Run by the lovely Mario since the dawn of time", this "welcoming"
media-land stalwart offers "cheap and filling" fare – not least "the best
breakfast in Soho" – in a no-nonsense setting.* /
Details: *www.thestarcafesoho.co.uk; L only, closed Sat & Sun; no Amex; no smoking
area.*

Star of India SW5 £ 39 ★★
154 Old Brompton Rd 7373 2901 4–2B
*The "flamboyant" owner and the "high camp" décor may set the tone,
but it's the "superb, authentic food" which makes this "posh" curry
house a continuing South Kensington favourite; "it's been run by the
same family for 50 years, so they must be doing something right".* /
Details: *www.starofindia.co.uk; 11.45 pm.*

Stone Mason's Arms W6 £ 29 A
54 Cambridge Grove 8748 1397
*"Relaxed" but still trendy, this Hammersmith gastropub manages
to rise above its trafficky location, and its menu offers a "good mix
of comfort food and interesting dishes".* / **Details:** *9.45 pm.*

Strada £31
15-16 New Burlington St, W1   7287 5967
31 Marylebone High St, W1   7935 1004
9-10 Market Pl, W1   7580 4644
6 Great Queen St, WC2   7405 6295
237 Earl's Court Rd, SW5   7835 1180
175 New King's Rd, SW6   7731 6404
105-106 Upper St, N1   7276 9742
4 South Grove, N6   8342 8686
40-42 Parkway, NW1   7428 9653
11-13 Battersea Rise, SW11   7801 0794
375 Lonsdale Rd, SW13   8392 9216
102-104 Clapham High St, SW4   7627 4847
8-10 Exmouth Mkt, EC1   7278 0800
"Really showing up PizzaExpress", this "superior" group is applauded
for its "wonderful" pizzas, its "excellent pasta selection" and its "fun"
(and "child-friendly") service; relentless growth, though, is hitting its
ambience ratings – "some branches are definitely better than others". /
Details: www.strada.co.uk; 11 pm; no smoking area; some booking restrictions
apply.

Stratford's W8 £38 ★
7 Stratford Rd   7937 6388   4–2A
It may be "low-key" and on a "quiet street", but this Kensington fish-
specialist is "hard to beat for consistency", offering "superb" seafood
and "always-welcoming" service. / **Value tip:** set weekday L
£26(FP). **Details:** www.stratfords-restaurant.com; 11.30 pm.

Sugar Hut SW6 £41 🅐
374 North End Rd   7386 8950   4–3A
"Hide away from the outside world", at this "amazingly-decorated"
Fulham Thai (whose seductive ambience is boosted by a bar complete
with "big mattresses to cosy up on"); the food is "not bad", but it
is "very expensive". / **Details:** www.sugarhutfulham.com; 11.30 pm; D only;
no smoking area.

Sumosan W1 £55 ★★
26b Albemarle St
7495 5999   2–3C
The "truly memorable" cuisine of this Mayfair Japanese clearly outdid
Nobu and Zuma in the survey; it's not nearly as well-known as it should
be, though, perhaps because the décor – even if it's quite "chic" and
"right for business" – can seem "a bit grey and cold". /
Details: 11.30 pm; closed Sat L & Sun L; no smoking area.

Sweetings EC4 £39 🅐★
39 Queen Victoria St   7248 3062   5–3B
"A City legend, and deservedly so", this "wonderful, olde-worlde
institution" has "been first-class for as long as anyone can remember";
"full of suits every day", it offers "no gimmicks, just great fish at good
prices" (or a sandwich with character, standing at the bar). /
Details: L only, closed Sat & Sun; no booking.

Taman gang W1 £61 🅐
141 Park Ln   7518 3160   1–2A
As a "beautiful people" scene, this ambitious Mayfair basement
newcomer has been an immediate hit; coming from the backers
of nightclub Chinawhite, that's no great shock – what is a surprise
is that the oriental cooking is often "excellent" (if, of course, "vastly
overpriced"). / **Details:** www.tamangang.com; 11 pm; closed Sun.

Tamarind W1   £ 50   ★

20 Queen St   7629 3561   2–3B

It went through a change of personnel last year, but this "spacious" and "stylish" Mayfair basement maintains a high standard of "sophisticated" modern Indian cuisine − it still outscores its ex-head chef's new place, Benares! / **Value tip:** *set Sun L £32(FP).* **Details:** *www.tamarindrestaurant.com; 11.15 pm; closed Sat L; no smoking area.*

Tartine SW3   £ 33   𝔸

114 Draycott Ave   7589 4981   4–2C

"Delicious tartines" − made with pain Poilâne − have helped make this "lively" Brompton Cross "pit stop" quite a "hip" destination. / **Details:** *www.tartine.co.uk; 11 pm; no smoking area; need 6+ to book at D.*

Tas   £ 26

33 The Cut, SE1   7928 2111
72 Borough High St, SE1   7403 7200

"A super choice for a quick and cheap bite" − this chain of "fun" and "buzzing" South Bank Turks has a "winning formula" (see also next entry); it's "great for groups", too. / **Details:** *www.tasrestaurant.com; 11.30 pm.*

Tas Pide   £ 26   𝔸

20-22 New Globe Walk, SE1   7928 3300
37 Farringdon Rd, EC1   7430 9721

"Cosier than the other Tases", this spin-off chain (which now bestrides the Thames) notably outscores its cousins, not least with its "better" (rustic) décor; the cuisine is Anatolian, with the local flatbread 'pizza' the speciality. / **Details:** *www.tasrestaurant.com; 11.30 pm.*

Tate Britain SW1   £ 42   𝔸

Millbank   7887 8825   1–4C

"A quirky, eclectic selection of wine" − "the best-value list in London" − and "wonderful" Whistler murals draw many fans to the 'old' Tate's hidden-away dining room whose "inoffensive" cooking plays a decidedly supporting rôle; (late-morning breakfast is a recent innovation). / **Details:** *www.tate.org.uk; L only; no smoking.*

Tatsuso EC2   £ 80   ★

32 Broadgate Circle   7638 5863   5–2D

"There's lots to recommend" this City Japanese "...except the prices" (it's "only for the expense account"); on the ground floor, the "unbeatable" teppan yaki can be "fun", but aficionados head for the "sterile" basement for "sublime" sushi and sashimi. / **Details:** *9.45 pm; closed Sat & Sun; no smoking area.*

Teca W1   £ 48   ★

54 Brooks Mews   7495 4774   2–2B

In spite of offering "fantastic food at reasonable prices" (and an "imaginative wine list", too), this "discreet" modern Italian in Mayfair has remained relatively "undiscovered"; "sterile" décor doesn't help. / **Details:** *www.atozrestaurants.com; 10.30 pm; closed Sat L & Sun.*

Tendido Cero SW5   £ 28   𝔸★

174 Old Brompton Rd   7370 3685   4–2B

"If you can't afford Cambio de Tercio" (the parent establishment, opposite), this "excellent, laid-back alternative" offers "fabulous" tapas and "efficient" service; prices are "keen", and you can BYO, too − a rarity in South Kensington. / **Details:** *11 pm; no credit cards; no smoking.*

Thai Noodle Bar SW10   £ 27   𝔸

7 Park Walk   7352 7222   4–3B

In the heart of Chelsea, this "simple noodle bar" is a "classy and comfortable" affair, where "incredibly friendly" staff serve up "good, clean-tasting Thai dishes"; (hopefully, management changes post-survey won't disrupt things). / **Details:** *11.15 pm.*

Thai Pot WC2   £ 26
1 Bedfordbury   7379 4580   3–4C
*Like the adjacent Coliseum, this "popular" and "convenient"
Theatreland Thai has emerged reinvigorated by refurbishment –
its "good food at reasonable prices" attracts much more consistent
praise.* / **Details:** *www.thaipot.co.uk; 11.15 pm; closed Sun; no smoking area.*

Thyme
The Hospital WC2
24 Endell St   7170 9200   3–2C
*"Sublime" cuisine won 'destination' status for the Clapham forebear
of this ambitious Covent Garden newcomer; let's hope its "daring"
approach survives the transition to this larger-scale – and more self-
consciously fashionable – operation, scheduled to open in late-2004.* /
Details: *www.thymeandspace.com.*

Toff's N10   £ 25   ★
38 Muswell Hill Broadway   8883 8656
*"Crowded and noisy, but the fish and chips are perfect" – that's all you
really need to know about this famous Muswell Hill chippie, which
is now back on top form.* / **Details:** *10 pm; closed Sun; no smoking area;
no booking, Sat.*

Tom Aikens SW3   £ 70   ★
43 Elystan St   7584 2003   4–2C
*"Sensational", "subtle" and "intense" cooking has – in its first year –
rightly won every award going for Tom Aikens's "stark" Chelsea dining
room; the critical minority all share pretty much the same reservation:
that "he tries way too hard", and produces dishes that are just
"too clever".* / **Value tip:** *set weekday L £43(FP).* **Details:** *www.tomaikens.co.uk;
10.30pm; closed Sat & Sun; no smoking; booking: max 6.*

Tom's W11   £ 26   𝔸★
226 Westbourne Grove   7221 8818
*"An excellent brunch" attracts "huge queues" to Tom Conran's
"very trendy" Notting Hill delicatessen – at least you can often "star-
spot" while you wait.* / **Details:** *8 pm; closed Sat D & Sun D; no Amex;
no smoking; no booking.*

Toto's SW1   £ 55   𝔸★
Lennox Gardens Mews   7589 0075   4–2C
*"Professional" service, a "grand but cosy" setting, and "solid and
traditional" fare have long made this "charming and hidden-away"
Italian a Knightsbridge favourite – no surprise, then, that it can seem
"a bit pricey".* / **Details:** *11 pm.*

Les Trois Garçons E1   £ 55   𝔸
1 Club Row   7613 1924
*"You could spend all night admiring the décor", at this "offbeat" and
"glamorous" East Ender, whose "plush" interior ("filled with stuffed
animals and weird artifacts") "screams decadence and frivolity"; that's
just as well, as the Gallic cuisine is "average, and so expensive".* /
Details: *www.lestroisgarcons.com; 10.30 pm; D only, closed Sun.*

La Trompette W4   £ 45   𝔸★★
5-7 Devonshire Rd
8747 1836
*"Effortlessly spot-on" modern Gallic cooking – complemented
by "charming" service, a "fantastic" wine list and "classy" décor –
makes this Chiswick sibling to the fabled Chez Bruce a similarly
"perfect" local restaurant; it's even "realistically priced".* /
Details: *11 pm; smoking discouraged; booking: max 6.*

Troubadour SW5   **£ 27**   𝔸
265 Old Brompton Rd   7370 1434   4–3A
*"Great coffee, newspapers and breakfast in a quaint rustic
environment" are what this "wonderfully eclectic and Bohemian" Earl's
Court coffee shop has always done best; otherwise, it's pretty
"mediocre". / **Details:** www.troubadour.co.uk; 11 pm; no Amex.*

La Trouvaille W1   **£ 43**   𝔸★
12a Newburgh St   7287 8488   2–2C
*This "brilliantly Gallic" bistro, "tucked away off Carnaby Street",
is winning ever more enthusiastic praise for its "charming"
(if "idiosyncratic") service, its "original" cuisine and its "rustic"
ambience; it also offers a "well-priced list of wines from SW France". /
Details: www.trouvaille.co.uk; 11 pm; closed Sun.*

Tsunami SW4   **£ 33**   ★★
Unit 3, 5-7 Voltaire Rd
7978 1610   6–1D
*"Nobu without the pretensions!"; "dishes that are works of art" –
served "courteously and quickly", and "at prices you can afford" –
win nothing short of adulation for this "unlikely" Japanese, "in the
middle of nowhere" (or Clapham, as the locals call it). /
Details: 10.45 pm, Fri & Sat 11.15 pm; D only, closed Sun; no Amex; no smoking
area.*

Two Brothers N3   **£ 24**   ★
297-303 Regent's Park Rd   8346 0469
*"Arrive early, or be prepared to queue", if you want to dine at the
Finchley institution which locals hail as "the best chippie in London". /
Details: www.twobrothers.co.uk; 10.15 pm; closed Mon & Sun; no smoking area;
no booking at D.*

202 W11   **£ 25**   𝔸★
202 Westbourne Grove   7727 2722
*Nicole Farhi's "see-and-be-seen" lifestyle-store/brasserie has quickly
made itself a key Notting Hill hang-out, especially for brunch – for that
"Dean & DeLuca feel", homesick Manhattanites need look no further.
/ **Details:** L & afternoon tea only; no smoking; no booking.*

Ubon E14   **£ 70**
34 Westferry Circus   7719 7800
*"Super views" provide some antidote to the "corporate" feel of Canary
Wharf's Nobu-sibling; it similarly serves "so-fresh-it's-amazing" sushi
(and so on), but, similarly, "you pay through the nose for it". /
Details: www.noburestaurants.com; 10.15 pm; closed Sat L & Sun; no smoking
area.*

Uli W11   **£ 29**   𝔸★
16 All Saints Rd   7727 7511
*"An excellent host takes service to a new level", at this "cosy" family-
run Notting Hill "gem", where the pan-Asian food is "interesting and
of high quality"; there's a garden, too, which is "a special treat
in summer". / **Details:** www.uli-oriental.co.uk; 11 pm; D only, closed Sun;
no Amex.*

Vacherin W4   **£ 34**   ★
76 South Pde   8742 2121
*This "really, really good" newcomer is in the "brave" North Chiswick
location that once housed Riso (RIP); with its "provincial French
cooking" (très correcte), its uniformed Gallic staff and its authentic
(slightly naff) décor, it all seems remarkably "traditional" for such
a recent arrival. / **Details:** www.levacherin.co.uk; 10.30 pm; closed Mon L;
no Amex; no smoking.*

The Vale W9 £ 30 *A* ★

99 Chippenham Rd   7266 0990

This "friendly" linchpin of Maida Hill is unanimously tipped by reporters as a "great local", offering "good value". / **Details:** *11 pm; closed Mon L, Sat L & Sun D; no Amex; no smoking area.*

Vama SW10 £ 45 ★★

438 King's Rd   7351 4118   4–3B

For many reporters, "the best innovative Indian food in town" – "light", "aromatic" and "wonderfully spiced" – is to be found at this classy World's End spot. / **Details:** *www.vama.co.uk; 11 pm.*

Veeraswamy W1 £ 44 ★

Victory Hs, 99 Regent St   7734 1401   2–3D

There are often "interesting" meals to be had at London's oldest Indian restaurant, which is a "dependable" destination, near Piccadilly Circus; it's all very "nouvelle", though, nowadays – a "stylish" modern revamp in recent times swept away any 'heritage' feel. / **Value tip:** *set weekday L £28(FP).* **Details:** *www.realindianfood.com; 11.30 pm.*

El Vergel SE1 £ 16 ★★

8 Lant St   7357 0057   5–4B

"The best-value lunch in town" is served at this "tiny but packed" Latin American "café/deli" in Borough, where "quick and friendly" staff serve "awesome", "light and zesty" fare. / **Details:** *www.elvergel.co.uk; breakfast & L only, closed Sat & Sun; no credit cards; no smoking; no booking after 12.45 pm.*

Vertigo
Tower 42 EC2 £ 46 *A*

20-25 Old Broad St   7877 7842   5–2C

"Let's be honest, no one comes for the food" (which is "uneventful" and "very expensive") – it's the "intoxicating" view from the 42nd-floor bar of the former NatWest Tower that makes this a surprisingly "romantic" (as well as a business-friendly) destination. / **Details:** *www.vertigo42.co.uk; 9.15 pm; closed Sat & Sun; booking essential.*

Vijay NW6 £ 20 ★★

49 Willesden Ln   7328 1087

Some of "the best south Indian cooking in north London" – and at "fantastic" prices, too – make this "friendly" Kilburn curry house an infallibly popular destination. / **Details:** *www.vijayindia.com; 10.45 pm, Fri & Sat 11.45 pm.*

Vrisaki N22 £ 26 ★

73 Myddleton Rd   8889 8760

"Don't eat for a week before you visit" – the "bargain" mezze at this "fun" and "noisy" Greek/Cypriot taverna (in a Bounds Green backstreet) are a "stomach-blowing experience". / **Details:** *midnight; closed Sun.*

Wagamama   **£ 22**
109-125 Knightsbridge, SW1   7201 8000
8 Norris St, SW1   7321 2755
101a Wigmore St, W1   7409 0111
10a Lexington St, W1   7292 0990
4a Streatham St, WC1   7323 9223
1 Tavistock St, WC2   7836 3330
14a Irving St, WC2   7839 2323
26a Kensington High St, W8   7376 1717
11 Jamestown Rd, NW1   7428 0800
45 Bank St, E14   7516 9009
1a Ropemaker St, EC2   7588 2688
22 Old Broad St, EC2   7256 9992
Tower Pl, EC3   7283 5897
109 Fleet St, EC4   7583 7889
30 Queen St, EC4   7248 5766
*"The concept is excellent", say the many fans of these "cheap",
"healthy" and "reliable" canteens, which are "great for a quick noodle
meal"; their once-radical approach, though, can seem "a bit formulaic
nowadays". /* **Details:** *www.wagamama.com; 10 pm-midnight; EC4 & EC2 closed
Sat & Sun; no smoking; no booking.*

Wapping Food E1   **£ 46**   🄰
Wapping Power Station, Wapping Wall   7680 2080
*An "extraordinary" all-Oz wine list almost rivals the more obvious lure
of the "marvellous" post-industrial interior at this "curious" Docklands
destination; brunch – "a different class of fry-up" – is also a highlight. /*
Details: *10.30 pm; closed Sun D.*

White Horse SW6   **£ 31**
1 Parsons Grn   7736 2115   6–1B
*Given its widespread reputation as the 'Sloaney Pony', it's easy
to overlook the variety of "quality" pub food (including summer BBQs),
good ales and "brilliant" wines on offer at this large and "airy" Parson's
Green boozer. /* **Details:** *www.whitehorsesw6.com; 10.30pm; no smoking
in dining room.*

Willie Gunn SW18   **£ 36**   🄰
422 Garratt Ln   8946 7773   6–2B
*"A neighbourhood treasure" – this Earlsfield "institution" continues
to receive local adulation for its "consistent" cooking and "friendly"
spirit; it can seem "pricey for what it is", though. /* **Details:** *11 pm.*

Wiltons SW1   **£ 74**
55 Jermyn St   7629 9955   2–3C
*Famed for its "fresh" and "un-mucked-around" fish and seafood,
this "revered" clubland "time warp" is a "class act" which somehow
manages to be "greater than the sum of its parts"; prices are "scary",
though, and reporters can find the experience pretty "dull". /*
Details: *www.wiltons.co.uk; 10.30 pm; closed Sat & Sun; jacket & tie required;
booking: max 8.*

Windows on the World
Park Lane Hilton Hotel W1   **£ 89**   🄰X
22 Park Ln   7208 4021   2–4A
*"The views are second to none" and provide a "very romantic"
backdrop for diners, at this 28th-floor Mayfair dining room;
unfortunately, the "scandalous" prices reflect altitude rather than food
quality. /* **Details:** *10.30 pm, Fri & Sat 11.30 pm; closed Sat L & Sun D; jacket &
tie required at D; no smoking at breakfast.*

The Windsor Castle W8 £ 26 Ⓐ
114 Campden Hill Rd   7243 9551
*Few pubs match the charm of the "cosy" interior and "great" garden
of this ever-popular Georgian tavern, near Notting Hill Gate; it's winning
a bit of a name for "the best sausages in town", and its other fare
is perfectly competent, too.* / **Details:** www.windsor-castle-pub.co.uk; 11 pm;
no smoking area at L; no booking.

The Wine Library EC3 £ 23 ⒶX
43 Trinity Sq   7481 0415   5–3D
*"Excellent wines at retail prices" (plus modest corkage) helps create
"a buzz that's perfect for a boozy lunch, or all afternoon", at these
"unique" merchant's cellars near Tower Hill; "forget the food" –
the cheese and pâté buffet is OK, but incidental.* / **Details:** 8 pm; L &
early evening only, closed Sat & Sun.

The Wolseley W1 £ 42 Ⓐ
160 Piccadilly   7499 6996   2–3C
*"Corbin and King still have what it takes", say fans of their "fabulous"
new grand café – a "stunning" reincarnation of a magnificent
Edwardian building, by the Ritz; "teething pains" have included some
"dull" dishes, but the place may yet rival their earlier (re-)creation,
The Ivy; (it already does a "perfect" breakfast).* / **Details:** midnight;
no smoking area.

Wong Kei W1 £ 16
41-43 Wardour St   7437 8408   3–3A
*The debate rages on – are staff "friendlier" these days, or still "so rude,
it's theatre"?; whatever, many reporters still think this "infamous"
canteen is "the best place for a cheap Chinatown meal".* /
Details: 11.15 pm; no credit cards; no booking.

Yatra W1 £ 42
34 Dover St   7493 0200   2–3C
*Fans say it's an "exotic treat" to visit this "imaginative" modern Mayfair
Indian; as ever, it induces surprisingly little feedback, though, and one
or two reporters think its food is "overpriced and bland".* / **Value tip:** set
weekday L £24(FP). **Details:** www.yatra.co.uk; 11 pm, Thu-Sat 11.30 pm; closed
Sat L & Sun.

Yauatcha W1 £ 30 ★★
Broadwick Hs, 15-17 Broadwick St
7494 8888   2–2D
*"Perfect morsels" of "delectable" dim sum win "top marks" for Alan
Yau's new "designer" Soho sibling to the famed Hakkasan; the
basement setting – including tropical fishtank bar – is quite exotic, but
"tightly-packed".* / **Details:** 11.30 pm; no smoking.

Yming W1 £ 34 ★★
35-36 Greek St   7734 2721   3–2A
*"Christine Yau and her staff are so helpful", at this Soho Chinese
("50 yards north of Chinatown"); you could walk past it for years
without noticing it – that would be a shame as the food (including
a good number of "unusual dishes") can be "superb".* /
Details: www.yming.com; 11.45 pm; closed Sun; no smoking area.

Zafferano SW1 £ 53 Ⓐ★★
15 Lowndes St   7235 5800   4–1D
*"Marvellous", "sophisticated" cooking and "attentive but unfussy"
service maintain the outstanding reputation of this Belgravia Italian;
it's "cramped and awkwardly laid-out", but – "for somewhere of this
calibre" – "unusually relaxed and unpretentious".* /
Details: www.atozrestaurants.com; 11 pm.

Zaika W8 £ 52 ★
1 Kensington High St 7795 6533 4–1A
Vineet Bhatia's "exquisite" cooking propelled this former banking hall, opposite Kensington Gardens, to the top of the premier league of London's 'nouvelle' Indians – he left in the summer of 2004, and is going to be a hard act to follow. / Value tip: set weekday L £33(FP). Details: www.cuisine-collection.co.uk; 10.45 pm; closed Sat L.

Zamoyski NW3 £ 24 𝔸
85 Fleet Rd 7794 4792
"Vodka and Polish accordion folk music" help create the continuing romantic and party-popularity of this "cosy" Belsize Park fixture, where the simple, "cheap" scoff can be "surprisingly good". / Details: 11 pm; D only; no smoking area.

Zero Degrees SE3 £ 24 𝔸
29-31 Montpelier Vale 8852 5619
An unusual formula – "brilliant microbrewery beers, plus pizza" – helps make an ongoing success of this "fun" Blackheath bar/restaurant; at weekends, though, it can get "noisy and smokey". / Details: www.zerodegrees-microbrewery.co.uk; 11.30 pm.

Ziani SW3 £ 39 𝔸
45-47 Radnor Walk 7352 2698 4–3C
"Lots of buzz and hum" and "waiters who treat you like family" are the key strengths of this "overcrowded" Chelsea trattoria; since last year's refurb, though, it's not quite back to its former standards. / Value tip: set weekday L £23(FP). Details: 11 pm.

Zilli Fish W1 £ 48
36-40 Brewer St 7734 8649 2–2D
"Consistently good" Italian fish and seafood dishes maintain the fashionable appeal of Aldo Zilli's "seedily-located" and "noisy" Soho "stalwart"; prices are "high", though, and portions can be "small". / Details: www.zillialdo.com; 11.15 pm; closed Sun.

Zuma SW7 £ 60 𝔸★★
5 Raphael St 7584 1010 4–1C
You feel "like you've walked into an advert", at this "hip, see-and-be-seen" Knightsbridge Japanese; it's often favourably compared to Nobu, both for the value of its "heaven-sent" sushi (and other dishes), and also for being "more chic". / Details: www.zumarestaurant.com; 11 pm; no smoking.

LONDON
AREA OVERVIEWS

CENTRAL

Soho, Covent Garden & Bloomsbury
(Parts of W1, all WC2 and WC1)

£70+	Lindsay House	*British, Modern*	-
£60+	Savoy Grill	*British, Traditional*	𝔸
	Asia de Cuba	*Fusion*	𝔸
£50+	The Ivy	*British, Modern*	𝔸
	Rules	*British, Traditional*	𝔸
	Simpsons-in-the-Strand	*"*	𝔸
	J Sheekey	*Fish & seafood*	𝔸★★
	East@West	*Fusion*	★★
	Red Fort	*Indian*	-
£40+	Indigo	*British, Modern*	★
	Circus	*"*	-
	Zilli Fish	*Fish & seafood*	-
	La Trouvaille	*French*	𝔸★
	The Criterion Grill	*"*	𝔸✗
	Maggiore's	*"*	𝔸
	Mon Plaisir	*"*	𝔸
	L'Escargot	*"*	-
	Le Palais du Jardin	*"*	-
£35+	Joe Allen	*American*	𝔸
	French House	*British, Modern*	𝔸
	Randall & Aubin	*French*	𝔸
	Gay Hussar	*Hungarian*	𝔸
	Bohème Kitchen	*International*	𝔸
	Sarastro	*"*	𝔸✗
	St Moritz	*Swiss*	𝔸
	La Spiga	*Pizza*	-
	Fung Shing	*Chinese*	★★
	Café Lazeez	*Indian*	-
£30+	Andrew Edmunds	*British, Modern*	𝔸★
	Aurora	*"*	𝔸
	Balans	*International*	-
	Boulevard	*"*	-
	Aperitivo	*Italian*	𝔸
	Strada	*"*	-
	Café Pacifico	*Mexican/TexMex*	-
	Yauatcha	*Chinese*	★★
	Yming	*"*	★★
	Malabar Junction	*Indian*	-
£25+	Sapori	*Italian*	-
	06 St Chad's Place	*Mediterranean*	𝔸★
	Mildred's	*Vegetarian*	-
	Harbour City	*Chinese*	-
	Thai Pot	*Thai*	-
£20+	Gordon's Wine Bar	*International*	𝔸✗
	Star Café	*"*	-
	La Porchetta Pizzeria	*Italian*	-
	Ed's Easy Diner	*Burgers, etc*	𝔸
	Hamburger Union	*"*	-

	Masala Zone	*Indian*	-
	Itsu	*Japanese*	𝔸★
	Wagamama	*"*	-
	Busaba Eathai	*Thai*	𝔸
£15+	Wong Kei	*Chinese*	-
£10+	Paul	*Sandwiches, cakes, etc*	★
	Bar Italia	*"*	𝔸
£5+	Maison Bertaux	*"*	𝔸★
£1+	Bank Aldwych	*British, Modern*	-
	Thyme	*"*	-
	Monmouth Coffee Company	*Sandwiches, cakes, etc*	-

Mayfair & St James's (Parts of W1 and SW1)

£120+	Sketch (Lecture Rm)	*French*	X
£90+	Le Gavroche	*"*	𝔸★
£80+	The Greenhouse	*British, Modern*	𝔸
	The Ritz	*French*	𝔸X
	Windows on the World	*"*	𝔸X
£70+	Wiltons	*British, Traditional*	-
	G Ramsay at Claridges	*French*	-
	The Square	*"*	-
	Nobu	*Fusion*	★
	Connaught (Angela Hartnett)	*Mediterranean*	-
£60+	Dorchester Grill	*British, Traditional*	𝔸
	Mirabelle	*French*	𝔸
	L'Oranger	*"*	𝔸
	Cecconi's	*Italian*	𝔸
	Cipriani	*"*	𝔸
	Hakkasan	*Chinese*	𝔸
	Taman gang	*Thai*	𝔸
£50+	Osia	*Australian*	★
	Quaglino's	*British, Modern*	-
	Green's	*British, Traditional*	𝔸
	Sketch (Gallery)	*French*	X
	Kai	*Chinese*	★
	Tamarind	*Indian*	★
	Benares	*"*	-
	Shogun	*Japanese*	★★
	Sumosan	*"*	★★
£40+	Le Caprice	*British, Modern*	𝔸★
	Patterson's	*"*	★
	Inn the Park	*"*	𝔸
	Langan's Brasserie	*"*	𝔸
	The Wolseley	*"*	𝔸
	Boudin Blanc	*French*	𝔸
	Alloro	*Italian*	★
	Teca	*"*	★
	Momo	*Moroccan*	𝔸

	Fakhreldine	*Lebanese*	𝔸
	Veeraswamy	*Indian*	★
	Chor Bizarre	*"*	𝔸
	Mint Leaf	*"*	𝔸
	Yatra	*"*	-
	Patara	*Thai*	★★
£35+	Fortnum's, The Fountain	*British, Modern*	𝔸
	Pappagallo	*Italian*	-
	Sotheby's Café	*Mediterranean*	𝔸★
£30+	Strada	*Italian*	-
	Rocket	*Mediterranean*	𝔸
	Rasa	*Indian*	★★
£20+	Running Horse	*International*	-
	Wagamama	*Japanese*	-
£1+	Fuzzy's Grub	*Sandwiches, cakes, etc*	-

Fitzrovia & Marylebone (Part of W1)

£70+	Pied à Terre	*French*	★
£60+	Orrery	*"*	-
£50+	Archipelago	*Fusion*	𝔸
	The Providores	*"*	-
	Passione	*Italian*	★
£40+	Odin's	*British, Traditional*	𝔸
	Back to Basics	*Fish & seafood*	★★
	Elena's L'Etoile	*French*	𝔸
	Locanda Locatelli	*Italian*	𝔸★
	Fino	*Spanish*	★
	Maroush	*Lebanese*	★
	La Porte des Indes	*Indian*	𝔸★
	Roka	*Japanese*	★
	Crazy Bear	*Thai*	𝔸
£35+	Hardy's	*International*	-
	Latium	*Italian*	★
	Black & Blue	*Steaks & grills*	-
	Bam-Bou	*French-Vietnamese*	𝔸★
	Deya	*Indian*	★★
£30+	Strada	*Italian*	-
	La Rueda	*Spanish*	𝔸
	Fairuz	*Lebanese*	★
	Royal China	*Chinese*	★★
£25+	Giraffe	*International*	-
	Eagle Bar Diner	*Burgers, etc*	𝔸
£20+	Wagamama	*Japanese*	-
£10+	Paul	*Sandwiches, cakes, etc*	★

Belgravia, Pimlico, Victoria & Westminster (SW1, except St James's)

£80+	Pétrus	*French*	★
£70+	One-O-One	*Fish & seafood*	★
£60+	Roussillon	*French*	★★
	Foliage	*"*	-
	The Cinnamon Club	*Indian*	★
	Nahm	*Thai*	★
£50+	Goring Hotel	*British, Traditional*	Ⓐ
	Boxwood Café	*International*	
	Zafferano	*Italian*	Ⓐ★★
	L'Incontro	*"*	Ⓐ★
	Toto's	*"*	Ⓐ★
	Signor Sassi	*"*	Ⓐ
	Ken Lo's Memories	*Chinese*	★
£40+	Tate Britain	*British, Modern*	Ⓐ
	La Poule au Pot	*French*	Ⓐ
	Quirinale	*Italian*	★★
	Sale e Pepe	*"*	-
	Boisdale	*Scottish*	Ⓐ
	Salloos	*Pakistani*	★★
£35+	The Ebury	*International*	Ⓐ
	Caraffini	*Italian*	Ⓐ★
	Noura	*Lebanese*	Ⓐ★
	Hunan	*Chinese*	★★
£30+	Le Cercle	*French*	Ⓐ★★
	Just Oriental	*Pan-Asian*	Ⓐ
£25+	Page in Pimlico	*International*	-
	Kazan	*Turkish*	-
£20+	Jenny Lo's	*Chinese*	★★
	Wagamama	*Japanese*	-

WEST

Chelsea, South Kensington, Kensington, Earl's Court & Fulham (SW3, SW5, SW6, SW7, SW10 & W8)

£90+	Gordon Ramsay	French	A★★
	Blakes Hotel	International	A
£70+	Aubergine	French	A★★
	Capital Hotel	"	★★
	Tom Aikens	"	★
£60+	Clarke's	British, Modern	A★★
	1880	"	A★
	Bibendum	French	A
	Rasoi Vineet Bhatia	Indian	★
	Zuma	Japanese	A★★
£50+	Bluebird	British, Modern	X
	Belvedere	French	A
	Scalini	Italian	A
	Chutney Mary	Indian	A★
	Zaika	"	★
	Bombay Brasserie	"	A
£40+	Big Easy	American	A
	Launceston Place	British, Modern	A
	Admiral Codrington	"	-
	Maggie Jones's	British, Traditional	A★
	Lundum's	Danish	A★
	Racine	French	★
	Le Colombier	"	A
	Lucio	Italian	A
	Carpaccio's	"	-
	La Famiglia	"	-
	Floriana	"	-
	Cambio de Tercio	Spanish	A
	Pasha	Moroccan	A
	Maroush	Lebanese	★
	Ken Lo's Memories	Chinese	★
	Mr Wing	"	★
	Vama	Indian	★★
	Eight Over Eight	Pan-Asian	A★
	Patara	Thai	★★
	Blue Elephant	"	A★
	Sugar Hut	"	A
£35+	The Abingdon	British, Modern	A
	Ffiona's	British, Traditional	A
	Lou Pescadou	Fish & seafood	★
	Stratford's	"	★
	Ghillies	"	A
	Randall & Aubin	French	A
	Langan's Bar & Grill	"	-
	Elistano	Italian	A
	Frantoio	"	A
	Ziani	"	A
	Manicomio	Mediterranean	-
	Black & Blue	Steaks & grills	-

	Spiga	Pizza	-
	The Painted Heron	Indian	★★
	Star of India	"	★★
	Café Lazeez	"	-
£30+	The Ifield	British, Modern	Ⓐ
	Lots Road	"	-
	Le Metro	"	-
	White Horse	"	-
	Tartine	French	Ⓐ
	The Scarsdale	International	Ⓐ
	Balans West	"	-
	Balans	"	-
	Mirto	Italian	★
	Riccardo's	"	Ⓐ
	Strada	"	-
	La Rueda	Spanish	Ⓐ
	Sophie's Steakhouse	Steaks & grills	Ⓐ★
	(Ciro's) Pizza Pomodoro	Pizza	Ⓐ
£25+	The Builder's Arms	British, Modern	Ⓐ
	The Windsor Castle	International	Ⓐ
	Coopers Arms	"	-
	Giraffe	"	-
	Pappa e Ciccia	Italian	Ⓐ★
	Aglio e Olio	"	★
	Bersagliera	"	Ⓐ
	The Atlas	Mediterranean	Ⓐ★
	Tendido Cero	Spanish	Ⓐ★
	La Delizia	Pizza	Ⓐ
	Troubadour	Sandwiches, cakes, etc	Ⓐ
	Malabar	Indian	★
	Thai Noodle Bar	Thai	Ⓐ
£20+	Chelsea Bun Diner	International	-
	Gourmet Burger Kitchen	Burgers, etc	★
	Ed's Easy Diner	"	Ⓐ
	Itsu	Japanese	Ⓐ★
	Wagamama	"	
£15+	Churchill Arms	Thai	Ⓐ★
	Café 209	"	Ⓐ

Notting Hill, Holland Park, Bayswater, North Kensington & Maida Vale (W2, W9, W10, W11)

£50+	Assaggi	Italian	★★
£40+	Notting Hill Brasserie	British, Modern	Ⓐ★★
	Julie's	"	Ⓐ
	Electric Brasserie	International	-
	Esenza	Italian	★
	Café Maroush	Lebanese	★
	Maroush	"	★
	Maroush Garden	"	★
£35+	Formosa Dining Room	British, Modern	Ⓐ
	The Cow	Fish & seafood	Ⓐ★
	L'Accento Italiano	Italian	Ⓐ★
	The Oak	"	Ⓐ★

	Osteria Basilico	"	A★
	Mediterraneo	Mediterranean	-
	Bombay Palace	Indian	★★
	E&O	Pan-Asian	A★★
£30+	Lucky Seven	American	A
	The Vale	British, Modern	A★
	The Frontline Club	"	A
	The Red Pepper	Italian	★
	Fairuz	Lebanese	★
	Levantine	Middle Eastern	A★
	Mandarin Kitchen	Chinese	★★
	Royal China	"	★★
£25+	202	International	A★
	Tom's	Sandwiches, cakes, etc	A★
	Inaho	Japanese	★★
	Uli	Pan-Asian	A★
£20+	Gourmet Burger Kitchen	Burgers, etc	★
	Ben's Thai	Thai	-
£15+	Beirut Express	Lebanese	★★
	Mandalay	Burmese	★★
£5+	Lisboa Patisserie	Sandwiches, cakes, etc	★★

Hammersmith, Shepherd's Bush, Olympia, Chiswick & Ealing (W4, W5, W6, W12, W14)

£60+	The River Café	Italian	-
£40+	Fish Hoek	Fish & seafood	★★
	La Trompette	French	A★★
£35+	The Brackenbury	British, Modern	A★
£30+	The Anglesea Arms	"	A★★
	Cotto	"	★
	Snows on the Green	"	★
	Vacherin	French	★
	The Gate	Vegetarian	★★
£25+	The Havelock Tavern	British, Modern	A★★
	Ealing Park Tavern	"	A★
	Dove	"	A
	Stone Mason's Arms	"	A
	Giraffe	International	-
	Lowiczanka	Polish	-
	Blah! Blah! Blah!	Vegetarian	★★
	Madhu's	Indian	★★
£20+	Gourmet Burger Kitchen	Burgers, etc	★
	Adams Café	Moroccan	A
	Sagar	Indian, Southern	★★
£15+	Abu Zaad	Middle Eastern	A★
	Mohsen	Persian	★★
	Mirch Masala	Indian	★★

NORTH

Hampstead, West Hampstead, St John's Wood, Regent's Park, Kilburn & Camden Town (NW postcodes)

£50+	L'Aventure	*French*	A ★
£40+	Odette's	*British, Modern*	A ★
	Oslo Court	*French*	★ ★
	Rosmarino	*Italian*	-
	Sardo Canale	*"*	-
£35+	Lansdowne	*British, Modern*	A ★
	The Engineer	*"*	A
	Globe Restaurant	*"*	-
	Black & Blue	*Steaks & grills*	-
£30+	The Greyhound	*British, Modern*	A ★
	The Belsize	*"*	A
	Aperitivo	*Italian*	A
	Strada	*"*	-
	Manna	*Vegetarian*	★
	Mango Room	*Afro-Caribbean*	A ★
	Royal China	*Chinese*	★ ★
	Jin Kichi	*Japanese*	★ ★
£25+	Lemonia	*Greek*	A
	Giraffe	*International*	-
	La Brocca	*Italian*	A
	Marine Ices	*"*	-
	Don Pepe	*Spanish*	A
	Gung-Ho	*Chinese*	A ★
	Opera	*"*	-
	Sabras	*Indian, Southern*	★ ★
	Café Japan	*Japanese*	★
	Little Basil	*Thai*	A ★
£20+	The Little Bay	*Mediterranean*	A
	Zamoyski	*Polish*	A
	Gourmet Burger Kitchen	*Burgers, etc*	★
	Ed's Easy Diner	*"*	A
	Vijay	*Indian*	★ ★
	Wagamama	*Japanese*	-
£15+	Geeta	*Indian*	★ ★

Hoxton, Islington, Highgate, Crouch End, Stoke Newington, Finsbury Park, Muswell Hill & Finchley (N postcodes)

£70+	Fifteen	*Italian*	X
£40+	Frederick's	*British, Modern*	A
	Morgan M	*French*	★ ★
	The Almeida	*"*	-
£35+	The Drapers Arms	British, Modern	A
	Fig	*"*	-
	Bistro Aix	*French*	-

	Casale Franco	*Italian*	Ⓐ
£30+	The Haven	*British, Modern*	Ⓐ★
	The Barnsbury	*"*	-
	St Johns	*British, Traditional*	Ⓐ★
	Chez Liline	*Fish & seafood*	★★
	Les Associés	*French*	★
	Banners	*International*	Ⓐ
	Banners on the Hill	*"*	Ⓐ
	Florians	*Italian*	-
	Strada	*"*	-
	Rasa	*Indian*	★★
£25+	Vrisaki	*Greek*	★
	Giraffe	*International*	-
	San Daniele	*Italian*	-
	Toff's	*Fish & chips*	★
	Pasha	*Turkish*	Ⓐ
	Rasa Travancore	*Indian, Southern*	★★
£20+	La Porchetta Pizzeria	*Italian*	-
	Fine Burger Company	*Burgers, etc*	★★
	Two Brothers	*Fish & chips*	★
	La Piragua	*South American*	-
	Gallipoli	*Turkish*	Ⓐ
	Anglo Asian Tandoori	*Indian*	Ⓐ★
	Masala Zone	*"*	-

SOUTH

South Bank (SE1)

£60+	Oxo Tower (Rest')	*British, Modern*	A**X**
	Le Pont de la Tour	*"*	A
£40+	Oxo Tower (Bras')	*International*	A**X**
	Le Pont de la Tour Bar & Grill	*Steaks & grills*	A
£35+	RSJ	*British, Modern*	-
	The Anchor & Hope	*British, Traditional*	★
	Champor-Champor	*Fusion*	A★★
	Delfina Studio Café	*International*	A★★
	Laughing Gravy	*"*	-
£30+	La Lanterna	*Italian*	A★
	Bermondsey Kitchen	*Mediterranean*	-
	Bengal Clipper	*Indian*	-
£25+	The Real Greek Souvlaki	*Greek*	-
	Baltic	*Polish*	A
	Tas Pide	*Turkish*	A
	Tas	*"*	-
£20+	Amano Café	*Pizza*	★★
£15+	El Vergel	*South American*	★★

Greenwich, Lewisham & Blackheath (All SE postcodes, except SE1)

£35+	Lobster Pot	*Fish & seafood*	A★★
	The Painted Heron	*Indian*	★★
£30+	Inside	*British, Modern*	-
£25+	Chapter Two	*"*	-
	Barcelona Tapas	*Spanish*	-
£20+	Zero Degrees	*Pizza*	A
£15+	Sea Cow	*Fish & chips*	★★
£1+	Arancia	*Italian*	-

Battersea, Brixton, Clapham, Wandsworth Barnes, Putney & Wimbledon (All SW postcodes south of the river)

£40+	Chez Bruce	*British, Modern*	A★★
	Redmond's	*"*	★★
	Niksons	*"*	-
	Ransome's Dock	*"*	-
£35+	Sonny's	*"*	A★
	Lamberts	*"*	★

	Willie Gunn	"	A A
	Ghillies	Fish & seafood	A A
	Bombay Bicycle Club	Indian	★
£30+	Cinnamon Cay	Australian	A ★
	Strada	Italian	-
	Rocket Riverside	Mediterranean	A
	La Rueda	Spanish	A
	Royal China	Chinese	★★
	Tsunami	Japanese	★★
£25+	Earl Spencer	British, Modern	★★
	Rick's Café	"	A ★
	The Abbeville	"	A
	Emile's	French	★
	Giraffe	International	-
	Pappa e Ciccia	Italian	A ★
	Antipasto & Pasta	"	A
	Café Portugal	Portuguese	-
	Rebato's	Spanish	A ★
	El Rincón Latino	"	A
	Pizza Metro	Pizza	A ★★
	Eco	"	★
	Eco Brixton	"	★
	Sarkhel's	Indian	★★
£20+	Chelsea Bun Diner	International	-
	Little Bay	Mediterranean	A
	Fine Burger Company	Burgers, etc	★★
	Gourmet Burger Kitchen	"	★
	Brady's	Fish & chips	-
	Boiled Egg & Soldiers	Sandwiches, cakes, etc	A ★
	Kastoori	Indian	★★
	Amaranth	Thai	A ★★
£15+	Mirch Masala SW16	Indian	★★
	Sree Krishna	"	★★
	Fujiyama	Japanese	-
	The Pepper Tree	Thai	A

Outer western suburbs
Kew, Richmond, Twickenham, Teddington

£50+	Monsieur Max	French	★★
	McClements	"	-
£40+	The Glasshouse	British, Modern	A ★★
	A Cena	Italian	-
	Kew Grill	Steaks & grills	-
£35+	Murano	Italian	-
£30+	Chez Lindsay	French	A
£25+	Ma Cuisine	French	★
	don Fernando's	Spanish	A

EAST

Smithfield & Farringdon (EC1)

£50+	Smiths (Top Floor)	*British, Modern*	𝔸
£40+	St John	*"*	★
	Club Gascon	*French*	𝔸★★
	Bleeding Heart	*"*	𝔸★
	Moro	*North African*	𝔸★★
£35+	Malmaison	*British, Modern*	𝔸
	Café du Marché	*French*	𝔸★
	Flâneur	*Mediterranean*	-
	Potemkin	*Russian*	-
	Café City Lazeez	*Indian*	-
	Cicada	*Pan-Asian*	𝔸★
£30+	Coach & Horses	*British, Modern*	★
	Strada	*Italian*	-
	Smiths (Dining Rm)	*Steaks & grills*	𝔸
£25+	The Gunmakers	*British, Modern*	-
	The Real Greek Souvlaki	*Greek*	-
	Tas Pide	*Turkish*	𝔸
£20+	La Porchetta Pizzeria	*Italian*	-
	The Eagle	*Mediterranean*	𝔸★
	The Little Bay	*"*	𝔸
	Smiths (Ground Floor)	*Sandwiches, cakes, etc*	𝔸

The City (EC2, EC3, EC4)

£80+	Tatsuso	*Japanese*	★
£60+	1 Lombard Street	*British, Modern*	-
£50+	Rhodes 24	*"*	𝔸★
	Coq d'Argent	*French*	-
£40+	The Don	*British, Modern*	𝔸★
	The Rivington Grill	*"*	-
	Vertigo	*Fish & seafood*	𝔸
	Refettorio	*Italian*	-
	Bevis Marks	*Kosher*	𝔸★
	City Miyama	*Japanese*	★★
£35+	Sweetings	*Fish & seafood*	𝔸★
	Luc's Brasserie	*French*	-
	Imperial City	*Chinese*	𝔸★
	Miyabi	*Japanese*	★★
	Singapura	*Malaysian*	𝔸
£30+	(Ciro's) Pizza Pomodoro	*Pizza*	𝔸
	Gt Eastern Dining Room	*Pan-Asian*	𝔸★
£25+	Barcelona Tapas	*Spanish*	-
	K10	*Japanese*	★
	Ekachai	*Thai*	-

£20+	Simpson's Tavern	British, Traditional	𝔸
	The Wine Library	"	𝔸
	Wagamama	Japanese	-
£15+	Club Mangia	British, Modern	𝔸

East End & Docklands (All E postcodes)

£70+	Ubon	Fusion	-
£50+	Les Trois Garçons	French	𝔸
	Plateau	"	-
£40+	Lanes	British, Modern	★
	Wapping Food	"	𝔸
	Lightship	Scandinavian	𝔸
£35+	1802	British, Modern	-
	St John Bread & Wine	British, Traditional	-
	The Grapes	Fish & seafood	𝔸★
	Il Bordello	Italian	𝔸★
	Armadillo	South American	𝔸★★
	Café Spice Namaste	Indian	★
	Elephant Royale	Thai	𝔸
£30+	Bistrothèque	French	-
	Parco's	Italian	-
	Royal China	Chinese	★★
£25+	LMNT	British, Modern	𝔸
	Cat & Mutton	"	-
	Barcelona Tapas	Spanish	-
	Haz	Turkish	★
£20+	Faulkner's	Fish & chips	★
	Drunken Monkey	Chinese, Dim sum	𝔸
	Itsu	Japanese	𝔸★
	Wagamama	"	-
£15+	Mangal	Turkish	★★
	Lahore Kebab House	Indian	★★
	New Tayyab	Pakistani	★★
	Sông Quê	Vietnamese	★★
£1+	Brick Lane Beigel Bake	Sandwiches, cakes, etc	★★

LONDON INDEXES

BBREAKFAST
(WITH OPENING TIMES)

Central
Asia de Cuba *(7)*
Balans: *all branches (8)*
Bank Aldwych *(7 Mon-Fri, Sat 8)*
Bar Italia *(7)*
Cecconi's *(8)*
The Cinnamon Club *(7.30 Mon-Fri)*
Connaught (Angela
   Hartnett) *(7)*
Dorchester Grill *(7)*
Fortnum's, The Fountain *(8.30)*
Fuzzy's Grub *(7.30)*
Giraffe: *W1 (8, Sat & Sun 9)*
Goring Hotel *(7)*
Indigo *(6.30)*
Inn the Park *(8)*
Maison Bertaux *(9)*
Monmouth Coffee
   Company *(7.30)*
One-O-One *(7)*
Paul: *WC2 (7.30)*
The Providores *(9, Sat & Sun 10)*
The Ritz *(7, Sun 8am)*
Simpsons-in-the-Strand *(7.30
   Mon-Fri, 10.30 Sun)*
06 St Chad's Place *(8)*
Sotheby's Café *(9.30)*
Star Café *(7)*
Tate Britain *(10)*
Windows on the World *(7)*
The Wolseley *(9, Sat & Sun)*
Yauatcha *(10)*

West
Adams Café *(7.30, Sat 8.30)*
Balans West: *all branches (8)*
Beirut Express *(7)*
Blakes Hotel *(7.30)*
Capital Hotel *(7, Sun 7.30)*
Chelsea Bun Diner: *all branches (7)*
Clarke's *(Mon-Sat in café)*
La Delizia *(10)*
Ed's Easy Diner: *SW3 (9 Sat & Sun)*
Electric Brasserie *(8)*
Ghillies: *all branches (10)*
Langan's Bar & Grill *(10.30, Sat &
   Sun)*
Lisboa Patisserie *(8)*
Lucky Seven *(8)*
Lundum's *(9)*
Maroush: *I) 21 Edgware Rd W2 (10)*
Le Metro *(7.30, Sun 8.00)*
Sophie's Steakhouse *(11, Sat & Sun)*
Tartine *(11)*
Tom's *(8, Sun 10)*
Troubadour *(9)*
202 *(8.30)*

North
The Almeida *(9)*
Banners on the Hill: *N19 (9); N8 (9,
   Sat & Sun 10)*
The Engineer *(9)*
Florians *(11, Sat & Sun)*
Gallipoli: *Upper St N1, Upper St
   N1 (10.30)*

Giraffe: *all north branches (8, Sat & Sun 9)*
Sardo Canale *(10, Sat & Sun)*

South
Amano Café *(7)*
Boiled Egg *(9)*
Café Portugal *(8)*
Chapter Two *(8.30)*
Chelsea Bun Diner: *all branches (7)*
Delfina Studio Café *(10)*
Eco Brixton: *SW9 (8.30)*
Ghillies: *all branches (10)*
Giraffe: *SW11 (8, Sat & Sun 9)*
Inside *(11, Sat)*
Le Pont de la Tour
   Bar & Grill *(10, Sat & Sun)*
El Vergel *(8.30)*

East
Brick Lane Beigel Bake *(24 hrs)*
Club Mangia *(7)*
Coq d'Argent *(7.30 Mon-Fri)*
Flâneur *(9, Sat & Sun)*
Malmaison *(7, Sat & Sun 8)*
1 Lombard Street *(7.30)*
St John Bread & Wine *(8)*
Smiths (Ground Floor) *(7, Sat &
   Sun 9)*
Wapping Food *(10)*

BRUNCH MENUS

Central
Aurora
Balans: *W1*
Bank Aldwych
Boisdale
Le Caprice
Circus
Fuzzy's Grub
Giraffe: *all branches*
Indigo
Inn the Park
The Ivy
Joe Allen
The Providores
Windows on the World
The Wolseley

West
The Abingdon
Admiral Codrington
Balans West: *SW5*
Blue Elephant
Bluebird
Chelsea Bun Diner: *SW10*
Chutney Mary
Electric Brasserie
Giraffe: *all branches*
Langan's Bar & Grill
Lucky Seven
Lundum's
Notting Hill Brasserie
Sophie's Steakhouse
Stone Mason's Arms
Tom's
Troubadour
202

INDEXES

Goring Hotel
L'Incontro
Locanda Locatelli
Mon Plaisir
One-O-One
Patterson's
Pied à Terre
La Porte des Indes
Quirinale
Rules
Zafferano

West
Aglio e Olio
Blah! Blah! Blah!
Blue Elephant
Café 209
Chelsea Bun Diner: SW10
Esenza
Fish Hoek
Manicomio
Mohsen
Pappa e Ciccia: Munster Rd SW6
Stratford's
Tendido Cero
Vacherin

North
Frederick's
Geeta
Jin Kichi
Lansdowne
Rosmarino

South
A Cena
Amaranth
Delfina Studio Café
Eco Brixton: SW9
The Glasshouse
Mirch Masala: SW16, SW17
Royal China

East
Club Gascon
Lahore Kebab House
Malmaison
Mangal
New Tayyab
St John
Ubon

CHILDREN
(H – HIGH OR SPECIAL CHAIRS
M – CHILDREN'S MENU
P – CHILDREN'S PORTIONS
E – WEEKEND ENTERTAINMENTS
O – OTHER FACILITIES)

Central
Aperitivo: W1 (p)
Asia de Cuba (h)
Back to Basics (hp)
Balans: all branches (hp)
Bank Aldwych (hmo)
Bar Italia (hp)
Benares (h)
Boudin Blanc (hp)

Boxwood Café (mo)
Café Pacifico (hm)
Le Caprice (hp)
Cecconi's (h)
Chor Bizarre (h)
The Cinnamon Club (h)
Circus (hp)
Connaught (Angela
    Hartnett) (hm)
The Criterion Grill (h)
Deya (p)
Dorchester Grill (hm)
Ed's Easy Diner: Trocadero W1 (hm);
    Moor St W1 (m)
Fairuz: all branches (h)
Fakhreldine (hp)
Foliage (hm)
Fortnum's, The Fountain (hmpe)
Fung Shing (h)
Fuzzy's Grub (h)
Gay Hussar (hp)
Giraffe: all branches (hm)
Gordon Ramsay at
    Claridge's (h)
Goring Hotel (hm)
Green's (p)
The Greenhouse (h)
Hamburger Union: all branches (h)
Harbour City (h)
Hardy's (hp)
Indigo (hp)
Inn the Park (hp)
Itsu: all branches (h)
The Ivy (hp)
Just Oriental (h)
Kai (h)
Kazan (hp)
Langan's Brasserie (p)
Latium (h)
Locanda Locatelli (hpo)
Malabar Junction (m)
Maroush: III) 62 Seymour St W1 (hp)
Masala Zone: W1 (hp)
Mirabelle (h)
Mon Plaisir (p)
Nobu (h)
Noura (hp)
One-O-One (hm)
Orrery (h)
Passione (p)
Patterson's (h)
Paul: all branches (h)
Pétrus (h)
La Porchetta Pizzeria: WC1 (h)
La Porte des Indes (h)
La Poule au Pot (h)
The Providores (h)
Quaglino's (hm)
Quirinale (hm)
The Ritz (hm)
Rocket: W1 (ph)
Roka (h)
Royal China: all branches (h)
La Rueda: all branches (hp)
Rules (h)
Sale e Pepe (h)
Sapori (hp)

INDEXES

Smiths (Ground Floor) *(hm)*
Smiths (Dining Rm) *(h)*
Smiths (Top Floor) *(h)*
Strada: *EC1 (h)*
Ubon *(hp)*
Wagamama: *E14, both EC2, Fleet St EC4 (h)*
Wapping Food *(h)*

ENTERTAINMENT
(CHECK TIMES BEFORE YOU GO)

Central
Bank Aldwych
(jazz, Sun)
Bohème Kitchen
(DJ, Sun)
Boisdale
(classic jazz, Mon-Sat)
Le Caprice
(pianist, nightly)
Circus
(DJ, Wed-Sat)
Eagle Bar Diner
(DJ, Tue-Sat)
East@West
(DJ, Thu-Sat)
Foliage
(jazz, Mon-Sat)
Goring Hotel
(pianist, nightly)
Hakkasan
(DJ, nightly)
Indigo
(film brunches, Sun)
Joe Allen
(pianist, nightly (not Sun); jazz, Sun)
Kai
(harpist, Tue or Thu & Sat)
Langan's Brasserie
(jazz, nightly)
Mirabelle
(pianist Tue-Sat & Sun l)
Momo
(live world music, Mon-Wed)
O'Conor Don
(DJ, Thu)
La Porte des Indes
(jazz, Sun brunch)
Quaglino's
(jazz, nightly; pianist, Sat & Sun brunch)
The Ritz
(band, Fri & Sat (nightly in Dec))
La Rueda: *W1*
(Spanish music & dancing, Fri & Sat)
Sarastro
(opera, Sun & Mon)
Simpsons-in-the-Strand
(pianist, nightly)
Taman gang
(DJ, nightly)
Windows on the World
(dinner dance, Fri & Sat; jazz, Sun brunch)

West
Big Easy
(band, nightly)
Bluebird
(DJ , Fri & Sat)
Bombay Brasserie
(pianist & singer, nightly)
Chutney Mary
(jazz, Sun)
(Ciro's) Pizza Pomodoro: *SW3*
(live music, nightly)
Lowiczanka
(Gypsy music, Fri & Sat)

Maroush: *I) 21 Edgware Rd W2*
(music & dancing, nightly)
Mr Wing
(jazz, Fri & Sat)
Notting Hill Brasserie
(jazz, nightly)
Star of India
(live music, Thur)
Sugar Hut
(DJ, Fri & Sat)
Vama
(jazz, Sun)

North
La Brocca
(jazz, Thu)
Don Pepe
(singer & organist, Thu-Sat)
Globe Restaurant
(cabaret, fortnightly Thu)
Zamoyski
(Russian music, Sat)

South
Baltic
(jazz, Sun & Mon)
Bengal Clipper
(pianist, nightly)
Fujiyama
(DJ, Mon-Thu)
La Lanterna
(live music, Fri)
Laughing Gravy
(jazz, Thu)
Le Pont de la Tour
  Bar & Grill
(jazz pianist, nightly)
La Rueda: *SW4*
(DJ, Fri & Sat)
Tas: *Borough High St SE1*
(guitarist, nightly); The Cut SE1
(live music, nightly)
Tas Pide: *SE1*
(guitarist, nightly)

East
Barcelona Tapas: *EC4*
(disco, Thu & Fri)
Bistrothèque
(transvestite show Wed, Pianist Fri)
Café du Marché
(pianist & bass, nightly)
(Ciro's) Pizza Pomodoro: *EC2*
(live music, Mon-Fri)
Coq d'Argent
(pianist Sat; jazz Fri & Sun L)
Elephant Royale
(live music, Wed-Sat)
LMNT
(opera, Sun)
1 Lombard Street
(pianist, Mon & Fri, L & D)
Smiths (Dining Rm)
(DJ, Fri & Sat)

LATE
(OPEN TILL MIDNIGHT OR LATER AS SHOWN; MAY BE EARLIER SUNDAY)

Central
Asia de Cuba *(midnight, Sat 1 am)*
Balans: *W1 (5 am, Sun 2 am)*
Bar Italia *(3 am, Fri & Sat open 24 hours)*
Boulevard *(1)*
Le Caprice *(1)*
Circus *(1)*

Ed's Easy Diner: Moor St
W1 (midnight)
Fakhreldine (1)
Itsu: all branches (Fri & Sat only)
The Ivy (1)
Joe Allen (12.45 am)
Maroush: all central branches (1 am)
Quaglino's (midnight, Fri & Sat 1 am)
J Sheekey (1)
La Spiga: W1 (Wed-Sat only)
The Wolseley (1)

West
Balans West: SW5 (1 am Sun-Thu , 2am
Fri & Sat)
Beirut Express (1.45 am)
Big Easy (midnight, Fri & Sat 12.30 am)
Blue Elephant (1)
Café Lazeez: SW7 (1)
(Ciro's) Pizza
Pomodoro: SW3 (1 am)
La Delizia (1)
Fairuz: W2 (1)
Itsu: all branches (Fri & Sat only)
Levantine (1)
Lou Pescadou (1)
Café Maroush: all in W2§ (1 am);
SW3 (2.30 am)
Scalini (1)

North
Banners: N8 (Fri & Sat only)
Gallipoli: all branches (Fri & Sat only)
The Little Bay: NW6 (1)
Pasha (Fri & Sat only)
La Piragua (1)
La Porchetta Pizzeria: all north
branches (1)
Vrisaki (1)

South
Fujiyama (Sat & Sun)
Mirch Masala: all branches (1)
Ransome's Dock (Sat only)
Sree Krishna (Fri & Sat only)

East
Barcelona Tapas: EC4 (2.30 am)
Brick Lane Beigel Bake (24 hours)
(Ciro's) Pizza
Pomodoro: EC2 (midnight)
Itsu: all branches (Fri & Sat only)
Mangal (1)
La Porchetta Pizzeria: EC1 (1)

NO-SMOKING AREAS
(* COMPLETELY NO SMOKING)

Central
Archipelago
Asia de Cuba
Balans: all branches
Benares*
Black & Blue: all branches
Boulevard
Boxwood Café*
Busaba Eathai: all branches*
Café Lazeez: all branches
Le Cercle*

Chor Bizarre
The Cinnamon Club
Connaught (Angela Hartnett)*
Ed's Easy Diner: all central branches
Foliage
Fortnum's, The Fountain
Giraffe: all branches*
Gordon Ramsay at Claridge's*
Goring Hotel
Hakkasan
Hamburger Union: all branches*
Hardy's
Hunan
Indigo*
Inn the Park*
Itsu: all branches*
Joe Allen
Kazan
Maison Bertaux
Malabar Junction
Masala Zone: all branches*
Mildred's*
Mint Leaf
Mirabelle
Nobu
Odin's
One-O-One
L'Oranger
Patara: all branches
Paul: all branches*
Pétrus*
Pied à Terre
The Providores*
Rasa: all branches*
Roka*
Roussillon
Rules*
Sketch (Lecture Rm)
Sotheby's Café*
Star Café
Strada: all branches
Sumosan
Tamarind
Tate Britain*
Thai Pot
Wagamama: all branches*
Windows on the World*
The Wolseley
Yauatcha*
Yming

West
Abu Zaad
Balans West: all branches
Ben's Thai
Big Easy
Black & Blue: all branches
Bombay Brasserie
Bombay Palace
The Brackenbury*
Café Lazeez: all branches
Churchill Arms
Chutney Mary
Clarke's*
Ealing Park Tavern*
Ed's Easy Diner: SW3
1880*

Fish Hoek
Floriana
The Frontline Club
Giraffe: all branches*
Gordon Ramsay*
Gourmet Burger Kitchen: all branches*
Inaho*
Itsu: all branches*
Mandalay*
Manicomio
Le Metro
Notting Hill Brasserie
Patara: all branches
Rasoi Vineet Bhatia*
Sagar
Snows on the Green
Strada: all branches
Sugar Hut
Tartine
Tendido Cero*
Tom Aikens*
Tom's*
La Trompette*
202*
Vacherin*
The Vale
Wagamama: all branches*
White Horse*
The Windsor Castle
Zuma*

North
Anglo Asian Tandoori
Les Associés
The Barnsbury
Bistro Aix
Black & Blue: all branches
Café Japan*
Casale Franco
Fifteen*
Frederick's
Giraffe: all branches*
Globe Restaurant
Gourmet Burger Kitchen: all branches*
Lansdowne
Little Basil
The Little Bay: NW6
Manna*
Marine Ices
Masala Zone: all branches*
Rasa: all branches*
Rasa Travancore*
Rosmarino
Sabras
San Daniele
Sardo Canale
Strada: all branches
Toff's
Two Brothers
Wagamama: all branches*
Zamoyski

South
Amano Café*
Amaranth
Bermondsey Kitchen

Café Portugal
Chapter Two*
Chez Bruce*
Delfina Studio Café
don Fernando's
Eco: SW4
Emile's
Fujiyama
Giraffe: all branches*
The Glasshouse*
Gourmet Burger Kitchen: all branches*
Inside
Kew Grill*
Lamberts
La Lanterna
Lobster Pot
McClements
Mirch Masala: SW17*
Murano
Niksons
The Pepper Tree: all branches
Ransome's Dock*
Redmond's*
Sarkhel's
Sree Krishna
Strada: all branches
Tsunami
El Vergel*

East
Bevis Marks*
Brick Lane Beigel Bake*
Café City Lazeez: all branches
Cicada
Club Mangla
1802
Ekachai*
Elephant Royale
Faulkner's
Flâneur*
Haz
Itsu: all branches*
K10*
The Little Bay: EC1
Malmaison
Potemkin
Singapura: all branches
Strada: all branches
Tatsuso
Ubon
Wagamama: all branches*

OUTSIDE TABLES
(* PARTICULARLY RECOMMENDED)

Central
Aurora*
Back to Basics
Balans: all branches
Bar Italia
Boisdale
Boudin Blanc*
Boulevard
Busaba Eathai: WC1
Caraffini
Giraffe: W1

Gordon's Wine Bar*
The Greenhouse
Hardy's
Inn the Park*
Mirabelle*
Momo
L'Oranger
Orrery
Le Palais du Jardin
La Poule au Pot*
The Ritz*
Rocket: W1
Roka
La Rueda: all branches
Running Horse
Sapori
Sarastro
06 St Chad's Place
Strada: Market Pl W1*; New Burlington St W1
Tate Britain
Toto's*
La Trouvaille

West
The Abingdon*
Admiral Codrington*
The Anglesea Arms
The Atlas*
Balans West: all branches
Belvedere*
Big Easy
Black & Blue: all west branches
Bombay Brasserie
Bombay Palace
The Brackenbury*
The Builder's Arms
Café Lazeez: SW7*
Le Colombier*
Cotto
La Delizia
Dove
E&O
Ealing Park Tavern
Ed's Easy Diner: SW3
Electric Brasserie
Elistano
La Famiglia*
The Gate*
Giraffe: all west branches
Gourmet Burger Kitchen: W4
The Havelock Tavern
Julie's
Langan's Bar & Grill
Lisboa Patisserie
Lou Pescadou
Lundum's
Manicomio*
Mediterraneo
Mohsen
Osteria Basilico
The Painted Heron: all branches
Pappa e Ciccia: all branches
Randall & Aubin: SW10
The Red Pepper
Riccardo's
The River Café*

La Rueda: all branches
The Scarsdale*
Sophie's Steakhouse
Spiga: SW3
Stone Mason's Arms
Tom's*
La Trompette
Troubadour
202
Uli*
Vacherin
Vama
White Horse*
The Windsor Castle*

North
Les Associés
L'Aventure*
Banners on the Hill: N19
The Barnsbury
The Belsize
Bistro Aix
Black & Blue: NW3
La Brocca
Casale Franco*
The Drapers Arms
The Engineer*
Florians
Frederick's*
Gallipoli: Upper St N1, Upper St N1
Giraffe: N1
Gourmet Burger Kitchen: NW6
The Greyhound
Lansdowne
Lemonia
Little Basil
The Little Bay: all branches
Masala Zone: N1
Odette's
The Real Greek
Rosmarino
St Johns
Sardo Canale
Strada: N1

South
The Abbeville
Amano Café*
Antipasto & Pasta
Arancia
Baltic
Barcelona Tapas: SE22
Boiled Egg*
Chelsea Bun Diner: SW11
Cinnamon Cay
don Fernando's
Earl Spencer
Eco: SW4
Ghillies: SW18
Giraffe: SW11
Gourmet Burger Kitchen: SW11
La Lanterna
Laughing Gravy
Little Bay: all branches
Niksons
Oxo Tower (Bras')*
Oxo Tower (Rest')

The Painted Heron: *all branches*
Pappa e Ciccia: *all branches*
The Pepper Tree: *all branches*
Pizza Metro
Le Pont de la Tour*
Le Pont de la Tour
  Bar & Grill*
Ransome's Dock*
Rocket Riverside: *SW15*
La Rueda: *all branches*
Strada: *SW11*

East
Armadillo
Bevis Marks*
Bleeding Heart*
Cat & Mutton
Cicada
(Ciro's) Pizza Pomodoro: *EC2*
Coq d'Argent*
Drunken Monkey
The Eagle
Elephant Royale*
Lightship⁺
The Little Bay: *all branches*
LMNT
Moro
New Tayyab
Royal China: *E14*
Singapura: *EC4*
Smiths (Top Floor)*
Wapping Food

ROMANTIC

Central
Andrew Edmunds
Archipelago
Asia de Cuba
Aurora
Bam-Bou
Bohème Kitchen
Boudin Blanc
Boulevard
Le Caprice
Chor Bizarre
Crazy Bear
The Criterion Grill
Dorchester Grill
Elena's L'Etoile
L'Escargot
French House
Le Gavroche
Gay Hussar
The Greenhouse
Hakkasan
Inn the Park
The Ivy
Langan's Brasserie
Lindsay House
Locanda Locatelli
Mirabelle
Momo
Mon Plaisir
Nobu
Odin's
Orrery

Le Palais du Jardin
Passione
La Porte des Indes
La Poule au Pot
The Ritz
Roussillon
Sarastro
J Sheekey
Shogun
Taman gang
Toto's
La Trouvaille
Windows on the World
Zafferano

West
Assaggi
Aubergine
Belvedere
Bibendum
Blakes Hotel
Blue Elephant
The Brackenbury
Cambio de Tercio
Clarke's
Le Colombier
La Famiglia
Gordon Ramsay
Julie's
Launceston Place
Maggie Jones's
Manicomio
Mediterraneo
Mr Wing
Notting Hill Brasserie
Osteria Basilico
Pasha
The River Café
Star of India
Sugar Hut
La Trompette

North
Anglo Asian Tandoori
L'Aventure
Casale Franco
The Engineer
Frederick's
Odette's
Oslo Court
The Real Greek

South
Arancia
Champor-Champor
Chez Bruce
Cinnamon Cay
The Glasshouse
Monsieur Max
Oxo Tower (Bras')
Le Pont de la Tour
Ransome's Dock
RSJ
Sonny's

East
Bleeding Heart
Café du Marché

INDEXES

Club Gascon
Lightship
LMNT
Moro
Les Trois Garçons

ROOMS WITH A VIEW

Central
Fakhreldine
Foliage
Inn the Park
Orrery
The Ritz
Windows on the World

West
Belvedere

South
Oxo Tower (Bras')
Oxo Tower (Rest')
Le Pont de la Tour
Le Pont de la Tour
  Bar & Grill
Rocket Riverside: SW15

East
Coq d'Argent
Elephant Royale
Rhodes 24
Smiths (Top Floor)
Ubon
Vertigo

Le Colombier
Gordon Ramsay
Le Metro
Racine
The River Café
Tom Aikens
La Trompette
White Horse

North
Odette's
The Real Greek

South
Chez Bruce
The Glasshouse
McClements
Le Pont de la Tour
Ransome's Dock
Redmond's
RSJ

East
Bleeding Heart
Club Gascon
Coq d'Argent
The Don
Moro
Wapping Food
The Wine Library

NOTABLE WINE LISTS

Central
Andrew Edmunds
Boisdale
Connaught (Angela Hartnett)
The Ebury
L'Escargot
Foliage
Fortnum's, The Fountain
Le Gavroche
Gordon Ramsay at Claridge's
Gordon's Wine Bar
The Greenhouse
Hardy's
The Ivy
Locanda Locatelli
Maggiore's
Mirabelle
Orrery
Pétrus
Pied à Terre
Roussillon
Savoy Grill
Sotheby's Café
The Square
Tate Britain
Teca
Zafferano

West
Bibendum
Clarke's

LONDON MAPS

MAP I - WEST END OVERVIEW

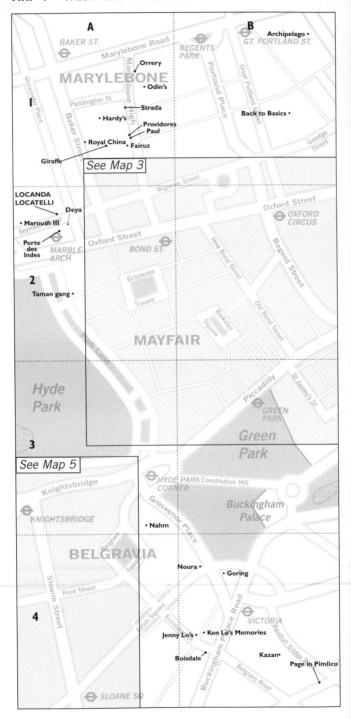

A

B

BAKER ST.

Marylebone Road

REGENTS PARK

Archipelago •
GT. PORTLAND ST.

• Orrery

MARYLEBONE

• Odin's

Portland Place

Great Portland

Paddington St

1

Gloucester Place

• Strada

Back to Basics •

Goodge Street

Baker Street

• Hardy's

Providores

Marylebone High

Paul

• Royal China.

Fairuz

Giraffe

See Map 3

Wigmore Street

Oxford Street

OXFORD CIRCUS

LOCANDA LOCATELLI

Deya

Oxford Street

BOND ST.

New Bond Street

Regent Street

• Maroush III

Seymour Street

Porte des Indes

MARBLE ARCH

Grosvenor

2

Park Lane

Taman gang •

Square

MAYFAIR

Berkeley Square

Old Bond Street

Hyde Park

Piccadilly

St James's St.

GREEN PARK

Green Park

3

See Map 5

Knightsbridge

HYDE PARK CORNER

Constitution Hill

Buckingham Palace

KNIGHTSBRIDGE

Grosvenor Place

• Nahm

BELGRAVIA

Belgrave Square

Noura •

• Goring

Sloane Street

Pont Street

4

Eaton Square

Buckingham Palace Road

VICTORIA

Vauxhall Bridge Road

Eccleston

Jenny Lo's • • Ken Lo's Memories

Boisdale •

Kazan•

Belgrave Road

Page in Pimlico •

SLOANE SQ

MAP 1 - WEST END OVERVIEW

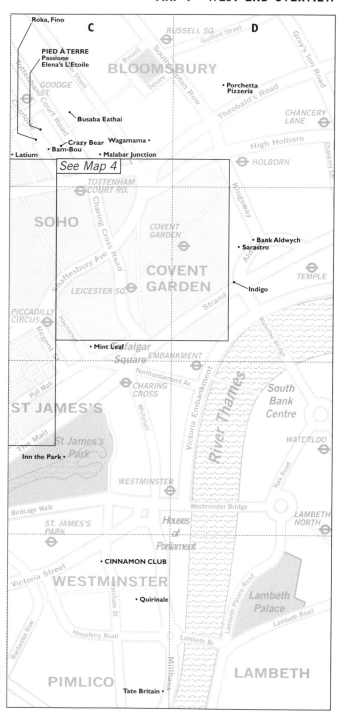

MAP 2 - MAYFAIR, ST JAMES'S & WEST SOHO

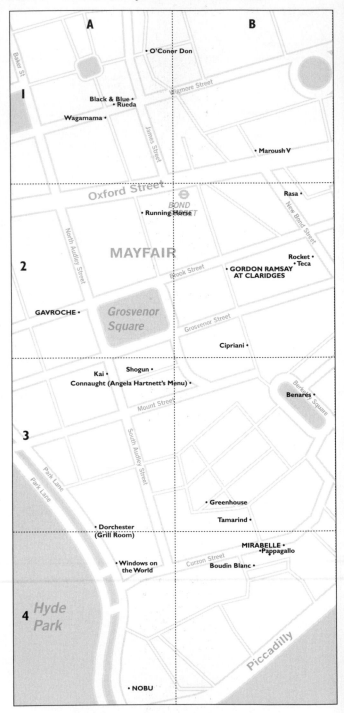

MAP 2 - MAYFAIR, ST JAMES'S & WEST SOHO

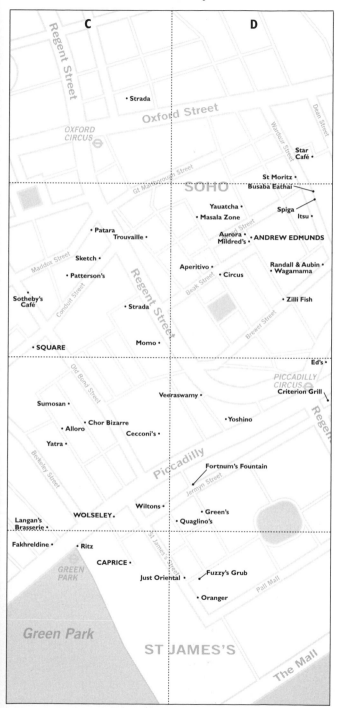

MAP 3 - EAST SOHO, CHINATOWN & COVENT GARDEN

MAP 3 - EAST SOHO, CHINATOWN & COVENT GARDEN

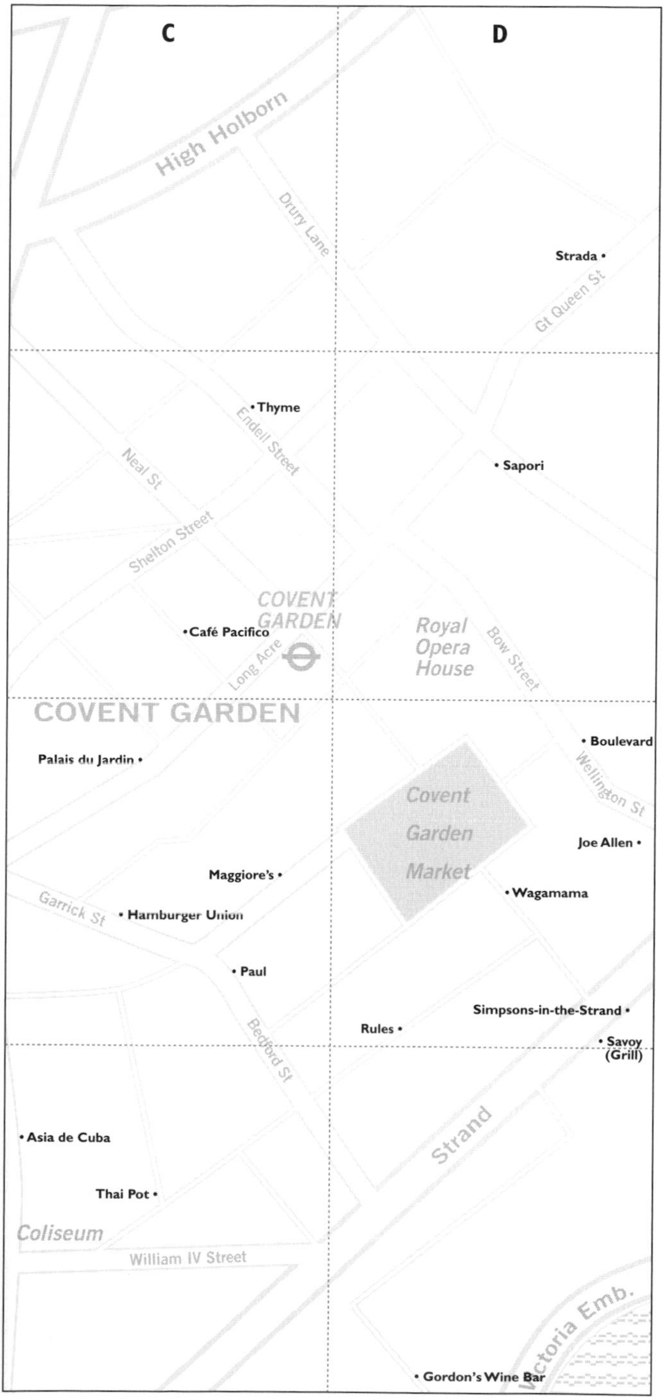

C

D

High Holborn

Drury Lane

Strada •

Gt Queen St

• Thyme

Endell Street

Neal St

• Sapori

Shelton Street

COVENT
GARDEN

•Café Pacifico

Long Acre

Royal
Opera
House

Bow Street

COVENT GARDEN

• Boulevard

Palais du Jardin •

Wellington St

Covent

Garden

Joe Allen •

Maggiore's •

Market

Garrick St

• Hamburger Union

• Wagamama

• Paul

Bedford St

Simpsons-in-the-Strand •

Rules •

• Savoy
(Grill)

• Asia de Cuba

Strand

Thai Pot •

Coliseum

William IV Street

Victoria Emb.

• Gordon's Wine Bar

MAP 4 - KNIGHTSBRIDGE, CHELSEA & SOUTH KENSINGTON

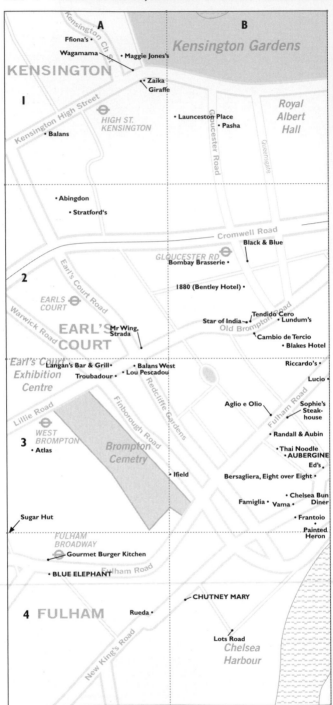

MAP 4 - KNIGHTSBRIDGE, CHELSEA & SOUTH KENSINGTON

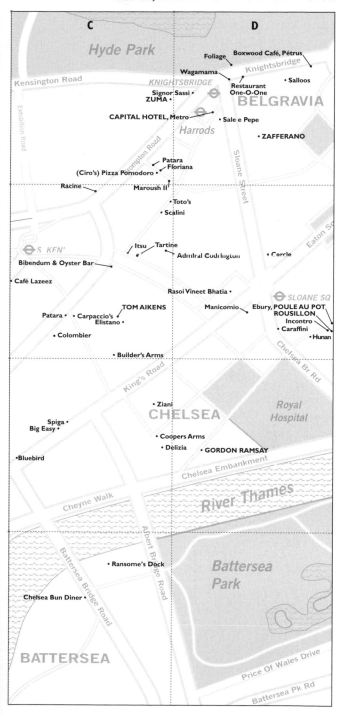

MAP 5 - NOTTING HILL & BAYSWATER

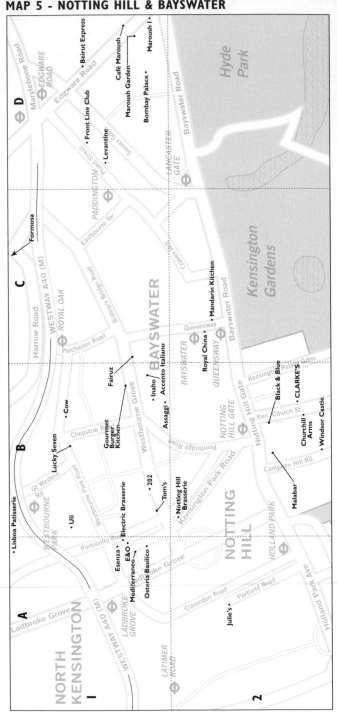

MAP 6 - HAMMERSMITH & CHISWICK

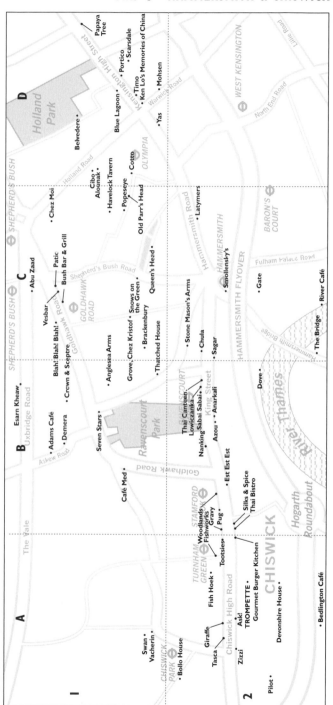

Papaya Tree

Scarsdale

Portico

Ken Lo's Memories of China

Timo

Mohsen

Blue Lagoon

Yas

Belvedere

Holland Park

WEST KENSINGTON

North End Road

Lillie Road

Holland Road

Cibo

Alounak

Cotto

Popeseye

Old Parr's Head

Havelock Tavern

Latymers

OLYMPIA

Chez Moi

Hammersmith Road

BARON'S COURT

SHEPHERD'S BUSH

Fulham Palace Road

Abu Zaad

Patic

Bush Bar & Grill

Vesbar

Queen's Head

HAMMERSMITH

Smollensky's

Shepherd's Bush Road

Blah! Blah! Blah!

Crown & Sceptre

GOLDHAWK ROAD

Grove, Chez Kristof

Snows on the Green

Brackenbury

Stone Mason's Arms

Gate

HAMMERSMITH FLYOVER

Esarn Kheaw

Goldhawk Road

Anglesea Arms

Thatched House

Chula

Sagar

The Bridge

River Café

Uxbridge Road

Adams Café

Demera

Seven Stars

Ravenscourt Park

Thai Canteen

Lowiczanka

Nanking Sabai Sabai

Azou

Anarkali

King Street

Dove

River Thames

Hammersmith Bridge

Askew Road

The Vale

Café Med

Goldhawk Road

Est Est Est

STAMFORD

TURNHAM GREEN

Woodlands

Fishworks

Gravy

Pug

Silks & Spice Thai Bistro

Hogarth Roundabout

Swan

Vacherin

Tasca

Zizzi

Giraffe

Fish Hoek

Tootsies

Chiswick High Road

Ask!

TROMPETTE

Gourmet Burger Kitchen

CHISWICK

CHISWICK PARK

Bollo House

Devonshire House

Bedlington Café

Pilot

1

2

A

B

C

D

UK SURVEY RESULTS
& TOP SCORERS

PLACES PEOPLE TALK ABOUT

These are the restaurants outside London that were mentioned most frequently by reporters (last year's position is shown in brackets). For the list of London's most mentioned restaurants, see page 25.

1	Manoir aux Quat' Saisons (1)	Great Milton, Oxon
2	Fat Duck (4)	Bray, Berks
3	Seafood Restaurant (2)	Padstow, Cornwall
4	Waterside Inn (3)	Bray, Berks
5	Yang Sing (5)	Manchester
6	Star Inn (9)	Harome, N Yorks
7=	Hotel du Vin et Bistro (-)	Brighton, E Sussex
7=	Magpie (6)	Whitby, N Yorks
9=	Chapter One (-)	Locksbottom, Kent
9=	Rick Stein's Café (-)	Padstow, Cornwall
11=	The Witchery (11=)	Edinburgh
11=	Croma (13=)	Manchester
13=	Vineyard/Stockcross (13=)	Stockcross, Berkshire
13=	The Angel (8)	Hetton, N Yorks
13=	Harts (15=)	Nottingham
13=	Chaing Mai (-)	Oxford
17	Terre à Terre (10)	Brighton
18	Winteringham Fields (7)	Winteringham, N Lincs
19=	Whitstable Oyster (11=)	Whitstable, Kent
19=	Auberge du Lac (-)	Lemsford, Hertfordshire
19=	Café 21 (-)	Newcastle-upon-Tyne

TOP SCORERS

All restaurants whose food rating is ★★; plus restaurants whose price is £50+ with a food rating of ★.

(Dublin restaurant prices have been converted to £.)

£110+	Waterside Inn *(Bray)*	★★A
	Le Manoir aux Quat' Saisons *(Great Milton)*	★A
£90+	Restaurant Patrick Guilbaud *(Dublin)*	★
£80+	Gidleigh Park *(Chagford)*	★★A
	Andrew Fairlie *(Auchterarder)*	★A
£70+	Winteringham Fields *(Winteringham)*	★★A
	Colette's *(Chandlers Cross)*	★A
	Gravetye Manor *(East Grinstead)*	★A
	Hambleton Hall *(Hambleton)*	★A
	Lucknam Park *(Colerne)*	★A
	The Fat Duck *(Bray)*	★
£60+	L'Enclume *(Cartmel)*	★★A
	Mallory Court *(Bishops Tachbrook)*	★★A
	Northcote Manor *(Langho)*	★★A
	Ynyshir Hall *(Eglwysfach)*	★★A
	Harry's Place *(Great Gonerby)*	★★
	Samling *(Windermere)*	★★
	Kinnaird House *(Dunkeld)*	★A
	Longueville Manor *(Jersey)*	★A
	Cameron House *(Loch Lomond)*	★
	Midsummer House *(Cambridge)*	★
	The Seafood Restaurant *(Padstow)*	★
	L'Ecrivain *(Dublin)*	★
£50+	Holbeck Ghyll *(Windermere)*	★★A
	Morston Hall *(Morston)*	★★A
	Underscar Manor *(Applethwaite)*	★★A
	Champignon Sauvage *(Cheltenham)*	★★
	Restaurant Martin Wishart *(Edinburgh)*	★★
	Shanks *(Bangor)*	★★
	Albannach *(Baddidarach)*	★A
	Ballathie House *(Kinclaven)*	★A
	The Buttery *(Glasgow)*	★A
	Fischers at Baslow Hall *(Baslow)*	★A
	Gilpin Lodge *(Windermere)*	★A
	Sharrow Bay *(Ullswater)*	★A
	Thackeray's House *(Tunbridge Wells)*	★A
	The Three Chimneys *(Dunvegan)*	★A
	Thornbury Castle *(Thornbury)*	★A
	Treacle Moon *(Newcastle upon Tyne)*	★A
	Auberge du Lac *(Lemsford)*	★
	Champany Inn *(Linlithgow)*	★
	Drakes On The Pond *(Abinger Hammer)*	★
	Fisherman's Lodge *(Newcastle upon Tyne)*	★
	Jessica's *(Birmingham)*	★
	Kaifeng *(Harrow)*	★
	Lumière *(Cheltenham)*	★
	Moss Nook *(Manchester)*	★
	Le Poussin at Parkhill *(Lyndhurst)*	★

TOP SCORERS

	Ripleys *(St Merryn)*	★
	36 on the Quay *(Emsworth)*	★

£40+	22 Mill Street *(Chagford)*	★★A
	Braidwoods *(Dalry)*	★★A
	Café du Moulin *(Guernsey)*	★★A
	Fairyhill *(Reynoldston)*	★★A
	Star Inn *(Harome)*	★★A
	Summer Isles *(Achiltibuie)*	★★A
	The Cellar *(Anstruther)*	★★A
	Anthony's *(Leeds)*	★★
	Hibiscus *(Ludlow)*	★★
	JSW *(Petersfield)*	★★
	Jacob's Ladder *(Dublin)*	★A
	Mermaid Café *(Dublin)*	★

£30+	The Angel *(Hetton)*	★★A
	Due South *(Brighton)*	★★A
	The Ebb *(Padstow)*	★★A
	Endeavour *(Staithes)*	★★A
	Gingerhill *(Glasgow)*	★★A
	Great House *(Lavenham)*	★★A
	Jeremy's at Borde Hill *(Haywards Heath)*	★★A
	Les Mirabelles *(Nomansland)*	★★A
	Let's Eat *(Perth)*	★★A
	Maison Bleue *(Bury St Edmunds)*	★★A
	Monachyle Mhor *(Balquhidder)*	★★A
	Pier House Hotel *(Port Appin)*	★★A
	Rowan Tree *(Askrigg)*	★★A
	Stagg Inn *(Titley)*	★★A
	Three Acres *(Shelley)*	★★A
	Crannog *(Fort William)*	★★
	Ee-Usk (Fish Café) *(Oban)*	★★
	Nutter's *(Cheesden)*	★★
	Quince & Medlar *(Cockermouth)*	★★
	Riverside *(Bridport)*	★★
	Terre à Terre *(Brighton)*	★★
	The Old Passage Inn *(Arlingham)*	★★
	Wheeler's Oyster Bar *(Whitstable)*	★★
	Yang Sing *(Manchester)*	★★
	Bang Café *(Dublin)*	★A
	Roly's Bistro *(Dublin)*	★A

£20+	Oyster Shack *(Bigbury)*	★★A
	Zeffirelli's *(Ambleside)*	★★A
	Koh Samui *(Manchester)*	★★
	Magpie Café *(Whitby)*	★★
	Cedar Tree *(Manchester)*	★★
	Mumtaz Paan House *(Bradford)*	★★
	Village Bakery *(Melmerby)*	★★
	Wee Curry Shop *(Glasgow)*	★★

£10+	The Company Shed *(West Mersea)*	★★A
	Cachumba *(Manchester)*	★★
	Chez Fred *(Bournemouth)*	★★
	Punjab Tandoori *(Manchester)*	★★
	The Mermaid Café *(Hastings)*	★★

£5+	Atlas *(Nottingham)*	★★A

UK DIRECTORY

Comments in "double quotation-marks" were made by reporters.

ABERAERON, CEREDIGION   4–3C
Harbourmaster   £ 36   A ★
Quay Pde   SA46 0BA   (01545) 570755
A "smart", "bright" and "contemporary" look distinguishes this
once-grotty harbourside boozer – now a "very good" restaurant,
specialising in "the best fresh fish and shellfish, and other local
ingredients". / **Details:** www.harbour-master.com; 9 pm; closed Mon L & Sun D;
no Amex; no smoking. **Accommodation:** 9 rooms, from £95.

ABERDEEN, ABERDEEN   9–2D
Silver Darling   £ 48   A
Pocra Quay, North Pier AB11 5DQ   (01224) 576229
Fans praise the "amazing" setting and the "superb" food at this
upper-floor fixture in a converted lighthouse at the harbour
mouth; it's "very expensive", though, and its style generally strikes
some reporters as "OTT". / **Sample dishes:** prawn ravioli with Parma
ham & lobster oil; sea bass with tapenade & aniseed butter; tarte Tatin with green
apple sorbet. **Details:** beside lighthouse; 9.30 pm; closed Sat L & Sun; no smoking.

ABERDYFI, GWYNEDD   4–3C
Penhelig Arms   £ 31   ★
LL35 0LT   (01654) 767215
"Exceptionally good seafood" and a "lovely" seaside location are
among the attractions of this well-established hotel dining room;
the owner "knows his wine", too. / **Sample dishes:** spinach & cream
cheese lasagne; char-grilled lamb with roast aubergines; raspberry frangipane tart.
Details: www.penheligarms.com; 9.30 pm; no Amex; no smoking.
Accommodation: 14 rooms, from £118.

ABERFORD, WEST YORKSHIRE   5–1C
Swan Hotel   £ 22
Great North Rd LS25 3AA   (0113) 281 3205
"Good pub food" comes in "huge portions", at this attractive
16th-century inn. / **Sample dishes:** seafood salad; chicken with sweet chili;
cheesecake. **Details:** www.swanaberford.co.uk; 10 pm; closed Mon & Tue, Wed-Sat
closed L; book only for restaurant.

ABERGAVENNY, MONMOUTHSHIRE   2–1A
Clytha Arms   £ 34
NP7 9BW   (01873) 840206
"Above-average" ingredients and a "beautiful" location are
features which help make this family-run inn "a great stop-over en
route to Wales". / **Sample dishes:** melon & avocado salad; roast hake with
herb salsa; Sauternes cream with spiced prunes. **Details:** www.clytha-arms.com; on
Old Abergavenny to Raglan Road; 9.30 pm; closed Mon & Sun D, no smoking.
Accommodation: 4 rooms, from £70.

Walnut Tree   £ 41
Llandewi Skirrid NP7 8AW   (01873) 852797
If you saw 'Kitchen Nightmares' you'll know this rural converted
pub has had difficulty living up to the legacy of Franco Taruschio;
it's clear the Italian cooking is "nothing like as good as the old
days", but while critics complain of "a mortgage job for average
results", others feel "the place seems to be looking up again".
/ **Sample dishes:** endive, pancetta & Dolcelatte salad; corned beef hash with
spinach & fried egg; steamed treacle sponge pudding.
Details: www.thewalnuttreeinn.com; 3m NE of Abergavenny on B4521; 9 pm;
closed Mon & Sun D; no Amex; no smoking.

ABINGER HAMMER, SURREY   3–3A
Drakes On The Pond   £ 52   ★
Docking Rd RH5 6SA   (01306) 731174
"Still very good despite the change of chef" (now Simon Attridge),
this *"fantastic"* restaurant continues to win praise from most
reporters for its *"superb"* cuisine; doubters, though, can find the
place *"overpriced"* or *"sterile"*. / **Sample dishes:** warm salad of asparagus
with rocket & pea purée; roast duck breast with potatoes & elderberry sauce;
orange & almond savarin with almond ice cream.
Details: www.drakesonthepond.com; 9.30 pm; closed Mon & Sun; no Amex;
no smoking; booking: max 6; children: 8+.

ACHILTIBUIE, HIGHLAND   9–1B
Summer Isles   £ 48   𝔸★★
IV26 2YG   (01854) 622282
"Incredible" dishes from *"outstanding quality produce"* combines
with *"friendly"* service and a *"relaxed"* atmosphere to create a
"magical" experience at this remote but famous hotel (which
looks out over the islands after which it's named).
/ **Sample dishes:** grilled mushrooms with Parmesan croutons; grilled turbot with
lime & capers; lemon soufflé crêpes. **Details:** www.summerisleshotel.co.uk; 25m N
of Ullapool on A835; 8 pm; no Amex; no smoking; children: 6+.
Accommodation: 13 rooms, from £98.

ALDEBURGH, SUFFOLK   3–1D
Lighthouse   £ 28   ★
77 High St IP15 5AU   (01728) 453377
"A continuously high standard of cooking" – with *"well-cooked
fish"* a highlight – makes this *"busy"* bistro quite a *"favourite"* in
these parts; it's *"very noisy"*, though, and some find its dining
room *"cramped"* and *"uncomfortable"*. / **Sample dishes:** celery & blue
cheese soup; sole with lime butter; boozy banana pancakes. **Details:** 10 pm; closed
for 2 weeks in Jan & 1 week in Oct; no smoking area.

152   £ 33
152 High St IP15 5AX   (01728) 454594
Under its new management, this *"quirky"* café has generated
slightly mixed commentary, but the food is generally found
"enjoyable" nonetheless. / **Sample dishes:** carrot, tomato & ginger soup;
lamb with pea purée & red pepper relish; cappucino crème brûlée.
Details: www.152aldeburgh.co.uk; 10 pm; closed Tue (& Mon in winter);
no smoking.

Regatta   £ 27   ★
171-173 High St IP15 5AN   (01728) 452011
With its *"delicate"* and *"excellent"* fish dishes, this popular and
well-established *"café-style"* fixture is still *"keeping up its
standards"*. / **Sample dishes:** smoked prawns; duck with French beans; crème
brûlée. **Details:** www.regattaaldeburgh.com; 10 pm; closed Mon-Wed in Nov-Mar;
no smoking area.

Wentworth Hotel   £ 24
Wentworth Rd IP15 5BD   (01728) 452312
Modernists mights find its approach a bit dated, but this smart,
"country house-style", family-owned hotel is hailed by some
reporters as a *"pleasing"* destination, where the cooking offers
"good value". / **Sample dishes:** platter of smoked salmon; oven baked sea
bream topped with roast vegetables; raspberry mousse cake with raspberry sauce &
cream. **Details:** www.wentworth-aldeburgh.co.uk; 9 pm; no smoking.
Accommodation: 35 rooms, from £90.

ALDFORD, CHESHIRE   5–3A

The Grosvenor Arms   **£ 32**
Chester Rd CH3 6HJ   (01244) 620228
"Reliably good food" and a *"comfortable"* setting commend this
"contemporary" (by local standards) ducal village pub to all who
report on it. / **Sample dishes:** corned beef & black pudding hash cake; pork
chops with Stilton rarebit topping; chocolate bread & butter pudding. **Details:** 6m S
of Chester on B5130; 10 pm; no smoking area; children: 14+ after 6 pm.

AMBERLEY, WEST SUSSEX   3–4A

Amberley Castle   **£ 60**   𝔸
BN18 9ND   (01798) 831992
No one doubts that this *"outstanding historic venue"* – 12th
century in origin – has a *"very special ambience"* (not least for
those with romance in mind); the cooking can sometimes be
"exciting", too, but not all reporters are impressed.
/ **Sample dishes:** game terrine with plum chutney; salmon pavé with celeriac
cream; roast pears with champagne sorbet. **Details:** www.amberleycastle.co.uk; N
of Arundel on B2139; 9.30 pm; jacket or tie required; no smoking; booking: max 8;
children: 12+. **Accommodation:** 19 rooms, from £155.

AMBLESIDE, CUMBRIA   7–3D

Drunken Duck   **£ 36**   𝔸
Barngates LA22 0NG   (01539) 436347
Located *"amidst fantastic scenery"*, this dining pub has become
very well-known, not least thanks to its *"good, lunchtime bar
snacks"*; the *"warm, cosy and candlelit"* dining room, however, can
seem *"terribly overpriced"*. / **Sample dishes:** chicken with sugar snap peas;
quail stuffed with prune risotto; lemon torte with spiced oranges.
Details: www.drunkenduckinn.co.uk; 3m from Ambleside, towards Hawkshead;
9 pm; no smoking; booking: max 6. **Accommodation:** 16 rooms, from £85.

The Glass House   **£ 34**   𝔸★
Rydal Rd LA22 9AN   (01539) 432137
*"In spite of its poor showing on Ramsay's Kitchen Nightmares, we
still think it a value-for-money destination"* – perhaps surprisingly
in the light of the revelations on the box, this attractive Lakeland
mill-conversion remains roundly praised for its *"great food and
atmosphere"*. / **Sample dishes:** tomato & Parmesan tart; roast monkfish with
Parma ham & vegetable crêpes; mint chocolate chip soufflé.
Details: www.theglasshouserestaurant.co.uk; behind Little Bridge House; 9.30 pm,
Sat 10 pm; closed Tue (& all of Jan); no Amex; no smoking; children: 5+ at D.

Lucy's on a Plate   **£ 30**   ★
Church St LA22 0BU   (01539) 431191
*"The fight/wait for a table is worth it as the food is very good (if a
little pricey)"* – thus speaks a typical fan of this *"outstanding"*
deli/café. / **Sample dishes:** scallops with cream & dill; roast lamb with minted
bacon jus; Belgian chocolate bread & butter pudding.
Details: www.lucys-on-a-plate.co.uk; centre of Ambleside; 9 pm; no Amex;
no smoking.

Rothay Manor £41 A★
Rothay Bridge LA22 0EH (01539) 433605
*Very limited commentary this year – but nothing approaching criticism – on this beautifully-located Regency country house hotel; such is the continuity of management (since 1967) and head chef (since 1976), that we judge former years' high standards to be being maintained. / **Sample dishes:** grilled sardines with rosemary; roast duck with red cabbage & juniper sauce; pavlova with summer fruits.*
Details: *www.rothaymanor.co.uk; 9 pm; no smoking; children: 7+ at D.*
Accommodation: *19 rooms, from £130.*

Sheila's Cottage £32
The Slack LA22 9DQ (01539) 433079
*"Reliable" and "unpretentious", this cutely-located tea-shop (which moonlights as a restaurant) is worth knowing about for a "cheap and cheerful" dinner. / **Sample dishes:** salmon mousse with roast tomatoes; roast pheasant with walnut & spinach risotto; treacle tart with custard.*
Details: *www.amblesideonline.co.uk; next to Queen's Hotel; 9 pm; closed Tue D & Wed D in winter; no Amex; no smoking; children: 8+ after 6 pm.*

Zeffirelli's £24 A★★
Compston Rd LA22 9AD (01539) 433845
*"Amazing" veggie dishes, including "really good pizza" (plus "wonderful coffee"), feature in comments on this ever-popular outfit (which combines a café and cinema); it's a "very stylish" operation, and was improved this year by the addition of a ground-floor restaurant. / **Sample dishes:** pesto & cherry tomato bruschetta; red chilli bean & Cheddar pizza; tiramisu.* ***Details:*** *www.zeffirellis.co.uk; 10 pm; no Amex; no smoking.*

AMERSHAM, BUCKINGHAMSHIRE 3–2A

Artichoke £39 ★
9 Market Sq HP7 0DF (01494) 726611
*"Show-stopping" French dishes are reported by fans of Laurie Gear's "smart" and "confident" two-year-old (in a 16th-century building on the market square); critics can feel it "tries much too hard". / **Details:** www.theartichokerestaurant.co.uk; 10 pm; closed Mon & Sun; no Amex; no smoking.*

Famous Fish £34
11 Market Sq HP7 0DF (01494) 728665
*"Very good ingredients" are a feature of this Old Amersham fish and seafood restaurant – "a friendly and buzzy place, with good-value food". / **Sample dishes:** grilled prawn tails with avocado; Cajun cod with tomato concasse; crème brûlée. **Details:** in Old Amersham; 10 pm; closed Sun; no smoking.*

Gilbey's £37
1 Market Sq HP7 0DF (01494) 727242
*"Wine at very reasonable prices" – from a "unique and personally-imported list" – are what this "cramped" and old-fashioned outfit is really all about; the food, though, is generally reckoned to be "consistently good". / **Sample dishes:** crab cakes with lime pickle; braised lamb with mint mash & red wine jus; rhubarb oat crumble.*
Details: *www.gilbeygroup.com; in Old Amersham; 9.30 pm; L & afternoon tea only.*

Kings Arms £35
30 High St HP7 0DJ (01494) 726333
"Old beams and coal fires" contribute to the appeal of this
ancient inn, best-liked as *"a great lunch spot"*; it's closed as we go
to press for a revamp by new owners Zola Hotels.
/ **Sample dishes:** *pheasant terrine; salmon & monkfish brochettes with ginger
dressing; chocolate & hazelnut galettes.* **Details:** *www.kingsarmsamersham.co.uk; in
Old Amersham; 9.30 pm; closed Mon & Sun D.*

Santhi £28
16 Hill Ave HP6 5BW (01494) 432621
*Consistent standards help make this "lavishly-decorated" Indian,
near the Metropolitan line terminus, an ever-reliable stand-by.*
/ **Sample dishes:** *prawn purée & poppadoms; hot, sweet & sour chicken curry;
chocolate mousse.* **Details:** *www.santhirestaurant.co.uk; 10.45 pm; no smoking
area.*

ANSTRUTHER, FIFE 9–4D

Anstruther Fish Bar £16 ★
42-44 Shore St KY10 3EA (01333) 310518
"The best fish 'n' chips ever" win acclaim for this busy chippie,
whose attractions include *"an excellent harbour view"*.
/ **Details:** *www.anstrutherfishbar.co.uk; 9.30 pm; no Amex; no smoking.*

The Cellar £44 🅐★★
24 East Grn KY10 3AA (01333) 310378
"The best fish in the UK", claim fans of Peter & Susan Jukes's
"friendly" basement fixture (in an historic building behind the
Scottish Fisheries Museum); one reporter was asked to wait ten
minutes extra for his lobster: *"they had to go and get me one
from the sea!"* / **Sample dishes:** *asparagus & leek soup; roast pesto-crusted
cod; hazelnut praline parfait.* **Details:** *9.30 pm; closed Mon L & Tue L; no smoking;
children: 8+.*

APPLECROSS, HIGHLAND 9–2B

Applecross Inn £27 🅐★
Shore St IV54 8LR (01520) 744262
"Fantastic fresh fish and seafood" (especially if you *"stick to the
simple dishes"*) wins praise for this waterside tavern; it has a
"pretty amazing setting", too. / **Sample dishes:** *hot-smoked salmon;
venison sausages with mash & onion gravy; chocolate brûlée.*
Details: *www.applecross.co.uk; off A896, S of Shieldaig; 9 pm; no Amex;
no smoking; need 4+ to book.* **Accommodation:** *7 rooms, from £60.*

APPLETHWAITE, CUMBRIA 7–3C

Underscar Manor £55 🅐★★
CA12 4PH (01768) 775000
"Outstanding cooking... fabulous location" – that's all there really
is to say about this small but *"opulent"* country house hotel,
overlooking Derwent Water. / **Sample dishes:** *Swiss cheese soufflé with
buttered spinach; roast lamb with moussaka gâteau; mini citrus desserts.*
Details: *on A66, 17m W of M6, J40; 8.30 pm; jacket required at D; no smoking;
children: 12+.* **Accommodation:** *11 rooms, from £180.*

ARLINGHAM, GLOUCESTERSHIRE 2–2B
The Old Passage Inn £ 39 ★★
Passage Rd GL2 7JR   (01452) 740547
"Fresh and excellent" fish dishes and a *"smashing"* position *"right on the edge of the River Severn"* make this former boozer – now a restaurant presided over by a Roux protégé – a unanimous hit with reporters. / **Details:** www.fishattheoldpassageinn.co.uk; 9 pm; closed Mon & Sun D; no smoking. **Accommodation:** 3 rooms, from £85.

ARMSCOTE, WARWICKSHIRE 2–1C
Fox And Goose £ 33 A★
Armscote CV37 8DD   (01608) 682293
"A bistro-type pub, done with style" – its *"good selection of above-average fare"* is prepared to a *"consistent"* standard.
/ **Sample dishes:** warm goats cheese with red onion marmalade; tagliatelle; panna cotta. **Details:** www.aboveaverage.co.uk; 10m S of Stratford-upon-Avon on the A4300; 9.30 pm; booking: max 10. **Accommodation:** 4 rooms, from £80.

ASCOT, BERKSHIRE 3–3A
Ascot Oriental £ 34 A★
London Rd SL5 0PU   (01344) 621877
"Much superior" for a Home Counties oriental – this *"original"* and *"very popular"* pan-Asian joint provides *"a great range"* of Chinese and Thai dishes of *"high quality"* in a stylish setting.
/ **Sample dishes:** tempura prawns; seared tuna with Asian greens; coconut & mango tart. **Details:** www.ascotoriental.com; 2m E of Ascot on A329; 10.15 pm.

The Thatched Tavern £ 35 A
Cheapside Rd SL5 7QG   (01344) 620874
"Great pub atmosphere plus good restaurant nosh" – that's how supporters see this *"marvellous 'Olde English' inn"*, whose *"quality"* cooking is in contemporary style. / **Sample dishes:** crispy oriental duck salad; steak & kidney pie; lemon & ginger crunch.
Details: www.thethatchedtavern.co.uk; 2m from Ascot, signed to Cheapside village; 10 pm.

ASENBY, NORTH YORKSHIRE 8–4C
The Crab & Lobster £ 42 A★
Dishforth Rd YO7 3QL   (01845) 577286
It's not just *"an interior crammed with lots of interesting things to look at"* which maintains the popularity of this knick-knack filled institution – after a 'wobble' on a change of ownership, its *"melt-in-the-mouth"* fish dishes are once again wowing reporters.
/ **Sample dishes:** Irish oysters on ice; crab-crusted salmon with saffron mash; chocolate torte. **Details:** www.crabandlobster.com; at junction of Asenby Rd & Topcliffe Rd; 9 pm; no smoking. **Accommodation:** 12 rooms, from £150.

ASHBOURNE, DERBYSHIRE 5–3C
Dining Room £ 43 ★
33 St. John's St DE6 1GP   (01335) 300666
"A superb tasting menu of nine courses, all beautifully presented" is the sort of experience that wins high praise for Peter and Laura Dale's tiny venture in an old town-centre building; the *"innovative"* cooking features *"marvellous use of local ingredients"*.
/ **Details:** www.thediningroomashbourne.co.uk; 8.30 pm; closed Mon & Sun; no Amex; no smoking; children: 12+.

ASHBURTON, DEVON   1–3D

Agaric   £39   ★
30 North St TQ13 7QD (01364) 654478
*"It looks like a café from the outside, but don't be deceived!" –
this place offers some "outstanding" cooking; even some fans,
though, rail at a staff attitude they find "pretentious".
/ Sample dishes: fresh soup with garlic croutons; steamed lemon sole fillets with
prawn mousseline & sauce; sticky toffee pudding.
Details: www.agaricrestaurant.co.uk; 9.30 pm; closed Mon & Tue, Sat L & Sun D;
no Amex; no smoking.*

ASKRIGG, NORTH YORKSHIRE   8–4B

The King's Arms   £32
Market Pl DL8 3HQ (01969) 650817
*"Cheerful" service and "solid" food make this walkers' pub just
the sort of place you might have expected to find in 'All Creatures
Great and Small' (which, of course, it was). / Sample dishes: spicy
salmon fishcakes; chicken & cheese wrapped in smoked bacon; sticky toffee pudding.
Details: www.kingsarmsaskrigg.com; 9 pm; no Amex; no smoking area.*

Rowan Tree   £33   𝔸★★
Market Pl DL8 3HT (01969) 650536
*"Dreamy" food and "unpretentious" service make Derek Wylie's
"intimate" 22-seater in the Dales a pure "gem", unanimously
acclaimed by reporters for its "superb" standards.
/ Sample dishes: Louisiana prawn & okra gumbo; lamb cutlets with colcannon &
Shiraz jus; coffee, chocolate & cardamom truffle torte. Details: 4m from Aysgarth
falls; 8.30 pm; D only Wed-Sat, L only Sun; closed Mon & Tue; no credit cards;
no smoking at D; children: 12+.*

ASTBURY, CHESHIRE   5–3B

Pecks   £42
Newcastle Rd CW12 4SB (01260) 275161
*It's a slightly love-it-or-hate-it experience ("fantastic, but
overbearing", says one reporter) to dine at this one-sitting-at-eight
venue, where the seven-course menu offers "top value", according
to fans; lunch is more standard. / Sample dishes: broad bean & goats
cheese risotto; braised lamb with black olive mash; rum & raisin cheesecake.
Details: www.pecksrest.co.uk; off A34; 8 pm; closed Mon & Sun D; no smoking at
D; booking essential.*

AUCHTERARDER, PERTH & KINROSS   9–3C

Andrew Fairlie
Gleneagles Hotel   £80   𝔸★
PH3 1NF (01764) 694267
*Andrew Fairlie's "top-class" modern French cuisine is "not as eye-
wateringly expensive as you might expect", at this "truly
outstanding" grand hotel dining room; all aspects of its operation
win praise from reporters for "brilliant attention to detail".
/ Sample dishes: foie gras terrine with caramelised apple; roast venison with wild
mushrooms; chocolate orange pudding. Details: www.gleneagles.com; 10 pm; L only,
closed Sun; no smoking; children: 12+. Accommodation: 273 rooms, from £320.*

AYLESBURY, BUCKINGHAMSHIRE   3–2A

Hartwell House   £ 59   𝔸
Oxford Rd HP17 8NL   (01296) 747444
Non-nobs "feel like they've joined the aristocracy", on visits to this
"magnificent" part-Jacobean country house hotel; its standard of
cuisine is generally found "reliably high", but there's no denying
that a minority claims it's "seriously over-rated and overpriced".
/ **Sample dishes:** smoked chicken & spring onion sausage; sea bass with spinach &
port wine sauce; mango mousse with pineapple crisps.
Details: www.hartwell-house.com; 2m W of Aylesbury on A418; 9.45 pm; jacket &
tie required at D; no smoking; children: 8+. **Accommodation:** 49 rooms,
from £260.

BABINGTON, SOMERSET   2–3B

Babington House   £ 42   𝔸
BA11 3RW   (01373) 812266
"Surprisingly good for such a self-consciously trendy
establishment" – in the culinary stakes, this rural country house
retreat for urban hipsters (owned by Soho House) pleased
reporters more consistently this year; you have to stay (or be a
member) to eat. / **Sample dishes:** smoked duck, dandelion & hazelnut salad;
monkfish with clams & bacon; trio of chocolate puddings.
Details: www.babingtonhouse.co.uk; 11 pm; open to residents & members only for
L & D all week; booking essential. **Accommodation:** 28 rooms, from £215.

BADDIDARACH, HIGHLAND   9–1B

Albannach   £ 56   𝔸★
IV27 4LP   (01571) 844407
It may be "even further north than the Summer Isles", but fans
say it's still worth seeking out this "unique" country house hotel –
a "very personal" place (run by "interesting" people), where the
food can be "incredible". / **Details:** www.thealbannach.co.uk; 8 pm; D only,
closed Mon; no Amex; children: 12+. **Accommodation:** 5 rooms, from £204.

BAKEWELL, DERBYSHIRE   5–2C

Aitch's Wine Bar   £ 36   ★
4 Buxton Rd DE45 1DA   (01629) 813895
"A small and intimate bistro", in an ancient town-centre building,
where the lunch menu ("great-value"), wine list ("extensive" and
"interesting") and breakfasts ("the best we have eaten anywhere,
including 5-star hotels") are singled out for special mention; jazz
evenings are also a feature. / **Sample dishes:** spicy Thai fishcakes; crispy
duck with stir-fried vegetables; champagne cheesecake with cassis ice cream.
Details: www.aitchswinebar.co.uk; 9.30 pm; closed Sun (open Sun D in summer);
no Amex; no smoking.

Monsal Head   £ 24   ★
DE45 1NL   (01629) 640250
"The most reliable eatery in the Peak District"; the "superb"
standards of this hotel in the middle of the National Park are
attested to by all reporters; "the main restaurant gets booked up,
but the bar food isn't far behind". / **Details:** www.monsalhead.com; just
outside the town; 9.30 pm; closed Mon-Wed in Winter; no Amex; no smoking.
Accommodation: 7 rooms, from £60.

Renaissance £31 ★
Bath St DE45 1BX (01629) 812687
"Simple fresh food" and a *"genuinely warm welcome"* make this comfortable Gallic restaurant a continuing success.
/ **Sample dishes:** *French onion soup; chicken stuffed with crab mousse; chocolate & pear terrine with claret sauce.* **Details:** *www.renaissance-restaurant.com; 9.30 pm; closed Mon & Sun D; no smoking.*

BALLACHULISH, HIGHLAND 9–3B

Ballachulish House £43 ★
PH49 4JX (01855) 811266
A piper sometimes announces dinner at this grand and remote restaurant-with-rooms; both the menu (which is quite complex) and the service are praised for *"excellent attention to detail"*.
/ **Details:** *www.ballachulishhouse.com; no smoking; children: 10+.*
Accommodation: *8 rooms, from £125.*

BALLATER, ABERDEEN 9–3C

Darroch Learg £48 🅐★
Braemar Rd AB35 5UX (01339) 755443
"Welcoming" and *"knowledgeable"* staff help make the Franks family's long-established country house hotel — which enjoys *"stunning views"* over the Dee Valley — an ever-reliable destination, not least for its *"superb"* cooking. / **Sample dishes:** *Loch Fyne scallops; loin of venison; lemon tart.* **Details:** *www.darrochlearg.demon.co.uk; 9 pm; D only, except Sun open L & D.* **Accommodation:** *17 rooms, from £130.*

Green Inn £43 ★
9 Victoria Rd AB35 5QQ (01339) 755701
"A change of ownership has made this place even better", says one of the fans of this welcoming inn, whose *"enjoyable"* cuisine is praised by all reporters. / **Sample dishes:** *duck with black pudding & sweet soy sauce; turbot with leek risotto & Arbroath smokie; treacle tart with liquorice ice cream.* **Details:** *www.green-inn.com; 9 pm; D only, closed Mon & Sun; no smoking.*
Accommodation: *3 rooms, from £119.*

BALQUHIDDER, PERTHSHIRE 9–3C

Monachyle Mhor £38 🅐★★
FK19 8PQ (01877) 384622
"Brilliant" food in *"beautiful"* surroundings — that's the gist of all commentary on this *"terrific"* farmhouse-hotel, *"overlooking a loch and surrounded by mountains"*; there are seven miles of single-track to get there, but the place is *"worth driving through snow for"*. / **Sample dishes:** *creamed spinich & quail tart; fillet of John Dory with garden vegetables; creamed sago pudding on carmelized banana with brown bread ice cream.* **Details:** *www.monachylemhor.com; 8.45 pm; no Amex; children: 12+ at D.* **Accommodation:** *11 rooms, from £95.*

BANBURY, OXFORDSHIRE 2–1D

Thai Orchid £29 🅐★
56 Northbar St OX16 0TL (01295) 270833
There's some *"exceptional"* and *"authentic"* food to be had at this *"traditionally-styled"* Thai; Tardis-like, its external appearance gives no hint of the spacious interior. / **Details:** *www.thaiorchidbanbury.co.uk; 10.30 pm; no Amex; no smoking area.*

BANGOR, COUNTY DOWN   10–1D

Shanks   £ 53   ★★
150 Crawfordsburn Rd BT19 1GB   (028) 9185 3313
*Implausibly located on a golf course, this "professional" and
"friendly" operation serves "inventive" cooking of a "consistently
very high standard" (and still arguably the best in Northern
Ireland). / Sample dishes: smoked salmon blinis; peppered pork with Parmesan
mash; chocolate mousse with raspberries. Details: www.shanksrestaurant.com; A2
to Bangor, follow signs for Blackwood golf centre; 10 pm; closed Mon, Sat L & Sun*

BANGOR, GWYNEDD   4–1C

The Fat Cat Café Bar   £ 23
161 High St LL57 1NU   (01248) 370445
*In many respects, this "popular" café/bar – the original member
of a northern chain – remains a worthwhile fixture; service,
though, "can really let it down". / Sample dishes: chicken quesadillas; tuna
with stir-fried vegetables in oyster sauce; Caribbean banana charlotte.
Details: www.fatcat.to; 10 pm; no smoking area; children: 18+ only.*

BARNARD CASTLE, COUNTY DURHAM   8–3B

Blagraves House   £ 33   𝔸★
30 The Bank DL12 8PN   (01833) 637668
*This "lovely and atmospheric" 16th-century townhouse again
produced only limited survey feedback – it's all to the effect that
the place is "hard to match", thanks to its "consistent" cooking
and "reasonable" prices. / Sample dishes: smoked salmon mousse; roast
loin of venison with wild mushrooms; orange parfait with fresh raspberry sauce.
Details: www.blagraves.co.uk; 9.30 pm; D only, closed Mon & Sun; no Amex;
no smoking; children: 8+.*

BARNSLEY, GLOUCESTERSHIRE   2–2C

Barnsley House   £ 63
GL7 5EE   (01285) 740000
*This trendy new boutique-hotel, in a 17th-century house, inspires
mixed views; even critics concede it "sets itself high standards",
but while some reporters find it "a beautiful all-rounder",
dissidents say it's "extortionately pricey for average service and
unexceptional food". / Sample dishes: bresaola with goats cheese; baked
pasta with mushroom and truffles; Mascarpone and raspberry brûlée.
Details: www.barnsleyhouse.com; 9.30 pm, Sat 10 pm; children: 12+ at D.
Accommodation: 9 rooms, from £250.*

The Village Pub   £ 33
GL7 5EF   (01285) 740421
*Since the former chef went to Barnsley House (same owners), the
food at this chilled Cotswold gastropub hasn't quite kept its lustre
– ingredients may be "first-class", but results can be a bit "hit-
and-miss". / Sample dishes: sausages with beans, potato, tomato & olives;
pan-fried sea bass with salad; baked pear puff pastry with toffee sauce.
Details: www.thevillagepub.co.uk; 9.30 pm; no Amex; no smoking area.
Accommodation: 6 rooms, from £80.*

BARTON UPON HUMBER, N LINCS   6–2A
Elio's   £ 36   ★
11 Market Pl DN18 5DA   (01652) 635147
"Exceptional, simply-cooked fresh fish" is what this Market Place
Italian does best (and has done *"for nearly 20 years"*); the recent
extension gives *"the impression of dining alfresco, all year round"*.
/ **Sample dishes:** cannelloni alla romana; seafood risotto; amaretto cheesecake.
Details: A15 towards Humber Bridge, first exit into Barton upon Humber; 9.45 pm;
D only, closed Sun; no smoking area. **Accommodation:** 8 rooms, from £65.

Rafters   £ 32   ★
24 High St DN18 5PD   (01652) 660669
"Good value, especially at lunchtime" – that's the commonest
theme of the consistently upbeat reports on this market-town
restaurant. / **Sample dishes:** antipasti with avocado; curried pork with dried
fruits; chocolate Scotch pancakes. **Details:** www.rafters.co.uk; just S of Humber
Bridge off A15; 10 pm; closed Mon & Sun D; no smoking.

BARWICK VILLAGE, SOMERSET   2–3B
Little Barwick House   £ 46   A★
BA22 9TD   (01935) 423902
The cooking at Tim & Emma Ford's *"lovely"* and *"quiet"* Georgian
country house hotel is always *"sound"*, and it's sometimes
"extremely good"; the *"carefully put-together wine list"* also merits
mention. / **Sample dishes:** pink-roast quail with mushroom risotto; brill with baby
leeks & girolles; hot plum soufflé. **Details:** www.littlebarwick.co.uk; 9 pm; closed
Mon, Tue L & Sun D; no Amex; no smoking. **Accommodation:** 6 rooms, from £94.

BASLOW, DERBYSHIRE   5–2C
Cavendish   £ 48   A★
Church Ln DE45 1SP   (01246) 582311
A *"fantastic"* location (*"overlooking the Chatsworth estate"*) is
matched by the *"delicious"* cooking at this ducally-owned hotel;
even some fans, though, can't help noticing that it's *"not cheap"*.
/ **Sample dishes:** timbale of black pudding with quails egg in hollandaise sauce;
roast squab breast with potato rosti buttered cabbage & port jus; lemon curd
bread & butter pudding with lemon meringue ice cream.
Details: www.cavendish-hotel.net; 10 pm; no smoking. **Accommodation:** 24
rooms, from £130.

Fischers at Baslow Hall   £ 55   A★
Calver Rd DE45 1RR   (01246) 583259
Max Fischer's cooking is *"always classy, and often sublime"*, in the
"fantastic" dining room at his *"romantic"* country house (*"at the
end of a long drive, on the fringe of the Chatsworth estate"*); if
there is a reservation, it is that the style can seem *"very formal"*.
/ **Sample dishes:** sea bream with butternut squash ratatouille; pigs trotter with
morels & truffle mash; passion fruit soufflé. **Details:** www.fischers baslowhall.co.uk;
9.30 pm; closed Mon L & Sun D; no jeans or trainers; no smoking; children: 12+
after 7 pm. **Accommodation:** 11 rooms, from £120.

BASSENTHWAITE LAKE, CUMBRIA   7–3C
Pheasant Hotel   £ 45   A
CA13 9YE   (01768) 776234
This *"lovely Lakeland inn"* is a *"favourite haven"* (*"whether in the
bar or the restaurant"*) for a more-than-local fan club; fish dishes,
in particular, can be *"very good"*. / **Sample dishes:** smoked breast of duck
with dressing; pan-fried fillet of red bream; pistachio parfait with white chocolate
wafers. **Details:** www.the-pheasant.co.uk; 8.30 pm; no Amex; no smoking.
Accommodation: 15 rooms, from £100.

BATH, BATH & NE SOMERSET 2–2B

Beautiful stone-built English cities seem to think their architectural riches will be enough to satisfy any visitor. How else to explain the fact that this affluent destination-city remains a culinary wilderness? There's a plethora of places to eat, of course, but pricey mediocrity seems to be the order of the day – even on the ambience front! For cooking, the *Moody Goose* is the only place that could be said to be of any real note. For an 'experience', seek out the *Pump Rooms* or *Pimpernel's*.

Bath Priory Hotel £68 Ⓐ
Weston Rd BA1 2XT (01225) 331922
"*Delightful*" service contributes to all-round satisfaction with this "*excellent*" hotel, in beautiful gardens on the outskirts of the city; the occasional doubter can find its approach "*a bit overblown*". / **Sample dishes:** crab & ginger ravioli with langoustine sauce; roast guinea fowl with lemon & sage, caramelised lemon tart. **Details:** www.thebathpriory.co.uk; 1m W of city centre, past Victoria Park; 9.30 pm; no jeans or trainers; no smoking; children: 7+ at D. **Accommodation:** 28 rooms, from £245.

Beaujolais £39 Ⓐ
5 Chapel Rw, Queen Sq BA1 1HN (01225) 423417
"*Very '70s and just great*", this "*very relaxed*" Gallic bistro is a local favourite, thanks to its "*authentic*" food and "*fun*" atmosphere. / **Sample dishes:** onion soup; coq au vin; crème brûlée. **Details:** www.beaujolaisbath.co.uk; next to Francis Hotel; 10.30 pm; closed Sun; no Amex.

Café Fromage £15 Ⓐ★
1 John St BA1 2JL (01225) 313525
"*Bath has lots of cafés, but this charming and unpretentious place is the best*", say fans of this tiny, "*friendly*" fixture over a cheese shop, serving "*simple*", "*light*" dishes; "*I just wish they were open in the evenings*". / **Sample dishes:** no starters; grilled mushrooms with roast vegetables and goat's cheese; warm Belgian apple tart with ice cream. **Details:** L & afternoon tea only; closed Sun & Mon, Tue-Sat L only; no credit cards; no smoking; no booking.

Demuths £32
2 North Parade Passage BA1 1NX (01225) 446059
This "*slightly hippy*" veggie is "*always full*", thanks to its "*original*" cuisine; it's become a bit of a "*victim of its own success*", though, and "*poor*" service is a recurrent complaint. / **Sample dishes:** feta, mint & pea pâté with walnut bread; goats cheese soufflé with tomato salsa; Indonesian black rice pudding. **Details:** www.demuths.co.uk; 10 pm, Sat 11 pm; no smoking; booking: max 4 at D, Fri & Sat; children: 6+ after 7 pm.

The Eastern Eye £22
8a Quiet St BA1 2JS (01225) 422323
"*An impressive Georgian room*" provides the "*surprising*" setting for this "*good value-for-money*" curry house; the dishes are usually "*tasty*" and "*well presented*". / **Details:** www.easterneye.com; 11 pm; no smoking area.

Firehouse Rotisserie £ 33
2 John St BA1 2JL (01225) 482070
*"The menu's nothing special, but if you want to chill out with
friends, this is the place"; don't be too laid-back, though – booking
for this "not-cheap" pizza-and-more Californian is "essential".*
/ *Sample dishes: Brie & grape quesadillas; Pacific crab & smoked salmon fishcakes;
chocolate pecan pie. Details: www.firehouserotisserie.co.uk; 10.30 pm; closed Sun;
no smoking area.*

FishWorks £ 44
6 Green St BA1 2JY (01225) 448707
*"A real find for fish-lovers in search of the unusual", this is the
original branch of the expanding national chain of fishmongers-
cum-cafés; "fish is the whole focus of the place", though – the
wine list is a bit "dull", the ambience "too informal for the prices"
and service "unsympathetic".* / *Sample dishes: crab salad with tarragon
mayonnaise; cod with mash & parsley sauce; Sicilian lemon tart.
Details: www.fishworks.co.uk; 10.30 pm; closed Mon & Sun D; no smoking.*

Hole in the Wall £ 37
16 George St BA1 2EN (01225) 425242
*One of the first notable post-war restaurants, this famous site has
been through many changes in recent years (most recently of
ownership, if not chef, in Jan 2004) – reports suggest the latest
régime is "good, but not exciting".* / *Sample dishes: warm scallop &
bacon salad; guinea fowl with beetroot & garlic sauce; caramelised pears with coffee
ice cream. Details: www.theholeinthewall.co.uk; 10 pm; no Amex; no smoking area.*

The Hop Pole £ 26
7 Albion Buildings, Upper Bristol Rd BA1 3AR
(01225) 446327
*"Cooking with care" and some "great beer" makes this "friendly"
place (owned by the Bath Ales brewery) "Bath's best gastropub";
the atmosphere of the "long and narrow" dining room strikes
some as "flat", especially compared to the "lively" bar.*
/ *Sample dishes: deep-fried whitebait with garlic mayonnaise; chargrilled ribeye
steak; cheeses. Details: www.bathales.co.uk; opp Victoria Park; 10 pm; closed
Mon & Sun D; no smoking area.*

Loch Fyne £ 34
24 Milsom St BA1 1DG (01225) 750120
*An old bank provides a setting that's "grand, without being too
cavernous" for this otherwise typical branch of the national
seafood chain – handy to know about, though, in this under-
served city.* / *Sample dishes: lobster bisque with garlic rouille; rosemary-infused
bream with tomatoes & black olives; lemon sorbet. Details: www.loch-fyne.com;
10 pm, Fri & Sat 11 pm; no smoking. Accommodation: 9 rooms, from £75.*

Mai Thai £ 24
6 Pierrepont St BA2 4AA (01225) 445557
*The occasional reporter feels that this central Thai is "not quite
what it used to be"; it's a "cosy" place, though, and its "excellent-
value set lunch" is worth seeking out.* / *Details: 10.30 pm, Fri & Sat
10.45 pm; no smoking area; children: 10+.*

Moody Goose   £42   ★
74 Kingsmead Sq BA1 2AB   (01225) 466688
Stephen Shore's "very thoughtful" cooking – quite possibly Bath's best – plus "first-class" service again win high praise for this "personal" and "intimate" cellar in the centre of town; it's "not overpriced", either. / Sample dishes: smoked haddock ravioli with goats cheese; chicken with crayfish & artichoke mousse; passion fruit soufflé.
Details: *www.moody-goose.com; 9.30 pm; closed Sun; no smoking; children: 7+.*

Moon & Sixpence   £34
6a Broad St BA1 5LJ   (01225) 460962
"One of the best casual dining experiences in a town full of disappointments" – this "cheerful" and "romantic" bistro, set in a courtyard, offers "a lovely retreat from the hustle and bustle of the city"; the food – if far from remarkable – is "generally good". / Sample dishes: guinea fowl & pistachio ballotine; sea bass with pak choy & sweet chilli; white, milk & dark chocolate mousses. Details: www.moonandsixpence.co.uk; 10.15 pm; no smoking area.

No 5 Bistro   £37
5 Argyle St BA2 4BA   (01225) 444199
This small French restaurant, just off Pulteney Bridge, inspires opposing views – doubters find it "expensive for what it is", but advocates say it's a "cosy" and "pleasing" place offering "good value for money". / Sample dishes: goats cheese mousse with grapefruit salad; pan-fried sea bass with aubergine caviar; chocolate truffle & pineapple cake. Details: www.no5restaurant.uk.com; 10 pm, Fri 10.30 pm, Sat 11 pm; no smoking.

Olive Tree
Queensberry Hotel   £43
Russell St BA1 2QF   (01225) 447928
Under its new régime, this well-known basement has been made over in what most – if not quite all – reporters judge "subtle and contemporary" style; the cooking is generally found "scrumptious", too, but "disappointing" results are not unknown. / Sample dishes: red mullet & roast aubergine salad; braised pork with morels & savoy cabbage; roast peach tart. Details: www.thequeensberry.co.uk; 10 pm; closed Mon L; no smoking. Accommodation: 29 rooms, from £120.

Pimpernel's
Royal Crescent Hotel   £65   Ⓐ
16 Royal Cr BA1 2LS   (01225) 823333
"Impressive (if flashy)" surroundings in gardens at the back of the hotel, and food "among the best in Bath" (well, you'd hope so, at these prices) create "special occasion" credentials for the restaurant at this famous townhouse (now part of the voracious Von Essen group); service, though, can prove "elusive". / Sample dishes: smoked salmon with capers & horseradish; rump of lamb Lyonnaise with white bean purée; Cointreau & pecan nougat parfait. Details: www.royalcrescent.co.uk; in centre of Royal Crescent; 9.30 pm; no smoking; booking: max 8. Accommodation: 45 rooms, from £210.

Pump Rooms   £27   Ⓐ
The Pump Room, Stall St BA1 1LZ   (01225) 444477
"A string quartet" creates "an ambience of a time gone by" at this famous Georgian landmark; "it's definitely on the tourist trail, but go anyway" – ideally for breakfast, or for tea. / Sample dishes: warm chilli garlic mushrooms; smoked haddock with spinach & ricotta tortellini. Details: www.searcys.co.uk; by the Abbey; L only, open until 10pm in Aug; no smoking; no booking, Sat & Sun.

Rajpoot £31
4 Argyle St BA2 2BA (01225) 466833
In quirky cellars near the Pulteney Bridge, this has long been regarded as a pre-eminent local Indian; it's cooking remains uneven, though, with rather too many reporters for comfort leaving "disappointed". / **Details:** www.rajpoot.com; 11 pm, Fri & Sat 11.30 pm; no smoking.

Sukhothai £23
90a Walcot St BA1 5BG (01225) 462463
"Good" food and a "pleasant" overall experience is the gist of most comments on this handy and inexpensive Thai stand-by. / **Details:** 10.30 pm; closed Sun L; no Amex; no smoking.

Tilley's Bistro £29 Ⓐ
3 North Parade Pas BA1 1NX (01225) 484200
A slight feeling of things "not as good as they used to be" pervades reports on this useful bistro, in a pretty, pedestrianised lane; fans, though, say it can still deliver "tasty dishes at attractive prices". / **Sample dishes:** Caesar salad; pork Dijonnaise; warm banana pancake with toffee sauce. **Details:** www.tilleysbistro.co.uk; 11 pm; closed Sun; no Amex; no smoking area.

Woods £34
9-12 Alfred St BA1 2QX (01225) 314812
"Never too original, but usually relaxing and very popular"; that's the whole story really on this "slightly down-at-heel" – but "consistent and congenial" – Gallic brasserie. / **Sample dishes:** roast tomato & basil soup; lamb & roast garlic casserole; chocolate torte. **Details:** www.bathshopping.co.uk; 10 pm; closed Sun D; no Amex.

BATTLE, EAST SUSSEX 3–4C

The Pilgrims £33 Ⓐ★
1 High St TN33 0AE (01424) 772314
In a "magical" medieval, half-timbered building, "in the shadow of Battle Abbey", this "creative" restaurant is unanimously hailed – if by a small fan club – for its "fabulous cooking, using local ingredients". / **Details:** www.thepilgrimsrestaurant.co.uk; 9 pm; closed Sun D; no Amex; no smoking.

BAWTRY, SOUTH YORKSHIRE 5–2D

China Rose £34 ★
16 South Parade DN10 6JH (01302) 710461
"Big and the best" – four words say it all about this vast oriental, which is unrivalled in these parts. / **Details:** 10 pm; D only; no jeans or trainers; no smoking.

BEACONSFIELD, BUCKINGHAMSHIRE 3–3A

Leigh House £39
53 Wycombe End HP9 1LX (01494) 676348
"By far the best Chinese restaurant in South Bucks", this is a "reliable" and "well-run" operation; the surroundings are "nice", too. / **Sample dishes:** sesame prawn toast; spicy lemon prawns with rice; toffee apples. **Details:** 10 pm; no smoking area.

BEARSTED, KENT   3–3C

Soufflé   £ 38   ★
31 The Grn ME14 4DN   (01622) 737065
"Delightfully located" by a green (and with a *"relaxing"* terrace for
the summer), this small restaurant is almost unanimously hailed
by reporters for its *"super"* food (even if the occasional doubter
finds it *"too 'nouvelle'")*. / **Sample dishes:** tiger prawns with chilli sauce; fillet
of beef with red wine sauce; soufflé with ice cream. **Details:** off M20; 9.30 pm;
closed Mon, Sat L & Sun D.

BEAUMARIS, ISLE OF ANGLESEY   4–1C

Ye Olde Bull's Head   £ 38   🄰 ★
Castle St LL58 8AP   (01248) 810329
"Unexpectedly good" – that's the unanimous verdict on the
surprisingly contemporary brasserie of this ancient and famous
coaching inn, near the castle. / **Sample dishes:** lettuce soup with smoked
goose ravioli; beef with horseradish crust; clementine sponge with Grand Marnier ice
cream. **Details:** www.bullsheadinn.co.uk; 9.30 pm; D only, closed Sun; no smoking;
children: 7+ at D. **Accommodation:** 13 rooms, from £92.

BEDFORD, BEDFORDSHIRE   3–1A

St Helena's   £ 43   🄰
High St MK42 9XP   (01234) 344848
"Always an experience to look forward to"; this attractive
restaurant in a pretty setting just outside the town is a
"consistently good" local destination (especially *"for a
celebration"*). / **Sample dishes:** marinated, smoked Scottish salmon with
dressing; fillet of beef stuffed with Stilton wrapped in bacon; apple bread & butter
pudding with custard. **Details:** 9 pm; closed Mon, Sat L & Sun; jacket & tie
required; no smoking; children: 12+.

BELFAST, COUNTY ANTRIM   10–1D

Belfast is slowly developing a restaurant scene with more to
interest the visitor, and we've added a number of new entries
this year. (Reports still suggest that, for the very best cooking
in the province, you should head out of town to Bangor's
Shanks.) Paul Rankin, of *Cayenne* is the big (read TV) name in
these parts. As this guide was going to press he relaunched a
new brasserie under his original brand name, Roscoff, at 7-11
Linenhall Street (tel 9031 1150).

Aldens   £ 38   ★
229 Upper Newtownards Rd BT4 3JF   (028) 9065 0079
*It may be in a "rough" area, but this "very good" venture (in a
converted supermarket) retains "first-choice" status for some
reporters; "the odd slip" was noted this year, but in general the
verdict is that the place is "excellent".* / **Sample dishes:** beetroot &
herring salad; roast cod with Parma ham butter; rhubarb granita with apple brandy.
Details: www.aldensrestaurant.com; 2m from Stormont Buildings; 10 pm, Fri & Sat
11 pm; closed Sat L & Sun; no smoking area.

Cayenne £35 A★
7 Ascot Hs, Shaftesbury Sq BT2 7DB (028) 9033 1532
"Cayenne is coming into its own after a slow transformation from Roscoff": one reporter says it all about the town's (re-)emerging top venue – an *"airy"* and *"comfortable"* place, where the food (from star local TV-chef Paul Rankin) is *"top-class"*.
/ **Sample dishes:** Caesar salad; salmon with coconut rice & black bean vinaigrette; spiced ginger pudding. **Details:** www.cayennerestaurant.com; near Botanic Railway Station; 10.15 pm, Sat & Sun 11.15 pm; closed Sat L & Sun L; no smoking area.

Deanes £40 A
34-40 Howard St BT1 6PF (028) 9056 0000
Feedback is still a mite mixed, but satisfaction with Michael Deane's *"baroque"* bistro is on the rise – it finds particular favour as a business lunch venue; upstairs, there's a fine dining restaurant that some would claim is *"NI's best"*.
/ **Sample dishes:** goats cheese with salami & asparagus; ground beef with onion mash & spiced ketchup; steamed pineapple pudding.
Details: www.michaeldeane.co.uk; near Grand Opera House; 11 pm; closed Sun.

James Street South £37
21 James Street South BT2 7AG (028) 9043 4310
This *"stark"* and *"formal"* city-centre newcomer is most popular as a *"business"* destination; its *"trendy"* food is well-received by reporters, though they can find it a fraction *"pricey"* for what it is.
/ **Details:** www.jamesstreetsouth.co.uk; 10.30 pm; closed Sun L.

Nick's Warehouse £37
35 Hill St BT1 2LB (028) 9043 9690
"Invariably good quality" has helped make this long-established wine bar-cum-restaurant famously *"the best place in Belfast for lunch"*. / **Sample dishes:** lemon & chilli chicken tempura; salmon & roast tomatoes with rocket mayonnaise; white peach cheesecake.
Details: www.nickswarehouse.co.uk; behind St Anne's Cathedral; 9.30 pm; closed Mon D, Sat L & Sun; children: before 9 pm only.

Red Panda £31
60 Great Victoria St BT2 7BB (028) 9080 8700
"Right in the heart of Belfast", this very large Chinese makes a handy stand-by, not least for a *"fast and cheap business lunch"*.
/ **Details:** www.theredpanda.com; 11.30 pm.

Zen £32 A★
55-59 Adelaide St BT2 8FE (028) 9023 2244
A style that's *"more 'Sex and the City' than downtown Belfast"* helps this *"stunning"* and *"glamorous"* oriental to stand out; on most reports the food is *"great"*, too (though the odd doubter does dismiss it as *"Japanese-lite"*). / **Sample dishes:** crispy king prawns; enoki mushroom; black sesame ice cream. **Details:** www.theredpanda.com; 9.30 pm.

Wednesdays £30
8 Wednesday Mkt HU17 0DG (01482) 869727
"Good food" – and especially *"good lunch deals"* – maintains the appeal of this unpretentious place near the Minster; you can BYO on the eponymous weekday. / **Sample dishes:** Thai fishcakes with sweet & sour cucumber sauce; lamb shank in pearl barley broth; spicy date & ginger pudding.
Details: www.wednesdaysathome.co.uk; near Beverley Minster; 9.30 pm; closed Sun.

BIDDENDEN, KENT   3–4C
Three Chimneys   £ 36   𝔸 ★

Hareplain Rd TN27 8LW   (01580) 291472
A "lovely" old pub, offering an "excellent choice" of "very good"
fare (using "fresh local produce") in "congenial" surroundings.
/ **Sample dishes:** baked mushrooms with goats cheese; sea bass with sweet
potato & coconut chowder; lemon tart with plum compote. **Details:** A262 between
Biddenden and Sissinghurst; 9.45 pm; no Amex; no booking, Sun L.

West House   £ 40

28 High St TN27 8AH   (01580) 291341
"Innovative" and often "excellent" food rewards visitors to this
"lovely" village two-year-old; it strikes some reporters as "a bit
overpriced", though, especially as neither service nor ambience is
much to write home about. / **Sample dishes:** samphire and lobster
hollandaise; fillet of sea trout; grappa marinated peach. **Details:** 9.30 pm; closed
Mon, Sat L & Sun D; no Amex.

BIGBURY, DEVON   1–4D
Oyster Shack   £ 29   𝔸 ★ ★

Millburn Orchard Farm, Stakes Hills TQ7 4BE
(01548) 810876
It may be "hard to find" and "in the middle of nowhere"
(overlooking Burgh Island), but "booking is essential" for this
"eccentric and charming" fixture; an "unrivalled choice of fresh
fish" is the principal attraction. / **Sample dishes:** grilled oysters with cream;
smoked fish medley with salad; raspberry pavlova. **Details:** www.oystershack.co.uk;
L only; L only, closed Mon; no smoking; booking essential.

BIRCHOVER, DERBYSHIRE   5–3C
Druid Inn   £ 28

Main St DE4 2BL   (01629) 650302
"A pleasant Peak District pub", where the food – from a "huge"
blackboard menu – is generally approved by reporters; doubters
feel it "could try harder". / **Sample dishes:** port & Stilton pâté; rack of lamb
with redcurrant & gooseberry sauce; date & ginger pudding with butterscotch sauce.
Details: www.druidinnbirchover.co.uk; Sw of Bakewell off B5056; 9 pm; closed Mon;
no Amex; no smoking.

BIRMINGHAM, WEST MIDLANDS   5–4C

Typical – you wait years for a decent restaurant, then two
come along at once! Birmingham has long been notable as the
major city without any interesting restaurants, but these
preconceptions are looking precarious following the arrival not
only of the immediately-hailed *Jessica's* but also, as this guide
goes to press, of *Simpson's*. Given the latter's track record
when it was in Kenilworth, it would be suprising if its standards
were not very high. At a slightly less ambitious level, the well-
established *Toque d'Or* continues to put in a very creditable
performance.

Otherwise, it remains the case that Brum – despite the huge
improvements to the cityscape of recent years – is a notably
also-ran culinary destination, with many of the new sites in the
revitalised city-centre given over to large and well-known but
bland operations (such as *Bank* and *Petit Blanc*). Apart from balti
houses (which are mostly concentrated in Moseley and
Sparkbrook), the city is also weak in ethnic appeal.

Adil £13 ★
148-150 Stoney Ln B12 8AJ (0121) 449 0335
Sparkbrook may offer "great competition" nowadays, but Brum's original balti house is still unanimously hailed by reporters for its "cheap, tasty and reliable" fare. / **Details:** www.adilbalti.co.uk; 3m from city centre on A41; midnight; no smoking area.

Bank £42
4 Brindleyplace B1 2JB (0121) 633 4466
"Classy breakfasts", "canal views" and "good business and pre-theatre menus" are among the features commending this '90s-style brasserie to some reporters; more generally, though, it can seem a pretty "boring" destination, and a "noisy" one, too. / **Sample dishes:** five-onion soup with cheese croutons; calves liver & bacon with red onion confit; rum & raisin cheesecake. **Details:** www.bankrestaurants.com; 10.30 pm, Fri & Sat 11 pm; no smoking area.

Bar Estilo £25
110-114 Wharfside St B1 1RF (0121) 643 3443
"A good selection of tapas – and in "good-sized portions", too – makes this large bar (an offshoot of a small London chain) a useful Mailbox rendezvous (especially "with children"). / **Details:** www.barestilo.co.uk; 11 pm; no smoking area.

Café Ikon £21
Ikon Gallery, Oozells Sq, Brindley Place B1 2HS
(0121) 248 3226
In some respects, the most consistent central Brum rendezvous, this art gallery café serves "good" tapas, and has "friendly" (if sometimes "overstretched") service; "it gets very packed – it's best to book". / **Sample dishes:** cured Spanish meats; seared tuna with roast vegetables; baked custard flan. **Details:** www.ikon-gallery.co.uk; 10 pm; closed Mon & Sun D; no smoking area; children: before 9 pm only.

Chez Jules £25
5a Ethel St, off New St B2 4BG (0121) 633 4664
This "lively" Gallic bistro may be "basic", but it's a "friendly" place that's often praised for delivering "value-for-money". / **Sample dishes:** chicken liver & mushroom pâté; pork in honey & grain mustard sauce; crème brûlée. **Details:** www.chezjules.co.uk; 11 pm; closed Sun D; no smoking area; no booking, Sat L.

Chung Ying Garden £29
17 Thorp St B5 4AT (0121) 666 6622
One of the two vast Cantonese landmarks (the older Chung Ying is at 16-18 Wrottesley Street, tel 622 5669), this Chinatown fixture generally makes a "decent" destination, and has quite a name for dim sum; even a fan, though, admits it's "nothing special compared to Manchester or London". / **Details:** www.chungying.co.uk; 11.30 pm.

Hotel du Vin et Bistro £39
25 Church St B3 2NR (0121) 200 0600
"Outshining other city-centre destinations", this "busy" design-hotel dining room is the number one venue hereabouts; the cooking is improving, but – as is invariably the case with this group – the "amazing and eclectic" wine list is "more interesting". / **Sample dishes:** Mozzarella & avocado salad; duck with apple & foie gras; butterscotch cheesecake with chocolate sauce. **Details:** www.hotelduvin.co.uk; 9.45 pm; no smoking; booking: max 10. **Accommodation:** 66 rooms, from £125.

Jessica's £50 ★
1 Montague Rd B16 9HN
(0121) 455 0999
"We had read such good reports, and it lived up to all expectations" – Glynn Purnell's elegant newcomer (part of a large Victorian house in Edgbaston, with conservatory and courtyard) has quickly won a name as *"the best restaurant in Brum"*.
/ **Sample dishes:** scallops with spring onion and mackerel beignet; sea bass with apple puree, ravioli of pigs trotters, smoked bacon & glazed baby onions; warm chocolate pudding with pear, almonds and sorbet. **Details:** www.eat-the-midlands.co.uk/jessicas; 10 pm; closed Mon L, Sat L & Sun; no Amex.

Jyoti £16 ★
569-571 Stratford Rd B11 4LS   (0121) 766 7199
"Consistently tasty Gujerati fare" makes it worth seeking out this Sparkhill subcontinental, especially if you're looking for somewhere that's just *"so cheap"*. / **Details:** 9.15 pm; closed Mon, Tue-Thu D only; no Amex; no smoking.

Kababish £26 ★
29 Woodbridge Rd B13 8EH   (0121) 449 5556
"Good baltis" and *"excellent naans"* are among the highlights at this *"consistent"* Moseley Indian. / **Details:** 11.15 pm; D only.

Living Room £30 Ⓐ
Regency Whf, 2 Broad St B1 2JZ   (0870) 442 2539
Part of a national chain of upmarket bar/restaurants, this busy city-centre operation wouldn't necessarily rate a mention in many cities; in Brum, however, it makes a *"good place"*.
/ **Sample dishes:** salt & pepper squid; cheese & bacon burger; hot chocolate fudge cake. **Details:** www.thelivingroom.co.uk; 11 pm, Wed & Thu 11.30 pm, Fri & Sat midnight.

Malmaison £40
Royal Mail St B1 1XL   (0121) 246 5000
Some discern a *"cooking by numbers"* quality to its cuisine (*"just like the rest of the chain"*), but this *"stylish"* design-hotel brasserie makes a useful Mailbox destination nonetheless, especially for business. / **Sample dishes:** eggs Benedict; poached salmon served with spinach & sorrel; iced banana parfait. **Details:** www.malmaison.com; 10.30 pm. **Accommodation:** 189 rooms, from £125.

Metro Bar & Grill £35
73 Cornwall St B3 2DF   (0121) 200 1911
A *"lively"* modern city-centre brasserie, that offers *"good"* cooking by Brummie standards; never less than *"pleasant"*, it's particularly popular for business. / **Sample dishes:** deep-fried squid with peanut butter & mango salsa; minted lamb with summer vegetables; apricot & nectarine crumble. **Details:** www.metrobarandgrill.co.uk; 9.30 pm; closed Sun.

Le Petit Blanc £30
9 Brindleyplace B1 2HS   (0121) 633 7333
Raymond Blanc is one of the UK's leading chefs, and it's very disappointing that he allows his name to be attached to this *"average"* (at best) modern brasserie; the new (Loch Fyne) régime is at best no improvement on the old. / **Sample dishes:** smoked chicken & chilli linguine; Thai-baked sea bass with coriander rice; sticky toffee pudding. **Details:** www.lepetitblanc.co.uk; 11 pm; no smoking.

Rajdoot £31
78-79 George St B3 1PY   (0121) 236 1116
*"Delicate", "different" and "spicy" dishes make this city-centre
subcontinental a destination of growing interest for reporters.
/ Details: www.rajdoot.co.uk; 11.15 pm; closed Sat L & Sun L.*

San Carlo £40
4 Temple St B2 5BN   (0121) 633 0251
*This "packed" Italian has long been one of the hottest tickets in
the city-centre; it has been through ups and downs in the last few
years, but more recent reports speak in terms of "good value"
and "friendlier service". / Sample dishes: barbecue spare ribs; veal in
wine & mushroom sauce; coffee bean ice cream. Details: www.sancarlo.co.uk; near
St Philips Cathedral; 10.45 pm.*

Shimla Pinks £31 X
214 Broad St B15 1AY   (0121) 633 0366
*This large and "trendy" subcontinental was once a major
'destination'; nowadays, however, all aspects of its operation strike
reporters as "too average". / Details: www.shimlapinks.com; 11 pm; closed
Sat L & Sun L.*

Simpson's £45
20 Highfield Rd B15 3DX   (0121) 454 3434
*When Andreas Antona's restaurant was in Kenilworth, some
reporters acclaimed his food as "the best in the Midlands" – let's
hope it's survived the transition to these grand new Edgbaston
premises, which opened in October 2004.
/ Details: www.simpsonsrestaurant.co.uk; 9.45 pm; no smoking.*

Thai Edge £34
7 Brindleyplace B1 2HS   (0121) 643 3993
*Fans still say you get "the best Thai food in the area by far", at
this large city-centre spot; the results it achieves, though, can be
"mixed". / Details: 11 pm, Fri & Sat 11.30 pm.*

La Toque d'Or £39 ★
27 Warstone Ln B18 6JQ   (0121) 233 3655
*Didier Philipot's "honest" Gallic cooking at "reasonable prices"
continues to win acclaim for this "small" (and "cramped")
venture, in a converted mill in the Jewellery Quarter.
/ Sample dishes: rainbow trout with lemon dressing; marinated lamb with
vegetables; vanilla crème brûlée. Details: www.latoquedor.co.uk; 9.30 pm; closed
Mon, Sat L & Sun; closed 2 weeks in Aug.*

BISHOPS STORTFORD, HERTFORDSHIRE 3–2B

The Lemon Tree £37
14-16 Water Ln CM23 2LB   (01279) 757788
*In a town without many gastronomic attractions, this pleasant
bistro has made something of a name – while it's "a favourite" for
some reporters, however, it strikes others as "uninteresting".
/ Sample dishes: cured salmon with avocado salsa; roast salmon with asparagus;
rhubarb & apple sponge. Details: www.lemontree.co.uk; 9.30 pm; closed Mon &
Sun D; no Amex; no smoking.*

BISHOPS TACHBROOK, WARWICKSHIRE   5–4C

Mallory Court   £ 63   𝔸★★
Harbury Ln CV33 9QB   (01926) 330214
"A sparkling jewel in the general mediocrity of the Midlands" –
this Lutyens-designed country house is emerging as a truly notable
destination, thanks to its *"utterly relaxing"* ambience and its
"unpretentious" service plus – not least – Simon Haigh's *"perfect"*
cooking. / **Sample dishes:** goats cheese ravioli with caramelised walnuts; sea bass
with tarragon mousse; raspberry soufflé. **Details:** www.mallory.co.uk; 2m S of
Leamington Spa, off B4087; 9.30 pm; no smoking; children: 9+.
Accommodation: 29 rooms, from £155.

BISPHAM GREEN, LANCASHIRE   5–1A

Eagle & Child   £ 29
Maltkiln Ln L40 3SG   (01257) 462297
A *"cosy"* country pub, whose popularity makes for a *"hectic"*
atmosphere at weekends; a *"friendly"* and *"professional"*
operation, it inspires consistently positive reports.
/ **Sample dishes:** deep-fried goats cheese; toasted chicken & red pepper panini;
sticky toffee pudding. **Details:** M6, J27; 8.30 pm; no Amex; no smoking area.

BLACKPOOL, LANCASHIRE   5–1A

Kwizeen   £ 26
47-49 King St FY1 3EJ (01253) 290045
Feedback is still limited, but the cooking at this inexpensive
"modern" bistro wins consistent praise from those reporters who
comment on it. / **Sample dishes:** wild mushroom soup with rosemary
shortbread; glazed duck breast with plum & blackberry sauce; vanilla panna cotta
with strawberries. **Details:** www.kwizeen.co.uk; 9 pm; closed Sat L & Sun; no Amex.

September Brasserie   £ 33
15-17 Queen St FY1 1PU   (01253) 623282
"A great find" – this *"tiny"* first-floor establishment generated
more consistent feedback this year for its *"good food,
professionally prepared and served"*. / **Sample dishes:** pumpkin & goats
cheese soufflé; braised pork knuckle; sticky date pudding.
Details: www.septemberbrasserie.co.uk; just past North Pier, opp Cenotaph;
9.30 pm; closed Mon & Sun.

BLAIRGOWRIE, PERTH & KINROSS   9–3C

Kinloch House   £ 46
PH10 6SG   (01250) 884237
A few reporters highly rate this grand, 19th-century country house
hotel; feedback remains thin on the ground, though, and one
reporter shares our intuition that *"given its acquisition by the Allen
family, late of the Airds Hotel, Port Appin, one would expect more
of the place"*. / **Sample dishes:** wild mushroom, chicken & sweetbread terrine;
fillet steak with Lanark Blue cheese; chocolate truffle cake with mint cream.
Details: www.kinlochhouse.com; 9 pm; jacket & tie required; no smoking; children:
7+ at D. **Accommodation:** 18 rooms, from £120.

BLAKENEY, NORFOLK   6–3C

The White Horse Hotel   £ 37
4 High St NR25 7AL   (01263) 740574
*"A genuine operation that rarely fails to please", this "traditional"
hotel – which has a great location overlooking the sea – won
more consistent praise this year for its "ambitious" and "tasty"
fare.* / **Sample dishes:** smoked cod, leek & Parmesan tartlet; roast black bream
with chilli & fennel dressing; chocolate mousse.
Details: www.blakeneywhitehorse.co.uk; 9 pm; D only, closed Mon; no Amex;
no smoking; children: 6+. **Accommodation:** 10 rooms, from £60.

BOLTON ABBEY, NORTH YORKSHIRE   8–4B

Devonshire Arms   £ 71
BD23 6AJ   (01756) 710441
*This grand (ducal) inn has quite a reputation, but its prices are
such that it really shouldn't attract gripes about "miniscule"
portions (in Yorkshire!) or "disinterested" service; the wine list,
though, is "fascinating".* / **Sample dishes:** goose, mango & smoked foie gras
salad; roast cod with fennel & olive sauce; chocolate & Turkish Delight soufflé.
Details: www.devonshirehotels.co.uk; on A59, 5m NE of Skipton; 9.30 pm; closed
Mon, Tue-Sat D only, Sun open L & D; no jeans; no smoking. **Accommodation:** 41
rooms, from £220.

BOSTON SPA, WEST YORKSHIRE   5–1C

Spice Box   £ 31
152 High St LS23 6BW   (01937) 842558
*"Homely, and not too expensive", this modern brasserie is an
ever-popular local stand-by.* / **Sample dishes:** fishcakes with Thai sauce;
duck with bacon & thyme potatoes; chocolate truffle. **Details:** www.spicebox.com;
2m E of A1, on A659; 9.30 pm; closed Mon & Sun D; no smoking.

BOUGHTON LEES, KENT   3–3C

Eastwell Manor   £ 50   Ⓐ
Eastwell Pk TN25 4HR   (01233) 213000
*Standards at this pretty Victorian country house hotel "have
fluctuated over the years" (unsurprisingly, as Marston Hotels have
both won and lost the management contract in recent times); it's
a "comfortable" place, though, and reports are rarely less than
satisfactory.* / **Sample dishes:** white bean soup with langoustine & truffles;
chicken supreme with mustard cream sauce; apple & rhubarb crumble.
Details: www.eastwellmanor.co.uk; 3m N of Ashford on A251; 9.30 pm; jacket &
tie required; no smoking; booking: max 8. **Accommodation:** 62 rooms, from £190.

BOURNEMOUTH, DORSET   2–4C

Bistro on the Beach   £ 33   Ⓐ
Solent Promenade BH6 4BE   (01202) 431473
*By day a beach café, by night this simple venue – with its
"brilliant" location (at the foot of the cliffs in Southbourne) – is
famed locally as "a great fresh fish café"; there's a growing
feeling, though, that it "could do better".* / **Sample dishes:** smoked
salmon & prawn terrine; braised lamb with mint mash; bread & butter pudding.
Details: www.bistroonthebeach.com; 2m E of town centre in Southbourne; 9.30 pm;
D only, closed Sun-Tue; no smoking.

Chez Fred   £16   ★★
10 Seamoor Rd BH4 9AN   (01202) 761023
You get "an excellent meal for under a tenner", at this brilliant long-established chippie, in Westbourne. / Sample dishes: no starters; cod & chips with mushy peas; treacle sponge & custard.
Details: *www.chezfred.co.uk; 1m W of town centre; 9.45 pm; closed Sun L; no Amex; no smoking; no booking.*

Mandarin   £26
194-198 Old Christchurch Rd BH1 1PD   (01202) 290681
A "favourite" town-centre Chinese, offering "good food in a nice atmosphere". / Details: www.themandarin.net; 11 pm; no smoking.

Ocean Palace   £31   ★
8 Priory Rd BH2 5DG   (01202) 559127
"Extremely good and reliable chow, with a bit more imagination than most" – plus "very friendly" service – has long made this veteran Chinese, a short walk from the pier, a "popular" destination; indeed, it can get very "crowded".
/ Sample dishes: deep-fried chicken in chilli sauce; crispy aromatic duck with pancakes, banana fritters. Details: www.oceanpalace.co.uk; 11 pm.

West Beach   £36   Ⓐ
Pier Approach BH2 5AA   (01202) 587785
"Watching the waves break on the beach" sets the tone at this "modern and trendy" seaside venture; locals say it's becoming the top place in the area, due to its "imaginative" and "ever-changing" menu, on which fish is the speciality. / Details: 10 pm; no smoking area.

BOWNESS, CUMBRIA   7–3D

Linthwaite House   £32   Ⓐ★
LA23 3JA   (01539) 488600
Reporters wax lyrical about this "comfortable", "relaxing" and "romantic" country house hotel, which comes complete with impressive views of Lake Windermere; the food is "fantastic", too, and "beautifully presented". / Details: www.linthwaite.com; 9 pm; children: 7+ after 7 pm. Accommodation: 26 rooms, from £125.

Miller Howe   £56
Rayrigg Rd LA23 1EY   (01539) 442536
Even some reporters who feel the food at this once-famous Lakeland dining room is "not as good as the view", think it a "sophisticated" venue – it continues to be commended "for romance". / Sample dishes: warm chicken liver salad; roast halibut with sage mash; sticky toffee pudding & toffee sauce. Details: www.millerhowe.com; on A592 between Windermere & Bowness; 8 pm; closed for 2 weeks in Jan; no smoking; children: 8+. Accommodation: 15 rooms, from £160.

Porthole   £40
3 Ash St LA23 3EB   (01539) 442793
This celebrated Italian restaurant of over 30 years' standing has recently been bought by its chef and its sommelier – most reports suggest a smooth transition, but, in these early days, we've felt it best to leave the place un-rated. / Sample dishes: antipasto; veal with mushrooms; sticky toffee pudding. Details: www.porthole.fsworld.co.uk; near Old England Hotel; 10 pm; closed Mon L & Tue, Wed-Sat D only; no smoking.

BRADFORD ON AVON, WILTSHIRE 3–3B

Thai Barn £35 ★
24 Bridge St BA15 1BY (01225) 866443
"Other restaurants are cheaper, but you just can't match the flavours at the Barn" – this "unexpected" and "consistent" oriental "gem" is very popular locally and, and it can get rather "crowded". / Sample dishes: royal platter; sauté pork, pineapple, onion, cucumber & tomato in sweet & sour sauce; pineapple ice cream. Details: opp Bridge St car park; 10.30 pm; closed Mon & Tue L; no Amex; no smoking area.

BRADFORD, WEST YORKSHIRE 5–1C

Aagrah £22 ★
483 Bradford Rd LS28 8ED (01274) 668818
Even in "England's curry capital", the "consistently good and imaginative food" at this outlet of the outstanding local chain is well worth seeking out. / Details: www.aagrah.com; on A647, 3m from city centre; 11.30 pm, Fri & Sat midnight; D only; no smoking area.

Akbar's Balti £18 ★
1276 Leeds Rd BD3 3LF (01274) 773311
"Lively", "friendly" and very popular, this "amazing value" subcontinental remains "an 'institution', of the best kind"; it offers everything from "bog-standard curries to more esoteric dishes". / Details: www.akbars.co.uk; midnight; D only; no smoking area.

Clark's £26
46-50 Highgate BD9 4BE (01274) 499890
"Especially for the early-bird menu", this "crowded" brasserie remains "very popular"; reports on the cooking were mixed this year, but on any analysis the place at least offers an alternative to curry. / Sample dishes: pea & mint soup; bacon chop with Cheddar mash & parsley sauce; treacle tart. Details: www.clarksrestaurant.co.uk; 5 mins from city centre on A650 to Shipley; 9.30 pm; closed Sat L; no smoking area.

Karachi £8 ★
15-17 Neal St BD5 0BX (01274) 732015
"Super tastes" continue to feature in reports on this "wonderful", "fantastic-value" curry house – there's been "no compromise in quality here for over 30 years". / Details: 1 am, Fri & Sat 2 am; no credit cards.

Kashmir £10 ★
27 Morley St BD7 1AG (01274) 726513
"It's impossible to spend much", at this "basic", "no-frills" veteran – the oldest Indian in town and fans say still "the best and most reliable". / Details: 3 am; no Amex; no smoking area.

Love Apple Cafe £18 Ⓐ★
34 Great Horton Rd BD7 1AL (01274) 744075
"Great main meals if you're hungry, plus a wide variety of snacks when you want something lighter" – this "friendly" all-day café is "much patronised by students, and by academic staff". / Sample dishes: nachos; chana massala with fresh tomatoes & coriander; chocolate truffle cheesecake served with cream & ice cream. Details: www.loveapplecafe.co.uk; 9 pm; no smoking area.

Mumtaz Paan House £21 ★★

Great Horton Rd BD7 3HS (01274) 571861
*"Revamped, enlarged and still excellent" – this "remarkable"
subcontinental "institution" has emerged pretty much unscathed
from its "OTT" ("steel, glass and marble") revamp, and still offers
"brilliant" ("hot") curries in a "strictly Muslim, no-alcohol"
environment. / Sample dishes: spiced chicken & sweetcorn in pastry; spiced cod
with pomegranate; mango ice cream. Details: www.mumtaz.co.uk; midnight, Fri &
Sat 1 am; no smoking area.*

Nawaab £24 ★

32 Manor Rw BD1 4QE (01274) 720371
*This eminent Indian has more "the feel of a real restaurant" than
some local competitors, and offers high standards all round.
/ Details: www.nawaab.co.uk; 11.30 pm; D only; no smoking area.*

BRANCASTER, NORFOLK 6–3B

White Horse £35

Main Rd PE31 8BY (01485) 210262
*"A jewel in North Norfolk", this "friendly" inn offers "huge
portions of fresh local fish"; its terrace has "great views".
/ Sample dishes: salmon & crab fishcakes, roast beetroot salad, lime créme fraiche;
pan-fried skate wing with capers; strawberry shortbread.
Details: www.whitehorsebrancaster.co.uk; 9 pm; no Amex; no smoking.
Accommodation: 15 rooms, from £84.*

BRANSCOMBE, DEVON 2–4A

Masons Arms £33

Main St EX12 3DJ (01297) 680300
*For most reporters, this is a "delightful", "real" pub with "cooking
to match"; doubters, however, find it "OK, but nothing special".
/ Sample dishes: smoked duck with pineapple pickle; grilled plaice with garlic &
prawns; chocolate truffle torte. Details: www.masonsarms.co.uk; 9 pm; D only,
closed Mon & Sun; no Amex; no smoking. Accommodation: 25 rooms, from £50.*

BRAY, WINDSOR & MAIDENHEAD 3–3A

The Fat Duck £78 ★

1 High St SL6 2AQ (01628) 580333
*Heston Blumenthal's "witty" molecular gastronomy does "mind-
blowing things to your taste-buds", and is nominated by many
reporters as "the most exciting cooking in the UK"; service can be
"joyless", though, and detractors (about one reporter in six) think
his cuisine "silly" or "ridiculously pricey". / Sample dishes: cuttlefish
cannelloni with duck & maple syrup; slow-cooked lamb with lambs tongue & onion
purée; tarte Tatin with bay leaf & almond foam. Details: www.fatduck.co.uk;
9.30 pm, Fri & Sat 10 pm; closed Mon & Sun D; closed 2 weeks at New Year;
no smoking.*

Jasmine Oriental £37 ★

Old Mill Ln SL6 2BG (01628) 788999
*This "elegant" new oriental has quickly been acknowledged as
"the best Chinese restaurant in the area", with "friendly" service
and "excellent" food; expansion is scheduled for 2005.
/ Details: 10.30 pm; no Amex.*

sign up for the survey at www.hardens.com 159

Riverside Brasserie　　　£ 42　　★
Monkey Island Ln, Bray Marina
SL6 2EB　(01628) 780553
*"We approached an unprepossessing shed, unaware of its
distinguished connections, to find very good food, and competent
and helpful service"* – one report says it all about this quirky,
"hard-to-find" riverside location; it was in fact sold by Heston
Blumenthal as this guide went to press, but chef Garrey Dylan
Dawson remains.* / **Sample dishes:** sardine tart; rib-eye steak & chips with
marrowbone sauce; strawberry soup with butter biscuits.*
Details: *www.riversidebrasserie.co.uk; follow signs for Bray Marina off A308;
10 pm; closed Mon & Sun D; no Amex.*

Waterside Inn　　　£116　　🅐★★
Ferry Rd　SL6 2AT　(01628) 620691
*Michel Roux's "idyllic" watersider is going from strength-to-
strength under his son Alain, and has an ever-stronger claim to
being "the best restaurant in England"; practically all of the many
reports recount "fairytale" experiences, with "fantastic" modern
cuisine delivered by "friendly" staff who "anticipate, without over-
doing it".* / **Sample dishes:** spiced foie gras terrine with poached figs; grilled
rabbit with glazed chestnuts; golden plum soufflé. **Details:** www.waterside-inn.co.uk;
off A308 between Windsor & Maidenhead; 10 pm; closed Mon & Tue (open Tue D
Jun-Aug); booking: max 10; children: 12+. **Accommodation:** 9 rooms, from £160.*

BREARTON, NORTH YORKSHIRE　　　8–4B

The Malt Shovel　　　£ 22
HG3 3BX　(01423) 862929
"Hopefully the standards will be maintained by the new owners"
– this popular boozer (in a former barn) was sold shortly before
this guide went to press (hence we've removed its ratings).
*/ **Sample dishes:** goats cheese & leek tart; steak & ale pie; treacle tart.
Details: off A61, 6m N of Harrogate; 9 pm; closed Mon & Sun D; no credit cards;
no smoking area; no booking.*

BRECON, POWYS　　　2–1A

Felin Fach Griffin　　　£ 40　　🅐★
Felin Fach　LD3 0UB　(01874) 620111
*The "huge secret" is now pretty much out about this "ultimate
gastropub", outside Brecon; "an oasis in a gastronomic desert", it
serves "great", "locally sourced" food in a "chilled" and
"characterful" setting. / **Sample dishes:** wild mushroom tagliatelli; rib of
welsh black beef with chips; lemon tart. **Details:** www.eatdrinksleep.ltd.uk; 20 mins
NW of Abergavenny on A470; 9.30 pm; closed Mon L; no Amex; no smoking at D.
Accommodation: 7 rooms, from £92.50.*

BRIDGWATER, SOMERSET　　　2–3A

The Hood Arms　　　£ 29
TA5 1EA　(01278) 741210
*There's nothing fancy about the cuisine at this traditionally-styled
17th-century inn; it's strongly tipped, though, for its "good-quality"
food at "reasonable prices". / **Details:** www.thehoodarms.co.uk; 9.30 pm;
no smoking. **Accommodation:** 12 rooms, from £65.*

BRIDPORT, DORSET   2–4B
Riverside   £ 35   ★★
West Bay DT6 4EZ (01308) 422011
"Always full, and no wonder"; "exquisite fresh fish, with a hint of France" helps make this *"simple"* and *"unpretentious"* operation – now coming up to its 40th year – *"the South West's best coastal restaurant"*, for some reporters. / **Sample dishes:** warm oysters with laver bread; halibut with rarebit topping; Limoncello panna cotta. **Details:** 9 pm; closed Mon & Sun D; no Amex; no smoking.

BRIGHTON, EAST SUSSEX   3–4B

It could only be a matter of time, and 'London by the Sea' really is at last beginning in some positive ways to mimic the restaurant scene of the metropolis, offering some pretty decent dining options at most levels.

At the middle level, there are now some restaurants of real note, including the new *Due South*, *The Saint* and *Strand*. *Terre à Terre* heads up a large veggie contingent and is now re-established as probably the best restaurant of that type in the country. For quintessential seaside seafood, the *Regency* remains hard to beat.

Diners on a budget (in particular) benefit from a good range of reasonably-priced ethnic restaurants, often of good quality.

Following a change of ownership, we've unfortunately not been able to award any rating to what's traditionally regarded as the top restaurant in these parts, *One Paston Place*.

Al Duomo   £ 24
7 Pavilion Building BN1 1EE (01273) 326741
Even some who feel it has "rather less charm since the recent renovation" say that this long-established Italian, near the Royal Pavilion, confounds its tourist trap potential; its *"good and inexpensive"* pizza is generally praised. / **Sample dishes:** calamari; fusilli with tomatoes & anchovies; tiramisu. **Details:** www.alduomo.co.uk; near the Royal Pavilion; 11 pm; no smoking area.

Blanch House   £ 48   X
17 Atlingworth St BN2 1PL (01273) 645755
"Style but no substance"; this Kemptown-fringe design hotel has a *"super bar"*, but its dining rooms attracts much flak from reporters for *"mingy"* portions and *"overpricing"*.
/ **Sample dishes:** celeriac ravioli with goats cheese; juniper-crusted lamb with ratatouille & rosemary polenta; pink peppercorn meringue with strawberries. **Details:** www.blanchhouse.co.uk; 10.30 pm; closed Mon, Tue L & Sun. **Accommodation:** 12 rooms, from £100.

Bombay Aloo   £ 13   ★
39 Ship St BN1 1AB (01273) 771089
You get "a pukka curry for under a fiver" at this *"simple and efficient"*, buffet-style veggie. / **Details:** www.bombay-aloo.co.uk; near the Lanes; midnight; no Amex; no smoking area; need 6+ to book; children: under 5s eat free.

Casa Don Carlos   £ 27   ★
5 Union St BN1 1HA (01273) 327177
"Very fresh" tapas makes it worth remembering this *"authentic"* and *"inexpensive"* bar in the Lanes; it is *"cramped"*, but otherwise reporters think it's just *"great"*. / **Details:** 11 pm.

China Garden £30 ★
88-91 Preston St BN1 2HG (01273) 325124
As ever, "excellent dim sum" is the highlight at this "great, cheap and cheerful canteen", which is popular with "Asians, students and those needing a post-pub refill". / **Details:** *opp West Pier; 11 pm; no smoking area.*

Donatello £30
1-3 Brighton Pl BN1 1HJ (01273) 775477
"Fast" and sometimes furiously-packed, this Lanes Italian offers "acceptable (only)" scoff; convenience and "reasonable prices", however, underpin a very high level of custom. / **Sample dishes:** *grilled sardines; tagliatelle with smoked salmon & cream; cherries in liqueur with ice cream.* **Details:** *www.donatello.co.uk; 11.30 pm; no smoking area.*

The Dorset Street Bar £28 Ⓐ
28 North Rd BN1 1YB (01273) 605423
A "Sunday morning favourite" sort of place, this North Laine ex-boozer is now a popular all-day café, perfect for brunch. / **Sample dishes:** *salmon fishcakes; grilled chicken with salami & Camembert; chocolate brioche.* **Details:** *www.thedorset.co.uk; 10 pm; no smoking area; booking: max 12.*

Due South £33 Ⓐ★★
139 King's Arches BN1 2FN
(01273) 821218

"A really encouraging newcomer", this "wonderful" establishment ("quirkily" built into "intimate" arches "under the seafront", and with a "nice terrace too") is resoundingly praised by reporters for its "expertly-cooked" dishes, "using local produce". / **Sample dishes:** *pan-fried red mullet fillets with lemon pickle; fish of the day with garlic, lemon and thyme; elderflower and vanilla panna cotta with gooseberry compote.* **Details:** *www.duesouth.co.uk; 10 pm; no smoking.*

English's £38
29-31 East St BN1 1HL (01273) 327980
Standards are again under pressure at this "cramped" fish restaurant – a Lanes fixture for 150 years – where too many "poor" meals were reported this year; if you decide to chance it, try to sit outside, and choose the simplest dishes. / **Sample dishes:** *avocado, feta & nectarine salad; Dover sole & prawns with sorrel & lobster sauce; apple Bakewell tart.* **Details:** *www.englishs.co.uk; 10 pm; no smoking area.*

Food for Friends £22
17-18 Prince Albert St BN1 1HF (01273) 202310
The changed format (expansion, plus waitress-service) had led to mixed reports on this long-established Lanes veggie, though its "good" food still generally finds favour. / **Sample dishes:** *Jerusalem artichoke soup; Cheddar & mushroom risotto with spicy tomato sauce; Bramley & blackberry crumble.* **Details:** *www.foodforfriends.com; 10 pm; no smoking area.*

La Fourchette £37
105 Western Rd BN1 2AA (01273) 722556
For fans, this recently re-located Gallic bistro is "Brighton's best place", and it's usually "busy"; up-and-down reports, though, tend to support those who find its performance "variable". / **Sample dishes:** *spinach, asparagus & Mozzarella lasagne; confit duck with mash & veal sauce; citron tart.* **Details:** *www.lafourchette.co.uk; 10.30 pm; closed Sun D.* **Accommodation:** *8 rooms, from £70.*

The George £20 𝔸★
5 Trafalgar St BN1 4EQ (01273) 681055
"Inexpensive", "tasty" and "filling" veggie grub, "good beer", a
"great buzz" and a "funky feel" – it's no wonder that this North
Laine boozer is a popular perennial. / **Sample dishes:** tomato &
Mozzarella bruschetta; smoked Applewood rarebit with leeks & salsa; tarte Tatin.
Details: 9.30 pm, Fri-Sun 8.30 pm; no smoking area; children: before 7.30 pm only.

Gingerman £36 ★
21a Norfolk Square BN1 2PD (01273) 326688
Ben McKellar's small Lanes fixture has a disproportionately large
following (and can therefore get "rather cramped and noisy"); the
draw is his "precise" and "thoughtful" cuisine, and at "good-
value" prices, too. / **Sample dishes:** beetroot & anchovy salad; swordfish with
plum tomato tart; passion fruit soufflé. **Details:** off Norfolk Square; 10 pm; closed
Mon & Sun; no smoking.

Harry's £25
41 Church Rd BN3 2BE (01273) 727410
"Good British fare" – with breakfasts of course a leading
attraction – helps make this Hove diner a popular destination
(and a "child-friendly" one, too); "great burgers" – and not just
beef – are a highpoint. / **Sample dishes:** prawn cocktail; cheese & chilli
burger; banoffi pie. **Details:** www.harrysrestaurant.co.uk; 10.30 pm.

Havana £45 𝔸
32 Duke St BN1 1AG (01273) 773388
It's a shame this "beautiful", spacious Lanes venture can seem
"overpriced" (and a touch "pretentious"), as the majority view is
that it's "a real gem", with "good" food and "very friendly"
service. / **Sample dishes:** haddock & poached egg tartlet; roast venison; Baileys
parfait with biscuits. **Details:** www.havana.uk.com; 10.30 pm; no trainers;
no smoking area; children: 6+ at D.

Hotel du Vin et Bistro £38 𝔸
Ship St BN1 1AD (01273) 718588
"Just what central Brighton has been crying out for" – seaside
diners now avail themselves of the "fun", "bustling bistro" style
which is the hallmark of this well-known boutique-hotel chain; as
usual, the "novel-like" wine list rather eclipses the cooking.
/ **Sample dishes:** moules marinière; duck with apple & foie gras; chocolate tart.
Details: www.hotelduvin.com; 9.45 pm; no smoking; booking: max 10.
Accommodation: 37 rooms, from £125.

Indian Summer £31 ★
69 East St BN1 1HQ (01273) 711001
"Well-presented cuisine, with a twist" is what this "interesting"
establishment is all about – "it's definitely not your regular curry
house". / **Details:** www.indian-summer.org.uk; 10.15 pm; closed Mon L.

One Paston Place £53
1 Paston Pl BN2 1HA (01273) 606933
In early-2004, this eminent Kemptown townhouse-restaurant
changed hands, though new chef Francesco Furriello maintains
the grand Gallic style of his predecessor; reports were unsettled in
this period of transition, so we've left it unrated.
/ **Sample dishes:** skate stuffed with potted shrimps & fennel; duck with balsamic
jus & butternut squash; caramel soufflé. **Details:** www.onepastonplace.co.uk;
between the pier & marina; 10 pm; closed Mon & Sun; booking: max 10; children:
no babies.

Regency £ 20 ★
131 Kings Rd BN1 2HH (01273) 325014
"Good fish and seafood, reasonable prices and a seafront position" make a *"rare combination"* that has helped this *"pleasant"* and *"reliable"* chippie become something of *"a Brighton institution"*; it's *"a great place to take the kids"*.
/ **Sample dishes:** oysters; dressed crab salad; peach Melba.
Details: www.theregencyrestaurant.co.uk; opp West Pier; 11 pm; no smoking area.
Accommodation: 30 rooms, from £65.

The Saint £ 34 ★
22 St James's St BN2 1RF (01273) 607835
"Imaginative dishes, well presented" (and a *"good wine list"*, too) maintain the popularity of this Kemptown spot; *"for a romantic meal, choose one of the intimate booths at the back"*.
/ **Sample dishes:** antipasti; roast duck with courgette cakes & liquorice sauce; trio of brûlées. **Details:** www.thesaintrestaurant.com; 10 pm; closed Mon.

Sanctuary Café £ 21 A
51-55 Brunswick Street East BN3 1AU (01273) 770002
A *"funky"* Brunswick café, which fans hail for its *"great, healthy food"* (and *"the best coffee in Brighton"*). / **Sample dishes:** vegetarian pâté with pitta bread; aubergine lasagne; carrot cake.
Details: www.sanctuarycafe.co.uk; 10 pm; no Amex; no smoking area.

Saucy £ 30
8 Church Rd BN3 2FL (01273) 324080
The cooking can be *"very good"* at this *"fun, cheap and cheerful"* Hove brasserie – pity about the *"terrible"* service.
/ **Sample dishes:** crayfish tails with linguine; beef with smoked anchovy tapenade; banana & butterscotch steamed pudding. **Details:** 10.30 pm; closed Sun D; no smoking area; booking: max 6, Fri & Sat.

Seven Dials £ 37
1-3 Buckingham Pl BN1 3TD (01273) 885555
A *"quirky"* venture, by a *"busy"* roundabout, praised for its *"above-average"* Gallic fare; up-and-down reports, though, support those who say it's *"temperamental"*. / **Sample dishes:** herb-crusted goats cheese salad; stuffed quail with pancetta & truffle jus; lavender panna cotta.
Details: www.sevendialsrestaurant.co.uk; 10.30 pm; closed Mon; no smoking area.

Strand £ 28 A ★
6 Little East St BN1 1HT (01273) 747096
"Book in advance", for the *"lovely food and wine"* on offer at this *"charming"* small restaurant, just off the seafront – prices are *"reasonable"*, and the ambience is quite *"romantic"*, too.
/ **Sample dishes:** Dolcelatte gnocchi; Thai fish wrapped in leeks; banana cream pie with honeycomb ice cream. **Details:** www.thestrandrestaurantbrighton.co.uk; 10 pm, Fri & Sat 10.30 pm; closed Mon L; booking: max 8, Fri & Sat.

Terre à Terre £ 37 ★★
71 East St BN1 1HQ (01273) 729051
"If all vegetarian restaurants were this good, we'd all be veggies", says one of the many fans of this *"ambitious"*, *"imaginative"* and *"friendly"* Lanes venture, which remains arguably the UK's best of its type. / **Sample dishes:** fried corn cakes with salsa; asparagus pasta parcel with sun-dried tomato pesto; rhubarb & rosehip sorbet.
Details: www.terreaterre.co.uk; 10.30 pm; closed Mon, Tue L & Wed L; no smoking; booking: max 8 at weekends.

BRIMFIELD, SHROPSHIRE   5–4A
The Roebuck Inn   £ 35
SY8 4NE   (01584) 711230
Under new ownership, this handsome pub (near Ludlow) is still generally approved for its "locally-sourced food, well cooked and in generous portions". / **Sample dishes:** gin-soused salmon with dill crème fraiche; steak & mushroom suet pudding with ale gravy; pear, rhubarb & ginger charlotte. **Details:** www.roebuckinn.com; 9.30 pm; no Amex; no smoking. **Accommodation:** 3 rooms, from £70.

BRINKWORTH, WILTSHIRE   2–2C
The Three Crowns   £ 32
The Street SN15 5AF   (01666) 510366
"Get there early", if you want to enjoy the "rich and unusual" menu on offer at this popular gastropub – "its no-booking policy and the dearth of places round Swindon make queues an ever-present risk". / **Sample dishes:** grilled kangaroo, venison & ostrich with vegetables; sticky toffee pudding. **Details:** www.threecrowns.co.uk; 9.30 pm; no smoking area; no booking.

BRISTOL, CITY OF BRISTOL   2–2B

For such a pleasant and affluent city, Bristol is surprisingly short of restaurant 'heavy hitters'. The opening of *Michael Caines* at the Royal Marriott helps fill this gap, despite a mixed reception.

Many of the city's best-known places are good-looking but culinarily undistinguished – both in the city centre (*Hotel du Vin*) and on the waterfront of the old docks (for example *riverstation* and *Severnshed*). Well-heeled Clifton has many places to go out, but, oddly, no outstanding destinations. All this may change if Stephen Markwick (who used to run the town's top dining room) is successful in his transformation of the premises that used to be Red Snapper into *Culinaria*.

Aqua   £ 29
Welsh Back BS1 4RR   (0117) 915 6060
"Busy, lively and fun", this bright and airy bar/restaurant makes a popular (and "reliable") destination for most (but not quite all) reporters; "beware the quantity of the puddings". / **Details:** www.aquarestaurant.com; 10.30 pm; no smoking.

Bell's Diner   £ 40   Ⓐ
1 York Rd BS6 5QB   (0117) 924 0357
This "casual" Montpelier "favourite" has long been known as "a cosy, candlelit venue, with an interesting and ever-changing menu"; the occasional reporter has found recent visits "disappointing", but to loyal fans (and there are many) the place "can't be faulted". / **Sample dishes:** braised octopus with black pudding; monkfish, saffron & broad bean risotto; Muscat jelly with Granny Smith sorbet. **Details:** www.bellsdiner.co.uk; 10 pm; closed Mon L, Sat L & Sun D; no smoking.

Bocanova   £ 38   Ⓐ
90 Colston St BS1 5BB   (0117) 929 1538
"Off the beaten track, but well worth finding"; this "slightly chaotic" – but "friendly" and "fun" – joint serves up cooking ("now more International than Brazilian") that's "always good". / **Sample dishes:** goats cheese salad with raspberry dressing; salmon with prawn & lime leaf sauce; panna cotta with plums & whisky syrup. **Details:** 10.30 pm, Fri & Sat 11 pm; closed Sun; no Amex; no smoking.

Boston Tea Party £20 Ⓐ
75 Park St BS1 5PF (0117) 929 8601
"The best coffee in the UK" and a "perfect" courtyard-garden help make this popular café a top local "hang-out" (in particular for brunch); the grub can be "variable", though, at worst like "a catering van at a hippy festival"; (it now has five spin offs across the West Country). / **Sample dishes:** *carrot & coriander soup; Spanish chicken; rum & raisin cheesecake.* **Details:** *10 pm, Sun 7 pm; closed Mon D & Sun D; no smoking; no booking.*

Budokan £23
Clifton Down, Whiteladies Rd BS8 2PH (0117) 949 3030
For "a cheap and tasty mixture of Asian street-foods" – "fantastic value for sushi, noodles and so on" – it's worth a visit to these wooden-benched noodle canteens (also at 31 Colston Street, tel 08708 377300); the lunchtime 'Rapid Refuel' once again attracts special mention. / **Sample dishes:** *Thai fish cakes; chicken ho fun noodles; mango sorbet.* **Details:** *www.budokan.co.uk; 10.30 pm; closed Sun; no Amex.*

Byzantium £39 Ⓐ
2 Portwall Ln BS1 6NB (0117) 922 1883
"Fantastic location, but the food's not good value for money" – so the situation is just as usual, then, at this wonderfully lavish Moroccan venue, near Temple Meads. / **Sample dishes:** *crab, chilli & coriander tart; smoked lamb with Swiss chard gratin; chocolate & Grand Marnier mousse.* **Details:** *www.byzantium.co.uk; near Temple Meads, opp St Mary's Redcliffe church; 11 pm; D only, closed Sun (open for L in Dec); no smoking area.*

A Cozinha £32 ★
40 Alfred Pl BS2 8HD (0117) 944 3060
This "authentic", "neighbourhood" Portuguese is a bit of a rarity, and its "informal" charm makes it quite romantic; the food is "good", too (with an "amazing fish stew" a highlight).
/ **Sample dishes:** *salt cod & chick pea salad; Catalan pork, fish & seafood stew; honey & cinnamon cake.* **Details:** *8.30 pm, Fri & Sat 9.30 pm; L only Tue-Fri, open Sat D; no Amex; children: 14+ at D.*

Culinaria £38
1 Chandos Rd BS6 6PG (0117) 973 7999
Just as our survey was drawing to a close, Stephen Markwick – who for years had a swanky city-centre operation – opened this bistro in the premises formerly occupied by Red Snapper (RIP); given his past form, it will be surprising if, next year, this isn't rated Bristol's best restaurant! / **Details:** *www.culinariabristol.co.uk; 9.30 pm; closed Sun-Tue, Wed L & Thu L; no smoking.*

Fishers £31
35 Princess Victoria St BS8 4BX (0117) 974 7044
"The menu is rather dull, but it has a convenient location and isn't too expensive" – like the Oxford original, this "relaxed" and "friendly" suburban fish restaurant has its uses.
/ **Sample dishes:** *grilled sardines with parsley & lemon; beer-battered fish & chips; banana fritters with Amaretto ice cream.* **Details:** *www.fishers-restaurant.com; 10.30 pm; closed Mon L; no Amex; no smoking.*

FishWorks £ 40 ★
128 Whiteladies Rd BS8 2RS (0117) 974 4433
*"Eating in a fish shop is a bit odd, but the food is great", say fans
of the "amazingly fresh" dishes on offer at this well-known branch
of a growing mini-chain; even some enthusiasts, however, find it
"relatively pricey" for what it is. / Sample dishes: spaghetti with crab &
chilli; grilled plaice with black butter; lemon tart. Details: www.fishworks.co.uk;
10.30 pm; closed Mon & Sun; no smoking.*

The Glass Boat £ 40 X
Welsh Back BS1 4SB (0117) 929 0704
*The setting of this moored barge in the docks makes it potentially
"perfect for a romantic meal"; it's a shame, therefore, that the
food is so "variable" (to the point that the occasional reporter
finds it "horrendous"). / Sample dishes: goats cheese with radish & chive
salad; roast duck with duck spring rolls & mango; Szechuan-peppered crème brûlée.
Details: www.glassboat.co.uk; below Bristol Bridge; 9.30 pm; closed Sat L & Sun;
no smoking area.*

Hope & Anchor £ 22 Ⓐ
38 Jacobs Wells Rd BS8 1DR (0117) 929 2987
*A "cosy" and "traditional" boozer that's a favourite "oasis in the
heart of the city", and which offers "standard but tasty" scoff
(including "legendary roasts", "a fantastic ploughman's" and
"evilly addictive chips"); it also has a "lovely" garden.
/ Sample dishes: crayfish tail & anchovy salad; lamb & rosemary pie; sticky toffee
pudding & custard. Details: 10 pm; no booking.*

Hotel du Vin Et Bistro £ 39 Ⓐ
The Sugar House, Narrow Lewins Mead BS1 2NU
(0117) 925 5577
*A "comfortably informal" candlelit dining room, in a former
warehouse, where "sexy sofas" contribute to the "fun" and
"romantic" feel; the food is "unadventurous", though, and notably
outclassed by the "extensive" and "interesting" wine list.
/ Sample dishes: gravadlax with citrus oil; braised lamb shank with olive jus;
banana tarte Tatin. Details: www.hotelduvin.com; 9.45 pm; no smoking; booking:
max 10. Accommodation: 40 rooms, from £130.*

Howards £ 34
1a-2a, Avon Cr BS1 6XQ (0117) 926 2921
*Maybe it has never set the Severn aflame, but this "intimate"
Hotwells veteran consistently pleases reporters with its "good food
and service"; (it changed hands in 2004, but the chef remained
the same). / Sample dishes: chicken, asparagus & leek terrine; seafood
tagliatelle; lemon meringue pie. Details: 11 pm; no smoking area.*

Michael Caines
The Royal Marriott Bristol £ 53
College Grn BS1 5TA (0117) 910 5309
*Many reporters say it offers "by far Bristol's best food", but the
second spin-off restaurant from the famous Gidleigh Park chef
inspires very mixed views — it's an "austere" sort of grand hotel
dining room which quite a few reporters found "didn't live up to
expectations". / Sample dishes: salad of Cornish lobster with Parmesan; turbot
with cannelloni of scallops; raspberry parfait with vanilla mousse.
Details: www.michaelcaines.com; 10 pm; closed Sun; no smoking.
Accommodation: 242 rooms, from £75.*

BRISTOL

Mud Dock £38   A
40 The Grove BS1 4RB   (0117) 934 9734
*This "buzzy" first-floor café-bar above a bike shop (and recently
expanded) makes a thoroughly "laid-back" destination – indeed,
given its perennially "erratic" service, it's probably best avoided if
you're in any sort of hurry. / Sample dishes: spinach, yoghurt & mint soup;
grilled tuna with olive oil mash; banoffi pie. Details: www.mud-dock.com; close to
the Industrial Museum & Arnolfini Gallery; 9.30 pm; no smoking area; no booking.*

Olive Shed £37
Floating Harbour, Princes Whf BS1 4RN   (0117) 929 1960
*"Great views of the waterside" are the special strength of this
harbourside bar; it does "nice tapas", too.
/ Details: www.therealolivecompany.co.uk; 10.30 pm; closed Mon; no Amex;
no smoking.*

One Stop Thali Cafe £20   A★
12 York Rd BS6 5QE   (0117) 942 6687
*This "quirky" Montpelier no-meat diner – decked out "in
Bollywood style" – is a top 'cheap eat'; "it's our favourite, and
we're not even veggies!". / Sample dishes: veggi pakora; three-curry plate
with rice & raita. Details: www.onestopthali.co.uk; 11.30 pm; D only, closed Mon;
no credit cards; no smoking.*

Primrose Café £33   A★
1 Boyces Ave BS8 4AA   (0117) 946 6577
*"Huge charm and delicious food" are a compelling combination at
this "friendly and buzzing café" in a "tiny Clifton backstreet"; an
"all-round-pleasant" place, it's attractions range from "pick-me-
up" Sunday breakfasts to "great seafood" in the evenings (BYO).
/ Sample dishes: crab risotto with avocado ice cream; curried Welsh mutton with
black pepper rice; brown sugar meringues with grilled bananas. Details: 9.30 pm;
closed Mon D & Sun D; no Amex; no smoking area; no booking at L.*

Quartier Vert £35
85 Whiteladies Rd BS8 2NT   (0117) 973 4482
*This Mediterranean joint in Clifton specialises in organic fare; fans
find it "one of Bristol's best places", but its prices can also seem
"unjustifiable" – first-timer visitors can hedge their bets by
checking out the "good tapas at the bar". / Sample dishes: pan-fried
scallops with pea purée; pork chops with smoked pimento mash; lemon & almond
polenta cake. Details: www.quartiervert.co.uk; 10.30 pm; no Amex.*

Rajdoot £25
83 Park St BS1 5PJ   (0117) 926 8033
*"Still a favourite after 20 years"; in default, it must be admitted,
of much local competition, this "smart" city-centre Indian
maintains its following. / Details: www.rajdoot.co.uk; 11 pm; closed Sun L.*

Rajpoot £33   ★
52 Upper Belgrave Rd BS8 2XP   (0117) 973 3515
*It's not just the "unusually smart" setting and "first-class" service
which make it "an occasion" to dine at this long-established,
"upmarket" Indian – the food is "expensive", but "worth it".
/ Details: 11 pm; D only, closed Sun; no smoking.*

riverstation £39 X
The Grove BS1 4RB (0117) 914 4434
This striking-looking, "smart but relaxed" dock-side establishment has a bar/deli downstairs, and a restaurant above; fans say it's a "great location" suited, say, to a family weekend brunch – as a general rule, though, there's a feeling that it "still doesn't live up to its looks". / **Sample dishes:** sautéed morels & asparagus; sea trout with summer vegetables & aioli; gooseberry & elderflower fool. **Details:** www.riverstation.co.uk; 10.30 pm, Fri & Sat 11 pm; no Amex; no smoking.

San Carlo £36
44 Corn St BS1 1HQ (0117) 922 6586
"Busy and bustling" and "in the heart of Bristol", this "very acceptable" Italian is hailed for its "classic" cooking – if "not exactly cheap", it's "worth sampling". / **Sample dishes:** oysters & calamari; rack of lamb. **Details:** 11 pm.

Sands £26 Ⓐ
95 Queens Rd BS8 1LW (0117) 973 9734
This "groovy" Lebanese is "popular with young and old alike"; "very good mezze" are a stand-out attraction, as are the "special Thursday exotic nights" (monthly). / **Sample dishes:** fried aubergine with chick peas; Lebanese mixed grill; lemon sorbet. **Details:** 11 pm; no smoking area.

Severnshed £37 Ⓐ
The Grove, Harbourside BS1 4RB (0117) 925 1212
"Much improved" – this "lively", "trendy" and "buzzing" spot is now said by most reporters to offer "reliably good" food" to complement its "great" waterside location; the all-day (till 7pm) weekday menu offers "outstanding value". / **Sample dishes:** fish mezze platter; hot chicken & rosemary salad; lemon curd tart.
Details: www.severnshed.co.uk; 10.30 pm; no smoking area.

Teohs £23 ★
26-34 Lower Ashley Rd BS2 9NP (0117) 907 1191
"Pan-Asian food that's full of interesting flavours" has helped make this "cheap and cheerful" venue very popular; the original St Agnes Branch now has a "great" sibling at The Tobacco Factory, Raleigh Road (tel 902 1122). / **Sample dishes:** spicy potatoes; roast duck with barbecue pork; ice cream. **Details:** 100 yds from M32, J3; 10.30 pm; closed Sun; no Amex; no smoking.

BROAD HAVEN, PEMBROKESHIRE 4–4B

Druidstone Hotel £31 Ⓐ★
Druidston Haven SA62 3NE (01437) 781221
A "great setting" – in twenty acres of wild gardens, by the sea – features in all reports on this "relaxed" seaside hotel; the food is not hugely ambitious, but it's almost always hailed for its "good value". / **Sample dishes:** Polish meat soup; sea bass & mullet with watercress cream; chocolate orange cheesecake. **Details:** www.druidstone.co.uk; from B4341 at Broad Haven turn right, then left after1.5m; 9.30 pm; closed Sun D; no smoking.
Accommodation: 11 rooms, from £58.

BROADHEMBURY, DEVON 2–4A

Drewe Arms £ 40 ★
EX14 3NF   (01404) 841267
"In a most picturesque village", this "cramped" but "characterful"
boozer has a massive reputation for its "imaginative" cooking,
which includes "especially good fish" and "delicious" seafood.
/ **Sample dishes:** mixed seafood selection; grilled turbot with hollandaise; bread
pudding with whisky butter. **Details:** 5m from M5, J28, on A373 to Honiton;
9.30 pm, 9 pm in Winter; closed Sun D; no Amex; no smoking.

BROADSTAIRS, KENT 3–3D

Marchesi £ 32 𝔸
19 Albion St CT10 1LU   (01843) 862481
"A recent refurbishment and a new chef have lifted this once-
pedestrian restaurant into a much better class", says a fan of this
"old-established, family-run fixture"; the terrace, with its
"wonderful sea views", remains the star attraction.
/ **Details:** www.marchesi.co.uk; 9.30 pm; no smoking. **Accommodation:** 19
rooms, from £92.

BROADWAY, WORCESTERSHIRE 2–1C

Lygon Arms £ 55
High St WR12 7DU   (01386) 852255
"We could have been in Hell's Kitchen"; the first year of post-
Savoy Group ownership saw standards (already in decline) nose-
dive at this "impressive" Cotswold coaching inn; no sign yet of any
'uptick' on the arrival of new chef Martin Blunos in early-2004 –
his best past form is very good indeed, though, so it's too early to
abandon hope. / **Sample dishes:** leek & mushroom lasagne with truffle oil; sea
bass with creamed leeks & chorizo; plum crumble soufflé with liquorice ice-cream.
Details: www.thelygonarms.co.uk; just off A44; 9.30 pm; D only, ex Sun open L &
D; no smoking. **Accommodation:** 69 rooms, from £240.

BROCKENHURST, HAMPSHIRE 2–4C

Simply Poussin £ 31 ★
The Courtyard, Brookley Rd SO42 7RB   (01590) 623063
A "fantastic bistro-style restaurant" (the original home of Le
Poussin at Parkhill), "tucked away in a yard off the main street";
it's praised by all reporters for offering "haute cuisine at café
prices". / **Sample dishes:** ham hock & foie gras terrine; chicken provençale;
chocolate truffle cake. **Details:** www.simplypoussin.co.uk; behind Bestsellers
Bookshop; 10 pm; closed Mon & Sun; no smoking; children: 8+.

BRODICK, ISLE OF ARRAN 7–1A

Creelers Seafood Restaurant £ 33 ★
Home Farm KA27 8DD   (01770) 302810
This "specialist fish & seafood restaurant" (a fairly humble
venture, that's since spawned an Edinburgh sibling) was much
better rated by reporters this year, and praised for some
"excellent" dishes. / **Sample dishes:** smoked fish pâté with Arran oatcakes;
sea bass with caper & lemon butter; strawberry cheesecake.
Details: www.creelers.co.uk; 9 pm; closed Mon; no Amex.

BROMLEY, KENT   2–1C
Tamasha   **£ 38**   A

131, Widmore Rd BR1 3AX   (020) 8460 3240
*The food is "good", but "excellent décor" is the "star of the show"
at this "very friendly" and "upmarket" subcontinental.*
/ **Details:** www.tamasha.co.uk; 10.30 pm; no smoking area.

BRUNDALL, NORFOLK   6–4D
Lavender House   **£ 38**   A★

39 The St NR13 5AA   (01603) 712215
*"Worth the trip", this ambitious restaurant – housed in a 16th-
century thatched house – won only praise from reporters; it's the
kind of place where "the inter-course 'extras'" can be "the best
part" of a meal.* / **Details:** www.thelavenderhouse.co.uk; 12.30 am; closed
Sun & Mon, D only, expect Fri when L & D; no Amex; no smoking.

BUCKLAND, OXFORDSHIRE   2–2C
Lamb at Buckland   **£ 34**

Lamb Ln SN7 8QN   (01367) 870484
*"Smart" and "well run" (if a little "cramped"), this Cotswold inn
wins praise for its "good but pricey" cooking.* / **Sample dishes:** lemon
sole with chive butter; pan-fried skate wing; peach & almond flan. **Details:** on A420
between Oxford & Swindon; 9.30 pm; closed Mon & Sun D; no Amex; no smoking.
Accommodation: 1 room, at about £90.

BURFORD, OXFORDSHIRE   2–2C
The Lamb   **£ 44**   A

Sheep St OX18 4LR   (01993) 823155
*It remains "a perfect romantic dinner location, just an hour from
London", but some reporters are not impressed with the new
régime at this "beautiful" Cotswold inn – perhaps recently arrived
chef Adrian Jones can jazz things up.* / **Sample dishes:** Parma ham &
Brie fritters; steak & Guinness pie; coffee profiteroles.
Details: www.lambinn-burford.co.uk; A40 from Oxford toward Cheltenham;
9.30 pm; no Amex; no smoking. **Accommodation:** 15 rooms, from £130.

BURLEY IN WHARFEDALE, WEST YORKSHIRE   5–1C
Mantra   **£ 34**

78 Main St LS29 7BT   (01943) 864602
*An "exceptional" welcome – which "makes you feel like you're
coming home" – is the norm at this recently modernised village
restaurant, where there's "always something new on the menu".*
/ **Sample dishes:** salmon platter; blackened duck with orange & honey; brown
bread parfait with butterscotch sauce. **Details:** www.mantra.uk.net; 10 pm; D only,
except Sun L only; no Amex; no smoking area.

BURNHAM MARKET, NORFOLK   6–3B
Fishes   **£ 43**   ★

Market Pl PE31 8HE   (01328) 738588
*"Unfussy and enthusiastic" – Caroline & Matthew Owsley-Brown's
"friendly" three-year-old is once again widely hailed for the
"delicious" use it makes of "fresh local ingredients".*
/ **Sample dishes:** potted brown shrimps; monkfish with fennel & cream sauce;
strawberry mousse. **Details:** www.fishesrestaurant.co.uk; 9 pm; Sat 9.30 pm; closed
Mon & Sun L; no Amex; no smoking; children: 8+ after 8.30 pm.

Hoste Arms   £ 33   A
The Green PE31 8HD   (01328) 738777
*Results can be "variable, due to fashionable over-popularity", but – for the great majority of reporters – this "easy-going" and "convivial" inn makes a "stylish", "reliable" and "good-value" destination. / **Sample dishes:** Cullen Skink with poached quails egg; honey-glazed ham hock with minted mash; apple tart with cinnamon ice cream. **Details:** www.hostearms.co.uk; 6m W of Wells-next-the-Sea; 8.45 pm; no Amex; no smoking area. **Accommodation:** 46 rooms, from £108.*

BURNSALL, NORTH YORKSHIRE   8–4B
Red Lion   £ 35
BD23 6BU   (01756) 720204
*"Hearty portions of well-cooked food" win praise for this well-known, "friendly" and "traditional" pub, which enjoys a "wonderful" out-of-the-way location, by a river in the Dales. / **Sample dishes:** gravadlax & avocado with lemon dressing; chilli-marinated chicken with spiced tomato sauce; treacle tart with candied lemon. **Details:** www.redlion.co.uk; off A59; 9.30 pm; no smoking. **Accommodation:** 13 rooms, from £100.*

BURY ST EDMUNDS, SUFFOLK   3–1C
Maison Bleue   £ 34   A★★
30-31 Churchgate St IP33 1RG   (01284) 760623
*"The food is divine, and the service unparalleled" – thus speaks one of the many fans of this "excellent" and "authentic" Gallic restaurant (which "has improved immeasurably over the past couple of years"); "perfectly-cooked fish" is the highlight. / **Sample dishes:** fish soup with garlic croutons; Dover sole with pink peppercorn butter; white chocolate & lime mousse. **Details:** www.maisonbleue.co.uk; 9.30 pm; closed Mon & Sun; no smoking.*

BUSHEY, HERTFORDSHIRE   3–2A
St James   £ 36
30 High St WD23 3HL   (020) 8950 2480
*"Noisy" but "reliable", this Italian-owned restaurant (with a modern British menu) is – for most reporters – "the only place round Watford worth considering". / **Sample dishes:** grilled vegetable antipasti; roast lamb with creamed leeks & basil jus; Toblerone cheesecake. **Details:** opp St James Church; 9.45 pm; closed Sun; no Amex; no smoking area.*

CAMBRIDGE, CAMBRIDGESHIRE   3–1B

For such an immemorially dreadful place to eat, Cambridge isn't actually that bad... as long as you don't mind eating either in a pub or in a restaurant of some grandeur. Indeed, the city now boasts, in *Midsummer House*, a restaurant deserving of 'destination' status. *22 Chesterton Road* is proving a good mid-range performer. Otherwise, the city seems to be stuck in something of a time warp.

Cazimir   £ 14
13 King St CB1 1LH   (01223) 355156
*This Polish-run café is a "colourful" and "friendly" place, serving an "interesting variety" of food, including some "good sarnies". / **Sample dishes:** roast vegetable bruschetta; Polish sausage & Mozzarella salad; chocolate cake. **Details:** L & afternoon tea only; no credit cards; no smoking area.*

Crown & Punchbowl £31 Ⓐ
High St CB5 9JG (01223) 860643
Just a short drive from Cambridge, this "lovely conversion" of an old boozer is well worth seeking out for its "imaginative" and "wide-ranging" menu. / **Sample dishes:** marinated goat cheese with peach, honey and peppercorn dressing; guinea fowl supreme with bacon and potato cake and onion sauce; sticky toffee pudding. **Details:** www.cambscuisine.com; 9 pm; closed Sun D; no smoking. **Accommodation:** 5 rooms, from £70.

Curry Queen £19
106 Mill Rd CB1 2BD (01223) 351027
In the face, it's fair to say, of little competition, this "reliable" veteran is "the most popular Indian in Cambridge". / **Details:** midnight.

Dojo £18
1-2 Millers Yd, Mill Ln CB2 1RQ (01223) 363471
"Decent noodles, cheap and in large portions" wouldn't necessary rate a guide entry in some cities, but in Cambridge... / **Sample dishes:** prawn tempura; salmon ramen. **Details:** www.dojonoodlebar.co.uk; off Trumpington St; 11 pm; no Amex; no smoking; no booking.

Fitzbillies £34
52 Trumpington St CB2 1RG (01223) 352500
"Sensible prices" and a "nice" location – adjacent to the famous bakery of the same name – win support for this intimate dining room. / **Sample dishes:** shrimp & leek tart; pink bream on crab cake with asparagus & lemon vinaigrette; fresh fruit tart with chantilly cream. **Details:** www.fitzbillies.com; 9.30 pm; closed Sun D; no smoking area.

Graffiti
Hotel Felix £40 Ⓐ
Whitehouse Ln CB3 0LX (01223) 277977
A "lovely situation" – in a Victorian mansion on the fringe of the city – and "arty" décor win praise for the dining room of this year-old design-hotel; its Mediterranean cooking is quite "inventive", too. / **Sample dishes:** venison carpaccio with baby artichokes & baked tomatoes; tournedos of beef with gorgonzola mousse potatoes; honey & bourbon mousse with candied filo pastry & strawberry salsa. **Details:** www.hotelfelix.co.uk; 10 pm, Sat 10.30 pm; no smoking. **Accommodation:** 52 rooms, from £158.

Kingston Arms £26 ★
33 Kingston St CB1 2NU (01223) 319414
"Classy pub food" – "much better than you'd expect from a street-side boozer" – makes this "busy" outfit near the station well worth knowing of. / **Details:** www.kingston-arms.co.uk; 9 pm; no Amex; booking: max 10; children: 18+ (but allowed in garden).

Loch Fyne £34
37 Trumpington St CB2 1QY (01223) 362433
It says much about Cambridge dining that this "just OK" outlet of the national seafood chain may be a useful place to remember. / **Sample dishes:** smoked salmon; lobster platter; ice cream. **Details:** www.lochfyne.com; opp Fitzwilliam Museum; 10 pm, Sat 11 pm; no smoking area.

Maharajah £22
9-13 Castle St CB3 0AH (01223) 358399
It inspires no great hymns of praise, but this above-average veteran subcontinental has its uses when only a curry will do. / **Details:** midnight.

Midsummer House £68 ★
Midsummer Common CB4 IHA (01223) 369299
*Daniel Clifford's "memorable" food – in "Fat Duck/El Bulli style,
with foams, jellies and so on" – is winning ever-loftier acclaim
from reporters; the "staid" and "precious" ambience of this
Victorian villa by the Cam is not an asset, though, and the wine
list (in particular) is often noted as being "painfully expensive".*
/ **Sample dishes:** deep-fried snails with bacon risotto; slow-roast beef with
mushroom gnocchi; prune & armagnac soufflé.
Details: www.midsummerhouse.co.uk; facing University Boathouse; 9.30 pm; closed
Mon & Sun; no smoking.

Peking Restaurant £34
21 Burleigh St CB1 IDG (01223) 354755
*Near the Grafton Centre, this "expensive" Chinese has long been
worth knowing about for its "fresh"-tasting cooking; the setting
though is "basic".* / **Sample dishes:** deep-fried squid in chilli; Szechuan
chicken; toffee bananas. **Details:** 10.30 pm; no credit cards; no smoking area.

Sala Thong £24
35 Newnham Rd CB3 9EY (01223) 323178
*Even the occasional reporters who accuse this small Thai of
appearing rather "downmarket" tip it as worth knowing about for
its "good food".* / **Details:** 9.45 pm; closed Mon; no Amex; no smoking.

22 Chesterton Road £35 A★
22 Chesterton Rd CB4 3AX (01223) 351880
*"Small and seductive", or "cosy, cottagey and cramped" – take
your pick of views on the ambience of the Edwardian house in
which this "personal" establishment is situated; foodwise, its
overall performance was "very good" this year.*
/ **Sample dishes:** pork & rabbit terrine with plum sauce; crab cakes with spring
onion risotto; steamed marmalade pudding. **Details:** www.restaurant22.co.uk;
9.45 pm; D only, closed Mon & Sun; no smoking; children: 12+.

Vaults Restaurant & Bar £22
14a Trinity St CB2 ITB (01223) 506090
*Start your night off with one of the "delicious" cocktails, and you
can have a "great evening out" at this subterranean tapas bar;
the scoff can be "very good", too.* / **Details:** www.localsecrets.com;
10.30 pm; no smoking area.

CANTERBURY, KENT 3–3D

Augustines £32 A★
1-2 Longport CT1 IPE (01227) 453063
*"Imaginative" food that's "very reasonably priced", would make
this "friendly", "intimate" and "efficient" Georgian townhouse-
restaurant worth seeking out anywhere – in this particular city, it's
a godsend.* / **Sample dishes:** provençale fish soup; marsh lamb with parsley
mash; lemon tart with raspberry sauce. **Details:** near the Cathedral; 9.30 pm;
closed Mon & Sun; no smoking; booking: max 7.

Café des Amis £29
95 St Dunstan's St CT2 8AD (01227) 464390
*No-one tips this long-popular Mexican, near one of the gates to
the city, as a major culinary destination; especially as "a place to
go in group", though, it remains a good option.*
/ **Sample dishes:** prawn & Serrano ham cakes; lamb with Merguez sausages;
pineapple tarte Tatin. **Details:** by Westgate Towers; 10 pm; no smoking area;
booking: max 6 at D, Fri & Sat.

Goods Shed £ 32 Ⓐ★
Station Road West CT2 8AN (01227) 459153
On a mezzanine above the Farmers' Market, this "satisfying and imaginative" destination does not just benefit from an "easy" atmosphere and a "very unusual" setting – it delivers "excellent" food (much of it sourced from down below) at "reasonable" prices. / **Details:** *9.30 pm; closed Mon & Sun D; L & afternoon tea only.*

CAPEL CURIG, GWYNEDD 4–1D

Bryn Tyrch £ 27 ★
LL24 0EL (01690) 720223
"Perfect for Snowdonia's hikers and campers", this "wonderful, cosy inn" offers "hearty" fare in "huge" portions – vegetarians do particularly well. / **Sample dishes:** smoked duck with orange & apricot chutney; Feta & spinach pie; bread & butter pudding.
Details: www.bryntyrch-hotel.com; on A5; 9 pm; no Amex; no smoking area.
Accommodation: 15 rooms, from £29.

CARDIFF, CARDIFF 2–2A

The Welsh capital still has yet really to join the 21st century as far as eating out is concerned. The only place of any real note is *Le Gallois Y Cymro* in the smart suburb of Canton. In the city centre, the vast and long-established complex based on a pleasant but dated steak 'n' fish formula incorporating *La Brasserie*, *Champers* and *Le Monde* continue to dominate (the last-mentioned being perhaps the best). Trendy Cardiff Bay still continues to show more style than substance, with *Tides* the best-known culprit in that respect.

Armless Dragon £ 29
97 Wyeverne Rd CF2 4BG (029) 2038 2357
"Reasonable food" and "friendly service" might be unremarkable in many parts of the world – this backstreet bistro, however, is notable as "one of the better places in Cardiff".
/ **Sample dishes:** liver parfait with date chutney; roast chicken with leeks & truffle oil; crème brûlée. **Details:** www.thearmlessdragon.co.uk; 10 min outside city centre; 9 pm, Fri & Sat 9.30 pm; closed Mon & Sun; no smoking; children: no babies on weekends.

La Brasserie £ 34
60 St Mary St CF10 1FE (029) 2023 4134
They don't stand on ceremony at this "easy", "sawdust-on-the-floor" spot, whose formula of "well-cooked" fish and meat ("self-selected from chill counters") have made it a leading local destination. / **Sample dishes:** frogs legs with garlic mayonnaise; lemon sole with new potatoes; apple tart. **Details:** www.labrasserierestaurant.co.uk; midnight; closed Sun D; need 8+ to book.

Champers £ 28
61 St Mary St CF10 1FE (029) 2037 3363
"If you're in the mood for a basic steak and chips", this "always busy" brasserie is a good option – being one of the three, adjacent chiller-cabinet restaurants (including Le Monde and La Brasserie) which dominate the city-centre's dining options.
/ **Sample dishes:** garlic prawns; stuffed chicken breast; chocolate truffle.
Details: www.le-monde.co.uk; nr Castle; midnight, 10.30 pm for tapas; closed Sun L.

Cibo £ 26 A
83 Pontcanna St CF11 9HS (029) 2023 2226
"Lovely food" and *"great service"* make it *"well worth the drive
from the city-centre"*, to seek out this funky pizza 'n' pasta stop,
in Poncanna. / **Sample dishes:** vegetable antipasti; salami & Mozzarella
ciabatta; lemon cheesecake. **Details:** 9 pm; no Amex; no smoking; booking:
max 10.

The Cinnamon Tree £ 23 ★
173 Kings Rd CF11 9DE (029) 2037 4433
"Tender flaming ostrich" is the sort of dish that means this
Canton curry house is *"not your typical Indian"*.
/ **Sample dishes:** lamb curry; duck cooked with dry chili; sponge pudding.
Details: www.thecinnamontree.co.uk; 10.45 pm; closed Fri L & Sun; no smoking
area.

Da Vendittos £ 48
7-8 Park Pl CF10 3DP (029) 2023 0781
"Spacious" tables, *"unhurried and discreet"* service and
"upmarket" cuisine make this modern Italian a key destination for
those willing to spend handsomely on Cardiff city-centre dining –
the low level of reports suggest that their number is few!
/ **Sample dishes:** risotto with Parma ham & peas; roast pigeon; basil ice cream.
Details: www.vendittogroup.co.uk; 10.45 pm; closed Mon & Sun; no smoking area.

Le Gallois Y Cymro £ 46 ★
6-10 Romilly Cr CF11 9NR (029) 2034 1264
This Canton restaurant stands head and shoulders over
everywhere else in Cardiff, and for its many fans it's simply *"a
delight"*, serving *"great"* Franco-Welsh cuisine (with a *"good
choice of wines"*) in an *"elegant setting"*; as ever, though, a
minority of reporters consider it *"pretentious"* and *"overpriced"*.
/ **Sample dishes:** Roquefort soufflé with poached pears; roast pork with truffle
mash & clove sauce; spiced pineapple with pepper ice cream.
Details: www.legallois-ycymro.com; 1.5m W of Cardiff Castle; 10.30 pm; closed
Mon & Sun; no smoking area.

The Greenhouse Café £ 26 ★
38 Woodville Rd CF24 4EB (029) 2023 5731
"A very good vegetarian and fish place that's reasonably-priced" –
key points on this ever-popular café, near the university.
/ **Sample dishes:** potato, leek & celeriac soup; parsley-crusted salmon with saffron
mayonnaise; banoffi pie. **Details:** near Cardiff University; 10.30 pm; D only, closed
Mon & Sun; no Amex; no smoking.

Happy Gathering £ 27
233 Cowbridge Road East CF11 9AL (029) 2039 7531
This large city-centre oriental is appropriately named and remains
a local favourite. / **Sample dishes:** chicken satay & crispy seaweed; steamed
duck in orange sauce; crispy toffee banana. **Details:** 10.45 pm, Fri & Sat
11.45 pm; no smoking area.

Izakaya £ 30
Mermaid Quay CF10 5BW (029) 2049 2939
"Fairly basic" but *"friendly"*, this Japanese tavern makes rather an
unlikely find, even in *"fashionable Cardiff Bay"*; its noodles and
other fare are *"good value"*, without in any way being earth-
shattering. / **Sample dishes:** grilled chicken and leek skewers; fried breaded
pork cutlet; green tea ice cream. **Details:** www.izakaya-japanese-tavern.com;
10.30 pm; no smoking area.

Le Monde £31 𝔸
62 St Mary St CF10 1FE (029) 2038 7376
"Fish, served by weight from the chiller" is what this well-known, rather upscale, first-floor venue (above La Brasserie) is all about; "very good-value lunch menus" help make it a popular business destination. / **Sample dishes:** *marinated seafood salad; venison with port wine sauce; Welsh cheeses.* **Details:** *www.le-monde.co.uk; midnight; closed Sun; no jeans; no booking.*

Scallops £35
Unit 2 Mermaid Quay CF10 5BZ (029) 2049 7495
A stark fish café, on the waterfront at Cardiff Bay, where the food is "OK", if "pricey" for what it is. / **Sample dishes:** *king scallops with roast tomatoes; monkfish wrapped in bacon with curried mussels; Eton Mess.* **Details:** *www.scallopsrestaurant.com; 10 pm.*

Thai House £36
3-5 Guiford Cr CF10 2HJ (029) 2038 7404
This "quiet" oriental, "right in the centre of Cardiff" – with its "friendly" staff and "good" food – has been a local fixture for almost 20 years. / **Details:** *www.thaihouse.biz; 11.15 pm; closed Sun.*

Tides
St David's Hotel & Spa £44 X
Havannah St CF10 5SD (029) 2031 3018
"It should be so much better in a five-star" – the "ultra-modern" dining room of Rocco Forte's modern landmark hotel continues to attract very mixed reports; a shame, as it has a "great location", overlooking the Bay. / **Sample dishes:** *kipper pâté with whisky; smoked haddock colcannon; sherry trifle.* **Details:** *www.thestdavidshotel.com; in Cardiff Bay; 10.15 pm; no smoking.* **Accommodation:** *132 rooms, from £165.*

Woods Brasserie £38
Pilotage Building, Stuart St CF10 5BW (029) 2049 2400
It has a lot of 'profile' locally, but this brasserie on the Bay attracts pretty mixed reports – for a "lively" place, it has (surprisingly) "little ambience", and sterner some feel the cooking is "by numbers". / **Sample dishes:** *crispy beef salad with Thai dressing; pan-fried John Dory with parsnip purée; Bakewell tart & custard.* **Details:** *www.old-post-office.com; in the Inner Harbour; 10 pm; closed Sun D.*

CARLISLE, CUMBRIA 7–2D
No 10 £35 𝔸
10 Eden Mount CA3 9LY (01228) 524183
A loyal local following hail the virtues of "Carlisle's Top Restaurant" – a well-established fixture run by a husband and wife team in a "cosy" old town house; it serves a "limited but ever-changing" menu of "first class food using local produce". / **Details:** *9.30 pm; D only, closed Mon & Sun; no smoking.*

CARTMEL, CUMBRIA 7–4D
Aynsome Manor £35 ★
LA11 6HH (015395) 36653
"Straightforward cooking from local produce", and at a reasonable price, wins praise from fans of this "reliable favourite" – a family-owned manor house hotel. / **Details:** *www.aynsomemanorhotel.co.uk; off A590,1/2m N of village; 8.30 pm; D only, ex Sun L only; no smoking; children: 5+ in restaurant.* **Accommodation:** *12 rooms, from £150.*

L'Enclume £ 60 A★★

Cavendish St LA11 6PZ
(01539) 536362
Thanks to Simon Rogan's "memorable" and "seriously foodie" cooking (and the "exciting" wine list), this "beautifully sited" and "pleasingly decorated" former smithy is still "the tops" for many reporters; to the extent there is an occasional let-down, it tends to be on the atmosphere front. / **Sample dishes:** pan-fried langoustine with sour grapefruit drops; poached brill with English mace and wild tree spinach; upside down coconut souflé, mango mousse, raspberry jelly and test tube. **Details:** www.lenclume.co.uk; 9.30 pm; closed Mon & Sun D; no jeans or trainers; no smoking; children: 12+ at D. **Accommodation:** cottage, plus 7 rooms, from £125.

Uplands £ 42 A★
Haggs Ln LA11 6HD (01539) 536248
The "delightful" dining room of this small country house hotel, with views towards Morecambe Bay, is hailed for its "terrific" cooking and its "very romantic" atmosphere. / **Sample dishes:** hot salmon soufflé; honey-roast duck; chocolate Grand Marnier mousse. **Details:** www.uplands.uk.com; 8 pm; closed Mon, Tue-Thu D only; no smoking; no booking, Sat; children: 8+ at D. **Accommodation:** 5 rooms, from £81.

CASTLE DOUGLAS, DUMFRIES & GALLOWAY 7–2B

Balcary Bay Hotel £ 38 ★
Shore Rd DG7 1QZ (01556) 640217
"First-class food" completes the "special experience", of visiting this "idyllically-located" country house hotel, which enjoys impressive coastal views. / **Details:** www.balcary-bay-hotel.co.uk; 8.30 pm; no Amex; no smoking. **Accommodation:** 20 rooms, from £112.

CAUNTON, NOTTINGHAMSHIRE 5–3D

Caunton Beck £ 34
Main St NG23 6AB (01636) 636793
The rural sibling to Lincoln's Wig & Mitre offers a broadly similar all-day formula in a "nice country location"; it's a "friendly" place, where standards are generally "above average".
/ **Sample dishes:** chicken laksa with pork wontons; duck with bean & chorizo cassoulet; passion fruit & ginger cheesecake. **Details:** www.wigandmitre.com; 6m NW of Newark past British Sugar factory on A616; midnight; no smoking.

CHADDESLEY CORBETT, WORCESTERSHIRE 5–4B

Brockencote Hall £ 48 A
DY10 4PY (01562) 777876
Monsieur Petijean's "formal" and very Gallic country house dining room didn't inspire quite such eloquent reports this year; generally, however, this seems to be a place that "lives up to expectations". / **Sample dishes:** scallops with juniper berry sauce; rabbit wrapped in Parma ham with marjoram sausages; lemon tart with Earl Grey sorbet. **Details:** www.brockencotehall.com; on A448, just outside village; 9.30 pm; closed Sat L; no smoking area; booking: max 6. **Accommodation:** 17 rooms, from £116.

CHAGFORD, DEVON   1–3D

Gidleigh Park   £ 85   A★★
TQ13 8HH   (01647) 432367
Michael Caines's "superlative" food – better than ever this year –
helps make the Hendersons' '30s country house ("idyllically
located" near Dartmoor) arguably the best place of its type in the
UK, not least for a "perfect romantic treat"; an "extensive" wine
list – with fixed mark-ups on grander vintages – is a further plus.
/ **Sample dishes:** langoustines & frogs legs with pasta in truffle cream; roast
duckling with honey & spices; hot apple tart. **Details:** www.gidleigh.com; from
village, right at Lloyds TSB, take right fork to end of lane; 9 pm; no smoking; children:
7+ at D. **Accommodation:** 14 rooms, from £420.

22 Mill Street   £ 43   A★★
22 Mill St TQ13 8AW   (01647) 432244
Duncan Walker's "passion for food is infectious" at this "intimate"
restaurant (down the road from his former employer, Gidleigh
Park); his "totally reliable, top-notch" modern cuisine makes a
meal here "terrific value". / **Sample dishes:** saffron lasagne of crab & red
pepper; roast pigeon with pea purée; hot raspberry soufflé.
Details: www.22millstreet.co.uk; 9 pm; closed Mon L, Tue L & Sun; no Amex;
no smoking; children: 14+. **Accommodation:** 2 rooms, from £75.

CHALFONT ST GILES, BUCKINGHAMSHIRE   3–2A

Cape Fish   £ 32   ★
London Rd HP8 4NL   (01494) 872113
"Freshly cooked fish, served in an unusual way" has made quite a
name for this former coaching inn; run by three South Africans
and a Frenchman, it could be said to combine the best of the
New World and the Old! / **Details:** www.capefish.co.uk; 10 pm; closed
Mon L & Sun D.

CHANDLERS CROSS, HERTFORDSHIRE   3–2A

Colette's
The Grove   £ 74   A★
WD3 4TG   (01923) 296015
The "wonderful" setting of this year-old, mega-swanky
resort/country house hotel offers a "tip top" fine-dining
experience, and Chris Harrod's cuisine is "of very high quality";
even so, some reporters find the experience "overpriced".
/ **Sample dishes:** leek terrine with langoustine & truffle; rabbit canneloni with
vegetables & mustard seed sauce; roast pear & fig pain perdu with pot ice cream.
Details: www.thegrove.co.uk; J19 or 20 on M25; 10.30 pm; closed Sun D;
no smoking area. **Accommodation:** 227 rooms, from £250.

CHEESDEN, LANCASHIRE   5–1B

Nutter's   £ 38   ★★
Edenfield Rd OL12 7TY   (01706) 650167
"The enthusiasm still shows"; TV-chef Andrew Nutter moved his
restaurant during the year, but his cooking is as "dynamic and
innovative" as ever; his base is now an ancient listed building, and
the ambience of the new setting pleases most (if not quite all)
reporters. / **Sample dishes:** black pudding wontons; pork with bubble 'n'
squeak & tomato jus; cappuccino panna cotta. **Details:** between Edenfield &
Norden on A680; 9.30 pm; closed Mon; closed 2 weeks in Aug; no smoking.

CHELMSFORD, ESSEX   3–2C
Waterfront Place   £ 33
Wharf Rd CM2 6LU (01245) 252000
The food is "not earth-shattering", but an "excellent" waterside location has helped win a fair-sized following for this "huge barn of a restaurant" (part of a canalside conference centre).
/ **Sample dishes:** goats cheese, prosciutto & fig bruschetta; char-grilled salmon with mango & lime salsa; banoffi brûlée in chocolate.
Details: www.waterfront-place.co.uk; 10 pm; closed Sun D; no smoking area.

CHELTENHAM, GLOUCESTERSHIRE   2–1C
Champignon Sauvage   £ 52   ★★
24-26 Suffolk Rd GL50 2AQ (01242) 573449
"Small but stunning"; David Everitt-Mathias's "outstanding combinations of flavours and textures" and his wife Helen's "exceptional" service win the highest acclaim from all quarters for this "friendly" foodie Mecca, just outside the town centre; veggies should pre-notify. / **Sample dishes:** eel tortellini with watercress cream; lamb with cauliflower dumplings; lemon mousse with milk sorbet.
Details: www.lechampignonsauvage.co.uk; near Cheltenham Boys College; 9 pm; closed Mon & Sun; no smoking.

Daffodil   £ 35   𝔸X
18-20 Suffolk Parade GL50 2AE (01242) 700055
For an Art Deco experience, this erstwhile cinema is "a Cheltenham must-see"; just go for a snack, though – "the ambitious cooking misses by a mile". / **Sample dishes:** rabbit confit with leek risotto; swordfish with Toulouse sausage & tomato cassoulet; lemon crème brûlée with chocolate shortbread. **Details:** www.thedaffodil.co.uk; just off Suffolk Square; 10.30 pm; closed Sun; no smoking.

Lumière   £ 50   ★
Clarence Pde GL50 3PA (01242) 222200
Though fans consider it "one of Cheltenham's top two places", Lin & Geoff Chapman's small, town-centre four-year-old still generates few reports; those there are speak of "very interesting and inventive" cooking (with perhaps a tendency to "over-complexity"). / **Sample dishes:** lime baked monkfish on wilted spinach with saffron jus; roast guinea fowl breast with sweet chilli potato puree; Stilton cheesecake with port syrup & pear. **Details:** www.lumiere.cc; 8.30 pm; D only, closed Mon & Sun; no Amex; no smoking; booking: max 10.

Mayflower   £ 31   ★
32-34 Clarence St GL50 3NX (01242) 522426
"Traditional Chinese food, well presented in comfortable surroundings" – that's the deal at this long-established town-centre spot, where a "good selection for veggies" is something of a feature. / **Sample dishes:** garlic & chilli frogs legs; roast duck with beansprouts; toffee bananas. **Details:** www.themayflowerrestaurant.co.uk; 10 pm; no smoking at D.

Le Petit Blanc   £ 31
Queen's Promenade GL50 1NN (01242) 266800
Perhaps a refurb' can buck up this "so-so" Blanc-branded brasserie, which – in the first year of the new (Loch Fyne) régime – has maintained the merely "adequate" standards of the recent past. / **Sample dishes:** twice-baked Roquefort soufflé; tuna with pine kernel crust & red pepper relish; chocolate fondant with pistachio ice cream. **Details:** www.lepetitblanc.co.uk; 11 pm; no smoking.

Ruby £29
52 Suffolk Rd GL50 2AQ (01242) 250909
A handy Chinese, worth knowing about in a town not well provided-for on the ethnic front. / **Details:** near Cheltenham Boys College; 11.30 pm.

Storyteller £30 A★
11 North Pl GL50 4DW (01242) 250343
"Who needs a wine list when you have a wine room?"; it's not just presentation, however, which sets apart this "atmospheric, conservatory-type outfit" – the "eclectic" cooking is "interesting" too. / **Sample dishes:** Mauritian beef skewers; roast lamb with new potatoes; chocolate mud pie. **Details:** www.storyteller.co.uk; 10 pm; no smoking area.

CHESTER, CHESHIRE 5–2A
Albion Inn £18
Park St CH1 1RN (01244) 340345
"Old-fashioned English grub" is served in "hearty" portions at this "proper pub" – a corner boozer of "great character", tucked away near the Newgate; pub anoraks take note – it is claimed that CAMRA was founded here. / **Sample dishes:** no starters; steak & kidney pie; bread & butter pudding. **Details:** www.albioninnchester.co.uk; 8 pm; no credit cards; no smoking; need 6+ to book; children: 18+ only.

Arkle
The Chester Grosvenor £75
Eastgate CH1 1LT (01244) 324024
The dining room of the Duke of Westminster's grand city-centre hotel – with its "top-quality" food and "stunning" wine list – has much going for it; sadly, it spoils everything by charging "rip-off" prices, and being "far too stuffy"; the much jollier brasserie, however, is "very popular". / **Sample dishes:** oxtail ravioli with langoustine tails; duck with black fig sauce; basil blancmange with iced gingerbread. **Details:** www.chestergrosvenor.co.uk; 9.30 pm; closed Mon & Sun; jacket required at D; no smoking. **Accommodation:** 80 rooms, from £185.

Blue Bell £36 ★
Northgate St CH1 2HQ (01244) 317758
This "black and white timbered building, complete with ghost" makes a "great" (but "not inexpensive") venue, near the Town Hall; fans say the food is "excellent", too. / **Sample dishes:** beignets with tomato fondue & avacado salsa; fillet of beef with blue cheese & tarragon; warm chocolate mousse with praline ice cream. **Details:** www.bluebellrestaurant.co.uk; 9.45 pm; no Amex; no smoking.

Francs £25
14 Cuppin St CH1 2BN (01244) 317952
"All-round, an acceptable experience" – this "lively" Gallic bistro is never going to set the world on fire, but almost all reporters find a visit here "enjoyable", in a city with surprisingly few decent places. / **Sample dishes:** smoked salmon, melon & avocado salad; lambs liver & bacon with mash; lemon tart. **Details:** www.francs.co.uk; 11 pm; no smoking area.

Pheasant Inn £29 A★
Higher Burwardsley CH3 9PF (01829) 770434
A "fantastic" location (overlooking the Cheshire Plain) – a few miles out of the city – is not the only attraction of this "old and characterful" pub (recently "extensively refurbished"); it offers "imaginative" cooking, too. / **Details:** www.thepheasant-burwardsley.com; 9.30 pm; no smoking. **Accommodation:** 10 rooms, from £80.

CHETTLE, DORSET   2–4C

Castleman Hotel   £ 27   ★
DT11 8DB   (01258) 830096
"Tucked away in a small village", this "lovely", "quiet" restaurant
(part of an elegant small hotel) is consistently praised for its "very
good" food and its "outstanding" service.
/ *Details:* www.castlemanhotel.co.uk; 9.30 pm; D only, ex Sun open L & D;
no Amex; no smoking. *Accommodation:* 8 rooms, from £75.

CHICHESTER, WEST SUSSEX   3–4A

Comme Ça   £ 39   𝔸★
67 Broyle Rd PO19 6BD   (01243) 788724
"A wonderful complement to a trip to the Chichester Festival" –
though some reports say the cooking at this "attractive", "entirely
French-run" operation is "merely decent", more say it's
"excellent". / *Sample dishes:* asparagus hollandaise; cured Scottish salmon;
summer pudding. *Details:* www.commeca.co.uk; 0.5m N of city centre; 10.30 pm;
closed Mon, Tue L & Sun D; no smoking area.

CHIGWELL, ESSEX   3–2B

The Bluebell   £ 44
117 High Rd IG7 6QQ   (020) 8500 6282
This "wonderful local restaurant" is "very, very popular" (albeit "in
a gastronomic desert"); it's "especially good for the set lunch", but
some reporters also say it's "fantastic" for dinner.
/ *Sample dishes:* smoked trout with baby spinach; rump of Welsh lamb with thyme
and rosemary; hot blueberry tart with homemade lemon curd ice cream.
Details: 10.45 pm; closed Mon, Sat L & Sun D.

CHILGROVE, WEST SUSSEX   3–4A

White Horse   £ 39
High St PO18 9HX   (01243) 535219
There's an "unbelievable" wine list (running to hundreds of bins)
at this celebrated South Downs boozer; the food has always been
secondary – even bearing this in mind, some reporters feel the
place is "resting on its laurels". / *Sample dishes:* chicken liver salad with
raspberry dressing; braised oxtail with potato pureé; warm chocolate gâteau.
Details: www.whitehorsechilgrove.co.uk; 8m NW of Chichester on B2141; 9.30 pm;
closed Mon & Sun D; no smoking. *Accommodation:* 8 rooms, from £85.

CHINNOR, OXFORDSHIRE   2–2D

Sir Charles Napier   £ 41   𝔸★
Spriggs Alley OX39 4BX   (01494) 483011
To some this is "the model of what a country restaurant should
be", which is perhaps why the crowd it attracts is, infamously,
"mainly from London"; a stylishly converted former Chilterns inn, it
offers "delicious" food and a wine list with "much of interest".
/ *Sample dishes:* butternut squash soup; skate wing with capers, saffron
potatoes & spinach; date cake with toffee sauce.
Details: www.sircharlesnapier.co.uk; M40, J6 into Chinnor, turn right at roundabout;
10 pm, 4pm Sun; closed Mon & Sun D; no smoking area; children: 6+ at D.

CHIPPING CAMPDEN, GLOUCESTERSHIRE   2–1C

Cotswold House   £42

Chipping Campden GL55 6AN   (01386) 840330

Grand and elegant, this Cotswold village hotel has both a restaurant and brasserie; most reporters found it "very pleasing" this year, if stopping short of more lavish endorsements.
/ **Sample dishes:** roast scallops with cauliflower purée & smoked bacon; rump of lamb with buttered spinach & tomatoes; ice strawberry parfait with hot banana spring rolls. **Details:** www.cotswoldhouse.com; 9.30 pm; D only, except Sun open L & D; no Switch; no smoking. **Accommodation:** 21 rooms, from £175.

Eight Bells   £30

Church St GL55 6JG   (01386) 840371

Nothing fancy, mind, but for "a very good standard of pub food", this ancient boozer achieves a consistent thumbs-up from reporters. / **Sample dishes:** twice-baked cheese soufflé; braised lamb with julienne vegetables; dark chocolate cheesecake. **Details:** www.eightbellsinn.co.uk; 10m S of Stratford upon Avon; 9.30 pm; no Amex; no smoking area. **Accommodation:** 5 rooms, from £85.

CHRISTCHURCH, DORSET   2–4C

FishWorks   £39

10 Church St BH23 1BW   (01202) 487000

An outpost of the West Country (and now London) chain of expensive café/fishmongers; as elsewhere, it offers great fish… but not much else. / **Sample dishes:** spaghetti with crab & chilli; grilled plaice with black butter; lemon tart. **Details:** www.fishworks.co.uk; 9.30 pm; closed Mon & Sun; no smoking.

CIRENCESTER, GLOUCESTERSHIRE   2–2C

Tatyan's   £26

27 Castle St GL7 1QD   (01285) 653529

This friendly town-centre Chinese offers a "very wide menu choice" – in this part of the world, such an establishment is of some note. / **Details:** www.tatyans.com; near junction of A417 & A345; 10.30 pm; closed Sun L.

CLACHAN, ARGYLL & BUTE   9–3B

Loch Fyne Oyster Bar   £34   🅰★

PA26 8BL   (01499) 600236

For "seafood at its best", this "stunningly"-located operation on the loch – now divorced from the namesake chain – wins consistent acclaim; it's "very reasonably priced", too ("if you discount the fact that you'll spend a fortune in the adjoining deli"). / **Sample dishes:** smoked haddock chowder; king scallops; ice cream. **Details:** www.loch-fyne.com; 10m E of Inveraray on A83; 11.15 pm; no smoking.

CLAVERING, ESSEX   3–2B

The Cricketers   £32

Wicken Rd CB11 4QT   (01799) 550442

"Jamie's influence is clear", say fans of this "popular" traditional village inn run by the Naked Chef's dad – doubters admit the food is "good", but say that there's "better and cheaper elsewhere". / **Sample dishes:** turmeric tempura monkfish; veal with Savoy cabbage & blue cheese sauce; chocolate cheesecake. **Details:** www.thecricketers.co.uk; on B1038 between Newport & Buntingford; 10 pm; no smoking. **Accommodation:** 14 rooms, from £100.

CLAYGATE, SURREY   3–3A
Le Petit Pierrot   £40   ★
4 The Parade KT10 0NU   (01372) 465105
"Small", "welcoming" and "very French", this fixture in a former
shop has long been a "reliable" source of "superb Gallic cuisine"
in an under-provided part of the world. / **Sample dishes:** pan-fried foie
gras with sweetcorn galette; guinea fowl with morel risotto; sweet chestnut & prune
pudding. **Details:** 9.30 pm; closed Sat L & Sun; children: 8+.

CLENT, WEST MIDLANDS   5–4B
Four Stones   £32   ★
Adams Hill DY9 9PS   (01562) 883260
"Outstanding Anglo-Italian cooking" and "relaxed and unobtrusive
service" make this a restaurant worth seeking out; it has a "very
pleasant" location, too – "good for a pre- or post-meal stroll".
/ **Details:** www.thefourstones.co.uk; 10 pm; closed Mon & Sun L; no smoking.

CLEOBURY MORTIMER, SHROPSHIRE   5–4B
Spice Empire   £26   ★
17 High St DY14 8DG   (01299) 270419
"High-standard classics" and a "varied" menu win continuing
support for this "superb" Indian. / **Details:** 11 pm; closed Mon.

CLEVEDON, BATH & NE SOMERSET   2–2A
Junior Poon   £29   Ⓐ
16 Hill Rd BS21 7NZ   (01275) 341900
Housed in an impressive Georgian building, this unusual Chinese
serves some "very fresh" cooking; there is also a "fantastic" wine
bar, which – with its "comfy sofas and cosy corners" – has a
following in its own right. / **Details:** www.juniorpoon.com; near Clevedon Pier;
10.30 pm.

CLIPSHAM, RUTLAND   6–4A
Olive Branch   £35   Ⓐ★
Main St LE15 7SH   (01780) 410355
This "excellent" rural gastro-boozer remains widely hailed as
"exactly what you want from a place in the country" – "friendly",
"very atmospheric" and in a "nice location"; the food can be
"very good", too (though reporters divide on whether Michelin's
star isn't over-egging it a bit). / **Sample dishes:** honey-roast parsnip soup;
roast sea bream with olive mash & tomato relish; coconut rice pudding.
Details: www.theolivebranchpub.com; 2m E from A1 on B664; 9.30 pm; no Amex;
no smoking area.

CLITHEROE, LANCASHIRE   5–1B
Inn at Whitewell   £33   Ⓐ★
Forest of Bowland BD7 3AT   (01200) 448222
"A heavenly riverside setting" (in the Trough of Bowland), a
"warm" and "eccentric" style and "delicious" cooking have long
been a winning formula for this "fabulous" inn, "in the middle of
nowhere"; a new dining room, kitchen and some new rooms are
planned for 2005. / **Sample dishes:** goats cheese cannelloni with sweet
pepper sauce; grilled black pudding with lambs kidneys; British & Irish cheeses.
Details: 9.30 pm; D only (bar meals only at L); no Amex. **Accommodation:** 17
rooms, from £89.

COBHAM, SURREY   3–3A

La Capanna   £ 42   Ⓐ
48 High St KT11 3EF   (01932) 862121
*All agree this barn-like Italian of over a quarter of a century's
standing has an extremely "attractive" interior – the cooking,
however, incites reactions all the way from "tired" to "excellent".
/ Sample dishes: fresh crab salad; veal & scallops with mushroom sauce;
profiteroles. Details: www.lacapanna.co.uk; 10.45 pm.*

Cricketers   £ 29
Downside KT11 3NX   (01932) 862105
*An "attractive location for the summer" is what this "reliable"
pub, overlooking the village green, is all about – "get there early, if
you want a seat at weekends", to enjoy a pint and some
"traditional" grub. / Sample dishes: smoked haddock & salmon with poached
egg; roast lamb with garlic & rosemary; cheesecake. Details: 2m from Cobham
High St; 9.30 pm; closed Mon & Sun D; no smoking.*

COCKERMOUTH, CUMBRIA   7–3C

Quince & Medlar   £ 34   ★★
13 Castlegate CA13 9EU   (01900) 823579
*Colin & Louisa Le Voi's "well-restored townhouse" is "a surprising
place to find a good veggie", but all reporters agree the food is
"excellent". / Sample dishes: French onion tart; lentil & apricot strudel with
wilted spinach; spiced quince cheesecake. Details: www.quinceandmedlar.co.uk;
next to Cockermouth Castle; 9.30 pm; D only, closed Mon & Sun; no Amex;
no smoking; children: 5+.*

COGGESHALL, ESSEX   3–2C

Baumann's Brasserie   £ 35
4-6 Stoneham St CO6 1TT   (01376) 561453
*This "relaxed" and "unpretentious" brasserie is "a rare find in a
dreary area foodwise"; its "good menu choice" and "friendly"
service made a better survey showing this year.
/ Sample dishes: watercress soup with crispy spring onions; blackened beef with
Worcestershire sauce butter; maple syrup custard with apple cookies.
Details: www.baumannsbrasserie.co.uk; 9.30 pm, Sat 10.30 pm; closed Mon &
Tue; no smoking area.*

COLCHESTER, ESSEX   3–2C

Lemon Tree   £ 26   Ⓐ★
48 St Johns St CO2 7AD   (01206) 767337
*An "interesting" location set into the town's Roman wall is not the
least of the attractions at this "good-value" bistro, which serves up
"hearty portions of well-cooked traditional food".
/ Sample dishes: pan-fried scallops & spicy chorizo salad; roast lamb with garlic &
rosemary with salsa; baked black cherry cheesecake.
Details: www.the-lemon-tree.com; 9 pm, weekends 10 pm; closed Sun; no smoking.*

COLERNE, WILTSHIRE   2–2B
Lucknam Park   £ 78   𝔸 ★
SN14 8AZ   (01225) 742777
"*Great since Hywell Jones took over*" (in early 2004), this
"*sophisticated but relaxed*" Georgian country house hotel dining
room now "*maintains an exceptional standard of cuisine and
service*". / **Sample dishes:** spinach cappuccino with truffled quails eggs; roast
venison with game chips & spiced pears; citrus sorbets with citrus jelly.
Details: www.lucknampark.co.uk; 6m NE of Bath; 9.30 pm; D only, except Sun
open L & D; jacket & tie required; no smoking; children: 8+ at D.
Accommodation: 42 rooms, from £225.

COLSTON BASSETT, NOTTINGHAMSHIRE   5–3D
Martins Arms Inn   £ 52
School Ln NG12 3FD   (01949) 81361
This grand dining pub (and restaurant) is generally hailed as a
"*formal*" but "*friendly*" place with "*lovely*" food (including, at the
budget end, "*the perfect ploughman's*"); as ever, though, not
everyone is convinced that its higher-end prices are quite justified.
/ **Details:** 1.5 miles off A46; 9.30 pm; closed Sun D; no smoking.

COMPTON, SURREY   3–3A
The Withies Inn   £ 40   𝔸
Withies Ln GU3 1JA   (01483) 421158
This ancient and "*cosy*" inn in the Surrey Hills makes a
"*romantic*" destination (which has a "*pretty summer garden*",
too); even fans, though, note that this happy formula comes at
"*London prices*". / **Sample dishes:** pan-fried sardines with lemon; roast lamb
with rosemary; treacle tart & custard. **Details:** off A3 near Guildford, signposted on
B3000; 10 pm, 3 pm Sun; closed Sun D; no smoking.

CONSTANTINE, CORNWALL   1–4B
Trengilly Wartha Inn   £ 35   𝔸
Nancenoy TR11 5RP   (01326) 340332
"*A must-visit if you're in the area*"; this "*beautifully located*" rural
inn has won a good following thanks to its "*agreeable ambience*"
and its "*out-of-the-ordinary*" food and wine selection.
/ **Sample dishes:** scallops with creamed cabbage; duck with sherry & puy lentils;
nougat parfait. **Details:** www.trengilly.co.uk; 1m outside village; 9.30 pm; D only;
no smoking area. **Accommodation:** 8 rooms, from £78.

COOKHAM, BERKSHIRE   3–3A
Bel & The Dragon   £ 41
High St SL6 9SQ   (01628) 521263
"*Great food*" in an "*olde worlde*" atmosphere is a formula that's
made this "*friendly*" gastropub – part of a small themed chain –
a "*favourite in the area*"; as ever, though, some find it a touch
"*expensive*" for what it is. / **Sample dishes:** goats cheese & spinach strudel;
roast lamb with herb mash & raspberry jus; banoffi cheesecake.
Details: www.belandthedragon.co.uk; opp Stanley Spencer Gallery; 10 pm.

Inn on the Green   £ 41
The Old Cricket Common SL6 9NZ   (01628) 482638
There is the occasional report of "*the best meal ever*" at Mark
Fuller and Gary Hollihead's fashionably revamped inn, but the
balance of commentary is that it's "*vastly over-rated*".
/ **Details:** www.theinnonthegreen.com; 9.30 pm; closed Mon & Sun D; no smoking
area; booking: max 6 on Sat. **Accommodation:** 9 rooms, from £130.

Maliks £ 34 🅰★
High St SL6 9SF   (01628) 520085
*"Exceptional curry in an unusual curry venue" – that's the deal at this "good if expensive" outfit, housed in an "atmospheric" Tudor inn. / **Details:** www.maliks.co.uk; 11 pm; no smoking area.*

CORBRIDGE, NORTHUMBERLAND 8–2B

The Angel of Corbridge £ 33
Main St NE45 5LA   (01434) 632119
*Opinions on the atmosphere vary (from "stark" to "charming"), but this inn serves up "probably the best bar food in this culinarily deprived county". / **Sample dishes:** smoked salmon soufflé; roast guinea fowl; chocolate tart. **Details:** www.theangelofcorbridge.co.uk; 8.45 pm; closed Sun D; no smoking. **Accommodation:** 5 rooms, from £79.*

The Valley £ 28
Old Station Hs NE45 5AY   (01434) 633434
*A rural curry house, sibling to Newcastle's Valley Junction; "for the full experience, book yourself a seat on the Passage to India 'curry train'" – you order en route from Newcastle, for service on arrival. / **Details:** www.thevalleyrestaurants.co.uk; 11 pm; D only, closed Sun; no smoking.*

CORSCOMBE, DORSET 2–4B

Fox Inn £ 33 🅰★
DT2 0NS   (01935) 891330
*New owner Clive Webb seems to be making a great success of this "charming" thatched inn in a tiny village; with its "very good food" and its "warm atmosphere", it "makes an excellent place to stay, too". / **Sample dishes:** roast aubergines with tomato & Mozzarella; chicken with celery, red pepper & cream sauce; plum crumble. **Details:** www.fox-inn.co.uk; 5m off A37; 9 pm, Fri & Sat 9.30 pm; no Amex; no smoking area; children: 5+. **Accommodation:** 4 rooms, from £80.*

CORSE LAWN, GLOUCESTERSHIRE 2–1B

Corse Lawn Hotel £ 46
GL19 4LZ   (01452) 780771
*The Hine family are "hands-on" proprietors, and ensure very "reliable" standards in the bistro of this Queen Anne building, overlooking the village green. / **Sample dishes:** char-grilled squid with rocket & chilli oil; pigeon with lentils & black sausage; poached fruits with vanilla cream. **Details:** www.corselawn.com; 5m SW of Tewkesbury on B4211; 9.30 pm; no jeans or trainers; no smoking; children: 6+ at D. **Accommodation:** 19 rooms, from £105.*

COTEBROOK, CHESHIRE 5–2B

Fox & Barrel £ 27
Forest Rd CW6 9DZ   (01829) 760529
*A "very busy" country boozer whose "good pub food" is attested to by most – if not quite all – reporters. / **Sample dishes:** warm salad of shredded duck with bacon & toasted pine kernels; char-grilled pork loin with pan-fried pear & parmentier potatoes; sticky toffee pudding. **Details:** www.thefoxandbarrel.com; on A49 NE of Tarporley; 9.30 pm; no smoking.*

COVENTRY, WEST MIDLANDS   5–4C
Thai Dusit   £ 24
39 London Rd CVI 2JP   (024) 7622 7788
*"Consistent quality and value" make this "friendly" oriental a
great find in these parts; "a view of the ring road" is the only real
drawback.* / **Details:** 10.45 pm; no Amex.

COWBRIDGE, VALE OF GLAMORGAN   2–2A
Farthings   £ 28
54 High St CF71 7AH   (01446) 772990
*Natalie and Nick Dobson's "bustling" brasserie is something an
"oasis" in these parts; "superb desserts" are a highlight.*
/ **Sample dishes:** *French onion soup; wild boar & pheasant sausages with grain
mustard mash; hazelnut & raspberry meringue.* **Details:** *10 pm; closed Mon D &
Sun D; no Amex; no smoking area.*

COWLEY, GLOUCESTERSHIRE   2–1C
Cowley Manor   £ 45   𝔸★
GL53 9NL   (01242) 870900
*"A great place for getting thoroughly chilled out and staring into
your loved one's eyes"; this cool country house hotel may offer
"excellent cuisine in fine surroundings", but it is in fact the "simply
exceptional" service which reporters rate most highly.*
/ **Sample dishes:** *seared Scotish scallops; fillet of wild trout; chocolate pudding.*
Details: *www.cowleymanor.com; 10 pm; closed Sat; no smoking.*
Accommodation: *30 rooms, from £220.*

COWLING, WEST YORKSHIRE   5–1B
Harlequin   £ 33
139 Keighley Rd BD22 0AH   (01535) 633277
*"No airs and graces" encumber this "friendly" restaurant-cum-
wine bar; as ever, it is hailed by its small fan club as "a joy".*
/ **Sample dishes:** *calamari & chorizo salad; roast duckling with rhubarb compote;
Yorkshire ginger sponge.* **Details:** *on A6068 towards Colne; 9.30 pm; closed Mon &
Tue; no smoking; children: 7+ at D.*

CRASTER, NORTHUMBERLAND   8–1B
Jolly Fisherman   £ 15   ★
NE66 3TR   (01665) 576461
*"Good crab and an amazing location" (with "superb views") are
the prime attractions of this "cheerful" seaside inn.*
/ **Sample dishes:** *crab soup with whisky; kipper pâté with melba toast; blackcurrant
crumble with custard.* **Details:** *near Dunstanburgh Castle; 7.45 pm; L only; no credit
cards; no booking.*

CREIGIAU, CARDIFF   2–2A
Caesars Arms   £ 31   ★
Cardiff Rd CF15 9NN   (029) 2089 0486
*"Consistently good standards" have long maintained the appeal of
this rural fish restaurant, whose choose-your-own formula is
similar to Cardiff's La Brasserie.* / **Sample dishes:** *smoked salmon with
eggs & capers; honey-roast duckling; raspberry pavlova.* **Details:** *beyond Creigiau,
past golf club; 10.30 pm; closed Sun D.*

CREWE, CHESHIRE   5–3B

Crewe Hall   £45
Weston Rd CW1 6UZ   (01270) 253333
*Newly converted into an hotel (by Marston Hotels), this very
grand house, once home to the Earls of Crewe, offers a "very
enjoyable" all-round dining experience, in an area without a huge
amount of competition.* / **Details:** www.crewehall.com; 9.15 pm; closed
Sat L & Sun D; no smoking; children: 7+. **Accommodation:** 65 rooms, from £165.

CRICKHOWELL, POWYS   2–1A

The Bear   £37
High St NP8 1BW   (01873) 810408
*"Sound" cooking and "very good" service help make this "great
old coaching inn" a stop-off that's still of note for today's traveller,
though it can seem a bit pricey.* / **Sample dishes:** seared king scallops with
noodles; swordfish with wild rice; summer fruit pudding. **Details:** 9.30 pm; D only,
ex Sun L only; no smoking area; children: 7⅂. **Accommodation:** 34 rooms,
from £75.

Nantyffin Cider Mill   £32   A★
Brecon Rd NP8 1SG   (01873) 810775
*"A great rural hideaway", this long-established gastropub once
again won nothing but praise from reporters for its "rich, tasty
and locally-sourced" food, its "charming" service and its
"amazing" atmosphere (especially in the bar).*
/ **Sample dishes:** chicken liver parfait with red onion confit; red mullet with saffron
linguine & crab; Drambuie panna cotta with figs. **Details:** www.cidermill.co.uk; on
A40 between Brecon & Crickhowell; 9.30 pm; closed Tue (& Sun D in winter);
no smoking.

CROSTHWAITE, CUMBRIA   7–4D

The Punch Bowl   £34   ★
LA8 8HR   (01539) 568237
*"Imaginative cooking" of "London standard" – as you might hope
for, from the ex-head chef of Le Gavroche – is the theme of
almost all of the many reports on this gastropub "in the middle of
nowhere", which is "not expensive", considering.*
/ **Sample dishes:** beetroot & goats cheese tart; slow-cooked lamb with leek & white
bean stew; chocolate & ginger tart with honey ice cream.
Details: www.punchbowl.fsnet.co.uk; off A5074 towards Bowness, turn right after
Lyth Hotel; 9 pm; closed Mon & Sun D; no Amex; no smoking. **Accommodation:** 3
rooms, from £75.

CROYDON, SURREY   3–3B

Banana Leaf   £23   ★
7 Lower Addiscombe Rd CR0 6PQ   (020) 8688 0297
*"Good South Indian food" puts this "fun" destination "miles
ahead of any other Croydon curry house"; the staff are "very
friendly", too.* / **Details:** www.a222.co.uk/bananaleaf; near East Croydon station;
11 pm; no smoking area.

CUCKFIELD, WEST SUSSEX   3–4B

Ockenden Manor   £51   Ⓐ
Ockenden Ln RH17 5LD   (01444) 416111
*"Realistically-priced food" helps inspire consistently positive
reports on the "charming" panelled dining room of this "very
pleasant" Elizabethan manor house – a destination "full of old
world charm".* / **Sample dishes:** *truffle risotto; grilled beef with mustard sauce;
warm apple fritters.* **Details:** *www.hshotels.co.uk; 9.30 pm; no jeans; no smoking.*
Accommodation: *22 rooms, from £155.*

CUPAR, FIFE   9–3D

Ostlers Close   £45   Ⓐ★
25 Bonnygate KY15 4BU   (01334) 655574
*"Very good food" rewards all reporters who have visited this
"excellent" family-run high-street favourite, of over 20 years'
standing; it had a major refit in mid-2004.* / **Sample dishes:** *monkfish
with red pepper salsa; oxtail & pigs trotter roly poly with oxtail gravy; pineapple syrup
sponge.* **Details:** *www.ostlersclose.co.uk; 9.30 pm; closed Sun & Mon,
Tue-Fri D only, Sat L & D; no smoking; children: 6+ at D.*

The Peat Inn   £38   Ⓐ★
KY15 5LH   (01334) 840206
*Thanks to its "marvellous" cooking and its "huge" wine list (with
"fine choices at reasonable prices"), David & Patricia Wilson's
famous coaching inn still lives up to its reputation as a "stunning"
destination.* / **Sample dishes:** *roast scallops with leeks & smoked bacon; roe
deer fillet with cocoa bean purée; trio of caramel desserts.*
Details: *www.thepeatinn.co.uk; at junction of B940 & B941, SW of St Andrews;
9.30 pm; closed Mon & Sun; no smoking.* **Accommodation:** *8 rooms, from £165.*

DALRY, AYRSHIRE   9–4B

Braidwoods   £45   Ⓐ★★
Drumastle Mill Cottage KA24 4LN   (01294) 833544
*"Unforgettable", "a revelation", "superb" – reporters are not shy
in their praise of Keith & Nicola B's "efficient and charming"
restaurant, in a "small but not overcrowded" former cottage.*
/ **Sample dishes:** *curried prawn & coriander soup; honey-glazed duck with spiced
beetroot; raspberry crème brûlée.* **Details:** *www.braidwoods.co.uk; 9 pm; closed
Mon, Tue L & Sun D; closed 2 weeks in Jan & Sep; no smoking; children: 12+.*

DARTMOUTH, DEVON   1–4D

New Angel   £47
2 South Embankment TQ6 9BH   (01803) 832465
*John Burton-Race – chef at L'Ortolan at Shinfield in its glory days,
and with a chequered career since – took over The Carved Angel
by the harbour in mid 2004, too late for survey commentary; the
place had badly lost its way, so it offers much scope for
improvement.* / **Sample dishes:** *Dartmouth crab with smoked pepper relish;
lamb with root vegetable strudel & cherry jus; rhubarb soufflé.*
Details: *www.thenewangel.co.uk; opp passenger ferry pontoon; 10.30 pm; closed
Mon & Sun D; no smoking; children: 10+ at D.*

DAVENTRY, NORTHANTS   2–1D

Fawsley Hall   £ 52   🔸🅰

NN11 3BA   (01327) 892000

This grand Elizabethan house has a "beautiful rural setting", and was converted a few years ago into a "lovely" hotel; the food hasn't generally aimed to push back new culinary frontiers, but some reporters feel it's been "wonderful" since Phil Dixon's arrival. / **Sample dishes:** foie gras terrine with pickled cherries; herbed lamb with creamed shallots; raspberry soufflé with chocolate sorbet. **Details:** www.fawsleyhall.com; on A361 between Daventry & Banbury; 9.30 pm; no smoking. **Accommodation:** 43 rooms, from £130.

DEAL, KENT   3–3D

Dunkerley's   £ 36

19 Beach St CT14 7AH   (01304) 375016

An "old-fashioned" hotel dining room, specialising in "local fish"; it wins praise for its "consistent quality". / **Sample dishes:** caramelized scallops served with smoked bacon & velouté; barbary duck breast with thyme roast vegetables; dark chocolate tart with lemon grass ice cream & kumquat syrup. **Details:** www.dunkerleys.co.uk; 9.30 pm; closed Mon L; no smoking. **Accommodation:** 16 rooms, from £100.

DEDHAM, ESSEX   3–2C

Milsoms   £ 32   🅰★

Stratford Rd CO7 6HW   (01206) 322795

About as unlike its parent (Le Talbooth) as possible, this "lively", "London-style" bistro is arguably better value, too, offering cooking that's "well prepared" and "well presented". / **Sample dishes:** glass noodle & tiger prawn salad; braised lamb with mustard mash & sage fritters; raspberry ripple cheescake. **Details:** www.milsomhotels.com; 9.30 pm, Fri & Sat 10 pm; no smoking area; no booking. **Accommodation:** 15 rooms, from £95.

Le Talbooth   £ 43   🅰

Gun Hill CO7 6HP   (01206) 323150

"An experience, not a restaurant" – over half a century, the Milsom family's "delightful" Constable Country fixture (in a timbered riverside building) has carved a formidable reputation (mainly amongst those of mature years); it can seem "very expensive", though, for what it is. / **Sample dishes:** foie gras terrine; seabass with braised fennel & cucumber; hot chocolate & orange fondant. **Details:** www.milsomhotels.com; 5m N of Colchester on A12, take B1029; 9.30 pm; closed Sun D. **Accommodation:** 10 rooms, from £165.

DENHAM, BUCKINGHAMSHIRE   3–3A

Swan   £ 35   🅰★

Village Rd UB9 5BH   (01895) 832085

This "pretty" pub in a "lovely village" attracts only upbeat reports, not least for its "good cooking" and its "attentive" service. / **Details:** 10 pm.

DERBY, DERBYSHIRE   5–3C

Darleys   £ 40
Darley Abbey Mill DE22 1DZ   (01332) 364987
*"A beautiful position by the River Derwent" helps make this
locally-celebrated restaurant "a perfect location on a summer
evening"; fans say its new owners have "brought the cooking into
the 21st century", but there are also occasional doubters who say
they've "ruined it".* / **Sample dishes:** scallops with crispy crab risotto cakes;
roast pork belly with black pudding & mustard mash; spiced poached pears with
cinnamon shortbread. **Details:** www.darleys.com; 2m N of city centre by River
Derwent; 10 pm; closed Sun D; no Amex; no smoking.

DINTON, BUCKINGHAMSHIRE   2–3C

La Chouette   £ 41   𝔸★
Westlington Grn HP17 8UW   (01296) 747422
*Belgian chef Frédéric Desmette's "fun" restaurant is "not to be
missed" – his style can seem a little "eccentric", but his
"challenging" menus are unanimously hailed as "superb".*
/ **Details:** on A418 between Aylesbury & Thame; 9 pm; closed Sat L & Sun;
no Amex; no smoking.

DODDISCOMBSLEIGH, DEVON   1–3D

Nobody Inn   £ 29   𝔸
EX6 7PS   (01647) 252394
*This ancient inn may be "in the middle of nowhere", but it has
made a huge name for its "outstanding" lists – of wines, of
cheeses and of malt whiskies – and it's a "beautiful" place, to
boot; other aspects of the operation, however, are surprisingly run-
of-the-mill.* / **Sample dishes:** pork meatballs with sweet & sour sauce; quail
stuffed with rice & apricots; sticky toffee pudding. **Details:** www.nobodyinn.co.uk; off
A38 at Haldon Hill (signed Dunchidrock); 9 pm; D only, closed Mon & Sun;
no smoking area; max: 8; children: 14+. **Accommodation:** 7 rooms, from £76.

DUBLIN, COUNTY DUBLIN, *ROI*   10–3D

*Though clearly not geographically within the ambit of a
guide called **UK** Restaurants, we have included a small
range of the best-known names in the Irish capital. These
tend to be 'destination' establishments. Visitors looking for
less expensive dining may like to bear in mind that, like
London's Covent Garden, the popular tourist area of
Temple Bar is generally best avoided by those in search of
decent value. All restaurants are now no-smoking.*

Bang Café   € 53   𝔸★
11 Merrion Row D2   (01) 676 0898
*"It's Dublin's best, pound-for-pound", say fans of this multi-level
dining experience near St Stephen's Green, which offers
"interesting" modern Irish cooking and "extremely pleasant"
service; "for atmosphere, downstairs is probably best".*
/ **Sample dishes:** pan roast scallops with muslin potato & grilled pancetta; baked
sea bass with fragrant rice & snake beans; warm chocolate brownie with vanilla ice
cream. **Details:** www.bangrestaurant.com; 10.30 pm, Thu-Sat 11 pm; closed Sun;
no Switch; no smoking.

Clarence Hotel (Tea Rooms)
Clarence Hotel   € 84
6-8 Wellington Quay D2   (01) 407 0800
Fans say it's "a real treat" – especially for weekend brunch – to visit the dining room of this U2-owned design-hotel; doubters, though, can just find it "up itself" – "trading on being somewhere people might want to be seen". / **Sample dishes:** deep-fried potato & bacon cakes; chicken with spinach & black pudding jus; chocolate clafoutis with tiramisu ice cream. **Details:** www.theclarence.ie; opp New Millennium Bridge; 10.30 pm; closed Sat L; no Switch; no smoking. **Accommodation:** 50 rooms, from £315.

L'Ecrivain   € 95   ★
109a Lower Baggot St D2   (01) 661 1919
The food is "always first-rate" at this Gallic restaurant, which is "consistently considered one of the best in Dublin" (and a favourite "for a business lunch"); an "interesting set-up hidden away off the street", its interior does include some "ambience-free pockets". / **Sample dishes:** baked rock oysters with cabbage & bacon; seared blue fin tuna; summer berry truffle cake. **Details:** www.lecrivain.com; opp Bank of Ireland; 10.30 pm; closed Sat L & Sun; no Switch; no smoking.

Eden   € 60
Meeting House Sq D2   (01) 670 5372
This "slightly pretentious haunt of Dublin's beautiful people" remains a popular Temple Bar rendezvous – no surprise, then, that the menu can seem a touch "overpriced".
/ **Sample dishes:** smoked eel salad; organic pork & apricot stew; crème brûlée. **Details:** www.edenrestaurant.ie; near Olympia Theatre; 10.30 pm; no Switch; no smoking.

Jacob's Ladder   € 60   Ⓐ★
4-5 Nassau St D2   (01) 670 3865
If you can get "a window seat" ("with picturesque views overlooking Trinity Green"), it's hard to beat this "elegant" first-floor venture, where Adrian Roche's "heavenly" modern cuisine is served "with style and discretion". / **Sample dishes:** roast quail with quails eggs & celeriac cream; roast pigeon with lentils; rum & raisin brûlée. **Details:** www.jacobsladder.ie; beside Trinity College; 10 pm; closed Mon & Sun; no Switch; no smoking.

King Sitric   € 76
East Pier, Howth   (01) 832 5235
"Good seafood" and a "great wine list" feature in nigh on all commentary on the MacManuses' long-established restaurant-with-rooms (in a pretty suburb at the end of the DART).
/ **Sample dishes:** grilled scallops with black & white pudding; poached fillet of turbot, gigas oysters & caviar cream sauce; iced hazelnut parfait with passion fruit coulis. **Details:** www.kingsitric.ie; 10.30 pm; closed Sat L & Sun; no smoking. **Accommodation:** 8 rooms, from £132.

Mermaid Café   € 60   ★
69-70 Dame Street D2   (01) 670 8236
"The best place to eat in Dublin by miles" – not such a ludicrous claim for this buzzy and informal corner-restaurant near Temple Bar, which serves thoughtful, California-influenced fare and interesting wines. / **Sample dishes:** smoked fish chowder with celery biscuits; rabbit fricassée with oyster mushrooms & pancetta; pecan pie with maple ice cream. **Details:** www.mermaid.ie; near Olympia Theatre; 11 pm, Sun 9 pm; no Amex or Switch; no smoking.

Restaurant Patrick Guilbaud €140 ★
21 Upper Merrion St D2 (01) 676 4192
This "eye-wateringly expensive" institution has long been known
as Dublin's grandest dining experience, thanks to its "fabulous"
Gallic cuisine, which is complemented by a wine list running to
many hundreds of bins. / Sample dishes: lobster ravioli in coconut cream;
venison with pumpkin cream & black radishes; black fig confit with fennel.
Details: www.merrionhotel.com; 10.15 pm; closed Mon & Sun; no Switch;
no smoking. Accommodation: 145 rooms, from £370.

Roly's Bistro € 56 Ⓐ★
7 Ballsbridge Ter D4 (01) 668 2611
"Terrific buzz" is a defining feature of this "impressive"
Ballsbridge brasserie; the cooking is "very decent", too.
/ Sample dishes: spiced crab with angel hair pasta; Dublin Bay prawns with
tarragon rice; Jaffa Cake torte. Details: www.rolysbistro.ie; near American Embassy;
9.45 pm; no Switch; no smoking.

La Stampa € 60 Ⓐ
35 Dawson St D2 (01) 677 8611
It's the magnificent setting – a former ballroom – which sets apart
this atmospheric "stalwart" of the Dublin scene; this is a 'good
time' place rather than a foodie Mecca, and quite "pricey", too –
all aspects of the operation win consistent praise nonetheless.
/ Sample dishes: pan-fried foie gras brioche; roast fillet of beef; chocolate fondant.
Details: www.lastampa.ie; off St Stephen's Green; midnight, Fri & Sat 12.30 am;
D only; no Switch; no smoking area. Accommodation: 24 rooms, from £185.

DUNKELD, PERTH & KINROSS 9–3C

Kinnaird House £68 Ⓐ★
Kinnaird Estate PH8 0LB (01796) 482440
"Must be the best restaurant in the UK without a Michelin star…
and it should have two!" – reporters speak only in glowing terms
of this "beautiful" Edwardian country house hotel, on the River
Tay; "the wine list looks pricey, but there are some bargains if you
look for them". / Sample dishes: squab pigeon salad; pan-fried John Dory with
peas; hot pear soufflé. Details: www.kinnairdestate.com; 8m NW of Dunkeld, off
A9 onto B898; 9.30 pm; closed Mon-Wed in Jan & Feb; jacket & tie at D;
no smoking; children: 12+. Accommodation: 9 rooms, from £275.

DUNVEGAN, ISLE OF SKYE 9–2A

The Three Chimneys £57 Ⓐ★
Colbost IV55 8ZT (01470) 511258
"Watch seals and otters on your pre-prandial stroll", at this
famously "remote" and "romantic" cottage dining room; a few
reporters found their meal "much anticipated, but disappointing",
but the majority still say that "absolutely faultless" cuisine – using
"wonderfully fresh" produce – makes it "worth the trip".
/ Sample dishes: carrot, orange & ginger soup; black pudding with leek & potato
mash; warm apple & almond tart. Details: www.threechimneys.co.uk; 5m from
Dunvegan Castle on B884 to Glendale; 9.30 pm; closed Sun L; closed part of Jan &
Feb; no smoking; children: 8+ at D. Accommodation: 6 rooms, from £215.

DURHAM, COUNTY DURHAM   8–3B
Bistro 21   £36   𝔸★
Aykley Heads Hs DH1 5TS   (0191) 384 4354
This "unexpected treasure" – in a converted riverside warehouse,
away from the centre – has long had a reputation as "the only
place in town which serves really good food"; a "consistent"
destination, its set-price lunch menu is particularly approved.
/ **Sample dishes:** Cheddar & spinach soufflé; slow-cooked beef with polenta &
Parmesan crisps; profiteroles with pistachio ice cream. **Details:** near Durham Trinity
School; 10.30 pm; closed Sun; no smoking; booking: max 10.

Hide Café Bar & Grill   £31
39 Saddler St DH1 3NU   (0191) 384 1999
"Very popular, I don't know why"; this "trendy" (for Durham) all-
day stand-by – "more of a bar which serves food", including pizza
– thrives in the absence of much in the way of competition.
/ **Sample dishes:** duck spring rolls with wasabi mayo; pizza with anchovies & roast
peppers; sticky toffee pudding. **Details:** www.hidebar.com; 9.30 pm; no Amex;
no smoking area.

Pump House   £39
Farm Rd DH1 3PJ   (0191) 386 9189
Set in a former pumping station, this "popular" bistro boasts an
"interesting" menu; even fans, though, can find it "a tad
expensive" for what it is. / **Sample dishes:** pan-roasted scallops; stuffed
monkfish; mixed berries and cream. **Details:** www.thepumphouserest.com; 9.30 pm;
no smoking.

Shaheens Indian Bistro   £22   ★
Old Post Office, 48 North Bailey DH1 3ET
(0191) 386 0960
A "popular" and "crowded" curry house that's "well worth
finding" in this under-served city. / **Details:** 11 pm; D only, closed Mon;
no Amex or Switch; no smoking area.

EAST CHILTINGTON, EAST SUSSEX   3–4B
Jolly Sportsman   £36
BN7 3BA   (01273) 890400
"It's a bit tucked-away, down a lane", near the South Downs, but
this "nugget" of a gastropub "now only nods to being a country
local"; thanks to food that's "more imaginative than most", it can
get "fantastically busy". / **Sample dishes:** ham, asparagus & Manchego
salad; grilled halibut with crab mash & capers; apricot, walnut & ginger toffee
pudding. **Details:** www.thejollysportsman.com; NW of Lewes; 9 pm, Fri & Sat
10 pm; closed Mon & Sun D; no Amex; no smoking.

EAST GRINSTEAD, WEST SUSSEX   3–4B
Gravetye Manor   £76   𝔸★
Vowels Ln RH19 4LJ   (01342) 810567
For a classic country house experience, this long-established hotel
– with its "gorgeous" gardens, its "beautiful" Elizabethan building
and its "impeccable" service – is "as good as it gets"; the Herbert
family (owners since the '50s) sold this year (to the chef and
manager), and reports suggest that the cooking is now more
"exemplary" than ever. / **Sample dishes:** quail, black pudding & lardon
salad; roast John Dory; panna cotta with rhubarb.
Details: www.gravetyemanor.co.uk; 2m outside Turner's Hill; 9.30 pm; no Amex;
jacket & tie required; no smoking; children: 7+. **Accommodation:** 18 rooms,
from £170.

EAST LINTON, EAST LOTHIAN   9–4D

Drovers Inn   £31
5 Bridge St EH40 3AG   (01620) 860298
They brew their own real ale at this busy coaching inn, where the cooking is generally "inventive" and "well prepared", too.
/ **Sample dishes:** *chicken liver pâté with oatcakes; beef stew with herb dumplings; raspberry trifle.* **Details:** *9.30 pm; no Amex; no smoking area.*

EAST LOOE, CORNWALL   1–4C

Trawlers   £40   ★
On The Quay PL13 1AH   (01503) 263593
"Locally caught seafood, given a twist by a Louisiana chef" is making quite a name for this quayside outfit – in the evening, it can get "crowded". / **Sample dishes:** *steamed mussels; fillet of John Dory with rocket, capers & olives; fresh raspberry shortbread with cream & ice cream.* **Details:** *www.trawlersrestaurant.co.uk; 9.30 pm; D only, closed Mon & Sun; no Amex; no smoking; booking: max 6.*

EAST WITTON, NORTH YORKSHIRE   8–4B

Blue Lion   £33   𝔸★
DL8 4SN   (01969) 624273
"Roaring fires, fine wines and honest local food" are the sort of virtues which have made a name for this "lovely" and "remote" gastropub. / **Sample dishes:** *onion & blue Wensleydale tart; chicken with smoked foie gras sauce; lemon mousse with lemon shortbread.* **Details:** *www.thebluelion.co.uk; between Masham & Leyburn on A6108; 9.30 pm; D only, except Sun open L & D; no Amex.* **Accommodation:** *12 rooms, from £69.*

EASTBOURNE, EAST SUSSEX   3–4B

The Mirabelle
The Grand Hotel   £55
King Edwards Parade BN21 4EQ   (01323) 412345
On a good night, Gerald Roser's "first-class food" – twinned with "good" service and "a lovely dining room" – make for a very grand experience at this eminent hotel; "over-fussy" staff can grate, though, and at quieter times (lunch especially), buzz is notable by its absence. / **Sample dishes:** *salmon terrine with sweet pepper coulis; pork with Cumberland stuffing & Bramley apple sauce; warm toffee & date pudding.* **Details:** *www.grandeastbourne.co.uk; 10 pm; closed Mon & Sun; jacket or tie required at D; no smoking; children: 12+ at D.* **Accommodation:** *152 rooms, from £165.*

Tiger Inn   £24   𝔸★
The Green BN20 0DA   (01323) 423209
"Arrive early", as there's "limited space" at the bar of this "picturesque" but "unpretentious" pub in the centre of "a pretty little village near Beachy Head"; it offers "delicious home cooking", with "plenty of choice". / **Details:** *9 pm; no credit cards; children: 14+.*

EDENBRIDGE, KENT   3–3B
Haxted Mill   £45
Haxted Rd TN8 6PU   (01732) 862914
This "lovely old water mill" has a name for its "confident" cooking (including some "very good seafood"); even a reporter for whom this is a "family favourite", however, thinks it's "cashing in on its reputation with a vengeance". / **Sample dishes:** grilled oysters with spinach; roast rack of lamb with rosemary jus; fig tarte Tatin.
Details: www.haxtedmill.co.uk; between Edenbridge & Lingfield; 9 pm; closed Mon, Tue & Sun D; no Amex; no smoking.

EDINBURGH, CITY OF EDINBURGH   9–4C

The options for eating out in Auld Reekie have improved considerably in recent times. There remains only one restaurant of true note, however, and *Restaurant Martin Wishart* – the modern 'destination' restaurant of a type the city so obviously lacked until a few years ago – maintains its pre-eminence.

For sheer charm of the setting, the city has two remarkable venues – the *Witchery by the Castle* (the best-known place in town) and the *Vintners' Rooms*. Two modern rooms-with-views have also gathered quite a following – *The Tower* and the more recent *Oloroso*. For lunch, the long-established Italian deli and wine merchant *Valvona & Crolla* remains one of the most fashionable destinations.

The city has a lot of 'bourgeois' restaurants of solid quality – there are many in a style which would seem very 'traditional' elsewhere, but there are some quite modern places, too. Leith, and its waterside, remains the best place to go for a range of fun and relatively inexpensive options.

Ann Purna   £23
44-45 St Patrick's Sq EH8 9ET   (0131) 662 1807
An ever-popular Southside Gujerati – "not quite up to Kalpna, but an interesting alternative". / **Details:** 10.30 pm; closed Sat L & Sun L; no Amex or Switch; no smoking.

Apartment   £24
7-13 Barclay Pl EH10 4HW   (0131) 228 6456
The elder sibling of The Outsider, this "jolly" modern hang-out on the fringe of the Old Town still wins sound support for its "crowded, noisy and fun" style, and its quite "interesting" food (designed for sharing). / **Sample dishes:** wild mushrooms with aubergine & sweet potato; peppered rib-eye steak & fries; profiteroles with Cointreau sauce.
Details: between Tollcross & Bruntsfield; 11 pm; D only Mon-Fri; no Amex; no smoking area.

The Atrium   £42
10 Cambridge St EH1 2ED   (0131) 228 8882
Auld Reekie's seminal "trendy" place (now over ten years old) has long divided opinion; at best it's praised for its "spacious" setting and "great" modern cooking, but even some fans admit "it's not particularly good value", and critics just find it "complacent".
/ **Sample dishes:** courgette & Parmesan soup; roast duck with cabbage & bacon; marjoram crème brûlée. **Details:** www.atriumrestaurant.co.uk; by the Usher Hall; 10 pm; closed Sat L & Sun (except during Festival); no smoking.

blue bar café £33

10 Cambridge St EH1 2ED (0131) 221 1222

*The Atrium's "noisy" upstairs sibling is still quite popular as a "casual" rendezvous; its hard-edged '90s décor is looking "a bit dated", though, nowadays, and both food and service can be "erratic". / **Sample dishes:** char-grilled tuna niçoise; sea bream with tomato & courgette galette; apple tart with Calvados parfait. **Details:** www.bluebarcafe.com; by the Usher Hall; 10.30 pm, Fri & Sat 11 pm; closed Sun (except during Festival); no smoking area.*

Café Royal Oyster Bar £39 🄺

17a West Register St EH2 2AA (0131) 556 4124

*Any visitor to Auld Reekie should pay at least one trip to this Victorian seafood bar/brasserie, with its "etched glass in the windows, its linen napery and its delicious oysters"; "it's a bit off the boil nowadays, but still a fabulous location". / **Details:** opp Balmoral Hotel; 10 pm.*

Le Café St-Honoré £37 🄺

34 NW Thistle Street Ln EH2 1EA (0131) 226 2211

*"The atmosphere and accents make you think you're in Paris", at this "authentic", family-fun New Town brasserie, where the food is generally (if not invariably) "well prepared" and "served with care". / **Sample dishes:** carrot & ginger soup; sirloin steak with caramelised shallots; chocolate & fig steamed pudding. **Details:** www.cafesthonore.com; 10 pm; no smoking area.*

Centotre £33

103 George St EH2 3ES (0131) 225 1550

*The involvement of the Contini family (of Valvona & Crolla fame) has ensured this new pizzeria/trattoria (in a converted New Town bank) has been "bustling" from day one; there have been "teething problems", but – as you'd expect – the food and wine are "carefully sourced and chosen". / **Details:** www.centotre.com; 10 pm; closed Sun D; no smoking.*

Daniel's £26

88 Commercial St EH6 6LX (0131) 553 5933

*This "friendly", if "hard-edged", modern bistro in Leith specialises in the cuisine of Alsace; it is invariably reported to be a "good-value" destination. / **Sample dishes:** tarte flambé; duck confit with spring greens; spicy ice cream terrine. **Details:** www.daniels-bistro.co.uk; 10 pm; no smoking area.*

Dusit £30 ★

49A, Thistle St EH2 1DY (0131) 220 6846

*"Impressive food in cool surroundings" makes this New Town Thai consistently popular with reporters – "presentation and quality are always outstanding". / **Details:** www.dusit.co.uk; 11 pm; no smoking area.*

Fishers Bistro £34 🄺★

1 The Shore EH6 6QW (0131) 554 5666

*Reporters speak only well of this "brilliant seafood restaurant on the shores at Leith" – a "relaxed" and "unpretentious" operation, offering "great fish". / **Sample dishes:** red snapper with sweet potato & Parmesan rosti; monkfish & swordfish brochette with spinach tagliatelle; Turkish delight in brandy snaps. **Details:** www.fishersbistros.co.uk; 10.30 pm.*

Fishers in the City £33

58 Thistle St EH2 1EN (0131) 225 5109

"Good, but not quite as good as Fishers Bistro" – in a reversal of last year's pattern, this New Town warehouse-conversion was less highly rated than the Leith original; most of the time, though, it still serves up "fantastically fresh food, interestingly prepared". / **Sample dishes:** squid & octopus salad; whole Dover sole topped with roast hazelnut; orange sorbet. **Details:** www.fishersbistros.co.uk; 10.30 pm; no smoking area.

Forth Floor
Harvey Nichols £38

30-34 St Andrew Sq EH2 2AD (0131) 524 8350

An "amazing view" (a theme of Harvey Nichols group restaurants) helps add lustre to this AbFab-style import; fans, insist that, for lunch, it's "the best place in town", but ultimately it's just rather "forgettable". / **Sample dishes:** cured salmon with buckwheat blinis; grilled sea bass; strawberry & Mascarpone tart. **Details:** www.harveynichols.com; 10 pm; closed Mon D & Sun D; no smoking area; booking: max 8.

Glass & Thompson £22　　🄰★

2 Dundas St EH3 6SU (0131) 557 0909

"Deli-style food, with all ingredients of the highest quality" – that's the creed of this "busy" but elegant New Town snackery (recently expanded); attractions include "fantastic" cakes and "excellent" coffee. / **Sample dishes:** selection of roast vegetables; seafood platter; passion cake. **Details:** L & afternoon tea only; no smoking.

Hadrian's
Balmoral Hotel £33

1 Princes St EH2 2EQ (0131) 557 5000

In its different way, the Balmoral's number 2, brasserie-style operation, is – like the main restaurant – similarly mainly of note as "a useful lunchtime rendezvous" (and it has natural light, too); the food it serves is "good" and "simple". / **Sample dishes:** saffron risotto Milanese; sirloin steak with fries & green beans; orange & grapefruit in Sauternes jelly. **Details:** www.thebalmoralhotel.com; 10.30 pm; no smoking area. **Accommodation:** 185 rooms, from £225.

Haldanes £45　　★

39a Albany St EH1 3QY (0131) 556 8407

"Interesting fish and meat dishes" lead a discerning clientèle to this New Town basement, where you dine "surrounded by the pictures of Jack Vettriano and the Scottish Colourists". / **Details:** www.haldanes.com; 9 pm, Fri & Sat 9.30 pm; no smoking.

Henderson's £20

94 Hanover St EH2 1DR (0131) 225 2131

For "good-value and filling veggie fare", this self-service New Town institution of some 40 years' standing still boasts quite a following; perhaps unsurprisingly, it can feel "a bit seedy" nowadays. / **Sample dishes:** vegetable soup; baked aubergine & tomato with Mozzarella; banoffi pie. **Details:** www.hendersonsofedinburgh.co.uk; 10 pm; closed Sun; no smoking.

Indian Cavalry Club £26　　🄰★

3 Atholl Pl EH3 8HP (0131) 228 3282

"Great curries" and a "dignified atmosphere" combine to make this Raj-style subcontinental "Edinburgh's best Indian", for some reporters; beware weekends, which can be "very busy". / **Details:** between Caledonian Hotel & Haymarket Station; 11.30 pm; no smoking area.

Jacksons £ 40   𝔸
209 High St EH1 1PZ (0131) 225 1793
*For the an authentic taste of Auld Reekie, this Royal Mile
basement is hard to beat; usually it's billed as a safe rather than
spectacular experience, but some local reporters rate it more
highly.* / **Sample dishes:** *potato soup with pea ravioli; lamb with spring greens &
pearl barley; pear & almond tart.* **Details:** *www.jacksons-restaurant.com; 10.30 pm,
Fri & Sat 11 pm.*

Kalpna £ 22   ★
2-3 St Patrick Sq EH8 9EZ (0131) 667 9890
*"Very good-value", "skillfully-spiced" Indian (Gujerati) cuisine has
long made this well-known vegetarian, near the University, a
"totally reliable" destination.* / **Details:** *www.kalpnarestaurant.com;
10.30 pm, Fri & Sat 11 pm; closed Sun L; no Amex or Switch; no smoking.*

La Partenope £ 34
96 Daltry Rd EH11 2AX (0131) 347 8880
*Fans tip this Haymarket "neighbourhood" destination, where the
Neapolitan chef/patron offers "a more adventurous menu than
many local Italians".* / **Details:** *11 pm, Fri & Sat 11.45 pm; closed Mon L &
Sun L.*

Malmaison £ 40   𝔸
1 Tower Pl EH6 7DB (0131) 468 5000
*The "lively" dining room of this Leith waterfront design-hotel
remains quite a popular destination; on a good day, the cooking
can be "well presented" and "well priced", too.*
/ **Sample dishes:** *black pudding & potato pancake with apple; roast lamb with
minted peas & beans; crème brûlée.* **Details:** *www.malmaison.com; 11 pm.*
Accommodation: *100 rooms, from £129.*

The Marque £ 35
19-21 Causewayside EH9 1QF (0131) 466 6660
*"Consistently good food", "reasonable prices" and "friendly staff"
make this, the original Marque, popular with all reporters.*
/ **Sample dishes:** *butternut squash & red lentil soup; baked cod with salsa &
pancetta; rhubarb, ginger & apple crumble.* **Details:** *10 pm, Fri & Sat 11 pm;
closed Mon & Tue, Wed-Fri D only; no smoking.*

Marque Central £ 32
Grindlay St EH3 9AX (0131) 229 9859
*"Simple ingredients put together with love and imagination" – and
at "great-value" prices – make this somewhat functional theatre
district restaurant (by the Lyceum) well worth knowing about.*
/ **Sample dishes:** *smoked haddock fish cake with bacon & egg salad; corn-fed
chicken with Parma ham & roast potatoes; warm chocolate pudding.*
Details: *www.marquecentral.com; 10 pm, Sat & Sun 11 pm; closed Mon & Sun;
no smoking.*

Martins £ 42   ★
70 Rose St, North Ln EH2 3DX (0131) 225 3106
*Martin Irons's "cheese board litany" ("including a photograph of
one of the cows concerned") helps make this discreet New Town
fixture something of a "national treasure"; its approach can seem
a tad "dated" nowadays, but most reporters still find it "very good
all round".* / **Sample dishes:** *sea trout cannelloni with artichoke confit; guinea
fowl with morel mousse; basil-marinated strawberries.*
Details: *www.edinburghrestaurants.co.uk; 10 pm; closed Mon, Sat L & Sun;
no smoking; children: 8+.*

Mussel Inn   £30   ★
61-65 Rose St EH2 2NH   (0131) 225 5979
*This "noisy-but-fun", "basic-but-good" New Town bistro is a
popular stand-by for those in search of "very fresh fish", plus the
"delicious" mussels which are, of course, the house speciality.
/ **Sample dishes:** hot-smoked salmon Caesar salad; mussels with leeks &
horseradish; sticky date pudding. **Details:** www.mussel-inn.com; 10 pm; no smoking
area; booking: max 12.*

Namaste   £27   ★
15 Bristo Pl EH1 1EZ   (0131) 225 2000
*A recent move to a better location (near the university) "will only
improve its recognition", say fans of what some reporters extol as
"the best Indian in town"; a small place, its ambience is described
as "rustic but pleasant". / **Details:** 11 pm.*

**North Bridge Brasserie
The Scotsman**   £35   ⓐ
20 North Bridge EH1 1YT   (0131) 556 5565
*For a "relaxed" lunch, this "interestingly located" brasserie – in
the former Scotsman building – makes a "very smart"
rendezvous; given its prominent location, though, it seems to
create few 'waves'. / **Sample dishes:** crabcakes with sweet chilli salsa; beef
fillet with pepper sauce; mango delice & melon sorbet.
Details: www.thescotsmanhotel.co.uk; 10 pm. **Accommodation:** 68 rooms,
from £180.*

**Number One
Balmoral Hotel**   £70
1 Princes St EH2 2EQ   (0131) 557 6727
*"Good table-spacing makes for excellent business discussions", in
the smart basement of this famous grand hotel; most reporters
availed themselves of "Edinburgh's best-value lunch menu" –
dinnertime "can be very empty", and generates little feedback.
/ **Sample dishes:** crab & avocado salad with caviar; Dover sole roulade with
langoustines; rice pudding with basil sorbet. **Details:** www.thebalmoralhotel.com;
10 pm, Fri & Sat 10.30 pm; closed Sat L & Sun L; no smoking.
Accommodation: 188 rooms, from £290.*

Off The Wall   £46   ★
105 High St EH1 1SG   (0131) 558 1497
*"Good ingredients well cooked" and "an ever-improving wine list"
win praise for David Anderson's low-key venture on the Royal Mile;
service is "notably pleasant", too. / **Sample dishes:** slow roast belly of
pork with caramelised turnip; saddle of venison & chicory with date sauce; coconut
parfait with Scottish strawberries. **Details:** www.off-the-wall.co.uk; 10 pm; closed
Sun.*

Oloroso   £43   ⓐ
33 Castle St EH2 3DN   (0131) 226 7614
*A "wonderful" rooftop location and "superb views" have helped
make this ambitious two-year-old big news in Auld Reekie; the
food is still not entirely consistent, though, and some reporters find
it no more than "adequate". / **Sample dishes:** tandoori quail with pickled
cucumber salad; halibut with linguine & champagne sauce; deep-fried jam sandwich
with custard. **Details:** www.oloroso.co.uk; 10.30 pm; closed Sun (in winter only);
no smoking.*

Original Khushi's £18 ★
26-30 Potterow EH8 9BT (0131) 667 0888
*"Modern" premises ("with teak furniture and uniformed staff")
now distinguish this Edinburgh institution of 50 years' standing;
you still BYO, though, and still get Indian home-cooking "dirt
cheap". / **Details:** www.khushis.com; 11 pm; closed Sun L; no Amex; no smoking.*

Outsider £24 Ⓐ★
15-16 George IV Bridge
EH1 1EE (0131) 226 3131
*"Excellent food at really surprising prices" (from a menu designed
for sharing) is ably served at this "bright", "airy" and "trendy"
joint (sibling to The Apartment); if you bag a window seat, you
even get "a view of the floodlit Castle". / **Sample dishes:** steamed
mussels; king prawns with pinapple & coriander dressing; warm apple tarte Tatin
with cinnamon & vanilla pod ice cream. **Details:** 11 pm; no Amex; no smoking area;
booking: max 10.*

Le Petit Paris £28 Ⓐ★
38-40 Grassmarket EH1 2JU (0131) 226 2442
*"More peasant than posh" – this "intimate" and "genuine" Gallic
spot, near the Castle, offers "good food at good prices".
/ **Sample dishes:** smoked chicken & wild mushroom pancake; broccoli-crusted
salmon with lemon butter; chocolate truffle with cherries.
Details: www.petitparis-restaurant.co.uk; near the Castle; 11 pm; no Amex.*

Point Hotel £24
34 Bread St EH3 9AF (0131) 221 5555
*"Good-value" prices feature in most feedback on the dining room
of this budget design-hotel (in a former office-block); its
"interesting" minimalist décor found more favour this year.
/ **Sample dishes:** smoked chicken salad with pineapple salsa; courgette & broccoli
frittata; champagne sorbet with raspberries. **Details:** www.point-hotel.co.uk;
9.30 pm; closed Sat L & Sun. **Accommodation:** 140 rooms, from £125.*

The Restaurant at the Bonham £39
35 Drumsheugh Gdns EH3 7RN (0131) 623 9319
*"Everything is first-class", say fans of the dining room of this
"elegant" townhouse-hotel; it can seem "pricey for what it is",
though, and there's a not insignificant number of doubters who
think it "very average". / **Sample dishes:** timbale of crab & avocado with
mango salsa; pan fried fillet of beef, spinach & roast potato.
Details: www.thebonham.com; off west end of Princes St; 10 pm; no smoking.
Accommodation: 48 rooms, from £185.*

Restaurant Martin Wishart £58 ★★
54 The Shore EH6 6RA (0131) 553 3557
*"Stunning" cooking puts this Leith water-sider beyond challenge as
"Scotland's best restaurant"; the atmosphere of his much-enlarged
venture can seem "a bit stiff", though, nowadays – no doubt
Mr Wishart hopes that the tyre men will be suitably impressed.
/ **Sample dishes:** tortellini of asparagus, leek cream & white wine velouté; roast
saddle of lamb, ratatouille, sage beignet, pomme croustillante & tapenade; Armagnac
parfait, poached pear, praline biscuit. **Details:** www.martin-wishart.co.uk; near Royal
Yacht Britannia; 10 pm; closed Mon, Sat L & Sun; no smoking; booking: max 10.*

Rogue £35

67 Morrison St EH3 8BU   (0131) 228 2700

*"Smart" and "contemporary", this bar/restaurant is hailed by some reporters for its "well-presented food" at "reasonable" prices; doubters, however, find it "too under-populated to have much atmosphere". / **Sample dishes:** potato, rocket & goats cheese soup; roast monkfish with black pudding & mushy peas; pineapple soup with citrus sorbet. **Details:** www.rogues-uk.com; 11 pm; closed Sun.*

Santini £49

8 Conference Sq EH3 8AN   (0131) 221 7788

*An outpost of the swanky fixture in London's Belgravia, this smart Italian is to be found behind one of the city's grander hotels; supporters find the food "superb", "simple" and "fresh", but prices are "high". / **Details:** 10.30 pm; closed Sat L & Sun; no jeans or trainers; no smoking area.*

The Shore £33 Ⓐ

3-4 The Shore EH6 6QW   (0131) 553 5080

*This "lovely and intimate" bar/restaurant near the Leith waterfront offers "a short, fish-based menu"; the cooking is generally dependable and, on occasions, "very good". / **Sample dishes:** grilled sardines with smoked paprika sauce; grilled fish with couscous; plum & orange crumble. **Details:** www.theshore.biz; 10 pm; no smoking.*

Skippers £33 Ⓐ

1a Dock Pl EH6 6LU   (0131) 554 1018

*This atmospheric, if "somewhat cramped" Leith waterfront bistro has long been a "friendly" destination; it still wins praise for its "wonderful fresh fish and seafood", but the occasional reporter senses that the place is "going downhill". / **Sample dishes:** chicken liver parfait; seared salmon with Prosciutto-wrapped asparagus; treacle tart. **Details:** www.skippers.co.uk; 10 pm.*

Stac Polly £42

29-33 Dublin St EH3 6NL   (0131) 556 2231

*The "Scottish cuisine with a twist" at this "quiet and unassuming" fixture finds favour with reporters; the branch listed is in New Town cellars – it has a sibling at 8-10 Grindlay Street (tel 229 5405). / **Sample dishes:** baked filo pastry parcels of haggis; pan-fried fillet of Aberdeen angus beef; chocolate tart with Mascarpone ice cream. **Details:** www.stacpolly.co.uk; 9.15 pm; closed Sat L & Sun L; no smoking area.*

Suruchi £25 ★

14a Nicolson St EH8 9DH   (0131) 556 6583

*The menu may be whimsically inscribed in "Scottish dialect", but the Indian fare at this "unpretentious" outfit overlooking the Festival Theatre is "authentic" and "served with a smile"; there is also a Leith branch at 21 Constitution St (tel 554 3268). / **Details:** www.suruchirestaurant.com; opp Festival Theatre; 11.30 pm; closed Sun L.*

Sweet Melindas £35 ★

11 Roseneath St EH9 1JH   (0131) 229 7953

*"First-class fish and game" are the special strengths of this small, all-female-run "neighbourhood restaurant"; it can sometimes get "too crowded". / **Details:** 10 pm; closed Mon L & Sun; no Amex; no smoking.*

Thai Orchid £ 28
44 Grindlay St EH3 9AP   (0131) 228 4438
*"A good reliable Thai, conveniently situated opposite Usher Hall
and the Lyceum Theatre"; that's the whole story, really, on this
"friendly" stand-by.* / **Details:** 10.45 pm; closed Sat L & Sun; no smoking.

Tinelli's £ 29
139 Easter Rd EH7 5QA   (0131) 652 1932
*"Good home-cooking" helps impart a feeling of "rural Italy (in
winter)" to this long-established, "unpromisingly located" fixture,
near Leith Links; "the atmosphere is better in the evenings, when
it's cosier".* / **Sample dishes:** snails with bacon & mushrooms; baked rabbit with
cream & rosemary sauce; strawberry gelati. **Details:** 11 pm; closed Mon & Sun.

The Tower
Museum of Scotland £ 44
Chambers St EH1 1JF   (0131) 225 3003
*"Exceptional" views help make this elevated and "pricey" dining
room "a great place to impress"; standards (in particular,
"amateur" service) are too often "unimpressive", though, and
some reporters feel the place is "just too expensive for what it
offers".* / **Sample dishes:** lobster claw & pickled vegetable salad; chicken with
cep mash & Madeira jus; chocolate truffle torte.
Details: www.tower-restaurant.com; at top of Museum of Scotland; 11 pm;
no smoking.

Valvona & Crolla £ 30 ★
19 Elm Row EH7 4AA   (0131) 556 6066
*With its "heavenly" Italian delicacies (including a huge array of
wine at retail plus corkage), this Edinburgh "institution" (attached
to a 70-year old deli) has acquired "national treasure" status;
prices are "steep", though, and you "often have to queue" –
"even for breakfast".* / **Sample dishes:** pumpkin tortellini; Italian spicy
sausage pizza; lemon tart. **Details:** www.valvonacrolla.com; at top of Leith Walk,
near Playhouse Theatre; L & afternoon tea only; L only; no smoking.

Vintners Rooms £ 44 𝔸★
87a Giles St EH6 6BZ   (0131) 554 6767
*"Oozing historical charm", the "romantic", candlelit setting of this
age-old fixture on the way to Leith makes for a "memorable"
meal; the Gallic cooking had drifted a bit of late, but – after a
recent change of ownership – is "much improved".*
/ **Sample dishes:** smoked salmon with sweet cucumber pickle; chicken supreme
with lime & Madeira; chocolate pecan pie with coffee sauce.
Details: www.thevintnersrooms.com; 9.45 pm; closed Mon & Sun D; no smoking.

The Waterfront £ 31 𝔸
1c Dock Pl EH6 6LU   (0131) 554 7427
*"A great place to sit outside with a bottle, read the paper and
chill" – this "relaxed" hang-out on the Leith waterfront scores
highly for its "informal" style; its "lovely" fish dishes also get the
thumbs-up.* / **Sample dishes:** grilled sardines with feta & chick peas; swordfish
with hot & sour sauce; white chocolate & Bailey's cheesecake.
Details: www.sjf.co.uk; near Royal Yacht Britannia; 10 pm, Fri & Sat 10.30 pm;
no smoking area.

The Witchery by the Castle **£45** A
Castlehill, The Royal Mile EH1 2NF (0131) 225 5613
A *"fairy-tale"* candlelit setting creates a *"magical"*, *"wonderfully romantic"* ambience at this famously *"Gothic"* destination, near the Castle; the cooking is *"competent"*, too, but it is somewhat eclipsed by a wine list *"of biblical proportions"*.
/ **Sample dishes:** home-smoked salmon with sautéed green beans; seared scallops with lobster risotto; lemon meringue pie with rhubarb sauce.
Details: www.thewitchery.com; 11.30 pm. **Accommodation:** 7 rooms, from £250.

EGHAM, SURREY 3–3A
Great Fosters Hotel **£47** A
Stroude Rd TW20 9UR (01784) 433822
"Lovely surroundings and real old-fashioned service" provide the backdrop to a meal at this Elizabethan country house hotel, where the food *"has improved"* in recent times.
/ **Details:** www.greatfosters.co.uk; 9.15 pm; closed Sat L; no jeans or trainers; no smoking; booking: max 12. **Accommodation:** 46 rooms, from £150.

EGLINGHAM, NORTHUMBERLAND 8–1B
Tankerville Arms **£30**
15 The Village NE66 2TX (01665) 578444
A cosy coaching inn, worth knowing about if you're travelling; even a local fan, though, concedes that the fare *"can sometimes be a bit disappointing"*. / **Sample dishes:** smoked trout salad with lime dill sauce; rump steak with creamed green peppercorn sauce; fruits of the forest cheesecake.
Details: 9 pm; no smoking.

EGLWYSFACH, POWYS 4–3D
Ynyshir Hall **£60** A★★
SY20 8TA (01654) 781209
"A terrific place for a special treat", this *"superb"* restaurant-with-rooms in a Georgian house inspires only rave reviews; new chef Adam Simmons took over halfway through the survey year, but reports remained a model of consistency throughout.
/ **Sample dishes:** prawn cannelloni with caviar; seared turbot with lemon potatoes; hot mango & apricot soufflé. **Details:** www.ynyshir-hall.co.uk; signposted from A487; 8.45 pm; no jeans or trainers; no smoking; children: 9+. **Accommodation:** 10 rooms, from £160.

ELLAND, WEST YORKSHIRE 5–1C
La Cachette **£26** ★
31 Huddersfield Rd HX5 9AW (01422) 378833
"A vibrant wine bar/brasserie, serving excellent food in pleasant surroundings"; its *"superb wine list"* is also commended.
/ **Details:** 9.30 pm; closed Sun; no Amex.

ELSTEAD, SURREY 3–3A
Woolpack **£28**
The Green GU8 6HD (01252) 703106
"Home-cooked food and many ales on tap" are the sort of homely virtues commending this town-centre pub; with its *"very good salads and quiches"*, it's *"especially good for veggies"*.
/ **Sample dishes:** deep-fried calamari; steak & kidney pie; fruit pavlova.
Details: 7m SW of Guildford, on village green; 9.45 pm; no Amex; no smoking; no booking.

ELY, CAMBRIDGESHIRE 3–1B
Old Fire Engine House £ 37 Ⓐ★
25 St Mary's St CB7 4ER (01353) 662582
"Nothing is too much trouble", for staff at this *"wonderfully
quirky"* city-centre *"institution"*, which remains *"very popular"*; it
offers the rarest of all cuisine-styles – *"English home-cooking, with
a bit of flair"*. / **Sample dishes:** lovage soup; lemon sole with prawn & dill
sauce; old-fashioned sherry trifle. **Details:** www.theoldfireenginehouse.co.uk; 9 pm;
closed Sun D; no Amex; no smoking area.

EMSWORTH, HAMPSHIRE 2–4D
Fat Olives £ 35 ★
30 South St PO10 7EH (01234) 377914
"Book well in advance", for this *"attractive"* family-run operation
in a former fisherman's cottage, where *"good fish"* provides the
backbone of a *"varied"* menu. / **Details:** www.fatolives.co.uk; 10 pm;
closed Mon & Sun; no Amex; no smoking; children: 8+.

36 on the Quay £ 58 ★
47 South St PO10 7EG (01243) 375592
Ramon Farthing's cooking is often *"beautifully judged"*, and
reporters acclaim his *"very smart"* restaurant – overlooking a
picturesque harbour – as *"the best in the area"*.
/ **Sample dishes:** pan-fried mullet with pesto; scallops with chicken & goose liver
sausage; quartet of lemon desserts. **Details:** www.36onthequay.co.uk; off A27
between Portsmouth & Chichester; 10 pm; closed Mon L, Sat L & Sun; no smoking.
Accommodation: 4 rooms, from £85.

ENGLEFIELD GREEN, SURREY 3–3A
Edwinns £ 38
Wick Rd TW20 0HN (01784) 477877
"Reliable" and *"consistent"* are the sort of words which crop up in
reports on the *"posh"* small chain of which this is a leafy outpost
(on the fringe of Windsor Great Park); *"prices are slightly high for
the area, but then there's not much competition"*.
/ **Sample dishes:** warm duck salad; lamb steak; sticky pudding.
Details: www.edwinns.co.uk; 9.45 pm; closed Sat L & Sun D; no smoking.

EPSOM DOWN, SURREY 3–3B
Le Raj £ 36 ★
211 Fir Tree Rd KT17 3LB (01737) 371371
"Standing out in the Surrey desert", this grand modern Indian
wins praise – and not just from locals – for its *"terrific"* (and
"unformulaic") cooking. / **Details:** www.lerajrestaurant.co.uk; next to Derby
race course; 11 pm; no smoking area.

ESCRICK, NORTH YORKSHIRE 5–1D
Sangthai £ 22 Ⓐ★
Church Cottage YO19 6EX (01904) 728462
"An unexpected location for really good Thai food" – this
"friendly" and *"efficient"* operation, in a small village near York,
delights many locals with its *"superb"* cooking and its *"very
pleasing"* environment; weather permitting, summer visitors can
even dine outside. / **Details:** www.sangthai.co.uk; 10 pm; closed Mon,
Tue-Thu & Sat D only; no smoking.

ESHER, SURREY   3–3A

Good Earth   £ 39
14-18 High St KT10 9RT   (01372) 462489
*Even if it is "quite expensive", this "upmarket" Chinese veteran –
decked out in "very modern" style these days – is consistently
praised for its "precise" and "subtle" cooking. / **Sample dishes:** spicy
spare ribs; Mongolian lamb; toffee apples & ice cream.*
***Details:** www.goodearthgroup.co.uk; 11.15 pm; booking: max 12, Fri & Sat.*

Sherpa   £ 23   ★
132 High St KT10 9QJ   (01372) 470777
*"Good Nepalese food, without having to climb Mt Everest!" –
that's the verdict on the "unusual" menu served at this "friendly"
and "calming" small subcontinental. / **Details:** 11 pm; no smoking area;
children: 10+.*

Siam Food Gallery   £ 32   ★
95-97 High St KT10 9QF   (01372) 477139
*It's a mite "pricey", but this "assured" Thai wins praise for its
"calm" ambience and its "delicious" cooking. / **Details:** 11 pm.*

ETON, WINDSOR & MAIDENHEAD   3–3A

Gilbey's   £ 36
82-83 High St SL4 6AF   (01753) 854921
*This pleasant establishment remains "by far the best place to eat
in Eton"; an "interesting selection" of wines is a highlight, and at
"very reasonable prices", too. / **Sample dishes:** pork chilli pistachio
galantine; grilled fillet of black bream with new potato & watercress salad; toffee
apple with brown bread ice cream. **Details:** www.gilbeygroup.com; 10 min walk
from Windsor Castle; 10.30 pm; no Switch.*

Renata's   £ 46
110 High Street SL4 6AN   (01753) 852359
*"Willing" staff help endear this "formal" but "relaxed" restaurant
to reporters; "it's a bit pricey, but the food is always good".
/ **Sample dishes:** carpaccio of tuna and salmon; wild sea bass; chocolate tart.
Details: www.christopher-hotel.co.uk; 9.30 pm; closed Sun; no smoking.
Accommodation: 33 rooms, from £145.*

EVERSHOT, DORSET   2–4B

Summer Lodge
Country House Hotel & Restaurant   £ 48   Ⓐ
DT2 0JR   (01935) 83424
*A "beautiful setting" and exceptional service contribute to the
"very intimate" experience of dining at this 18th-century house
(complete with walled gardens); the Gallic menu is often "lovely",
too, though perhaps rather a supporting attraction.
/ **Sample dishes:** assorted melons & ham with raspberry & mint coulis; seared cod
with orange butter sauce; iced honey parfait with seasonal berries.
Details: www.summerlodgehotel.co.uk; 12m NW of Dorchester on A37; 9.30 pm;
jacket required at D; no smoking; children: 7+ at D. **Accommodation:** 20 rooms,
from £185.*

sign up for the survey at www.hardens.com

EVESHAM, WORCESTERSHIRE   2–1C

Evesham Hotel   £37   𝔸
Coopers Ln WR11 1DA   (01386) 765566
"Quirky" and *"entertaining"*, this *"professionally run"* hotel is *"a
well-disguised gem"*; it certainly offers *"good food"*, but the real
point is the *"massive"* wine list – it comes *"photo-album"* style,
and in three volumes (but excluding anything Gallic).
/ **Sample dishes:** smoked chicken, cherry & watercress salad; baked cod with red
wine risotto & mushrooms; lemon meringue ice cream.
Details: www.eveshamhotel.com; 9.30 pm; no smoking; booking: max 12.
Accommodation: 40 rooms, from £118.

EXETER, DEVON   1–3D

Brazz   £32
10-12 Palace Gate EX1 1JA   (01392) 252525
*Fans find this branch of a south western brasserie chain "a great
all rounder", and praise its "something-for-everyone" menu; it can
seem "flashy", though, and quality can be "variable".*
/ **Sample dishes:** mushroom brioche; chicken with lemon, leeks & wild mushroom
sauce; chocolate brownie with white chocolate sauce. **Details:** www.brazz.co.uk;
10.30 pm, Fri & Sat 11 pm; no smoking.

Double Locks   £22   𝔸
Canal Banks, Alphington EX2 6LT   (01392) 256947
*A "wonderful canalside location" makes this "cheap 'n' cheerful"
boozer something of a destination; it serves "good pub grub using
local produce".* / **Sample dishes:** garlic bread with Cheddar; turkey &
mushroom pie; sticky toffee pudding. **Details:** through Marsh Barton industrial
estate, follow dead-end track over bridges to end of towpath; 10 pm; no Amex;
no booking.

Herbies   £22
15 North St EX4 3QS   (01392) 258473
*This long-established veggie "still packs a great punch"; soups, in
particular, can be "terrific".* / **Sample dishes:** houmous with garlic bread;
mushroom sundried tomato; apple pie. **Details:** 9.30 pm; closed Mon D & Sun;
no Amex; no smoking area.

Hotel Barcelona   £38
Magdalen St EX2 4HY   (01392) 281000
*The "great modern setting" is perhaps more of an attraction than
the (mainly Italian) cuisine, but – all things considered – this is "a
good restaurant" (and it's attached to quite a "hip" hotel).*
/ **Sample dishes:** beef carpaccio with rocket & Parmesan; magret of duck with
couscous; chocolate fondant pudding. **Details:** www.aliashotels.com; 9.45 pm;
no smoking; booking: max 8. **Accommodation:** 46 rooms, from £95.

**Michael Caines
Royal Clarence Hotel**   £51
Cathedral Yd EX1 1HD   (01392) 310031
*Gidleigh Park chef Michael Caines's "amazing transformation" of
this "once-awful" hotel dining room won more consistent support
from reporters this year, with the "elegant" fusion cooking
attracting much praise.* / **Sample dishes:** red mullet with saffron risotto; duck
with roast garlic & spiced jus; chocolate nougatine with cherries.
Details: www.michaelcaines.com; 10 pm; closed Sun; no smoking.
Accommodation: 56 rooms, from £130.

St Olave's Court Hotel £35 ★
Mary Arches St EX4 3AZ (01392) 217736
Under its new ownership, the dining room of this attractive, slightly old-fashioned city-centre hotel is praised by all reporters for its "delicious" cuisine. / **Sample dishes:** creamy sweet potato soup; braised duck with creamed potatoes & green peppercorn sauce; honey cheesecake with lemon curd ice cream. **Details:** www.olaves.co.uk; 8.45 pm; no Amex; no smoking; children: 10+. **Accommodation:** 15 rooms, from £105.

Thai Orchid £29
5 Cathedral Yd, Three Gables EX1 1HJ (01392) 214215
A "superior" Thai, by the cathedral, serving "reasonably-priced" food in "pleasant" surroundings. / **Details:** www.thaiorchidrestaurant.co.uk; next to Exeter Cathedral; 10.30 pm; closed Sat L & Sun.

FAIRFORD, GLOUCESTERSHIRE 2–2C
Allium £45 Ⓐ★
1 London St GL7 4AH (01285) 712200
James & Erica Graham recently upped sticks from Hampshire's Vineyard at Wickham to found this, their own venture – a modern makeover of a grade II listed Cotswold building; on the basis of one or two early reports, it's putting in an impressive performance across the board. / **Details:** www.allium.uk.net; 9 pm; closed Mon & Tue; no Amex; no smoking; booking: max 8.

FARNHAM, DORSET 2–3C
Museum £36 ★
DT11 8DE (01725) 516261
"Exemplary upmarket bar food" makes this "beautifully restored" but "relaxed" pub uniformly popular with reporters; "the dining room is open Fri & Sat only – otherwise, you eat in the bar". / **Sample dishes:** mini-fishcakes with lemon butter; fillet of lemon sole; crème brûlée with raspberry sorbet. **Details:** www.museuminn.co.uk; 9.30 pm; no Amex; no smoking; children: 8+. **Accommodation:** 8 rooms, from £75.

FAVERSHAM, KENT 3–3C
Read's £58
Macknade Manor, Canterbury Rd ME13 8XE
(01795) 535344
"Elegant but unstuffy" – this long-established venture (until recent years housed in a converted supermarket) is now settling nicely into its new "Georgian mansion" home; it makes "a good outpost in a culinary wilderness". / **Sample dishes:** smoked eel with beetroot; calves liver with chive mash & melted onions; lemon & white chocolate mousse. **Details:** www.reads.com; 9.30 pm; closed Mon & Sun. **Accommodation:** 6 rooms, from £150.

FERRENSBY, NORTH YORKSHIRE 8–4B
General Tarleton £36
Boroughbridge Rd HG5 0PZ (01423) 340284
Living "in the shadow" of its sibling (the famous Angel at Hetton), this civilised but unremarkable-looking roadside inn risks invidious comparisons; fans insist that it's "outstanding", but the reporter who finds it "average" is closer to the general view. / **Sample dishes:** Jerusalem artichoke soup; tuna with butter bean mash & Parmesan crisps; lemon & ginger cheesecake. **Details:** www.generaltarleton.co.uk; 2m from A1, J48 towards Knaresborough; 9.30 pm; D only, except Sun when L only; no smoking. **Accommodation:** 14 rooms, from £85.

FLETCHING, EAST SUSSEX 3–4B
The Griffin Inn £ 38   🄰
TN22 3SS (01825) 722890
*"Great food, a traditional interior, good beer and a large garden
with splendid views"* – fans find all they could want in this *"posh"*
but popular pub; some find it *"expensive"*, but still it gets
"overcrowded". / **Sample dishes:** grilled sardines with chilli & wild garlic; roast
lamb with Mediterranean vegetables; rhubarb, honey & saffron tart.
Details: www.thegriffininn.co.uk; off A272; 9.30 pm; closed Sun D (in winter only);
no smoking. **Accommodation:** 8 rooms, from £85.

FORT WILLIAM, HIGHLAND 9–3B
Crannog £ 34   ★★
Town Pier PH33 7NG (01397) 705589
"Wonderful fresh fish and seafood" (*"interestingly prepared"*) and
"superb views down Loch Linnhe" win continuing rave reviews for
this excellent pier sider. / **Sample dishes:** surf clams & mussels with lemon
mayonnaise; pistachio-crusted halibut with risotto; treacle toffee pudding.
Details: www.crannog.net; 10 pm, 9 pm Dec-Mar; no Amex; no smoking.

Inverlochy Castle £ 80   🄰
Torlundy PH33 6SN (01397) 702177
"Be prepared for a serious dent in the wallet", at this epitome of
a Scottish Baronial pile, in the foothills of Ben Nevis – given the
"fabulous" food, reporters perennially seem to think it's worth it.
/ **Sample dishes:** wild mushroom tart with veal kidneys; roast duck with vanilla
mash & pickled cherries; orange crème brûlée with lemon & lime sorbet.
Details: www.inverlochycastlehotel.com; off A82, 4 m N of Ft. William; 9.15 pm;
closed Jan & part of Feb; jacket & tie required; no smoking; children: 12+.
Accommodation: 17 rooms, from £395.00.

Old Pines £ 42
Old Pines Spean Bridge PH34 4EG (01397) 712324
It's part of the deal that, chalet-style, you sometimes have to
share tables at this prettily located and well-reputed restaurant-
with-rooms; its cuisine, however, has recently struck some
reporters as being *"rather too home-made"*. / **Sample dishes:** scallops
with lobsters, mussels & spinach; loin of venison with spiced red cabbage, wild
fungi & thyme sauce; brown sugar meringue with pink gooseberries & elderflower ice
cream. **Details:** www.oldpines.co.uk; 8 pm; closed Mon; no Amex; no smoking;
children: 6+. **Accommodation:** 8 rooms, from £117.

FOWEY, CORNWALL 1–4B
Food For Thought £ 34   🄰★
4 Town Quay PL23 1AT (01726) 832221
This *"excellent fish restaurant"* on the quayside is *"slightly
expensive, but worth it"*… especially if you bear in mind its
"comfortable" dining room (*"with fine views"*), its
"comprehensive" wine list and its *"good"* service.
/ **Sample dishes:** pan-fried scallops; roast shellfish with garlic olive oil; chocolate
marquise. **Details:** www.foodforthought.com; 9 pm; no Amex; no smoking; children:
10+ at D.

Fowey Hall £ 47   🄰★
Hanson Drive PL23 1ET (01726) 833866
An Italianate member of the Luxury Family (country house) Hotels
group – its *"great"* location enjoys *"fabulous"* views over the
estuary, and the food can be *"imaginative"*, too. / **Sample dishes:** foie
gras; sea bass; raspberry & basil soufflé. **Details:** www.luxuryfamilyhotels.com; on
the main road next to the car park; 9.30 pm; no smoking; booking: max 10;
children: 12+. **Accommodation:** 24 rooms, from £155.

Sam's The Other Place   £35   ★
41 Fore St PL23 1AQ   (01726) 833636
*"A wide selection of very fresh fish and seafood", "imaginatively"
served, makes Sam Saxton's "relaxed" and "family-friendly"
restaurant a hit with all who comment on it.* / **Details:** *9 pm; no Amex;
no smoking.*

FOWLMERE, CAMBRIDGESHIRE   3–1B

Chequers   £30   ★
SG8 7SR   (01763) 208369
*"Pub food of a high order" again wins approval for this small
country inn, not far from Cambridge.* / **Sample dishes:** *Spinach & walnut
risotto; calves liver with horseradish mash & spinach; rhubarb & almond crumble.*
Details: *on B1368 between Royston & Cambridge; 10 pm; no smoking area.*

FRIDAY STREET, SURREY   3–1D

Stephan Langton   £30   ★
RH5 6JR   (01306) 730775
*John Coombe's "imaginative" cooking makes it worth seeking out
this Surrey Hills boozer.* / **Sample dishes:** *terrine of chicken livers; duck
confit; chocolate brownies.* **Details:** *10 pm; closed Mon & Sun D; no Amex;
no smoking.*

FRITHSDEN, HERTFORDSHIRE   3–2A

Alford Arms   £35   ★
HP1 3DD   (01442) 864480
*"Everything that a gastropub should be"; the only problem is that
you "need to book months ahead", if you want to savour its
"innovative" dishes, which are served in a "friendly" and "relaxed"
atmosphere.* / **Sample dishes:** *Dolcelatte & fig tart; roast cod & chorizo with
spinach; lemon crème brûlée.* **Details:** *www.alfordarms.co.uk; near Ashridge College,
by vineyard; 10 pm; booking: max 12.*

GANTS HILL, ESSEX   3–2B

Elephant Royale   £36
579-581 Cranbrook Rd IG2 6JZ   (020) 8551 7015
*"A desperately needed half-decent restaurant in an area where
there is a serious lack of such places" – this "cheesy" Thai, right
on the A12, offers "fairly authentic" cooking at "reasonable"
prices; it has a sibling on the Isle of Dogs.*
/ **Details:** *www.elephantroyale.com; 11.15 pm; children: no babies.*

GATESHEAD, TYNE & WEAR   8–2B

Eslington Villa Hotel   £33   𝔸★
8 Station Rd NE9 6DR   (0191) 487 6017
*"Quality" cooking that's "always good" helps make it "a real
treat" to dine at this "elegant" Victorian country house hotel.*
/ **Sample dishes:** *smoked haddock & chive risotto; pork & pancetta with sage &
onion mash; British cheeses with quince jelly.* **Details:** *A1 exit for Team Valley Retail
World, then left off Eastern Avenue; 9.30 pm; closed Sat L & Sun D; no smoking.*
Accommodation: *18 rooms, from £69.50.*

GLASGOW, CITY OF GLASGOW   9–4C

Glasgow has quite a line in 'institutions'. The fame of two of them – the very Art Deco *Rogano* in the city-centre and the rather '70s *Ubiquitous Chip* in the West End – is considerable (and you can expect to pay accordingly). *The Buttery* – the city's classic comfortable businessman's destination – is currently on top form. At less exalted price levels, such places as *Babbity Bowster* and *Café Gandolfi* are much treasured by the locals.

The city also has an extensive contemporary restaurant scene, but real highlights remain relatively thin on the ground. *Gamba* – a notable destination for fish-lovers – is an honourable exception, and another is the quirky *Gingerhill*.

At the lower price levels, many of the better choices are subcontinental.

Air Organic   £ 34
36 Kelvingrove G3 7SA   (0141) 564 5200
The Kelvingrove location may be "hard to find", but "good organic food" has won quite a name for this "original", "friendly" and "laid-back" outfit; after major upheavals on a recent change of ownership, however, a rating is not appropriate.
/ **Sample dishes:** roast tomato & Mozzarella crostini; beef fillet bento box; white chocolate & lemon cheesecake. **Details:** www.airorganic.co.uk; near Kelvingrove art galleries; 10 pm; no smoking area; booking: max 10 at weekends.

Amber Regent   £ 38
50 West Regent St G2 2RA   (0141) 331 1655
"Consistently good food" – it should be, at the prices – makes this grand city-centre Chinese a continuing local favourite.
/ **Sample dishes:** spring rolls; duck with garlic & plum sauce; toffee apples.
Details: www.amberregent.com; 10.45 pm; closed Sun.

Ashoka   £ 25   ★
19 Ashton Ln G12 8SJ   (0800) 454817
The "consistently good" Ashoka brand covers quite a number of Glaswegian curry houses (not all of them under the same ownership); favourite for many, though, is the "densely packed" and "buzzing" branch on Ashton Lane. / **Sample dishes:** vegetable & fish pakoras; chicken in coconut & chilli sauce; 'death by chocolate' cake.
Details: www.harlequin-leisure.co.uk; behind Hillhead station; 11.30 pm; closed Sun L.

Babbity Bowster   £ 31   Ⓐ
16-18 Blackfriar's St G1 1PE   (0141) 552 5055
"A good Scottish-French fusion" ("using fresh local produce") is proclaimed by the fans of this elegant (James Adam) Merchant City pub; for more formal events, choose the Schottische restaurant upstairs. / **Sample dishes:** poached Scottish oysters; beef with port & foie gras sauce; chocolate terrine. **Details:** 11 pm; D only, closed Mon & Sun. **Accommodation:** 6 rooms, from £50.

Brian Maule at Chardon D'Or   £ 45
176 West Regent St G2 4RL   (0141) 248 3801
"Interesting" Scottish cuisine has helped make a name for this "reliable" and "well-spaced" Gallic venture, near Blythswood Square; it's most popular for business, though, when it's easier to forgive the tendency some reporters discern to "stuffiness" and "overpricing". / **Sample dishes:** salmon with cucumber & dill dressing; coley with warm celery & lentil salad; roast pears with caramel sauce.
Details: www.lechardondor.com; 10 pm; closed Sat L & Sun; no smoking.

The Buttery   £ 55   A★
652 Argyle St G3 8UF   (0141) 221 8188
*You may have to "fight your way round the one-way system", to
find this "darkly inviting" Victorian restaurant, near the SECC; with
its "panelled" quarters and "very good, essentially French" food,
it's "a great expense-account destination, and priced accordingly".*
/ **Sample dishes:** *apple & beetroot pasta pave on a confit of venison; lamb with a
minted sausage hotpot; tiramisú with white chocolate & vanilla ice cream.*
Details: *10 pm; closed Mon, Sat L & Sun; no smoking.*

Café Gandolfi   £ 31   A
64 Albion St G1 1NY   (0141) 552 6813
*With its "great interior" and "brilliant laid-back atmosphere", this
Merchant City veteran is "a Glasgow institution"; "poor" service
can be a let-down, but the food – in both the bar and the
restaurant – is generally realised to a "good" standard.*
/ **Sample dishes:** *warm potato & chorizo salad; polenta with wild mushrooms &
Gorgonzola; rhubarb summer pudding.* **Details:** *near Tron Theatre; 11.30 pm;
no smoking area; no booking, Sat.*

Café India   £ 26
171 North St G3 7DA   (0141) 248 4074
*"Sean Connery and Billy Connolly are regulars", apparently, at this
"cool" and cavernous, "only-in-Scotland" curry-house, hailed by
fans for its "delicious" cooking.* / **Details:** *www.cafeindia-glasgow.com; next
to Mitchell Library; midnight; no smoking area.*

Café Mao   £ 28
84 Brunswick St G1 1ZZ   (0141) 564 5161
*"Tasty" fare draws a constant crush to this "noisy" oriental fusion
café, in the Merchant City.* / **Sample dishes:** *fishcakes; lemongrass & chilli
tiger prawns; frozen yoghurt.* **Details:** *www.cafemao.com; 11 pm; no smoking area.*

City Merchant   £ 37   A
97-99 Candleriggs G1 1NP   (0141) 553 1577
*"A good range of fish specials" is the culinary highlight at this
congenial, rather traditional Merchant City stalwart.*
/ **Sample dishes:** *smoked duck & bacon salad; venison with black pudding
mousse & apple jus; meringue nest with berry compote.*
Details: *www.citymerchant.co.uk; 10.30 pm; closed Sun; no smoking area; children:
5+.*

Crème de la Crème   £ 28
1071 Argyle St G3 8LZ   (0141) 221 3222
*"Glasgow's biggest curry house" is most notable, well, for being
just that; given the scale of the operation, in a former cinema,
though, the surprise is that it satisfies reporters on such a
consistent basis.* / **Details:** *near Scottish Exhibition Centre; 11.45 pm; closed
Sun L; no smoking area.*

étain   £ 44
The Glass Hs, Springfield Ct G1 3JX   (0141) 225 5630
*Conran's self-proclaimed 'first signature restaurant outside
London' occupies an elegant space on an upper floor of the
Princes Square Shopping Centre; early reports are broadly
favourable (if no more so than one would hope at the price).*
/ **Details:** *www.conran-restaurants.co.uk; 11 pm; closed Sat L; no smoking.*

Gamba £45 ★
225a West George St G2 2ND   (0141) 572 0899
"Great fish" and *"high-quality seafood"* are what this city-centre
cellar is all about (and they are most economically enjoyed from
the *"bargain-basement"* pre-theatre menu); in other respects, the
place is fairly unremarkable. / **Sample dishes:** mackerel with potato &
horseradish salad; roast cod with mussel & thyme stew; panna cotta with
strawberries & mint syrup. **Details:** www.gamba.co.uk; 10.30 pm; closed Sun;
children: 14+.

Gingerhill £36 A★★
1 Hillhead St G62 8AF   (0141) 956 6515
"Adventurous cooking using the freshest ingredients" makes Alan
Burns's (now licensed) dining room, above a suburban chemist's
shop, a surprisingly *"exciting"* culinary destination; it's to be found
a few minutes' walk uphill of Milngavie station.
/ **Sample dishes:** boudin of halibut, monk fish & lentils; confit of beef shin with veal
loin & sweetbreads; strawberry consommé with basil ice cream.
Details: www.gingerhillrestaurant.co.uk; 9.30 pm; closed Mon & Tue,
Wed-Sun D only; no Amex; no smoking; booking: max 12; children: 14+.

Ho Wong £35 ★
82 York St G2 8LE   (0141) 221 3550
"Yet to be beaten north of Manchester" – this *"excellent"* but
"expensive" Chinese may not have the most inspiring location
(near Central Station), but it inspires only rave reviews.
/ **Details:** www.ho-wong.com; 11.30 pm.

Ichiban £17 ★
50 Queen St G1 3DS   (0141) 204 4200
"Ideal after the theatre or cinema", this *"top noodle bar"* is
almost unanimously hailed for its *"quick service, great food and
great prices"*; there is another branch at 184 Dumbarton Road
(tel 334 9222). / **Sample dishes:** assorted sushi; pork chop curry & rice; green
tea. **Details:** www.ichiban.co.uk; 9.45 pm, Thu-Sat 10.45 pm; no smoking;
no booking at weekends.

Kama Sutra £26
331 Sauchiehall St G2 3HW   (0141) 332 0055
There was modest commentary this year on this trendily-styled
city-centre Indian (part of the Harlequin group), but such as there
was insists it offers *"amazing food in an amazing setting"*.
/ **Sample dishes:** chicken pakora; pan-fried machi fish & creamed spinach curry;
ice cream. **Details:** www.kama-sutra-restaurant.com; midnight; closed Sun L.

Killermont Polo Club £24 A
2022 Maryhill Rd G20 0AB   (0141) 946 5412
This colonial-themed Maryhill subcontinental doesn't inspire raves,
but is consistently well-rated, and noted for its *"reasonable"*
prices. / **Sample dishes:** prawn tikka; chicken stuffed with cheese &
pomegranate; fruit pavlova. **Details:** www.killermontpoloclub.co.uk; near Maryhill
station; 10.30 pm; no smoking area.

Lux £36 A
1051 Great Western Rd G12 0XT   (0141) 576 7576
A former railway station provides interesting premises for this
stylish bar & restaurant, on the leafy fringes of the West End;
even some who think the food is *"not refined"* find a visit here
"pleasant overall". / **Sample dishes:** roast pear & Stilton cheese puffs with
port compote; baked supreme of chicken with black pudding & apple risotto; crème
brûlée with homemade short bread. **Details:** www.lux.5pm.co.uk; 2m W of city
centre; 10.30 pm; D only, closed Sun; no smoking area; children: 12+.

Mitchell's   **£30**

157 North St G3 7DA   (0141) 204 4312
"A well-run family-owned bistro", praised by all reporters for
"simple fare, well cooked"; there is also a Carmunnock branch at
*107 Waterside Rd (tel 644 2255). / **Sample dishes:** grilled squid with*
chorizo; beef with crispy potatoes & mustard lentils; coconut tart with orange sorbet.
***Details:** 10 pm, Fri & Sat 10.30 pm; closed Mon & Sun; no smoking.*

Mother India   **£26**   ★

28 Westminster Ter G3 7RU   (0141) 221 1663
"The best authentic Indian food in Glasgow, perhaps Scotland" –
this long-running favourite, south of Kelvingrove Park, is hailed by
almost all reporters as "really excellent"; it now has a "tapas-
style" offshoot at 1355 Argyle Street (tel 339 9145).
*/ **Sample dishes:** aubergine fritters; chicken tikka passanda; gulab jaman.*
***Details:** beside Kelvingrove Hotel; 10.30 pm, Fri & Sat 11 pm; closed Mon L,*
Tue L & Sun L.

Mr Singh's India   **£27**

149 Elderslie St G3 7JR   (0141) 204 0186
A friendly Kelvingrove Park venture, where Scottish culture collides
with that of the subcontinent; fans say it's all-round "wonderful",
but there was also the odd gripe about standards this year.
*/ **Sample dishes:** pan-fried prawns with lime; south Indian garlic spiced chicken;*
*toffee pudding. **Details:** 11.30 pm.*

Mussell Inn   **£30**   ★

157 Hope St G2 2UQ   (0141) 572 1405
As at its more famous Edinburgh sibling, this basic and "vibrant"
city-centre establishment is praised for its "fresh" and "un-
*gimmicky" seafood, at "reasonable" prices. / **Details:** 10 pm;*
no smoking in bar.

Number 16   **£31**   ★

16 Byres Rd G11 5JY   (0141) 339 2544
"Small and solid", "tiny and reliable", "excellent food in cramped
conditions"… – the language may differ, but all reports on this
bistro near the Dumbarton Road come to pretty much the same
conclusion. / ***Sample dishes:** hot cheese fritters with apple & port sauce; roast*
*venison with spiced red cabbage; sticky toffee pudding. **Details:** 9.45 pm; no Amex;*
no smoking at D.

Parmigiana   **£34**   Ⓐ

447 Great Western Rd G12 8HH   (0141) 334 0686
"A loyal following much larger than the restaurant itself" attests
to the charms of this long-established, family-run Kelvinbridge
Italian, whose "discreet" atmosphere is "perfect for business";
now back on more regular form, it's "going from strength to
strength". / ***Sample dishes:** lobster ravioli; fish & shellfish soup with bruschetta;*
*lemon tart with cherries. **Details:** www.laparmigiana.co.uk; near Kelvinbridge*
station; 10.30 pm; closed Sun.

Rogano   **£50**   Ⓐ

11 Exchange Pl G1 3AN   (0141) 248 4055
An "amazing", "stylish" '30s Art Deco interior (apparently
modelled on the first Queen Mary) makes this "classy" local
institution a true rarity among British restaurants; "wonderful
fresh seafood" is the culinary highlight – there's a choice of places
to eat it, but the ground floor is "where the action is".
*/ **Sample dishes:** smoked salmon with quails eggs & caperberries; sea bream with*
*cabbage & bacon; chocolate & ginger snap cheesecake. **Details:** www.rogano.co.uk;*
10.30 pm; no smoking.

Room £ 40
I Devonshire Gdns G12 0UX   (0141) 341 0000
On the site of Gordon Ramsay's Amaryllis (RIP), this new offshoot of a groovy Leeds outfit – whose hallmark menu includes retro '70s dishes – has taken up residence at this grand boutique-hotel; it will be interesting to see if the new boys can succeed where local hero Gordon did not. / Details: www.roomrestaurants.com; 10 pm; no smoking.

Sarti's £ 27
121 Bath St G2 2SZ   (0141) 204 0440
Is complacency a besetting sin of Glasgow institutions? – it's certainly manifest at these "atmospheric" and "authentic" Italians (best known for their pizza), where some recent visits have been plain "disappointing"; the second branch is at 42 Renfield St (tel 572 7000). / Sample dishes: minestrone soup; four cheese pizza; tiramisu. Details: www.fratellisarti.com; 11 pm; no smoking area; no booking at L.

78 St Vincent £ 36
78 St Vincent's St G2 5UB   (0141) 248 7878
This impressive former banking hall can seem "uninspiring", but – as city-centre stand-bys go – it's "usually a safe choice"; it has also – as someone who admits to being part of the management proudly informs us – "been voted one of the city's top places for breakfast". / Sample dishes: rainbow trout with sweet pepper butter; halibut with braised fennel & rocket; white chocolate praline tart. Details: www.78stvincent.com; 2 mins from George Sq; 10 pm, Fri & Sat 10.30 pm; no smoking area.

Shish Mahal £ 22 ★
66-68 Park Rd G4 9JF   (0141) 334 7899
"One of the oldest in Glasgow, and still one of the best" – this "hardy perennial" curry house is notable for its "large" menu and its "generous" portions. / Details: 11 pm; closed Sun L; no smoking area.

Stravaigin £ 40
28 Gibson St G12 8NX   (0141) 334 2665
"Great Scottish ingredients with a fusion twist" have made this quirky bar (upstairs)/restaurant (cellar), near the University, a consistent local favourite; shortly before we went to press, a new chef (Daniel Blancowe) took over – let's hope he maintains his predecessor's "intelligent" standards. / Sample dishes: roast artichoke & garlic broth; chicken stuffed with red pepper & pesto; Belgian chocolate & ginger truffle tart. Details: www.stravaigin.com; 11 pm; closed Mon, Tue-Thu D only; no smoking.

Stravaigin 2 £ 31
8 Ruthven Ln G12 9BG   (0141) 334 7165
Prettily located in a mews, Colin Clydesdale's West End offshoot of Stravaigin remains fairly popular with locals, but the feedback it inspires is both more limited and less rapturous. / Sample dishes: mackerel on tapenade toast with balsamic bacon relish; spiced coconut crusted bream with yoghurt-dressed leaves; Sherry soaked lemon & poppy seed trifle with vanilla anglaise. Details: www.stravaigin.com; 11 pm; no smoking.

Thai Fountain £ 37
2 Woodside Cr G3 7UL   (0141) 332 1599
A classy oriental ten-year-old; it was (more) consistently favourably rated this year. / Details: www.thai-fountain.com; 11 pm, Fri & Sat midnight; children: 7+.

Two Fat Ladies £34
88 Dumbarton Rd G11 6NX (0141) 339 1944
For most reporters, this long-time fixture remains a "lovely" place, serving "great" fish and "superb" puddings; the occasional reporter, however, suspects "slipping standards". / **Sample dishes:** asparagus spears with hollandaise; lemon sole & salmon roulade with spinach; strawberry pavlova. **Details:** www.twofatladies.5pm.co.uk; 10.30 pm; closed Mon & Sun L.

Ubiquitous Chip £50
12 Ashton Ln G12 8SJ (0141) 334 5007
Ronnie Clydesdale's "romantic" West End venue, with its "great courtyard", is a famous destination for "good old-fashioned Scottish cuisine at its best"; it rather "trades on past glories", nowadays, but "the best wine list north of the Border" offers much compensation. / **Sample dishes:** vegetarian haggis & neeps; Loch Fyne herrings with tapenade mash & aubergine caviar; Caledonian oatmeal ice cream. **Details:** www.ubiquitouschip.co.uk; behind Hillhead station; 11 pm.

Wee Curry Shop £20 ★★
Buccleuch St G3 6SJ (0141) 353 0777
"An offshoot of the excellent Mother India", this "tiny" venture offers a "limited" menu of "first-class" Indian food at "very reasonable" prices; "on the downside, the tables are rather close together". / **Details:** 10.30 pm; closed Sun; no credit cards.

GODALMING, SURREY 3–3A

Bel & The Dragon £38 🄺
Bridge St GU7 3DU (01483) 527333
It's the "fantastic setting in a converted church", and the "helpful" service that make this foodie pub (part of a mini-chain) of note; praise for the cooking – though it generally pleases – is lukewarm by comparison. / **Sample dishes:** Thai crab & spring onion dumplings; Cumberland sausages with cabbage & bacon mash; apricot & honeycomb cheesecake. **Details:** www.belandthedragon.co.uk; 10 pm.

GOLCAR, WEST YORKSHIRE 5–1C

The Weavers Shed £39 ★
Knowl Rd HD7 4AN (01484) 654284
"Homely and professional" service adds to the "comfortable" ambience of this restaurant-with-rooms, housed in former cloth-finishing mill; the menu "flies the flag for home-grown ingredients". / **Sample dishes:** potted crab & avocado with egg mayonnaise dressing; rib-eye steak with potato wedges; sticky toffee pudding. **Details:** www.weaversshed.co.uk; 9 pm, Sat 10 pm; closed Mon, Sat L & Sun; no smoking. **Accommodation:** 5 rooms, from £75.

GORING, BERKSHIRE 2–2D

Leatherne Bottel £52 🄺
Bridleway RG8 0HS (01491) 872667
"Somehow both formal and relaxed", this "superbly-located" Thames-side "retreat" is a "consistent" performer, even if it's (unsurprisingly) "not cheap by any means"; "on a sunny day, nowhere beats its terrace". / **Sample dishes:** flat mushrooms on black olive toast; steak with chilli onions & deep-fried cabbage; sticky toffee pudding. **Details:** www.leathernebottel.co.uk; 0.5m outside Goring on B4009; 9 pm; closed Sun D; children: 10+.

GRANGE MOOR, WEST YORKSHIRE   5–1C

Kaye Arms   £ 34   ★
29 Wakefield Rd WF4 4BG   (01924) 848385
"More brasserie than country pub" – this very popular local is "a
little oasis" of "very good" cooking (complemented by "quality
wines at sensible prices"). / **Sample dishes:** smoked duck with sweetcorn &
walnuts; Cheddar cheese soufflé with stuffed peppers; coconut tart. **Details:** 7m W
of Wakefield on A642; 9.30 pm; no Amex; no smoking area; no booking on Sat;
children: 14+ at D.

GRASMERE, CUMBRIA   7–3D

The Jumble Room   £ 33   𝔸★
Langdale Rd LA22 9SU   (01539) 435188
"Lovely food and owners" is the gist of all reports on this pretty
little restaurant (which offers more formal dinners than its
daytime style might suggest) – "make sure you book ahead if you
want a weekend table". / **Details:** www.thejumbleroom.co.uk; 10.30 pm;
closed Mon & Tue; no Amex.

Lancrigg Country House Hotel   £ 34   ★
Easedale Rd LA22 9QN   (01539) 435317
An "excellent" Lakeland location and (generally) "great"
vegetarian food make this "fun" country house dining room
(owned by Robert and Janet Whittington for the last 20 years) a
popular destination for reporters. / **Sample dishes:** Parmesan & pine
kernel soufflé; chestnut, wild mushroom & cranberry tart; orange, sultana & pecan
pudding. **Details:** www.lancrigg.co.uk; 8 pm; no smoking. **Accommodation:** 13
rooms, from £100.

GREAT BARROW, CHESHIRE   5–2A

The Foxcote   £ 34   ★
Station Ln CH3 7JN   (01244) 301343
"Seemingly in the middle of nowhere", this pub has quite a name
for its "great range of seafood" (though "all tastes are catered
for"); fans say it offers "excellent value", especially for lunch.
/ **Sample dishes:** battered haggis with mustard; Thai red snapper with sticky rice;
sticky toffee pudding. **Details:** www.thefoxcote.com; 10 pm; closed Sun D; no Amex;
no smoking.

GREAT DUNMOW, ESSEX   3–2C

Starr   £ 51   𝔸
Market Pl CM6 1AX   (01371) 874321
There's "bags of character" at this "formal" inn, which has stood
on the market square for over half a millennium; the cooking is
"very good", if perhaps a mite "expensive" for what it is.
/ **Sample dishes:** smoked salmon with marinated vegetables; roast guinea fowl &
celery with grapes; aniseed parfait. **Details:** www.the-starr.co.uk; 8m E of M11, J8
on A120; 9.30 pm; closed Sun D; no jeans or trainers; no smoking.
Accommodation: 8 rooms, from £115.

GREAT GONERBY, LINCOLNSHIRE 5–3D

Harry's Place £67 ★★
17 High St NG31 8JS (01476) 561780
Harry Hallam's "small but special" front-room venture was rated
"still wonderful" by reporters this year; for first-timers, it's a
"fabulous surprise to find such good food in Lincolnshire!"
/ **Sample dishes:** mushroom soup with truffle oil; roe deer fillet with black
pudding & Madeira sauce; cherry brandy jelly. **Details:** on B1174 1m N of
Grantham; 9.30 pm; closed Mon & Sun; no Amex; no smoking; booking essential;
children: 5+.

GREAT MILTON, OXFORDSHIRE 2–2D

Le Manoir aux Quat' Saisons £110 A★
Church Rd OX44 7PD (01844) 278881
"A truly amazing experience" rewards most visitors to Raymond
Blanc's "simply perfect" manor house hotel near Oxford (which is
"particularly magical if you stay"); critics may complain of
"crucifying" prices, but this remains the UK's No. 1 dining
'destination'. / **Sample dishes:** quail egg ravioli with Parmesan & truffles; roast
Trelough duck with vinegar & tamarind sauce; pistachio soufflé with bitter cocoa
sorbet. **Details:** www.manoir.com; from M40, J7 take A329; 9.30 pm; no smoking.
Accommodation: 32 rooms, from £265.

GREAT TEY, ESSEX 3–2C

The Barn Brasserie £33 A
Brook Rd CO6 1JE (01206) 212345
Occupying a barn that's half a millennium old, this rural brasserie
has a "wonderful" setting; the prices for the "indifferent" cooking,
though, "cannot be justified". / **Sample dishes:** grilled garlic mushrooms;
crispy duck on sea-spiced aubergine; deep-fried chocolate ravioli with raspberries.
Details: www.barnbrasserie.co.uk; 10 pm; no smoking.

GREAT YELDHAM, ESSEX 3–2C

White Hart £34 A
Poole St CO9 4HJ (01787) 237250
"Each visit is a delight", says a fan of this ancient beamed inn ("in
pleasant grounds"), whose straightforward cuisine continues to
satisfy. / **Sample dishes:** wild mushroom & pigeon salad; steamed venison &
onion pudding; raspberry & Amaretto trifle. **Details:** www.whitehartyeldham.co.uk;
between Haverhill & Halstead on A1017; 9.30 pm; no smoking.

GRIMSTON, NORFOLK 6–4B

Congham Hall £45 A
PE32 1AH (01485) 600250
"Attention to detail" commends the dining experience at this part-
Georgian country house hotel, which has a "fantastic setting", a
few miles outside the town; (a major – £5m – expansion,
including to the dining room, is planned for 2004/05).
/ **Details:** www.conghamhotel.co.uk; 9.15 pm; no smoking; children: 7+.
Accommodation: 14 rooms, from £165.

GUERNSEY, CHANNEL ISLANDS

Auberge £38 A
Jerbourg Rd, St Martin's GY4 6BH (01481) 238485
A reputation as THE trendy modern restaurant on the island rather precedes this welcoming coastal spot; reporters say the food is "superb" – though in our own experience it's wholly unremarkable – but the distant view of St Peter Port is certainly impressive. / **Details:** www.theauberge.gg; 9 pm; no smoking.

Café du Moulin £44 A★★
Rue de Quanteraine GY7 9DP (01481) 265944
"Sublime food, superb service and a sensational setting" – as ever, all reports on Christo Vincent's rural Gallic venture, in a former granary, are a pure hymn of praise. / **Sample dishes:** lobster salad with mango & ginger dressing; oxtail cannelloni with truffle shavings & Parmesan; crème brûlée. **Details:** www.cafedumoulin.com; 9 pm; closed Mon & Tue L; closed Sun D in winter; no Amex; no smoking.

Da Nello £30 ★
46 Lower Pollet St, St Peter Port GY1 1WF
(01481) 721552
The top choice for a stylish meal in the heart of 'Town', this "friendly and attentive" Italian of long standing hides an impressive interior behind its tiny façade; "good ingredients are well cooked in the traditional manner". / **Details:** 10 pm; no smoking area.

New Fisherman's £33 A★
Rue de la Lague, St Peter Port GY7 9HU (01481) 263333
In a former fisherman's cottage, a Mauritian chef adds that bit of spice which is all too often missing from the local seafood cuisine; this is a cosy place, too, and, in a kitsch way, quite romantic. / **Details:** 9 pm; closed Mon.

GUILDFORD, SURREY 3–3A

Café de Paris £38
35 Castle St GU1 3UQ (01483) 534896
This long-established (and recently expanded) Gallic brasserie may not be earth-shattering, but it's a "reliable" and "friendly" place that makes a popular choice in a not over-provided town. / **Sample dishes:** onion & anchovy tartlet; guinea fowl casserole with tarragon sauce; lemon tart. **Details:** www.cafedeparisguildford.co.uk; 10.30 pm, Fri & Sat 11 pm; closed Sun.

Cambio £41
2-4 South Hill GU1 3SY (01483) 577702
This "slightly upmarket" Italian fixture moved to modern premises a year-or-so ago; if you find yourself in the area it's "recommended without hesitation" (though doubters note that it's "not really up to London standards"). / **Sample dishes:** black lasagne with crab; veal with Parma ham & sage; Amaretto mousse. **Details:** www.cambiorestaurant.com; by Guildford Castle; 10.30 pm, Fri & Sat 11 pm; closed Sun D; no smoking.

Thai Terrace £34   A★
Castle Car Pk, Sydenham Rd
GU1 3RT (01483) 503350
"Exciting and busy", this new opening is "raising the bar in Guildford" – with its "unusual", "super" food and "wonderful" views over the town from a "magic" terrace, it's widely hailed by locals as a "star" all-rounder. / Details: 10.30 pm; closed Sun; no Amex; no smoking.

GULLANE, EAST LOTHIAN   9–4D
La Potinière £48   ★
Main St EH31 2AA (01620) 843214
The dining room may be "slightly cramped and almost cottagey", but there are "some exceptional dishes" on offer at this "delightful" and "friendly" destination; it was relaunched by Keith Marley & Mary Runciman in late-2002 and is already again proclaimed "easily the equal of many more expensive London and Edinburgh venues". / Sample dishes: crispy salmon with vierge sauce; honey-roast venison; lemon tart. Details: www.la-potiniere.co.uk; 20m E of Edinburgh, off A198; 9 pm; closed Mon & Tue; no Amex; no smoking.

GULWORTHY, DEVON   1–3C
Horn of Plenty £49   A
PL19 8JD (01822) 832528
"Breathtaking views" help make this celebrated rural restaurant-with-rooms, near Tavistock, quite a "special" venue; while fans say it's still "all-round excellent", however, critics say "the food's not quite up to the surroundings". / Sample dishes: millefeuille of smoked salmon & crab; roast lamb with mint & pesto tagliatelle; cappuccino parfait & coffee meringue. Details: www.thehornofplenty.co.uk; 3m W of Tavistock on A390; 9 pm; closed Mon L; no smoking; children: 13+ at D. Accommodation: 10 rooms, from £115.

HALIFAX, WEST YORKSHIRE   5–1C
Design House £30
Dean Clough HX3 5AX (01422) 383242
Reports on this "ambitious" ultra-modern restaurant, in a former mill, remain relatively few – such as there are say that the wide-ranging menu "can be very good". / Sample dishes: smoked salmon & saffron risotto; pork belly with noodles & tempura vegetables; pear & cinnamon fritters. Details: www.designhouserestaurant.co.uk; from Halifax follow signs to Dean Clough Mills; 9.30 pm; closed Sat L & Sun; no Amex; no smoking.

Shibden Mill Inn £33   A
Shibden Mill Fold HX3 7UL (01422) 365840
This 17th-century inn – complete with a "beautiful location" and "roaring fires" – is a popular destination; foodwise, portions are "huge", but reports on its quality are very variable. / Details: www.shibdenmillinn.com; 9 pm. Accommodation: 12 rooms, from £65.

HAMBLETON, RUTLAND   5–4D
Finch's Arms £28   A
Oakham Rd LE15 8TL (01572) 756575
"Good food, well presented" helps make this "superbly located" inn a "reliable" destination; its large garden overlooking Rutland Water, makes it an ideal place to head for on a sunny day. / Sample dishes: artichoke tagliatelle; steamed beef with marrow & thyme dumplings; panna cotta with glazed kumquats. Details: www.finchsarms.co.uk; 9.30 pm; no Amex; no smoking. Accommodation: 6 rooms, from £75.

Hambleton Hall   £70   A★
LE15 8TH   (01572) 756991

"Excellent, if a bit formal and rather expensive" – that's the overview on this grand country house hotel, which has a *"magnificent location"*, overlooking Rutland Water; the food is usually *"sublime"*, and its complemented by a *"most extensive"* wine list. / **Sample dishes:** langoustine cannelloni; roast pigeon with foie gras ravioli & truffle sauce; pavé of white & dark chocolate. **Details:** www.hambletonhall.com; 9.30 pm; no smoking. **Accommodation:** 17 rooms, from £165.

HAMPTON COURT, SURREY   3–3A
Caffe La Fiamma   £30   A
Hampton Court Rd   KT8 9BY   (020) 8943 2050

"Watch the deer grazing while you eat", at this *"lovely Italian restaurant"*, next to Bushy Park; it *"never disappoints"*… *"well, except for the parking"*. / **Sample dishes:** prawns with white wine sauce & mango salsa; pasta with seafood & white wine tomato sauce; zabaglione. **Details:** www.clfuk.com; 11 pm.

HARLECH, GWYNEDD   4–2C
Maes y Neuadd   £43   A★
LL47 6YA   (01766) 780200

Cooking that's *"always competent and sometimes outstanding"* has carved out quite a name for this *"enterprising"* country house hotel restaurant; with its views of Snowdonia, it also benefits from *"one of the most beautiful locations in Britain"*.
/ **Sample dishes:** soused mackerel with Waldorf salad; chicken with bacon & garlic risotto; strawberry & mint delice. **Details:** www.neuadd.com; 3m N of Harlech off B4573; 8.45 pm; no smoking area; children: 8+. **Accommodation:** 16 rooms, from £150.

HAROME, NORTH YORKSHIRE   8–4C
Star Inn   £40   A★★
YO62 5JE   (01439) 770397

"The best pub food in the UK" maintains a huge reputation for Andrew and Jacquie Pern's thatched 14th-century inn – located in a *"sweet"* village – where the hospitality is *"second to none"*; (*"you can eat the same scoff in the bar without a reservation, but get there early"*). / **Sample dishes:** gammon terrine with fried quails eggs; braised rabbit with pea & mint risotto; lemon tart with blueberry sauce. **Details:** www.thestaratharome.co.uk; 3m SE of Helmsley off A170; 9.30 pm; closed Mon & Sun D; no Amex; no smoking. **Accommodation:** 11 rooms, from £90.

HARPENDEN, HERTFORDSHIRE   3–2A
Bean Tree   £40
20a Leyton Rd   AL5 2HU   (01582) 460901

Fans say you get *"West End quality"* at this *"great"* recent addition to the local dining scene; *"London prices"* to match, though, are a source of some disquiet. / **Details:** www.beantree.com; 9.30 pm; closed Mon, Sat L & Sun D; no smoking.

Chef Peking   £26
5-6 Church Grn   AL5 2TP   (01582) 769358

"One of the best Chineses in the area"; it's *"somewhat pricey compared to the other restaurants in town"*, but *"very popular"* nonetheless, especially *"at weekends"*. / **Sample dishes:** satay chicken; chicken in black bean sauce; ice cream. **Details:** just off the High Rd; 10.45 pm; no smoking area.

HARROGATE, NORTH YORKSHIRE   5–1C

Bettys   £30   Ⓐ
1 Parliament St HG1 2QU (01423) 877300
*"1920s service and ambience twinned with 2010 prices" – that's
the deal at the famous "tea shop that's become an institution";
it's very popular for breakfast, as well as for lunch and tea.*
/ **Sample dishes:** *Yorkshire rarebit; sausages & mash; fresh fruit tart.*
Details: *www.bettysandtaylors.co.uk; 9 pm; no Amex; no smoking; no booking.*

The Boar's Head   £39   Ⓐ★
Ripley Castle Estate HG3 3AY (01423) 771888
*A "posh" feel characterises this consistently-praised village inn
(owned by the local bigwig), which enjoys a "marvellous" rural
setting; the "excellent bar food" won particular praise this year.*
/ **Sample dishes:** *rabbit with caramelised apples; duck with summer vegetable
risotto; hot strawberry soufflé.* **Details:** *www.boarsheadripley.co.uk; off A61 between
Ripon & Harrogate; 9 pm; no smoking.* **Accommodation:** *25 rooms, from £125.*

Drum & Monkey   £29   ★
5 Montpellier Gardens HG1 2TF (01423) 502650
*"Book well in advance", if you want a table at this tiny and
"overcrowded" bar/restaurant, which – with its characterful
Victorian premises – has a huge name for offering "fantastic
seafood at brilliant prices"; reporters find it slightly less special
under its new ownership, but, as "an 'in' destination", it's still very
hard to beat.* / **Sample dishes:** *lobster delice; smoked haddock florentine; crème
brûlée.* **Details:** *10.15 pm; closed Sun; no Amex; L & afternoon tea only; booking:
max 10.*

Hotel du Vin et Bistro   £38   Ⓐ
Prospect Pl HE1 1LB (01423) 856800
*Most reporters agree that this new outpost of the celebrated
hotel-cum-bistro chain is a "really pleasant" destination, even if –
typically for the group – the "great" wine list and the "romantic"
setting outshine the workmanlike cuisine.* / **Details:** *www.hotelduvin.com;
9.45 pm.* **Accommodation:** *43 rooms, from £95.*

Quantro   £29   ★
3 Royal Pde HG1 2SZ (01423) 503034
*"Excellent food at reasonable prices" is the gist of all reports on
this "small and elegant modern restaurant".*
/ **Details:** *www.quantro.co.uk; 10 pm; closed Sun; no smoking; children: 8+.*

Rajput   £22   ★
11 Cheltenham Pde HG1 1DD (01423) 562113
*"One of Harrogate's best-kept secrets", this "welcoming" family-
run establishment dishes up "really wonderful Indian food"(using
"beautifully fresh" ingredients) at "fantastic" prices.*
/ **Details:** *midnight; D only, closed Mon; no Amex.*

Villu Toots
Balmoral Hotel   £34   ★
Franklin Mount HG1 5EJ (01423) 705805
*"A surprisingly good restaurant, attached to a small hotel" – all
reports agree this stylish modern venue offers, in particular,
"outstanding value at lunchtime".* / **Sample dishes:** *game terrine with
chicory & apple salad; tuna teriyaki with mango, lychee & red chard salad; apple &
cinnamon crumble tart.* **Details:** *www.villutoots.co.uk; 9.45 pm; D only; no smoking.*
Accommodation: *23 rooms, from £110.*

HARROW, MIDDLESEX   3–3A

Golden Palace   £ 28   ★
146-150 Station Rd HA1 2RH   (020) 8863 2333
*"The quality of the food is up to Hong Kong" – "and certainly to
Chinatown or Bayswater" – say fans of this "exceptionally good"
suburban Chinese; for lunchtime dim sum, the place is very
"busy" – "arrive early or queue". / Details: 11.30 pm; no booking, Sat &
Sun.*

Kaifeng   £ 50   ★
51 Church Road NW4 4DU   (020) 8203 7888
*For kosher Chinese, this "high-class" suburban fixture is "as good
as it comes" – "at a price", though, especially given the
"cramped" setting and the sometimes "grudging" service.
/ Details: www.kaifeng.co.uk; 10.30 pm; closed Fri & Sat L.*

Old Etonian   £ 31   Ⓐ★
38 High St, Harrow On The Hill HA1 3LL   (020) 8422 8482
*"Quirky" fare and a "stunning" view from the "romantic" terrace
combine to win only favourable feedback for this long-established
Gallic/Mediterranean bistro. / Sample dishes: crêpe aux fruits de mer; fillet
Dijon. Details: 10.30 pm; closed Sat L & Sun D. Accommodation: 5 rooms,
from £75.*

HARWICH, ESSEX   3–2D

The Pier at Harwich   £ 38   ★
The Quay CO12 3HH   (01255) 241212
*"Watch the ships come in", as you consume "good-quality fish
dishes" in the dining room of this traditional hotel (run by the
Milsom family, of Talbooth fame). / Sample dishes: roast pigeon breast
salad with fresh figs; Dover sole with nut brown butter & lemon; basket of
chocolate & hazelnut parfait with white chocolate sauce.
Details: www.pieratharwich.com; 9.30 pm; no smoking. Accommodation: 14
rooms, from £95.*

HASCOMBE, SURREY   3–3A

White Horse   £ 42   ★
The Street GU8 4JA   (01483) 208258
*"Welcoming" and "friendly" service adds to the appeal of this
cosy 16th-century inn, and it has a nice garden, too; the cooking –
in the bar or the restaurant – is not inexpensive, but wins
consistent praise from reporters. / Sample dishes: Thai fishcakes; roast
rack of lamb; sticky toffee pudding. Details: 10 pm.*

HASSOP, DERBYSHIRE   5–2C

Hassop Hall   £ 38   Ⓐ★
DE45 1NS   (01629) 640488
*"Excellent setting, wonderful building and great food" – one
reporter speaks for all about the "formal" dining room of this
"outstanding" country house hotel. / Sample dishes: smoked chicken &
avocado salad with bacon, orange & honey dressing; grilled fillet steak Rossini;
vanilla & dark chocolate mousse. Details: 9 pm; closed Mon L & Sun D;
no smoking.*

HASTINGS, EAST SUSSEX   3–4C
The Mermaid Café   £18   ★★
2 Rock-a-Nore Rd TN34 3DW   (01424) 438100
*"Great fresh fish, cooked fresh, and served with traditional English
trimmings by friendly folk in a simple place" – that's the winning
formula that's earned a very big name for this "topping" seaside
café; its breakfasts also get the thumbs-up. / **Sample dishes:** prawn
salad; skate & chips; spotted dick & custard. **Details:** 7.30 pm; no credit cards;
no booking, except D in winter.*

HATCH END, GREATER LONDON   3–3A
Rotisserie   £32   ★
316 Uxbridge Rd HA5 4HR   (020) 8421 2878
*A "friendly" place which "does what its name says"; "always
reliable" and offering "good value for money", it's "always busy".
/ **Sample dishes:** char-grilled spare ribs; ostrich with red wine & garlic sauce;
maple & pecan bread pudding. **Details:** www.therotisserie.co.uk; 10.30 pm;
Mon-Thu D only, Fri-Sun open L & D.*

Sea Pebbles   £24   ✦
348-352 Uxbridge Rd HA5 4HR   (020) 8428 0203
*"Very fresh, good fish" and a "pleasant" dining room combine to
make this family-owned chippie a reliable hit with reporters.
/ **Sample dishes:** calamari rings; deep-fried scampi & chips; bread & butter
pudding. **Details:** 9.45 pm; closed Sun; debit cards only; need 10+ to book.*

HATFIELD PEVEREL, ESSEX   3–2C
Blue Strawberry   £35
The Street CM3 2DW   (01245) 381333
*This "busy" bistro makes a "rare find" in a thatched rural cottage
building; it's still quite well-rated, but the feeling remains that
"over its ten years in business, it's lost some edge".
/ **Sample dishes:** Colchester oysters; duck with prune & pistachio stuffing; dark
chocolate & raisin pudding. **Details:** 3m E of Chelmsford; 10 pm; closed Sat L &
Sun D; no smoking.*

HAWORTH, WEST YORKSHIRE   5–1C
Weaver's   £35   𝔸
15 West Ln BD22 8DU   (01535) 643822
*"A delightful setting in a former weavers' shed" adds interest to
the Rushworth family's "lovely and relaxed" fixture of over 20
years' standing; the cooking is "original and well-sourced".
/ **Sample dishes:** monkfish, scallops & prawns; seared pork with wilted greens;
sticky toffee pudding. **Details:** www.weaverssmallhotel.co.uk; 1.5m W on B6142
from A629, near Parsonage; 9.15 pm; closed Mon, Tue L, Sat L & Sun D;
no smoking. **Accommodation:** 3 rooms, from £80.*

HAYWARDS HEATH, WEST SUSSEX   3–4B
Jeremy's at Borde Hill   £38   𝔸★★
Balcombe Rd RH16 1XP   (01444) 441102
*"Adventurous" dishes at "amazing value-for-money" prices win
enduring popularity for Jeremy Ashpool's civilised five-year-old; it's
set in gardens, so leave time for "drinks on the terrace" – when
the weather is fine, you can dine outside, too. / **Sample dishes:** prawn
bisque with prawn & coriander dumplings; rabbit with bubble 'n' squeak; apple &
rhubarb tart. **Details:** www.homeofgoodfood.co.uk; 15m S of M23, J10a; 10 pm;
closed Mon & Sun D; no smoking.*

HAZLEWOOD, NORTH YORKSHIRE   5–3C

1086
Hazlewood Castle Hotel   £ 40
Paradise Ln LS24 9NJ   (01937) 535354
*An impressive castle, which, say fans, offers "innovative" food
(and "caters well for big business events and weddings"); as usual,
though, reporters' views are mixed, and to detractors it just seems
"pretentious". /* **Sample dishes:** *hot smoked salmon with dried fruit chutney;
salmon with oriental greens; 'predictable' cheese & biscuits.*
Details: *www.hazlewood-castle.co.uk; signposted off A64; 9.30 pm; closed Mon,
Tue-Sat D only, Sun open L & D; no smoking; children: before 7 pm only.*
Accommodation: *21 rooms, from £140.*

HENLEY IN ARDEN, WEST MIDLANDS   5–4C

Edmunds   £ 33   ★
64 High St B95 5BX
(01564) 795666
*"Our London friends plead with us to book Edmunds… nuff said"
– indeed, you must "reserve well in advance" if you want to visit
this half-timbered house, and enjoy Andy Waters's "very good"
cooking. /* **Sample dishes:** *pan-fried sea scallops; fillet of lamb with hotpot;
poached pear with hazelnut cream & caramel sauce.* **Details:** *9.45 pm; closed
Mon, Sat L & Sun; no Amex; no smoking; booking: max 6.*

HEREFORD, HEREFORDSHIRE   2–1B

Floodgates
Left Bank   £ 38   𝔸★
20-22 Bridge St HR4 9DF   (01432) 349009
*Part of an impressive new riverside development, this "upmarket
brasserie/coffee house" benefits from "a very good ambience"
and "beautiful views"; it generated less feedback this year, but
ratings for its cooking remained consistently high.
/* **Details:** *www.leftbank.co.uk; 10 pm; no smoking area.*

La Rive at Castle House
Castle House Hotel   £ 55
Castle St HR1 2NW   (01432) 356321
*The "slightly formal" dining room of this Georgian townhouse-
hotel serves modern cuisine which is judged "very good" by most
(if not quite all) reporters. /* **Sample dishes:** *Thai risotto with tempura frogs
legs; salmon & crab brandade with lobster won tons; Pimm's jelly with cucumber ice.*
Details: *www.castlehse.co.uk; 10 pm; no jeans or trainers; no smoking.*
Accommodation: *15 rooms, from £165.*

HERSHAM, SURREY   3–3A

Dining Room   £ 34   𝔸
10 Queens Rd KT12 5LS   (01932) 231686
*This "higgledy-piggledy house" was converted over 20 years ago
into the "cosy" and "atmospheric" favourite it has become today;
its loyal local fan club finds the cuisine "good and reasonably
priced". /* **Sample dishes:** *Double Gloucester, ale & mustard pot; lamb & mint
pie; spotted dick.* **Details:** *www.the-dining-room.co.uk; just off A3, by village green;
10.30 pm; closed Sat L & Sun D; no smoking area.*

HERSTMONCEUX, EAST SUSSEX   3–4B

Sundial   £ 50
Gardner St BN27 4LA   (01323) 832217
*Mary & Vincent Rongier's "delightful" restaurant is still praised for
its "imaginative use of local produce" and its "warm and
attentive" service; doubters find it "not what it was", though,
saying prices are "unjustified".* / **Sample dishes:** *langoustine tails with
vegetable tempura; sea bass with stuffed courgette flowers; Breton shortbread with
lime & basil sorbet.* **Details:** *9.30 pm; closed Mon & Sun D; no Amex; no smoking.*

HETTON, NORTH YORKSHIRE   5–1B

The Angel   £ 38   A★★
BD23 6LT   (01756) 730263
*"It's still overcrowded, but for food of this quality that's to be
expected" – this Dales legend (England's best-known dining pub)
remains a phenomenally popular destination, due to its "haute
pub cuisine" (with fish a highlight), its "excellent" and "varied"
wine list, and its "lovely" rural location.* / **Sample dishes:** *black pudding
with lentils & pancetta; rack of lamb with thyme mash; sticky toffee pudding.*
Details: *www.angelhetton.co.uk; 5m N of Skipton off B6265 at Rylstone; 9 pm;
D only, except Sun when L only; no smoking area.* **Accommodation:** *5 rooms,
from £120.*

HINTLESHAM, SUFFOLK   3–1C

Hintlesham Hall   £ 55   A
Dodge St IP8 3NS   (01473) 652334
*The "delightful" and "incredibly romantic" dining room of this
country house hotel (first made famous by Robert Carrier) is a
"good all-rounder"; the setting, in particular, is "amazing" and
service is "excellent", too.* / **Sample dishes:** *smoked haddock, mussel &
roast vegetable salad; lamb chump with harissa mash; iced raspberry parfait.*
Details: *www.hintleshamhall.com; 4m W of Ipswich on A1071; 9.30 pm; closed
Sat L; jacket & tie required; no smoking; children: 12+.* **Accommodation:** *33
rooms, from £110.*

HISTON, CAMBRIDGESHIRE   3–1B

Phoenix   £ 26
20 The Green CB4 4JA   (01223) 233766
*This popular oriental near the village green remains "the best
Chinese in the area"; there is a view, though, that "that isn't
saying much".* / **Sample dishes:** *pepper & salt squid; smoked chicken salad; ice
cream.* **Details:** *10.30 pm; no Amex; no smoking area.*

HOCKLEY HEATH, WARWICKSHIRE   5–4C

Nuthurst Grange   £ 60
Nuthurst Grange Ln B94 5NL   (01564) 783972
*In the lush countryside south of Brum, this grand country house
hotel is a natural for "a celebratory business lunch" (or, on
Sunday, en famille); dinner time can seem "not nearly such good
value".* / **Sample dishes:** *tomato, red pepper & olive oil soup; smoked sirloin
steak with artichokes & wild mushrooms; Victoria plum & ginger soufflé.*
Details: *www.nuthurst-grange.com; J4 off M42, A3400; 9.30 pm; closed Sat L;
no jeans or trainers; no smoking area.* **Accommodation:** *15 rooms, from £165.*

HOLKHAM, NORFOLK   6–3C
Victoria Hotel   £ 43
Park Rd NR23 1RG   (01328) 711008
"A real port in a storm" for those seeking modern style on the
Norfolk coast, this trendified beach-facing pub serves quite an
"interesting" menu; the crowd can *"be a bit South Kensington"*,
though, and some find service *"laid-back"* to the point of being
"supercilious". / **Sample dishes:** smoked eel with apple & horseradish
vinaigrette; venison with creamed cabbage & chocolate sauce; tarte Tatin with green
apple sorbet. **Details:** www.victoriaatholkham.co.uk; 9.30 pm; no Amex; no smoking
area; children: 7+ at D. **Accommodation:** 11 rooms, from £120.

HOLT, NORFOLK   6–3C
Yetman's   £ 48   A★
37 Norwich Rd NR25 6SA   (01263) 713320
"We love Peter and Alison!" – *"simple and stylish"* cooking that's
"to die for" makes this *"snug"* husband-and-wife outfit *"Norfolk's
best restaurant"*, for some reporters; it has an *"interesting"* wine
list, too. / **Sample dishes:** Louisiana crabcakes with red pepper mayonnaise;
char-grilled duck with spiced figs; passion fruit & mango bombe.
Details: www.yetmans.net; on A148, 20m N of Norwich; 9.30 pm; D only, except
Sun when L only (open Sun D Jul & Aug); no smoking.

HORNDON ON THE HILL, ESSEX   3–3C
The Bell Inn   £ 35   A★
High Rd SS17 8LD   (01375) 642463
A *"wonderful"* half-timbered inn that's uniformly praised for its
"sophisticated pub food"; you can't book, and *"getting a table can
be difficult"*. / **Sample dishes:** sweet potato & garlic soup; roast duck with
stuffed squid & parsnips; apple crumble with praline ice cream.
Details: www.bell-inn.co.uk; signposted off B1007, off A13; 9.45 pm; no smoking;
booking: max 12. **Accommodation:** 15 rooms, from £50.

HORTON, NORTHANTS   3–1A
The New French Partridge   £ 36   ★
Newport Pagnell Rd NN7 2AP   (01604) 870033
"Superb" and *"beautifully presented"* cooking (mainly French) is
creating quite a following for Mr and Mrs Banerjee's village
restaurant; even fans, though, can sometimes find it *"expensive
for what it is"*. / **Sample dishes:** galatine of chicken, boudin noir, guinea fowl,
sauce gribiche; rack of lamb, three-peppercorn crust with vegetable gâteau &
redcurrant jus; raspberry brulée with blackcurrant sorbet.
Details: www.newfrenchpartridge.co.uk; on B526 between Newport Pagnell &
Northampton; 9.30 pm; closed Mon & Sun D; no jeans; no smoking.
Accommodation: 10 rooms, from £170.

HOUGHTON CONQUEST, BEDFORDSHIRE   3–2A
Knife & Cleaver   £ 35
The Grove MK45 3LA   (01234) 740387
"An unlikely location for a good fish restaurant", this conservatory
attached to a 17th-century inn wins consistent praise for its
"intelligently-prepared" food. / **Sample dishes:** salt cod tortilla with black
olive sauce; beef with wild mushrooms, Stilton & crispy onions; chocolate marquise
with raspberry coulis. **Details:** www.knifeandcleaver.com; off A6, 5m S of Bedford;
9.30 pm; closed Sat L & Sun D; no smoking. **Accommodation:** 9 rooms,
from £53.

HOYLAKE, MERSEYSIDE 5–2A

Lino's £32 ★

122 Market St CH47 3BH (0151) 632 1408

"Never fails to impress, and we've been going for 15 years"; the Galantini family's Anglo-French fixture still inspires consistently positive critiques, not only for its "never-had-a-bad-meal" cooking, but also for service that's "second-to-none". / **Sample dishes:** three cheese & onion tartlet; roast duck with bitter sweet orange sauce; nut, rum & raisin chocolates. **Details:** www.linosrestaurant.co.uk; 3m from M53, J2; 10 pm; closed Mon & Sun; closed Aug; no Amex.

HUDDERSFIELD, WEST YORKSHIRE 5–1C

Bradley's £26 ★

84 Fitzwilliam St HD1 5BB (01484) 516773

"Crowded, but full of fun", this "lively" town-centre bistro is "overseen by an engagingly hyperactive proprietor"; it enjoys a big local reputation, thanks not least to its "good-value" menus. / **Sample dishes:** chicken fritters with peanut & lime dip; roast lamb with cherry tomato couscous; mango tart with caramel ice cream. **Details:** www.bradleys-restaurant.co.uk; 10 pm; closed Sat L & Sun L; no Amex; no smoking area.

Nawaab £26 ★

35 Westgate HD1 1NY (01484) 422775

"A good town-centre Indian" – not much to add, really, on this ever-popular spot. / **Details:** www.nawaab.co.uk; between bus & railway stations; 11.30 pm; D only; no smoking area.

HULL, KINGSTON UPON HULL 6–2A

Cerutti's £38

10 Nelson St HU1 1XE (01482) 328501

"A strange place to find tucked away on the port side of Hull", this fish restaurant in an old Georgian house overlooking the Humber has quite a name locally; "the food can be very good, but less elaborate dishes are best". / **Sample dishes:** seared scallops served with black pudding; roast fillet of turbot with a crayfish sauce; double chocolate mousse. **Details:** www.ceruttis.co.uk; follow signs to the fruit market; 9.30 pm; closed Sat L & Sun; no smoking.

HUNTINGDON, CAMBRIDGESHIRE 3–1B

Old Bridge Hotel £38 Ⓐ

1 High St PE29 3TQ (01480) 424300

"An 18th-century house near the river" is the setting for this "welcoming" and "particularly well-organised" establishment; its dining room inspires consistently positive reports (not least for its "extensive" and "interesting" wine list). / **Sample dishes:** garlic & mushroom risotto with parsley; roast salmon with Swiss chard & mussels; lemon tart. **Details:** www.huntsbridge.com; off A1, off A14; 10 pm; no smoking. **Accommodation:** 24 rooms, from £125.

Pheasant Inn £36

Loop Rd PE28 0RE (01832) 710241

"Interesting dishes, and friendly staff" make this thatched inn (part of the Huntsbridge group) a superior destination of its type. / **Sample dishes:** deep-fried Brie de meaux; lamb fillet with vegetables & bread; vanilla & lavender panna cotta with red fruits. **Details:** www.huntsbridge.com; 1m S of A14 between Huntingdon & Kettering, J15; 9.30 pm; no smoking area.

ILKLEY, WEST YORKSHIRE   5–1C

Bettys   £30   A
32-34 The Grove LS29 9EE   (01943) 608029
*"Pricey, but delicious", this famously "old-fashioned" tea-room
"institution" continues to do what it does very well; sadly,
therefore, "there's always a queue".* / **Sample dishes:** *Swiss potato rosti;
Yorkshire rarebit with apple chutney; fresh fruit tart.*
Details: *www.bettysandtaylors.com; L & afternoon tea only; no Amex; no smoking;
no booking.*

The Box Tree   £44
35-37 Church St LS29 9DR   (01943) 608484
*The previous ownership (a "black cloud") has moved on from this
famous 'destination'; recently refurbished and re-opened shortly
before this guide went to press, it's now in the hands of chef
Simon Gueller, who brings with him a formidable 'name' from his
Leeds days.* / **Sample dishes:** *roast quail & hazelnut salad; sea bass with
lobster & fennel; honey & lime crème brûlée.* **Details:** *www.theboxtree.co.uk; on
A65 near town centre; 9.30 pm; closed Mon & Sun D; closed 2 weeks in Jan;
no smoking.*

Far Syde   £31   ★
1-3 New Brook St LS29 8DQ   (01943) 602030
*"Improved by its move to larger premises", this linchpin of the
local scene has mercifully retained its "unfussy" charms (and its
"excellent" wine list); you still "always have to book".*
/ **Sample dishes:** *chicken & prawn risotto; lamb wrapped in Mozzarella &
aubergine; cappuccino cup.* **Details:** *www.thefarsyde.co.uk; 10 pm; closed Mon &
Sun; no Amex; no smoking.*

ILMINGTON, WARWICKSHIRE   2–1C

The Howard Arms   £32   A
Lower Grn CV36 4LT   (01608) 682226
*"For a reasonable meal in a lovely Cotswold setting, this pub on
the village green is the place" – attractions include "friendly"
service and "an excellent wine selection".* / **Sample dishes:** *avocado,
French bean & bacon salad; beef, ale & mustard pie; pear, plum & apple flapjack
crumble.* **Details:** *www.howardarms.com; 8m SW of Stratford-upon-Avon off A4300;
9 pm; no Amex; no smoking area; children: 8+ after 7 pm.* **Accommodation:** *3
rooms, from £90.*

IPSWICH, SUFFOLK   3–1D

Baipo   £23   ★
63 Upper Orwell St IP4 1HP   (01473) 218402
*"The best Thai food in the region" is to be had at this "unlikely"
town-centre spot; it would seem to be pretty authentic – "when
we dine in Thailand", says one reporter, "we use Baipo as a
yardstick".* / **Details:** *www.baipo.co.uk; 10.45 pm; closed Mon L & Sun.*

Bistro on the Quay   £23
3 Wherry Quay IP4 1AS   (01473) 286677
*"A basic bistro occupying Mortimers' old premises, near the
Marina"; "good food, for the price" is the gist of most reports,
and there's also a "nice view".* / **Details:** *9.30 pm; closed Sun D.*

The Galley   £41   ★

25 St Nicholas St IP1 1TW   (01473) 281131
Ugur Vata produces "consistently excellent"
Mediterranean/Turkish fare (and "goes the extra mile with
customers", too) at this "good-value" town-centre bistro; it now
has an offshoot in Woodbridge – one reporter wonders how it will
do, "given that Mr V is so much part of the success of the
original". / Sample dishes: crispy Feta & parsley filo pastry; Norfolk smoked
trout; Belgian chocolate delice. Details: www.galley.uk.com; 10 pm, 11 pm in
Summer; closed Mon & Sun; no smoking area.

Mortimer's Seafood Restaurant   £33

1 Duke St IP3 0AE   (01473) 230225
"Today's fish, cooked simply but with imagination" is the highlight
at this long-established restaurant (which is not, in fact, any longer
on the quay); service can be "slow", though, and "the décor offers
little to distract you while you're waiting". / Sample dishes: Brittany
sardines with garlic butter; swordfish & tuna kebab with smoked paprika; baked
apple & almond pudding. Details: www.mortimersrestaurant.com; 9.15 pm, Mon
8.30 pm; closed Sun; no smoking.

Il Punto   £33   Ⓐ★

Neptune Quay IP4 1AX   (01473) 289748
"For a romantic evening", this "little French restaurant" – "on a
boat moored in the newly refurbished docks" – is hard to beat;
given the obvious constraints on the kitchen, the quality of the
cooking can seem "amazing". / Sample dishes: foie gras; grilled T-bone
steak; iced apricot and pistachio nougat. Details: www.ilpunto.co.uk; 9.30 pm;
closed Mon, Sat L & Sun.

Trongs   £32   ★

23 St Nicholas St IP1 1TW   (01473) 256833
"By far the best Chinese restaurant in the region" (and "usually
fully booked at night"), this "small but perfectly formed"
establishment provides "good and authentic" cooking, and
"discreet" service. / Details: 10.30 pm; closed Mon; no smoking area.

IRELAND, BEDFORDSHIRE   3–2A

Black Horse   £40   Ⓐ★

2 Church St   (01462) 811398
"Generally you need to book two weeks ahead, such is the local
popularity" of this "beautiful" country pub ("in an otherwise
unremarkable hamlet") – and no wonder, given the consistency of
commentary on the "excellent" food. / Details: 9 pm; no Amex or Switch;
no smoking.

ITTERINGHAM, NORFOLK   6–4C

Walpole Arms   £35   ★

The Common NR11 7AR   (01263) 587258
Locals say "it's worth the drive" to this "friendly" rural gastropub,
which is praised for its "very varied and really interesting menu".
/ Details: www.thewalpolearms.co.uk; 9.30 pm; closed Sun D; no Amex;
no smoking.

IVINGHOE, BEDFORDSHIRE   3–2A

Kings Head   £ 55
Station Rd LU7 9EB   (01296) 668388
*"Everything about this old-fashioned restaurant is very good
except the inflated prices"; if you don't mind paying, however, the
"traditional fare" – with duck a speciality – is of "consistently high
quality". / **Sample dishes:** tomato, Mozzarella & chorizo tartlet; pink bream with
lobster risotto & fennel; lemon tart with berry compote.*
***Details:** www.kingsheadivinghoe.co.uk; 3m N of Tring on B489 to Dunstable;
9.45 pm; closed Sun D; jacket & tie required at D; no smoking.*

JERSEY, CHANNEL ISLANDS

Bohemia   £ 46   𝔸★
Green St, St Helier JE2 4UH   (01534) 880588
*"Finally bringing Jersey into the 21st century" – and "doing it in
style" – this "romantic" yearling is consistently praised by all
reporters; as you might expect, "superb crab and lobster" are
among the menu highlights. / **Details:** www.bohemiajersey.com; 10 pm;
closed Sun; no smoking.*

Longueville Manor   £ 63   𝔸★
Longueville Rd, St Saviour JE2 7WF   (01534) 725501
*"A stunning restaurant in a lovely setting" – this "very high-
quality" country house hotel attracts only the most positive
reports, and fans say it offers nothing less than "the ultimate
dining experience". / **Sample dishes:** foie gras terrine with orange salad &
brioche; brill & calamari with aromatic noodles; mint & white chocolate soufflé.*
***Details:** www.longuevillemanor.com; 9.30 pm; no smoking area.*
***Accommodation:** 31 rooms, from £230.*

JEVINGTON, EAST SUSSEX   3–4B

Hungry Monk   £ 42
BN26 5QF   (01323) 482178
*Even fans of this cutely-housed '60s veteran concede that "it can
be disappointing at times"; it rather seems to rely on the fact that
it's "an oasis in a gastro-desert" (as well, of course, as being the
self-proclaimed birthplace of Banoffi Pie). / **Sample dishes:** crab &
avocado tian; lamb with Moroccan spiced crust & butternut squash; baked
chocolate & raspberry Alaska. **Details:** www.hungrymonk.co.uk; 5m W of
Eastbourne; 9.30 pm; D only, ex Sun open L & D; no smoking; children: 5+.*

KELSALE, SUFFOLK   3–1D

Harrisons   £ 31   𝔸★
Main Rd IP17 2RF   (01728) 604444
*"Food prepared with verve from local ingredients" – and sold at
"reasonable prices" – is carving a name for Peter Harrison's four-
year-old venture, in a "wonderful" old house. / **Sample dishes:** spiced
aubergine with yoghurt & mint; rack of lamb with haricot beans. **Details:** off the
A12; 9.45 pm; closed Mon & Sun; no Amex; no smoking; children: no babies at D.*

KENILWORTH, WARWICKSHIRE · 5–4C

Bosquet · £45 · ★

97a Warwick Rd CV8 1HP (01926) 852463

The "unprepossessing" location can make it "a real surprise" to visit Jane & Bernard Lignier's pint-sized Gallic fixture – it's an establishment "of genuine note", offering "traditional cuisine of the sort you feared might have died out". / *Sample dishes: watercress soup with caviar; roast veal with chive & cream sauce; blueberry & almond tart.* **Details:** *9.30 pm; closed Mon, Sat L & Sun; closed Aug.*

Simply Simpsons · £35

101-103 Warwick Rd CV8 1HL (01926) 864567

The standards at Andreas Antona's restaurant have long been far above average, but October 2004 saw the move of his main operation to Brum; there's every reason to hope that his original site, now a bistro, will remain a worthwhile destination. / *Sample dishes: crab tart with smoked salmon; roast brill with spring vegetables; turrón parfait with marinated pineapple.* **Details:** *www.simpsonsrestaurant.co.uk; 10 pm; closed Mon & Sun; no smoking area.*

KIBWORTH BEAUCHAMP, LEICESTERSHIRE · 5–4D

Firenze · £32 · ★

9 Station St LE8 0LN (0116) 2796260

Fans find food "well up to the best metropolitan standards", at this small family-run venture, where the chef boasts experience of some of Italy's best restaurants; there is sometimes "a real buzz about the place", too. / *Details: www.firenze.co.uk; 10 pm; closed Mon & Sun; no Amex; no smoking.*

KILLIECRANKIE, PERTH & KINROSS · 9–3C

Killiecrankie Hotel · £35 · 𝔸

PH16 5LG (01796) 473220

A "lovely" position helps distinguish this "charming and welcoming" Victorian country house hotel; there is some feeling among reporters that the "discerning" wine list may be a greater attraction than the food. / *Details: www.killiecrankiehotel.co.uk; 9 pm; no Amex; no smoking.* **Accommodation:** *10 rooms, from £160.*

KINCLAVAN, PERTH & KINROSS · 9–3C

Ballathie House · £50 · 𝔸★

PH1 4QN (01250) 883268

A "great location overlooking the Tay" is not the only strength of this grand country house hotel – its "consistently good" cooking contributes to an often-"wonderful" overall experience. / *Sample dishes: game sausage with lentils & bacon; seared scallops with chilli polenta & pesto; citrus tart.* **Details:** *www.ballathiehousehotel.com; off B9099, take right from 1m N of Stanley; 8.45 pm; jacket & tie; no smoking.* **Accommodation:** *42 rooms, from £170.*

KINGSTON UPON THAMES, SURREY · 3–3B

Ayudhya · £30 · ★

14 Kingston Hill KT2 7NH (020) 8549 5984

"A lovely little local Thai that's highly recommended" – that's the whole story on this "really good neighbourhood spot". / *Sample dishes: chicken sauté; spicy seafood; butternut toffee pudding.* **Details:** *www.ayudhya-kingston.com; 10.30 pm; no Amex; no smoking area.*

Frère Jacques **£33** A
10-12 Riverside Walk KT1 1QN (020) 8546 1332
"*A pretty location*" by Richmond Bridge and a "*credible French
ambience*" make this "*reasonably-priced*" restaurant-bar-café ever
popular with reporters. / *Sample dishes:* smoked salmon; liver; crème
brûlée. *Details:* www.frerejacques.co.uk; next to Kingston Bridge and the market
place; 11 pm; no smoking area.

Riverside Vegetaria **£26**
64 High St KT1 1HN (020) 8546 7992
"*The absence of meat and fish is completely unnoticeable*", says a
fan of "*one of the best vegetarians around the capital*" (whose
menu incorporates "*a whole variety of ethnic styles*"); being by the
Thames, it makes an especially nice summer destination.
/ *Details:* www.rsveg.plus.com; 10 mins walk from Kingston BR; 11 pm; no Amex;
no smoking.

KINGUSSIE, HIGHLAND 9–2C

The Cross **£48** A★
Tweed Mill Brae, Ardbroilach Rd PH21 1LB
(01540) 661166
"*The management are keen to please*", at this "*charming
restaurant-with-rooms, on the banks of a Highland stream*" – "*a
perfect setting for a romantic evening*"; the cooking is "*careful*",
too, and "*uses the best ingredients*". / *Sample dishes:* scallop & prawn
sausage with fennel; saddle of lamb with rosemary & red wine sauce; lime
cheesecake. *Details:* www.thecross.co.uk; head uphill on Ardbroilach Rd, turn left
into private drive after traffic lights; 8.30 pm; D only, closed Mon & Sun; no smoking
area. *Accommodation:* 8 rooms, from £95.

KIRKHAM, LANCASHIRE 5–1A

Cromwellian **£32** ★
16 Poulton St PR4 2AB (01772) 685680
"*A two-person band dispenses honest cooking at cracking prices*",
at these "*tea-shop-sized*" premises, which offer "*a totally
dependable experience*". / *Details:* 9 pm; closed Mon, Sat & Sun; no Amex.

KNIGHTWICK, WORCESTERSHIRE 2–1B

The Talbot **£34**
WR6 5PH (01886) 821235
"*Good country cooking*" (with an emphasis on "*local produce*")
makes this riverside coaching inn (with an adjoining brewery) a
pretty consistent stand-by. / *Sample dishes:* warm game liver salad; roast
sea bass with pesto; sticky toffee pudding. *Details:* www.the-talbot.co.uk; 9m from
Worcester on A44; 9 pm; no smoking area. *Accommodation:* 11 rooms,
from £75.

KNUTSFORD, CHESHIRE 5–2B

Belle Époque **£38** A
King St WA16 6DT (01565) 633060
This long-established institution leans quite heavily on its "*classy*"
and "*charming*" Art Nouveau setting nowadays; the cooking has
its fans, but others feel it's "*nice enough, but not at the prices
charged*". / *Sample dishes:* Tuscan spring salad; sea bass with red onion salsa;
apricot fritters with Cointreau mousse. *Details:* www.thebelleepoque.com; 1.5m
from M6, J19; 10 pm; closed Sat D & Sun D; no smoking area; booking: max 6, Sat;
children: 10+. *Accommodation:* 6 rooms, from £80.

LACOCK, WILTSHIRE   2–2C

At the Sign of the Angel   £35   Ⓐ
6 Church St SN15 2LB   (01249) 730230
An "historic inn" in a National Trust village offering "English pub
food in an idyllic 'Moll Flanders' setting"; a visit is generally held to
be "a nice experience", even if the fodder is "decidedly average".
/ *Sample dishes:* Stilton & walnut pâté; steak & kidney pudding; crème brûlée.
Details: www.lacock.co.uk; close to M4, J17; 9 pm; closed Mon L.
Accommodation: 10 rooms, from £105.

LANCASTER, LANCASHIRE   5–1A

Bay Horse   £35   ★
Bay Horse Ln LA2 0HR   (01524) 791204
Most reporters leave "very impressed" from this "good country
pub", thanks not least to Craig Wilkinson's "accomplished"
cuisine. / *Sample dishes:* potted Morecambe Bay shrimps; braised lamb with
ale & thyme sauce; lemon tart & lemon fruit ice. *Details:* www.bayhorseinn.com;
0.75m S of A6, J33 M6; 9.30 pm; closed Mon & Sun D; no Amex; no smoking.

Pizza Margherita   £22   ★
2 Moor Ln LA1 1QD   (01524) 36333
Standards remain very consistent at the Lancaster institution
founded by the sister of the man who created PizzaExpress; its
menu also includes "limited but good pasta dishes".
/ *Sample dishes:* garlic bread with cheese; pizza; dime bar crunch pie.
Details: www.pizza-margherita.co.uk; 10.30 pm.

Simply French   £24   Ⓐ
27a St Georges Quay LA1 1RD   (01524) 843199
"Reliably good simple food, well served" is what this "very French"
bistro is all about, and it has a pleasant ambience, too – "it could
be the Mediterranean outside", raves one reporter… "rather than
the River Lune". / *Sample dishes:* baked courgette stuffed with spinach &
salmon mousse; chicken marinated in lemon & olive oil; apricot tart.
Details: 9.30 pm; Mon-Thu D only, Fri-Sun open L & D; no Amex.

Sultan of Lancaster   £17   Ⓐ★
Old Church, Brock St LA1 1UU   (01524) 61188
"A Methodist church, attractively converted to Islam" provides the
unlikely but atmospheric setting for this "dependable" curry
house; "the food is so good, you don't even miss the alcohol".
/ *Sample dishes:* tikka masala; coconut supreme.
Details: www.sultanoflancaster.com; 11 pm; D only; no Amex; no smoking area.

Sun Café   £34
Sun Street Studios, 25 Sun St LA1 1EW   (01524) 845599
This café adjoining an art gallery "should be high on the list of
any visitor to Lancaster" – "it makes a serious effort to present
modern European dishes with local produce, often successfully".
/ *Sample dishes:* asparagus & poached egg with Parmesan; scallops & shrimps
with teriyaki dressing; cheesecake with pistachios & honey. *Details:* 9.30 pm; closed
Sun D; closed Mon-Tue D unless booked; no Amex.

LANGAR, NOTTINGHAMSHIRE   5–3D

Langar Hall   £ 44   *A*

NG13 9HG   (01949) 860559

It's as *"a lovely place for a leisurely lunch"* (and *"good value"*, too) that this *"peaceful"* country house excites most interest from reporters. / **Sample dishes:** *asparagus & pea soup; roast duck with citrus sauce; banana parfait with caramel ice.* **Details:** *www.langarhall.com; off A52 between Nottingham & Grantham; 9.30 pm, Sat 10 pm; no Amex; no smoking.* **Accommodation:** *12 rooms, from £130.*

LANGHO, LANCASHIRE   5–1B

Northcote Manor   £ 62   *A*★★

Northcote Rd BB6 8BE   (01254) 240555

Nigel Haworth's *"faultless"* cooking (*"proudly promoting local producers"*) combines with Craig Bancroft's *"extensive and varied"* wine list to make *"a total gastronomic experience"* at this *"relaxing"* Ribble Valley restaurant-with-rooms; it's not just *"a benchmark in the North West"*, but also of real note nationally. / **Sample dishes:** *black pudding & pink trout with nettle sauce; Pendle lamb with lemon marmalade & chive mash; apple crumble soufflé with Lancashire cheese ice cream.* **Details:** *www.northcotemanor.com; M6, J31 then A59; 9.30 pm; no smoking.* **Accommodation:** *14 rooms, from £140.*

LANGTON GREEN, KENT   3–4B

The Hare   £ 29

Langton Rd TN3 0JA   (01892) 862419

A village inn, *"popular with families"*, which offers a *"varied"* and *"dependable"* menu; even the most ambivalent reporter says it's *"miles better than anything else of its type round Tunbridge Wells"*. / **Sample dishes:** *bacon, lentil & goats cheese tart; seared salmon with sweetcorn fritters; Malibu roulade with pineapple.* **Details:** *www.hare-tunbridgewells.co.uk; on A264 to East Grinstead; 9.30 pm; no Amex; no smoking area.*

LAPWORTH, WARWICKSHIRE   5–4C

The Boot   £ 35

Old Warwick Rd B94 6JU   (01564) 782464

"What a surprise!"; this large boozer by a canal is quite a destination hereabouts, and the food – if not hugely ambitious – can be *"very good"*. / **Sample dishes:** *rustic bread with olive oil; chicken with goats cheese & saffron; Bailey's cheesecake.* **Details:** *www.thebootatlapworth.co.uk; off A34; 10 pm.*

LAUGHARNE, CARMARTHANSHIRE   4–4C

Hurst House   £ 42   *A*★

East Marsh SA33 4RS   (01994) 427417

It may be *"in the middle of nowhere"*, but the few reporters who truffled out this *"delightful"* restaurant-with-rooms heap praise on its *"excellent"* cuisine and its *"laid-back"* atmosphere. / **Details:** *www.hurst-house.co.uk; 10 pm; no smoking.* **Accommodation:** *6 rooms, from £125.*

LAVENHAM, SUFFOLK   3–1C

Angel   £28
Market Pl CO10 9QZ   (01787) 247388
A 14th-century inn on the marketplace, where the "choice and quality" of the fare generally gets the thumbs-up.
/ **Sample dishes:** smoked salmon trout; ducks breast with juniper & mushroom sauce; sticky pudding. **Details:** www.lavenham.co.uk/angel; on A1141 6m NE of Sudbury; 9.15 pm; no smoking; booking: max 14. **Accommodation:** 8 rooms, from £75.

Great House   £36   A★★
Market Pl CO10 9QZ   (01787) 247431
"Top French food from the Gallic staff and owners" make the Crépy family's "lovely" half-timbered, town-centre restaurant-with-rooms a sort of "gastronomic utopia", for many reporters.
/ **Sample dishes:** moules marinière; venison in red wine with duck foie gras sauce; saffron crème brûlée. **Details:** www.greathouse.co.uk; follow directions to Guildhall; 9.30 pm; closed Mon & Sun D; closed Jan; no smoking. **Accommodation:** 5 rooms, from £76.

Swan Hotel   £38
High St CO10 9QA   (01787) 247477
Reporters aren't always enamoured with Macdonald Hotels properties, so it's nice to record that "good experiences every time" are the gist of all commentary on this ancient inn.
/ **Sample dishes:** scallops & Parma ham with green bean salad; sea bass with salt crust & lemon sauce; peach & thyme ice cream.
Details: www.theswanatlavenham.co.uk; 9.30 pm; no smoking.
Accommodation: 51 rooms, from £160.

LEEDS, WEST YORKSHIRE   5–1C

Especially as its city-centre restaurant scene is not large compared to, say, Manchester's, it's impressive how Leeds achieves occasional flashes of brilliance of a type which have tended to elude its larger rival. The long-term success story, *Pool Court at 42* (not admittedly on absolutely top form in recent times), has in recent years been complemented by *No 3 York Place* and now by the extraordinary *Anthony's* – one of the most notable restaurants to have opened in England in recent years.

Otherwise, Leeds can offer something for most tastes, even if a number of places have reputations rather bigger than – reports suggest – the quality of their operation.

Aagrah   £24   A★
Aberford Rd LS25 2HF   (0113) 287 6606
"Consistently a winner"; a chain outlet it may be, but that does nothing to stop this eminent subcontinental restaurant from being "excellent all round". / **Details:** www.aagrah.com; from A1 take A642 Aberford Rd to Garforth; 11.30 pm; D only; no smoking area.

Amigos   £20   A
70 Abbey Rd LS5 3JG   (0113) 228 3737
"A Latino vibe", "fabulous beers" and "great food" all win approval for this "noisy" tapas bar, near Kirkstall Abbey.
/ **Sample dishes:** meatballs in chilli & tomato sauce; paella; Manchego cheese with apple. **Details:** www.amigostapasbar.com; on A65 in Kirkstall; 11 pm; closed Sun; no Amex.

Anthony's £42 ★★

19 Boar Ln LS1 6EA
(0113) 245 5922

"The next star in the British cooking firmament" – Anthony Flinn (an ex-El Bulli 'stagiaire') cooks with such "innovation" and "technical wizardry" that reporters wonder how "one so young" – he's 24 – can cook "with such confidence"; indeed this small but "knowledgeable" enterprise is often compared with the Fat Duck... which some reports say it "beats hands down"! / **Sample dishes:** *roast langoustine with fennel tea consomme; roast duck with chocolate & olive oil bonbon; peanut ice cream in artichoke caramel.* **Details:** *9.30 pm; closed Mon & Sun; no Amex; no smoking.*

Art's £29 Ⓐ
42 Call Ln LS1 6DT (0113) 243 8243

This "anytime favourite" has been a remarkably "consistent" stand-by for many years – a "cool" and "laid-back" destination, it "attracts all ages and all types"; the "wonderful-value lunch plate" is a highlight. / **Sample dishes:** *roast garlic & thyme risotto; crispy duck with halloumi & herb salad; Belgian chocolate cake.* **Details:** *www.artscafebar.co.uk; near Corn Exchange; 10 pm, Fri & Sat 10.30 pm; no smoking area; no booking, Sat & Sun L.*

Bibis £38 Ⓐ
Criterion Pl, Swinegate LS1 4AG (0113) 243 0905

Initial reports on the 'new' Bibis (occupying "OTT", Art Deco-style new premises near the railway station) suggest that its essential style has survived the move – the Italian cooking is still "very over-rated", and the place is still "very busy". / **Sample dishes:** *beef tomatoes with basil oil dressing; pigeon & foie gras terrine; chocolate & Amaretto cake.* **Details:** *www.bibisrestaurant.com; 11.30 pm, Sun 10.30 pm; no booking, Sat.*

Brasserie Forty Four £38
44 The Calls LS2 7EW (0113) 234 3232

A "lively" atmosphere, underpins the long-term popularity of this well-known (recently refurbished) canalside brasserie; it's also generally praised for its "tasty" cooking too. / **Sample dishes:** *home-made corned beef with beetroot relish; smoked cod with leeks & Gorgonzola; Toblerone & Amaretto fondue.* **Details:** *www.brasserie44.com; 10.30 pm, Fri & Sat 11 pm; closed Sat L & Sun; no Amex.*

Brio £36
40 Great George St LS1 3DL (0113) 246 5225

It's difficult to unscramble commentary on this "successful" city-centre Italian from that on its offshoot in The Light shopping centre (Brio Pizza, 28 The Headrow, tel 243 5533), but both are "bustling" places hailed for offering "good food at reasonable prices". / **Sample dishes:** *haricot beans in chilli & wine sauce; seared tuna niçoise; panna cotta.* **Details:** *www.brios.co.uk; 10.30 pm; closed Sun.*

Bryan's £27
9 Weetwood Ln LS16 5LT (0113) 278 5679

For its "good Yorkshire fish 'n' chips", this celebrated chippy remains especially "popular with families"; as ever, the occasional reporter thinks it's "coasting". / **Sample dishes:** *chicken goujons with spicy BBQ dip; Jumbo deep-fried haddock & chips; treacle sponge & custard.* **Details:** *off Otterley Rd; 9.30 pm; no Amex; no smoking; need 8+ to book.*

The Calls Grill £37
Calls Landing, 38 The Calls LS2 7EW (0113) 245 3870
*"Nothing fancy", just "a good canalside brasserie" which "does
what it says on the tin" – the occasional reporter finds its style
better pitched for lunch than dinner. / Sample dishes: smoked tuna with
Spanish omelette; Dover sole with citrus butter; rice pudding bavarois.
Details: www.callsgrill.co.uk; opp Tetleys brewery on waterfront; 10.30 pm; D only,
closed Sun; booking: max 6, Sat.*

Casa Mia Grande £30
33-35 Harrogate Rd LS7 3PD (0870) 444 5154
*They're very big news locally, but some reporters are beginning to
fear that this Chapel Allerton Italian and its spin-offs "think they're
better than they are" – while "great fish", in particular, is still a
highlight, reports are becoming more mixed; there are now two
sibling establishments – at 10-12 Steinbeck Lane (tel 239 2555),
and a grander new one at Millennium Square (tel 245 4121).
/ Sample dishes: smoked chicken salad with mango vinaigrette; honey-roast salmon
with spinach & lemon sauce; tiramisu. Details: www.casamiaonline.co.uk;
10.30 pm, Fri & Sat 11 pm; no smoking area.*

Darbar £35   𝔸 ★
16-17 Kirkgate LS1 6BY (0113) 246 0381
*Most reports still confirm that "food and décor exceed
expectations" at this veteran Indian just off Briggate; its first-floor
premises are decked out on "a grand scale".
/ Details: www.darbar.co.uk; midnight; closed Sun.*

Dare Café £19
49 Otley Rd LS6 3AB (0113) 230 2828
*"Quirky", "friendly" Mexican café in Headingley that's mainly
prized by reporters for its laid-back charms, but whose food is at
least "enjoyable". / Sample dishes: tomato & Mozzarella salad; chicken
fajitas; chocolate fudge cake. Details: 10 pm; no Amex; no smoking area.*

Dough Bakery £28   ★
293 Spen Ln LS16 5BD (0113) 278 7255
*This "bright" and basic BYO bistro is the latest venture of
peripatetic local chef Wayne Newsome; enthusiastic locals attest
that his "interesting and original" food is "beautifully served" (and
"with flair"). / Details: 9.30 pm; D only, closed Mon & Sun; no credit cards;
no smoking.*

Flying Pizza £29
60 Street Ln LS8 2DQ (0113) 266 6501
*"If you don't fall off your chair laughing at the pseudo-glitterati,
you might survive to enjoy the best pizzas in town" – this ever-
"popular" Italian is world-famous hereabouts for being "full of
people with more money than taste". / Sample dishes: rolled Italian
ham with Mozzarella; chicken with farfalle in spicy tomato sauce; tiramisu.
Details: www.theflyingpizza.co.uk; just off A61, 3m N of city centre; 11 pm,
Thu-Sat 11.30 pm; no smoking area; no booking at weekends.*

Fourth Floor Café
Harvey Nichols £34
107-111 Briggate LS1 6AZ (0113) 204 8000
*This "buzzy", "light" and "airy" department store venue makes a
popular and "interesting" choice, especially for a snack or brunch,
even if some reporters find it "a little overpriced for what you
get". / Sample dishes: smoked chicken with pears & Roquefort; rib-eye steak with
sweet potato mash; passion fruit mousse. Details: www.harveynichols.com; 10 pm;
L only, except Thu-Sat when L & D; no smoking area; no booking, Sat L.*

Fuji Hiro   £16   ★
45 Wade Ln LS2 8NJ   (0113) 243 9184
"Cramped but authentic", this Japanese café *"puts the chains to
shame"* with its *"enormous bowls of noodles"*; all-in-all, the place
offers *"excellent value"*. / **Details:** 9.45 pm, Fri & Sat 10.45 pm; no credit
cards; no smoking; need 5+ to book.

La Grillade   £29
Wellington St LS1 4HJ   (0113) 245 9707
"For steak frites and red wine" – this *"authentic"*, *"cave-like"*
Gallic fixture is a long-standing favourite, especially for business
types. / **Sample dishes:** French onion soup; char-grilled rib-eye steak; bread &
butter pudding. **Details:** 10.30 pm; closed Sat L & Sun.

Hansa's   £21   ★
72-74 North St LS2 7PN   (0113) 244 4408
"Fantastic" Gujerati (vegetarian) cuisine makes this *"interesting"*
destination a *"refreshing change from your usual beer and curry
house"*; it has long been deservedly popular.
/ **Details:** www.hansasrestaurant.com; 10 pm, Sat 11 pm; D only, ex Sun L only;
no Amex; no smoking area; children: under 5s eat free.

Leodis   £38
Victoria Mill, Sovereign St LS1 4BJ   (0113) 242 1010
Views on this brassy canal-side brasserie become ever more
divided; fans say its a *"buzzy"* place, serving *"very good food"* in
"attractive" surroundings – for doubters, it's just an
"unremarkable", *"see-and-be-seen"* destination, and overpriced,
too. / **Sample dishes:** warm bacon & poached egg salad; steak & kidney sausages
with mash; chocolate nut brownie. **Details:** www.leodis.co.uk; 10 pm; closed Sat L &
Sun.

Lucky Dragon   £25
Templar Ln LS2 7LP   (0113) 245 0520
This long-established city-centre Chinese – long thought of as the
best in town – has a strong local fan club who applaud its
"knowledgeable" staff and its *"unfailing high-quality food"*;
"excellent dim sum" is a highlight. / **Details:** 11.30 pm.

Maxi's   £28   X
6 Bingley St LS3 1LX   (0113) 244 0552
"Dropping standards" are becoming quite a turn-off at this huge –
and increasingly *"average"* and *"overpriced"* – city-centre fringe
Chinese. / **Sample dishes:** spare ribs in Peking sauce; sizzling steak with
ginger & spring onions; toffee bananas. **Details:** www.maxi-s.co.uk; 11.30 pm;
no smoking area.

Millrace   £35   ★
2-4 Commercial Rd LS5 3AQ   (0113) 275 7555
"Wholesome, organic food that melts in the mouth" is the gist of
most reports on this *"cosy"* (if recently enlarged) operation; like
many organic places *"it's on the pricey side"*, though, and dishes
can occasionally seem *"over-complicated"*. / **Sample dishes:** seared
scallops; roast ham with smoked Cheddar hash; triple chocolate cheesecake.
Details: www.themillrace-organic.com; near Kirkstall Abbey; 10 pm; D only, except
Sun open L & D; no Amex; no smoking.

No 3 York Place £40 A★
3 York Pl LS1 2DR (0113) 245 9922
This "sleek" and "stylish" venue is hailed for its "sexy",
"seasonally-led" cooking ("which proves to London clients that
there is life outside the capital"); service is "personal", too.
/ *Sample dishes:* lobster, mango & avocado salad with basil oil; pigs trotter stuffed
with ham hock & morels; blood orange mousse. *Details:* www.no3yorkplace.co.uk;
10 pm; closed Sat L & Sun; no smoking; children: 5+.

Pool Court at 42 £61
44 The Calls LS2 7EW (0113) 244 4242
This design-hotel dining room by the canal – long known as the
best place in town – still wins much praise for "high-quality
everything"; even fans are aware that "not everyone likes the
setting", though, and the cooking sometimes seemed a bit
"average" this year. / *Sample dishes:* beef tartare with quail eggs; roast sea
bass with anchovy-stuffed squid; chilled pineapple & lemongrass soup.
Details: www.poolcourt.com; 10 pm, Sat 8.30 pm; closed Sat L & Sun; no Amex;
no smoking; children: 3+.

Quantro £32
62 Street Ln LS8 2DQ (0113) 288 8063
It has still to measure up to the Harrogate original, but this
Roundhay sibling is still praised by most reporters for its
"unpretentious" charms, including sometimes "very good"
cooking. / *Sample dishes:* Parma ham celeriac remoulade; lamb with black olive
mousse; green apple & grapefruit bavarois. *Details:* www.quantro.co.uk; 10 pm;
closed Sun; no smoking; children: 8+.

The Reliance £26 A
76-78 North St LS2 7PN (0113) 295 6060
"Consistent standards" have made this "laid-back and chilled" all-
day venue, near the Grand Theatre, a "firm favourite" for almost
all reporters; for Sunday brunch, it's "the best place in town".
/ *Sample dishes:* pan-fried smoked haddock fish cakes with fresh herb salad &
chutney; roast chicken breast with Parma ham, stuffed with spinich & Parmasan;
banoffi pie. *Details:* 10.30 pm; no booking.

Room £40 A
Bond Hs, The Bourse Courtyard LS1 5DE (0113) 242 6161
"Retro food with an interesting twist" has helped make this "cool"
lounge bar/restaurant, near the Marriott Hotel, a "welcome
addition" to the dining scene. / *Details:* www.roomleeds.com; 9.30 pm.

Sala Thai £26 ★
13-17 Shaw Ln LS6 4DH (0113) 278 8400
Back on more consistent form, this "friendly" Headingley spot is –
once again – clearly "Leeds's best Thai".
/ *Details:* www.salathaileeds.com; just off Otley Rd, near Arndale Centre; 10.30 pm;
closed Sat L & Sun; no smoking.

Salvo's £29
115 Otley Rd LS6 3PX (0113) 275 5017
It's a bit "busy" and "noisy" for some tastes, but this "fun" family-
run Headingley Italian is praised by almost all reporters for its
"imaginative" and "well-cooked" food (with pizza a highlight).
/ *Sample dishes:* deep-fried Brie with raspberry vinaigrette; veal with field
mushrooms & Parma ham crisps; Malteser mousse. *Details:* www.salvos.co.uk; 2m
N of University on A660; 10.30 pm; closed Sun; no smoking area; no booking at D.

Sheesh Mahal £19 ★
346-348 Kirkstall Rd LS4 2DS (0113) 230 4161
"A warm welcome from Azram, the ever-present owner" helps
make this Burley Indian a "fun" destination; the cooking is "good"
too ("especially by Leeds standards"). / *Details:* www.sheeshmahal.co.uk;
next to Yorkshire TV centre; midnight; D only; no smoking area.

Simply Heathcote's £32
Canal Whf, Water Ln LS11 5PS (0113) 244 6611
Although fans applaud traditional English dishes served "with
panache" at these canalside premises (once known as Rascasse),
not all reporters are so impressed; this seems to be a difficult
location, and more than one reporter found the place "half
empty". / *Sample dishes:* warm black pudding & poached egg salad; herb-roast
chicken with oyster mushrooms; bread & butter pudding.
Details: www.heathcotes.co.uk; off M621, J3, behind Granary Wharf; 10 pm, Sat
11 pm; no smoking.

Sous le Nez en Ville £30
Quebec House, Quebec St LS1 2HA (0113) 244 0108
This "subterranean hide-away" has been a popular "cosy" city-
centre rendezvous for some years now; the Gallic food is "nothing
fancy", but the wine list is "really good" ("and it won't break the
bank"). / *Sample dishes:* deep-fried Brie with pepper & mango sauce; rib of beef
with béarnaise sauce; white chocolate pâté. *Details:* 10 pm, Fri & Sat 10.30 pm;
closed Sun; no Amex.

Sukhothai £25 ★
8 Regent St LS7 4PE (0113) 237 0141
"A Thai gem in Chapel Allerton" – this "small" establishment is
praised by many enthusiastic locals for its "beautifully presented"
and "fresh-tasting" cuisine. / *Details:* www.thaifood4u.co.uk; 11 pm; D only,
closed Mon; no Amex; no smoking.

Tampopo £25
15 South Pde LS1 5QS (0113) 245 1816
"Reliably good, cheap eating" makes this city-centre noodle joint –
part of a chain that's recently spread to the capital – a handy
stand-by. / *Sample dishes:* vegetable gyoza; prawns with coconut & Asian basil
sauce; mango sorbet. *Details:* 10.45 pm; no smoking; need 7+ to book.

Whitelocks Luncheonette £20 AX
Turk's Head Yd, off Briggate LS2 6HB (0113) 245 3950
"What you see is what you get", at this extraordinary Victorian
pub and dining room, hidden away in a courtyard off Briggate; the
cooking? – well, let's say: "you don't leave hungry".
/ *Sample dishes:* crispy haddock fingers; steak & Stilton pie; jam roly-poly with
custard. *Details:* 7 pm, Sun 4 pm; children: 18+ only.

LEICESTER, LEICESTER CITY 5–4D

Bobby's £20 ★
154-156 Belgrave Rd LE4 5AT (0116) 266 0106
It may be "basic" – "awful"-looking even – but this Gujarati
canteen and sweet shop remains a very popular, "cheap and
authentic" Golden Mile destination; its "genuine" simple veggie
dishes deliver "lovely fresh flavours". / *Sample dishes:* deep-fried potato
baskets; aubergine stuffed with peanut & potato; caramelised ice cream.
Details: www.eatatbobbys.com; 10 pm; no Amex; no smoking.

Case   £35   A
4-6 Hotel St LE1 5AW   (0116) 251 7675
This "stylish", "loft-style" venue, near St Martins, is a local
"favourite", and offers a good degree of "London style"; the food
is "reliable", too, if "quite pricey". / *Sample dishes:* red onion & goats
cheese tart; turkey escalope with roast polenta; brioche pudding.
Details: www.thecase.co.uk; near the Cathedral; 10.30 pm; closed Sun; no smoking
area.

Friends Tandoori   £25   ★
41-43 Belgrave Rd LE4 6AR   (0116) 266 8809
"Fresh-tasting dishes" from an "interesting" menu – plus décor
that's comfortable and quite stylish, for the Golden Mile – make
this well-established subcontinental a top choice in this curry-mad
town. / *Details:* 11.30 pm; closed Sat L & Sun; no smoking.

Jones Cafe   £29
93 Queens Rd LE2 1TT   (0116) 270 8830
Even critics say "you can't beat the Sunday morning brunch" at
this breezy Clarendon Park café; at other times, though, the
cooking can be "poor". / *Sample dishes:* warm duck salad with Thai
dressing; coriander-crusted chicken with red onion confit; Malteser tiramisu.
Details: 9.30 pm, Sat & Sun 10 pm; closed Sun D; no Amex; no smoking area.

Opera House   £41
10 Guildhall Lane LE1 5FQ   (0116) 223 6666
It has a "superb" setting in an historic building of real charm, so
it's shame that this central fixture "has gone downhill" – its
cooking "doesn't match up to the cost or the ambience".
/ *Sample dishes:* twice-baked Cheddar soufflé; plaice with herb risotto & lobster
sauce; chocolate tart with praline ice cream.
Details: www.theoperahouserestaurant.co.uk; 10 pm; closed Sun; no Amex;
no smoking.

Sakonis   £19   ★
2 Loughborough Rd LE4 5LD   (0116) 261 3113
"The fifth branch of a London-based chain", this new "hangar-
sized" outlet (done out in "hard-edged", "modern" style) is
"always full" due to its "bargain" cooking – "mostly Indian
vegetarian". / *Details:* 10 pm; closed Mon L; no smoking.

Shimla Pinks   £24
65-69 London Rd LE2 0PE   (0116) 247 1471
This "contemporary-style" subcontinental is part of a chain that
has generally lost its way; this "smart" branch, though, inspired
very satisfactory reports. / *Details:* www.milesfromdelhi.com; opp railway
station; 11 pm; closed Sat L & Sun; no smoking area.

Stones   £38
29 Millstone Ln LE1 5JN   (0116) 291 0004
A trendy city-centre venture in an attractive mill-conversion; it
attracted limited survey commentary, mainly to the effect that it
has "gone badly downhill". / *Sample dishes:* antipasto platter;
harissa-glazed salmon with saffron fettuccine; chocolate pudding.
Details: www.stonesrestaurant.co.uk; 10.30 pm, weekends 11.30 pm; closed Sun;
no smoking.

The Tiffin £26
I De Montfort St LEI 7GE (0116) 247 0420
A "warm welcome from the owner" helps ensure this upscale
Indian near the station is "often packed"; the cooking is OK, but
can tend to "average". / **Sample dishes:** chilli-fried chicken; aubergine &
tamarind curry; kulfi. **Details:** www.the-tiffin.co.uk; near railway station; 10.45 pm;
closed Sat L & Sun; no smoking area.

Watsons £27
5-9 Upper Brown St LEI 5TE (0116) 222 7770
"The food can be hit-and-miss" at this locally well-known
warehouse-conversion, and the atmosphere can be on the clinical
side; for business, though, "you can't fault it". / **Sample dishes:** fish
soup with rouille; salmon with wok-fried greens; strawberry millefeuille. **Details:** next
to Phoenix Art Theatre; 10.30 pm; closed Sun; no smoking.

LEIGH ON SEA, ESSEX 3–3C

Boat Yard £44 Ⓐ
8-13 High St SS9 2EN (01702) 475588
A "wonderful" location, with "lovely views of fishing boats and the
sea", helps focus attention on this modern waterside spot; the
quality of the cooking, however, "is some way behind the prices".
/ **Sample dishes:** seared tuna with pickled vegetables; beef with green peppercorn
sauce; chocolate tart with clotted cream. **Details:** www.theboatyardrestaurant.co.uk;
near railway station; 10 pm; closed Mon, Tue L & Sun D; no Amex.

LEINTWARDINE, SHROPSHIRE 5–4A

Jolly Frog £35 Ⓐ★
The Todden SY7 0LX (01547) 540298
"A real find", this pub in "lovely countryside" evokes a hymn of
praise from reporters, not least for its "fabulous" food (with fish
and desserts singled out) and its "great" beer.
/ **Sample dishes:** seared king scallops with beetroot reduction; grilled Torbay sole
with butter; white chocolate lasagne with lemon ice cream.
Details: www.jolly-frog.com; 10.30 pm; closed Mon, Tue D & Sun D; no Amex;
no smoking area.

LEMSFORD, HERTFORDSHIRE 3–2B

Auberge du Lac
Brocket Hall £55 ★
AL8 7XG (01707) 368888
"A delightful lakeside setting in the grounds of Brocket Hall" sets a
"romantic" tone at JC Novelli's "picturesque" lodge (though the
interior is a mite "dated"); the cuisine shows "flair", but is "pricey
even by London standards" – perhaps this just reflects the rarity
of "the only gastronomic destination in Herts"! / **Sample dishes:** foie
gras terrine with Szechuan pepper; brill with endives & red wine sauce; frozen vanilla
soufflé with rhubarb compote. **Details:** www.brockethall.co.uk; on B653 towards
Harpenden; 10 pm; closed Mon & Sun D; no jeans or trainers.
Accommodation: 16 rooms, from £185.

LEWDOWN, DEVON   1–3C

Lewtrenchard Manor   £ 45   A ★

EX20 4PN   (01566) 783256

*Early-days reports on the new (Von Essen Hotels) régime at this
impressive Elizabethan house suggest that the cooking is now
"much improved", and that the dining experience is "delightful in
every way".* / **Sample dishes:** langoustine cappuccino with truffled leeks;
sautéed liver with garlic mash & crispy bacon; apricot bread & butter pudding.
Details: www.lewtrenchard.co.uk; off A30 between Okehampton & Launceston;
9 pm; closed Mon L; no jeans or trainers; no smoking; children: 8+.
Accommodation: 9 rooms, from £135.

LEWES, EAST SUSSEX   3–4B

Circa   £ 36

145 High St BN7 1XT   (01273) 471777

*"Fun fusion food in twee Lewes" has made quite a name for this
"imaginative" Asian–Italian oddity; most still find it an
"interesting" destination, but reports of "fusion-confusion" rose
this year – perhaps the strain of opening a sibling, Circa Fish, in
Westgate Street (tel 471333).* / **Sample dishes:** Thai butternut squash
soup; tandoori trout with potatoes & tzatziki; red gooseberry crème brûlée.
Details: www.circacirca.com; 10 pm; closed Mon & Sun D; no smoking area.
Accommodation: 22 rooms, from £140.

LICKFOLD, WEST SUSSEX   3–4A

Lickfold Inn   £ 36   A ★

GU28 9EY   (01798) 861285

*It can seem "expensive, for a pub", but the food at this
beautifully-sited establishment in the South Downs is usually "very
good"; it's a charming place, too, with a nice garden for the
summer, and roaring fires in winter.* / **Sample dishes:** grilled goats cheese
with red pepper relish; pan-fried sea bass with black olive mash; white chocolate
crème brûlée. **Details:** 3m N of A272 between Midhurst & Petworth; 9.30 pm;
closed Mon L & Sun D; no Amex.

LIDGATE, SUFFOLK   3–1C

Star Inn   £ 33   A

The Street CB8 9PP   (01638) 500275

*"It's rather surprising to find authentic Spanish food in rural
Suffolk", but the formula works remarkably well at this "beautiful"
old pub, where the menu stretches "from paella to potted
shrimps".* / **Sample dishes:** Catalan salad; paella Valenciana; treacle tart.
Details: on B1063 6m SE of Newmarket; 10 pm; closed Sun D; no smoking.

LIFTON, DEVON   1–3C

Arundell Arms   £ 43

Fore St PL16 0AA   (01566) 784666

"Long-established, but continuing to impress" – this grand, old-
school hotel dining room again won more consistent praise this
year for its *"outstanding set menus"* and its *"reasonably-priced
wine list"*. / **Sample dishes:** spiced potted chicken with apricot chutney; roast
monkfish with scallop & lentil fricassée; passion fruit delice.
Details: www.arundellarms.com; 0.5m off A30, Lifton Down exit; 9.30 pm;
no smoking. **Accommodation:** 27 rooms, from £136.

LINCOLN, LINCOLNSHIRE   6–3A

Browns Pie Shop   £28
33 Steep Hill LN2 1LU   (01522) 527330
*It's "not just a pie shop", but otherwise there's little consensus on
this once-excellent fixture, near the cathedral; fans still hail its
"different and mouth-watering" traditional scoff, but its standards
struck too many reporters this year as "tourist-trappy".*
/ *Sample dishes: Yorkshire pudding with spiced onion gravy; fish pie; Bailey's
cheesecake. Details: near the Cathedral; 10 pm; no smoking area.*

Jew's House   £38
15 The Strait LN2 1JD   (01522) 524851
*"Exceptional historic surroundings" are an undisputed plus at this
"high-class" establishment (in what is probably the oldest building
in the city); some reporters describe "excellent" cooking to match,
but others are unconvinced. / Sample dishes: wild mushroom vol-au-vents;
braised monkfish with spinach; white chocolate cheesecake.
Details: www.thejewshouse.co.uk; halfway down Steep Hill from Cathedral;
9.30 pm; closed Mon & Sun; no smoking.*

The Wig & Mitre   £34
30-32 Steep Hill LN2 1TL   (01522) 535190
*"Not what it used to be at all"; this once-celebrated inn by the
cathedral (open breakfast till midnight daily) has badly lost its way
– too many reporters now just see it as a "touristy" and
"overpriced" place, with "grudging" service. / Sample dishes: wild
mushroon & Madeira soup; chicken in Parma ham with pistachio & lemon stuffing;
baked vanilla cheesecake. Details: www.wigandmitre.com; between Cathedral &
Castle; 11 pm; no smoking.*

LINLITHGOW, WEST LOTHIAN   9–4C

Champany Inn   £53   ★
EH49 7LU   (01506) 834532
*"For the extravagant blow-out every carnivore should try at least
once in a lifetime", this famous and "beautiful" inn – with its "out-
of-this-world" steak and an "encyclopaedic" wine list – fits the bill
nicely; prices are "even above London", though, but for fans "this
is the high point of a visit to Scotland". / Sample dishes: quail with
bacon & tarragon stuffing; steak with chips & asparagus; hazelnut meringues.
Details: www.champany.com; 2m NE of Linlithgow on junction of A904 & A803;
10 pm; closed Sat L & Sun; no jeans or trainers; children: 8+.
Accommodation: 16 rooms, from £125.*

LITTLE SHELFORD, CAMBRIDGESHIRE   3–1B

Sycamore House   £35   Ⓐ★
1 Church St CB2 5HG   (01223) 843396
*"Elegant and homely at the same time"; reporters unanimously
find a visit to Michael & Susan Sharpe's "peaceful" village house
restaurant – with its "personal" service and its "relaxed"
atmosphere – "a real tonic". / Sample dishes: Stilton & celery soup;
steamed prawns with sour cream & sweet chilli; Campari & orange sorbet.
Details: 1.5m from M11, J11 on A10 to Royston; 9 pm; D only, closed Sun-Tue;
no Amex; no smoking; children: 12+.*

LIVERPOOL, MERSEYSIDE   5–2A

As Liverpool gears up to be European City of Culture 2008, its appearance is being transformed (rather in the same way as Birmingham's has in recent years). As in Brum, however, developments in the culinary scene seems to be lagging behind those in the architecture. The recent arrival of the *London Carriage Works*, however – not far from the other local beacon, *60 Hope Street* – may signal better times ahead. Many of the European restaurants of note, however, still huddle together in a remarkably small area, between the cathedrals. One of these, the *Everyman Bistro*, has maintained its 'top stand-by' reputation for three decades.

There is quite a number of Chinese restaurants of some interest – and a Chinatown – but the 'scene' could not in any sense be said to rival Manchester's.

L'Alouette   £38   𝔸
2 Lark Ln l 17 8US   (0151) 727 2142
*The sort of French restaurant that does "the best Banoffi pie" – this Sefton Park spot may perhaps be more notable for its romantic ambience than for its cuisine, but is a well-established local institution nonetheless. / **Sample dishes:** snails & frogs legs in garlic; steak with Roquefort; lemon tart.* **Details:** 10 pm; closed Mon.

Casa Italia   £22   𝔸
40 Stanley St L1 6AL   (0151) 227 5774
*"Still the best place in town for a pizza" – this "lively" Italian occupies a former warehouse. / **Sample dishes:** smoked & cured meat platter; Ventresca bacon & olive pizza; cassata.* **Details:** off Victoria St; 10 pm; need 8+ to book.

Chung Ku   £26   ★
Riverside Drive, Columbus Quay L3 4DB   (0151) 726 8191
*"Stunning river views" are a defining characteristic of this "architecturally-striking" oriental, but it's the "excellent" food which gets the most consistent support from reporters; watch out, though, for "pricey" drinks. / **Sample dishes:** pork and prawn dumplings; sweet and sour chicken; chocolate ice cream.*
Details: www.chungkurestaurant.co.uk; 11.30 pm, Fri & Sat midnight, Sun 10 pm.

Ego   £30
Federation Hs, Hope St L1 9BS   (0151) 706 0707
"Good value for a pre-concert dinner" – this "buzzy" bistro next to the Philharmonic Hall offers "unfussy" Mediterranean food; allow plenty of time, though, as service can be "slow".
*/ **Sample dishes:** Andalucian chicken salad; roast salmon fillet served with a langoustine & spinach sauce; summer berries in wine jelly, served with greek yoghurt.* **Details:** www.egorestaurants.com; 10.30 pm; no Amex; no smoking.

Everyman Bistro   £20   𝔸
5-9 Hope St L1 9BH   (0151) 708 9545
"A lovely bustling friendly place, with a very Bohemian feel" – this theatre basement bistro has, for over thirty years, been the Pool's most popular 'cheap eat'; for its many fans, it still "never fails".
*/ **Sample dishes:** nutty parsnip soup; red chilli chicken with yellow rice; apricot & almond cobbler.* **Details:** www.everyman.co.uk; midnight, Thu-Sat 2 am; closed Sun; no Amex; no smoking area.

Far East £19
27-35 Berry St L1 9DF (0151) 709 3141
"Very reasonable prices" feature in most reports on this cavernous Chinatown fixture (above an oriental cash & carry). / **Details:** by church on Berry St; 11 pm; no smoking area.

Gulshan £25 ★
544-548 Aigburth Rd L19 3QG (0151) 427 2273
"The only Indian worth a visit in these parts", this surprisingly "tasteful" outfit consistently serves up "very good" dishes. / **Details:** www.gulshan-liverpool.com; 10.45 pm; D only; no smoking area.

Keith's Wine Bar £16 🄰
107 Lark Ln L17 8UR (0151) 728 7688
"A long-standing institution on trendy Lark Lane", this Sefton Park "classic" offers "lovely snacks and main meals" (with "lots for veggies"), plus "a massive selection of wines" (many by the glass). / **Sample dishes:** grilled halloumi with pitta bread; Spanish-style chicken with rice; sticky toffee pudding. **Details:** 10.30 pm; no smoking area; need 6+ to book.

Left Bank £34
1 Church Rd L15 9EA (0151) 734 5040
This "cramped" but "lovely" Gallic bistro moved into new hands in July 2004, and a rating is therefore inappropriate. / **Sample dishes:** tomato & Mozzarella tart; roast duck with honey & thyme glaze; crème brûlée. **Details:** www.leftbankrestaurant.co.uk; off Penny Lane; 10 pm; closed Mon L, Sat L & Sun.

The Living Room £28 🄰
15 Victoria St L2 5QS (0870) 442 2535
"Really nice bar food, in addition to the more sophisticated grub" makes this "lively" bar/restaurant (part of a national chain) worth knowing about in this still under-served city. / **Sample dishes:** duck spring rolls with shitake salsa; Cumberland bangers & mash; Belgian waffles. **Details:** www.thelivingroom.co.uk; 11 pm, Fri & Sat 12 pm; no jeans or trainers; no smoking area.

London Carriage Works £38 🄰★
40 Hope St L1 9DA 9DA
(0151) 705 2222
"Competition for 60 Hope Street" (a few doors away) – this "sophisticated" but "relaxed" newcomer (part of a trendy new design-hotel) is winning instant acclaim for its "cool" and "well-designed" setting and its "interesting" and "deft" cuisine; "the bistro is good, too". / **Details:** www.tlcw.co.uk; 10 pm. **Accommodation:** 48 rooms, from £115.

The Other Place £29 🄰★
141-143 Allerton Rd L18 2DD (0151) 724 1234
This Allerton restaurant has "old favourite" status in these parts, offering "well-cooked" fare in "cramped" but characterful surroundings; it recently opened a "more upmarket" city-centre outpost – on the site vacated by Becher's Brook (RIP) at 29a Hope Street (tel 707 7888). / **Sample dishes:** goats cheese & red pepper spring rolls; grilled cod with hazelnut & herb potato cake; passion fruit & coconut tart. **Details:** 10 pm; closed Mon & Sun D; no Amex; L & afternoon tea only.

Pod £22 𝔸★
137-139 Allerton Rd L18 2DD (0151) 724 2255
"A good range of 'world' tapas" is the culinary draw to this buzzy
Allerton destination; it's *"always a big hit with the nearby students
and trendy professionals"*, and can get *"too noisy and crowded at
weekends".* / ***Sample dishes:*** *prawn & squid tempura with wasabi mayonnaise;
chicken stuffed with chorizo & coriander; sticky toffee pudding.* ***Details:*** *9.30 pm;
booking: max 6 at weekends.*

Quarter £32
7-11 Falkner St L8 7PU (0151) 707 1965
*"An Italian café owned by the same people as 60 Hope Street
(across the road)";* reporters don't find it an exciting destination,
but it does offer *"good pizza, pasta and salads, plus good coffee
and lovely cakes".* / ***Sample dishes:*** *antipasto; arabiatta pasta with pepperoni;
profiteroles.* ***Details:*** *11 pm; no Amex; no smoking area; no booking.*

Simply Heathcote's £30
Beetham Plaza 25, The Strand L2 0XL (0151) 236 3536
*Near the Liver Building, this "bustling, brasserie-style venue" –
part of Paul Heathcote's North Western mini-empire – is hailed
by fans as "bright, pleasant and ever-popular" (especially for
business); overall, though, its standards are "OK-ish", at best.*
/ ***Sample dishes:*** *pan-fried sardines with tomato salsa; char-grilled chicken Caesar
salad; bread & butter pudding.* ***Details:*** *www.heathcotes.co.uk; 10 pm; no smoking.*

60 Hope Street £40 𝔸
60 Hope St L1 9BZ
(0151) 707 6060

*This "friendly" modern establishment (with a café/bar below) is a
"polished operation", which – for its many fans – "still leads the
Liverpool scene"; some feel it's "not as good as it used to be",
though, complaining of "oddly uninspiring" recent meals.*
/ ***Sample dishes:*** *fishcakes with smoked pepper aioli; lamb with crispy spinach
risotto; peanut butter brûlée.* ***Details:*** *www.60hopestreet.com; between the
Cathedrals; 10.30 pm; closed Sat L & Sun; no Amex; no smoking area.*

Tai Pan £21 ★
WH Lung Building, Gt Howard St L5 9TZ (0151) 207 3888
"Only let down by its warehouse-like setting", this *"sprawling"*
dining room (above a Chinese supermarket) is consistently praised
for its *"good value"* and its *"quality nosh".* / ***Sample dishes:*** *chicken
satay; pork & green peppers in black bean sauce; ice cream.* ***Details:*** *11.30 pm,
Sun 9.30 pm.*

Yuet Ben £21 ★
1 Upper Duke St L1 9DU (0151) 709 5772
"Still just as good after three decades", this *"friendly"* veteran, by
the Chinatown arch, is – for some reporters – still Liverpool's
"best Chinese"; it offers *"a smaller menu than most orientals,
which is probably why it's so good!"* / ***Details:*** *www.yuetben.co.uk; 11 pm;
D only, closed Mon.*

Ziba £42

Hargreaves Building, 5 Chapel St L3 9AG (0151) 236 6676
*The high-ceilinged, new city-centre premises may be "cool and stylish" and the modern British cooking generally "good", but there's no denying that a sense of "something missing" permeates reports from those who knew the 'old' Ziba. / **Sample dishes:** tian of crab, mango & avocado with shellfish dressing; roast veal with crushed potato & shallot jus; soft-centered chocolate cake, with greek yoghurt sorbet.
Details: www.racquetclub.org.uk; 10 pm; closed Sun; no smoking area.
Accommodation: 8 rooms, from £120.*

LLANDEGLA, WREXHAM 5–3A

Bodidris Hall Hotel £43 Ⓐ

LL11 3AL (0870) 729 2292
*Descriptions of the "lovely" setting and "amazing" views pepper feedback on this romantic manor house; the food is "good", too. / **Sample dishes:** confit duck terrine with Cumberland sauce; lamb with leek & mint mousse; roast pear & almond tart. **Details:** www.bodidrishall.com; on A5104 from Wrexham; 8.45 pm; no smoking; children: 14+. **Accommodation:** 9 rooms, from £99.*

LLANDRILLO, DENBIGHSHIRE 4–2D

Tyddyn Llan £46 Ⓐ★

LL21 0ST (01490) 440264
*Bryan & Susan Webb's rural restaurant-with-rooms is hailed by most reporters as "a real class act", where local ingredients are intelligently used to create dishes that are "spot on every time". / **Sample dishes:** Lamb sweetbreads; roast pigeon with wild mushrooms; rhubarb and champagne trifle. **Details:** www.tyddynllan.co.uk; on B4401 between Corwen and Bala; 9 pm; closed Mon (Tue-Thu L by prior arrangement only); no Amex; no smoking; booking essential Tue L-Thu L. **Accommodation:** 12 rooms, from £130.*

LLANDUDNO, CONWY 4–1D

Bodysgallen Hall £45 Ⓐ

LL30 1RS (01492) 584466
*"A wonderful country house in a magnificent setting" (on a hill outside the town); the food can be "very good", too, but a regular notes that it can also be rather "variable". / **Sample dishes:** roast tomato soup with pesto tortellini; lamb with bacon potato cake & mint jus; grape & grenadine jelly. **Details:** www.bodysgallen.com; 2m off A55 on A470; 9.30 pm; no Amex; jacket required at D; no smoking; booking: max 10; children: 8+. **Accommodation:** 36 rooms, from £165.*

Richards £35

7 Church Walks LL30 2HD (01492) 877924
*Under Richard Hendey, this "intimate" bistro in a characterful Victorian seaside resort has built a good name for its "lovely, freshly-cooked fare"; let's hope new owners, Donald & Gillian Hadwin, keep the flag flying. / **Sample dishes:** chicken, venison & pistachio terrine; pork with Bramley apple sauce; Caribbean rum, raisin & coffee ice cream.
Details: 11 pm; D only, closed Mon & Sun.*

St Tudno Hotel   £ 47   ★
Promenade LL30 2LP   (01492) 874411
"Excellent food and terrific personal service" help make this "tranquil" hotel dining room (near the pier) an "exceptional" seaside destination; the recent "lavish refurbishment", however, is not to all tastes. / **Sample dishes:** *crab risotto with parmesan; lamb with cabbage & oatmeal; warm chocolate fondant with coconut ice cream.*
Details: *www.st-tudno.co.uk; 9.30 pm; no smoking area; children: no babies or toddlers at D.* **Accommodation:** *19 rooms, from £100.*

LLANGOLLEN, DENBIGHSHIRE   5–3A

Corn Mill   £ 26   A
Dee Ln LL20 8PN   (01978) 869555
A "beautiful setting" (looking down on the fast-flowing River Dee) plus "lots of choice" help make this "interesting" mill-conversion brasserie a destination of some note locally; culinary standards, though, tend to be "hit-and-miss". / **Sample dishes:** *melon, feta & pine kernel salad; aubergine & goats cheese with red pepper dressing; bread & butter pudding.* **Details:** *www.brunningandprice.co.uk; 9.30 pm; no smoking area.*

LLANWDDYN, POWYS   4–2D

Lake Vyrnwy Hotel   £ 42   A★
Lake Vyrnwy SY10 0LY   (01691) 870692
It's not just the "stunning location" – "with beautiful views over a lake" – which again wins raves for this Victorian hotel dining room; service is "wonderful" and the food – often making use of produce from the surrounding estate – is "very good", too.
/ **Sample dishes:** *tuna carpaccio with smoked quails eggs; pot-roast pork with sage mash; lime panna cotta with peppered strawberries.* **Details:** *www.lakevyrnwy.com; on B4393 at SE end of Lake Vyrnwy; 9.15 pm; no smoking.* **Accommodation:** *35 rooms, from £120.*

LLANWRTYD WELLS, POWYS   4–4D

Carlton House Hotel   £ 42   A★
Dolecoed Rd LD5 4RA   (01591) 610248
For a "gourmet break", this townhouse restaurant-with-rooms – with its "small" but very comfortably-furnished dining room – makes a "great-value" destination; if offers Mary-Ann Gilchrist's "excellent" cooking accompanied by husband Alan's "interesting" wines. / **Sample dishes:** *seared king scallops; warm peppered beef salad; apple & Calvados sorbet.* **Details:** *www.carltonrestaurant.com; 8.30 pm; closed Mon L, Sat L & Sun; no Amex; no smoking; booking: max 10.* **Accommodation:** *5 rooms, from £65.*

LLYSWEN, POWYS   2–1A

Llangoed Hall   £ 59   A
LD3 0YP   (01874) 754525
An "amazing location" helps make a visit to Sir Bernard Ashley's country house hotel "a pleasure and delight" for many reporters; it's all change on the personnel front, though, with both a new chef (Sean Ballington) and manager moving into position as this guide goes to press. / **Sample dishes:** *butternut squash velouté with smoked chicken; herb-crusted lamb with pea purée; seared pineapple with tarragon sorbet.* **Details:** *www.llangoedhall.com; 11m NW of Brecon on A470; 9 pm; jacket required; no smoking; children: 8+.* **Accommodation:** *23 rooms, from £180.*

LOCH LOMOND, DUNBARTONSHIRE   9–4B

Cameron House   £61   ★
G83 8QZ   (01389) 755565
A new chef (Paul Tambourini) is "setting very good standards", at
this "magnificent" Loch Lomond-side dining room; it's undeniably
"pricey", though, and doubters can find the atmosphere on the
"clinical" side. / **Sample dishes:** asparagus, leek & mushroom terrine; lobster &
langoustine with black olive pasta; banana tarte Tatin with pineapple sorbet.
Details: www.cameronhouse.co.uk; over Erskine Bridge to A82, follow signs to Loch
Lomond; 9.45 pm; D only, closed Mon & Tue, except Sun when L & D; jacket & tie
required; no smoking; children: 14+. **Accommodation:** 96 rooms, from £245.

LOCKSBOTTOM, KENT   3–3B

Chapter One   £40   ★
Farnborough Common BR6 8NF   (01689) 854848
"A top-notch West End restaurant in the suburbs" – that's the
theme of practically all commentary on this well-established
suburban "oasis", whose "excellent-value" modern cuisine has
won an enormous following. / **Sample dishes:** smoked goose, walnut &
raspberry salad; provençale salmon, clam & mussel confit; apple tart & thyme ice
cream. **Details:** www.chaptersrestaurants.co.uk; 2m E of Bromley on A21;
10.30 pm; booking: max 12.

LONG CRENDON, BUCKINGHAMSHIRE   2–2D

Angel   £41   ★
47 Bicester Rd HP18 9EE   (01844) 208268
"You never seem to get a bad meal", at this "great" Chilterns pub,
whose "top-notch" cooking – in particular, the "ever-changing"
fish and seafood menu – has quite a reputation.
/ **Sample dishes:** feta, tomato & olive gateau; duck & smoked bacon with
blueberry sauce; cranberry toffee tart. **Details:** 2m NW of Thame, off B4011;
9.30 pm; closed Sun D; no Amex; no smoking area; booking: max 12, Fri & Sat.
Accommodation: 3 rooms, from £75.

LONG MELFORD, SUFFOLK   3–1C

Scutchers Bistro   £39   ★
Westgate St CO10 9DP   (01787) 310200
The Barrett family's smartly turned-out modern venture serves up
an "eclectic" range of dishes – from "straightforward" to more
complex, but all "from good ingredients" and "properly prepared".
/ **Sample dishes:** seared scallops; roast lamb with stuffed tomatoes; crêpes Suzette.
Details: www.scutchers.com; 9.30 pm; closed Mon & Sun; no smoking.

LONGRIDGE, LANCASHIRE   5–1B

The Longridge Restaurant   £38
104-106 Higher Rd PR3 3SY   (01772) 784969
Relaunched a couple of years back, the original, rural cradle of
Paul Heathcote's North Western group continues to attract mixed
reports; even some fans say it's "only occasionally memorable",
and critics simply think it's "overpriced". / **Sample dishes:** herb polenta
with char-grilled vegetables; crispy pork belly with spinach & red wine; iced apricot &
gingerbread parfait. **Details:** www.heathcotes.co.uk; follow signs for Jeffrey Hill;
10 pm; closed Mon & Sat L; no smoking.

LOUGHBOROUGH, LEICESTERSHIRE   5–3D

Thai House   £26
5a High St LE11 2PY   (01509) 260030
"Reliably good food" ensures that there's "often a crowd" at this
consistent town-centre oriental. / **Sample dishes:** spare ribs.
Details: 11 pm.

LOWER ODDINGTON, GLOUCESTERSHIRE   2–1C

The Fox Inn   £29   A
GL56 0UR   (01451) 870555
Some accuse it of being "chichi", but most reporters sing the
praises of this "warren-like" Cotswold gastropub, which offers
"consistently good" (and wide-ranging) cooking at "reasonable"
prices. / **Sample dishes:** smoked haddock & watercress tart; braised lamb shank
with lemon zest; steamed treacle sponge. **Details:** www.foxinn.net; on A436 near
Stow on the Wold; 10 pm; no Amex. **Accommodation:** 3 rooms, from £68.

LOWER WOLVERCOTE, OXFORDSHIRE   2–2D

Trout Inn   £26   A
195 Godstow Rd OX2 8PN   (01865) 302071
Even excessive popularity cannot dent the appeal of "Inspector
Morse's pub", with its "wonderfully atmospheric interior and its
riverside location"; the food is incidental. / **Sample dishes:** salmon &
broccoli fishcakes; Mediterranean chicken with new potatoes; toffee apple bread &
butter pudding. **Details:** www.mbplc.com; 2m from junction of A40 & A44; 9 pm;
no smoking; no booking; children: no children.

LUDLOW, SHROPSHIRE   5–4A

The Cookhouse   £32
Bromfield SY8 2JR   (01584) 856565
"Very obliging" and "reliable", this unpretentious spot offers "good
fresh food"… and some relief from the culinary striving to be
found everywhere else in town. / **Sample dishes:** Cornish crab with saffron
lemon & crème fraîche; noisette of lamb with herb crust, scented with lavender
honey; vanilla & lime panacotta. **Details:** 2m N of Ludlow on A49 to Shrewsbury;
9.30 pm; no Amex; no smoking area. **Accommodation:** 15 rooms, from £60.

Hibiscus   £45   ★★
17 Corve St SY8 1DA   (01584) 872325
Fans hail Claude Bosi as "the most exciting chef in the UK" and
his "progressive" cuisine is rated towards the top of the survey's
premier league; the décor at his manor house dining room can
occasionally seem a bit "chilly", but, for most reporters, the
"super" staff contribute to a "charming" overall experience.
/ **Sample dishes:** white onion & lime ravioli with broad beans; roast turbot with
tarragon & orange; chocolate tart with star anise. **Details:** 9.30 pm; closed Mon,
Tue L & Sun; no Amex; no smoking; booking: max 14.

Koo   £25
127 Old St SY8 1NU   (01584) 878462
"Freshly cooked and delicate" Japanese–Thai fare generally wins
the thumbs-up for this "friendly" spot. / **Details:** www.koo-ook.com;
9.45 pm; closed Mon & Sun.

Merchant House £ 42 ★
Lower Corve St SY8 1DU (01584) 875438
Shaun Hill put Ludlow on the map, and his "interesting, if rather spare" townhouse venture still makes a "fabulous" and "unpretentious" destination; he has let it be known he's thinking of moving on, though, and one or two reports suggest that the food may be "slightly slipping". / **Sample dishes:** grilled sea bass with allspice; roast pigeon with morels; Hungarian apricot trifle.
Details: www.merchanthouse.co.uk; 9 pm; closed Mon & Sun, Tue-Thu D only; no Amex or Switch; no smoking; booking: max 8.

Mr Underhill's £ 44 𝔸★
Dinham Wier SY8 1EH (01584) 874431
"Excellent cooking compensates for the absence of choice", at Chris & Judy Bradley's riverside restaurant-with-rooms, where an impressive proportion of reports note a "perfect" dinner in "relaxed" surroundings. / **Sample dishes:** smoked haddock with confit tomatoes; Perigord duck with olives & honey; Italian bread & butter pudding.
Details: www.mr-underhills.co.uk; 8.30 pm; D only, closed Tue; no Amex; no smoking. **Accommodation:** 9 rooms, from £95.

Overton Grange £ 48
Hereford Rd SY8 4AD (01584) 873500
This "formal" establishment in an Edwardian house is, according to its fans, "utterly wonderful"; it doesn't generate a huge amount of feedback, though, and other reporters only go so far as to say that it's "usually sound". / **Sample dishes:** roast scallops & langoustines with truffles; seared turbot with salsify & roast shallots; chocolate cup with pistachio ice cream. **Details:** www.overtongrangehotel.com; off A49, 1.5m S of Ludlow; 9.30 pm; no Amex; no smoking area; children: 5+ after 7 pm. **Accommodation:** 14 rooms, from £130.

LUND, NORTH YORKSHIRE 5–1D

Wellington Inn £ 36 ★
19 The Grn YO25 9TE (01377) 217294
A "nice 'village' atmosphere" pervades this attractive inn; fans find the food simply "excellent", and even those who find it "expensive" concede that it's "reliable every time".
/ **Details:** 9.30 pm; closed Mon & Sun; no Amex; children: 14+.

LYDFORD, DEVON 1–3C

The Dartmoor Inn £ 32 ★
EX20 4AY (01822) 820221
"Beautifully presented food" wins widespread praise for this "charming old inn" – "an oasis in the wilderness", on the fringe of the National Park. / **Sample dishes:** artichoke purée tart with baby onions; grilled mixed fish with courgette flower fritters; Bramley apple ice cream with roasted cob nuts. **Details:** 9.30 pm; closed Mon & Sun D; no Amex; no smoking; children: 5+ at weekends. **Accommodation:** 3 rooms, from £90.

LYDGATE, GREATER MANCHESTER   5–2B
White Hart   **£ 35**   ★

51 Stockport Rd OL4 4JJ (01457) 872566

*That home-made sausages are the speciality might give the wrong impression about this "wonderful inn", on the moors outside Manchester – the bangers may be "a great hit", but there are also plenty of more "interesting" choices, from a very varied menu. / Sample dishes: grilled tandoori chicken with cucumber yoghurt; calves liver with pickled cabbage & thyme; lime & raspberry cheesecake. **Details:** www.thewhitehart.co.uk; 2m E of Oldham on A669, then A6050; 9.30 pm; no smoking. **Accommodation:** 12 rooms, from £110.*

LYME REGIS, DORSET   2–4A
Fish Restaurant   **£ 33**   Ⓐ★

Cliff Cottage, Cobb Rd DT7 3JP (01297) 444111

*"High on the hill overlooking the sea", this small, singular, summer-only venture wins rave reviews as a "magical" experience; chef/patron Clive Cobb offers "the local catch, cooked to perfection". / **Details:** www.thefishrestaurant.net; 8.30 pm; closed Mon, Tue L & Sun D; no Amex; no smoking. **Accommodation:** 3 rooms, from £50.*

LYMINGTON, HAMPSHIRE   2–4D
Egan's   **£ 37**   ★

Gosport St SO41 9BE (01590) 676165

*"Consistently good" food and service make John Egan's bistro popular with reporters; lunchtime prices are particularly "reasonable", but you "have to book" at pretty much any time. / Sample dishes: seafood tempura; rack of lamb with leeks; strawberries & ice cream. **Details:** 10 pm; closed Mon & Sun; no Amex; no smoking; booking: max 6, Sat.*

Gordleton Mill   **£ 36**   Ⓐ★

Silver St SO41 6DJ (01590) 682219

*This tranquil site in the New Forest (a converted 17th-century water mill on the River Avon) has quite a gastronomic history; feedback is limited these days, confirming the view that its "simple and fairly priced" food and "outstanding" service are something of "a local secret". / **Details:** www.gordeltonmill.co.uk; 9 pm; closed Sun D; no smoking area. **Accommodation:** 7 rooms, from £120.*

LYNDHURST, HAMPSHIRE   2–4C
Le Poussin at Parkhill   **£ 51**   ★

Beaulieu Rd SO43 7FZ (023) 8028 2944

*"Formal but friendly", this country house hotel maintains "high standards" of cuisine in "beautiful" New Forest surroundings; critics, though, find it too "pricey". / Sample dishes: salmon with cucumber salad & caviar; rare beef with red wine sauce; hot chocolate fondant. **Details:** www.lepoussin.co.uk; 9.30 pm; no smoking; children: 8+ at D. **Accommodation:** 19 rooms, from £110.*

LYTHAM, LANCASHIRE   5–1A
Chicory   **£ 28**   ★

5-7 Henry St FY8 5LE (01253) 737111

*"Chicory saves Lancashire's bacon", opines one reporter otherwise dismayed by local restaurant standards – an informal brasserie, it offers "imaginative" and "plentiful" cooking, sometimes "slowly". / **Details:** 9.30 pm; no smoking.*

MADINGLEY, CAMBRIDGESHIRE 3–1B
Three Horseshoes £37
CB3 8AB (01954) 210221
"Ideal for parents visiting their Cambridge offspring", this "old stalwart" dining pub remains a pretty reliable, if somewhat "pricey"-for-what-it-is, destination. / **Sample dishes:** leek & morel tortellini with leek mousse; venison with star anise noodles & pak choy; lemon tart with cherry vodka sorbet. **Details:** www.huntsbridge.com; 2m W of Cambridge, off A14 or M11; 9.30 pm; closed Sun D; no smoking.

MAIDENHEAD, BERKSHIRE 3–3A
Cookham Tandoori £32 🄰★
High St SL6 9SL (01628) 522584
Its name may be prosaic, but this is a "sophisticated" subcontinental – its style is "about as far from a curry and a pint as you could imagine". / **Details:** www.spicemerchantgroup.com; 11 pm; no smoking.

MALMESBURY, WILTSHIRE 2–2C
Old Bell £35 🄰
Abbey Rw SN16 0AG (01666) 822344
"Well-cooked, locally-sourced cooking" rewards visitors to 'the oldest hotel in England' – a "friendly" and "delightful" place, of which reporters speak only well. / **Sample dishes:** chicken liver crostini; shepherds pie; chocolate fondant with pistachio ice cream. **Details:** www.oldbellhotel.com; next to Abbey; 9 pm; no smoking; children: 12+ at D. **Accommodation:** 31 rooms, from £110.

MANCHESTER, GREATER MANCHESTER 5–2B

Manchester has, by some margin, the largest restaurant scene outside London, and with some characteristics all of its own. For example, although there are exceptions – such as *Mont* and the quirky quarter-centenarian *Market* – the city-centre remains, to a surprising extent, free of European restaurants of real quality. Many central places tend to be very much 'atmosphere-led'. For good European cooking, diners still tend to head towards the south western suburbs – to the long-established *Moss Nook* (near the Airport), to West Didsbury's consistently impressive *Lime Tree* or to Altrincham's ambitious *Juniper*.

However, the city-centre boasts a very impressive range of oriental restaurants, including the most notable Chinatown in the UK outside London. The legendary *Yang Sing* – by far the best known place in Manchester – is also the country's most famous Chinese restaurant, and justifiably so. *Koh Samui* is arguably England's top Thai outside the capital. There are lots of Indian restaurants, too, mainly in Rusholme. Some of them are quite good, but they are, to a surprising extent, still stuck in a pretty downmarket mould.

Western Europe's largest student population – bolstered nowadays by a growing army of young professionals resident in the city-centre – helps to support a growing number of places, such as *Kro,* which are fun and relatively affordable.

Armenian Taverna
£25 ★
3-5 Princess St M2 4DF (0161) 834 9025
It's worth descending the "gloomy and uninviting steps" to seek out this long-established city-centre "Eastern grotto"; "excellent-value kebabs" are a highlight, but there are also "some interesting options for veggies". / **Sample dishes:** *stuffed cabbage leaves; Armenian goulash; baklava.* **Details:** *11.30 pm; closed Mon; children: 3+.*

The Assembly Rooms
£35
6 Lapwing Ln M20 2WS (0161) 445 3653
This "noisy" and "stylish" newcomer "could not be more different" from The Nose (RIP), which formerly occupied this Didsbury site; it has no great foodie aspirations, but the menu is "wide-ranging" and "reasonably priced". / **Details:** *between Palatine Road & Withington hospital; midnight; no smoking area.*

The Bridge
£23 ★
53 Bridge St M3 3BW (0161) 834 0242
"Nice twists on standard British fare" often lead to "outstanding" results at this recently relaunched boozer, just off Deansgate; with its "generous" portions, it's already "deservedly popular". / **Details:** *www.thebridgemanchester.co.uk; 9.30 pm.*

The Bridgewater Hall
£30 🄰
Lower Mosley St M2 3WS (0161) 950 0000
The menu "could sometimes be a bit more exciting", but – by the standards of cultural-facility catering – this "cool" dining room inspires consistently positive feedback. / **Sample dishes:** *shredded chicken salad; roast cod with pesto gnocchi; chocolate marquise with poached apricots.* **Details:** *www.bridgewater-hall.co.uk; 7.30 pm; openings affected by concert times; no smoking.*

Cachumba
£16 ★★
220 Burton Rd M20 2LW (0161) 445 2479
"An amazing fusion of world cuisines, with strong African and Asian influences" draws a devoted fan club to this "easy-going" BYO West Didsbury café, where chef Seema Gupta creates "marvellous" dishes "with love". / **Sample dishes:** *red chicken curry; fish curry; mango & berry crumble.* **Details:** *9.30 pm; closed Sun D; no credit cards.*

Café Paradiso
Hotel Rossetti
£29 ★
107 Piccadilly M1 2DB (0161) 200 5665
"Simple Italian-influenced food" makes this "quirky" design-hotel brasserie, near Piccadilly Station, well worth seeking out in the still under-served city-centre. / **Sample dishes:** *blue cheese tart; halibut fillet seared with couscous & oil dressing; oriental spiced rice pudding.* **Details:** *www.aliasrossetti.com; 10 pm; no smoking; booking: max 8.* **Accommodation:** *61 rooms, from £100.*

Cedar Tree
£23 ★★
69 Thomas St M4 1LQ
(0161) 8345016
It "looks like a café", but this simple newcomer in the Northern Quarter wins raves for its "really welcoming" service and "superb", "carefully prepared" dishes – "I've travelled extensively in the Middle East and I had some of the best dishes ever here"; unlicensed but you can BYO. / **Details:** *www.sugarcane.com; 10 pm; no Amex; no smoking area.*

Choice   £32   A★
Castle Quay M15 4NT   (0161) 833 3400
An "interesting" menu ("modern British, with a hint of the
North") – twinned with "stylish" design and "reasonable" prices –
contributes to high levels of reporter satisfaction with this
"intimate" spot, "pleasantly situated" in Castlefield.
/ *Details:* www.choicebarandrestaurant.co.uk; 10 pm.

Croma   £23   A
1 Clarence St M2 4DE   (0161) 237 9799
Arguably it's only "one step above PizzaExpress" – the owners
once ran the local franchise – but this "stylish" and "really buzzy"
pizza joint has established itself as central Manchester's 'default'
stand-by for an informal bite. / *Sample dishes:* goats cheese bruschetta;
chicken Caesar salad pizza; crème brûlée cheesecake.
Details: www.cromamanchester.co.uk; off Albert Square; 11 pm; no smoking area;
need 6+ to book.

Dimitri's   £26
Campfield Arc M3 4FN   (0161) 839 3319
"A fun place for groups, but very noisy" – this "solid and
consistent" mezze bar (in a Victorian arcade off Deansgate) is an
ever-popular destination (if perhaps one that's "a bit frantic for
couples"). / *Sample dishes:* chorizo salad; ribs with vegetable couscous; baklava.
Details: www.dimitris.co.uk; near Museum of Science & Industry; 11.30 pm.

Dukes 92   £22   A
19-25 Castle St M3 4LZ   (0161) 839 8646
"Good-value pub food" (featuring "good cheese" and "large
helpings") makes this "relaxed" Castlefield boozer a handy stand-
by; in late-summer 2004, the same owners opened a restaurant:
Albert's Shed. / *Sample dishes:* roast tomato soup; ciabatta with bacon &
pesto; hot fudge cake. *Details:* www.dukes92.com; off Deansgate; 6 pm; L only;
no Amex.

Eighth Day Café   £14   ★
111 Oxford Rd M1 7DU   (0161) 273 4878
Inevitably, some reports find the old magic missing from the new
building of this student-land institution; for "vegetarian home-
cooking with flair", at "low prices", however, it remains well worth
knowing about. / *Sample dishes:* Armenian lentil soup; vegan pâté with pitta
bread & salad; vegan chocolate cake. *Details:* www.eighth-day.co.uk; 7 pm; Sat &
Sun 9.30 pm; closed Sun; no smoking; no booking.

Etrop Grange   £45
Thorley Ln M90 4EG   (0161) 499 0500
"Only a few minutes from the airport, but very quiet", this
attractive, old-fashioned country house hotel is ideally located for
savvy travellers; it's unsurprisingly quite "expensive", but standards
are consistently high. / *Details:* www.corushotels.com/etropgrange; J5 off the
M56; 10 pm; closed Sat L; no smoking. *Accommodation:* 64 rooms, from £85.

Evuna   £29   ★
277 Deansgate M3 4EW   (0161) 819 2752
Over 500 Spanish wines are on offer at this "very relaxed and
chilled" new wine bar/restaurant; it offers "quality throughout",
not least in its "innovative" modern Hispanic cuisine.
/ *Details:* 11 pm; closed Sun.

Francs £28
2 Goose Grn WA14 1DW   (0161) 941 3954
*It's never going to set the world on fire, but this "reliable local
bistro" is consistently hailed as a "good value-for-money"
destination. / Sample dishes: salmon dauphinoise; chicken in coconut & lime;
chocolate praline tartlet. Details: www.francs-altrincham.com; 10.30 pm, Fri & Sat
11 pm; no Amex; no smoking area.*

Great Kathmandu £18 ★
140 Burton Rd M20 1JQ   (0161) 434 6413
*"Very cramped" and "full every night", this "unfancy" West
Didsbury subcontinental continues to please most reporters with
its "tasty" Nepalese food that's "always good".
/ Details: www.greatkathmandu.com; near Withington hospital; midnight.*

Green's £27 ★
43 Lapwing Ln M20 2NT   (0161) 434 4259
*"Innovative" veggie dishes and "decent" prices (with a BYO policy,
too) help make this West Didsbury café very popular – indeed a
major expansion took place post our survey. / Sample dishes: feta,
watermelon & cucumber salad; aubergine & potato Massaman curry; chocolate &
honeycomb mocha pot. Details: 4m S of city centre; 10.30 pm; closed Mon L &
Sat L; no Amex.*

The Greenhouse £19
331 Great Western St M14 4AN   (0161) 224 0730
*It's rather "like eating in your mad veggie uncle's front room", but
this Rusholme end-terrace retains quite a following; the menu
seems "huge" (but "many of the dishes are really very similar").
/ Sample dishes: houmous & pitta bread; peppers stuffed with cashews & pilau
rice; Knickerbocker glory. Details: www.dineveggie.com; 9.30 pm, Sat 10 pm; closed
Aug; no Amex; no smoking.*

The Grinch £24 Ⓐ
5-7 Chapel Walks, off Cross St M2 1HN   (0161) 907 3210
*"Just around the corner from the Royal Exchange", this "bustling"
and slightly Bohemian café-diner is an ever-popular city-centre
rendezvous. / Sample dishes: crispy duck & Japanese cucumber salad; grilled
chilli chicken Caesar salad; marshmallow ice cream & chocolate fudge sauce.
Details: www.grinch.co.uk; 10 pm.*

Gurkha Grill £23 ★
198 Burton Rd M20 1LH   (0161) 445 3461
*"It has strange décor, but the food is really tasty and a refreshing
change from the bland horrors of the Curry Mile" – one
representative reporter sings the praises of this "consistently
good" Nepalese. / Details: www.gurkhagrill.com; midnight, Fri & Sat 12.30 am;
D only.*

Jem And I £29 ★
School Ln M20 6RD   (0161) 445 3996
*"A simple modern restaurant serving brasserie-style food", this
"buzzy" and "fun" Didsbury newcomer is almost invariably
acclaimed for its "tasty" cuisine and its "good value"; (in fact, it's
already planning to double in size). / Details: 10 pm; closed Mon L &
Sun D; no smoking area.*

Juniper £55
21 The Downs WA14 2QD   (0161) 929 4008
*The "sheer inventiveness" of Paul Kitching's "totally different
culinary combinations" leads fans of his well-known Altrincham
HQ to hail it as "Manchester's best"; a (not so small) minority of
detractors, though, dismiss the cuisine as "ridiculously pretentious"
and "over-rated".* / **Sample dishes:** scallops with curried pea sauce; lamb with
raisins & sweetbreads in espresso sauce; lemon tart with Florida fruit cocktail.
Details: www.juniper-restaurant.co.uk; 10 pm; closed Mon, Sat L & Sun;
no smoking.

Koh Samui £26 ★★
16 Princess St M1 4NB   (0161) 237 9511
*"Fabulous food at reasonable prices" makes this "top-class" city
centre Thai a smash hit with reporters; service is "very friendly",
too.* / **Sample dishes:** seafood papaya salad; roast pork with chilli and sweet basil;
sticky coconut rice with mango. **Details:** www.kohsamuirestaurant.co.uk; opp City
Art Gallery; 11.30 pm; closed Sat L & Sun L.

Koreana £21 ★
40a, King St West M3 2WY   (0161) 832 4330
*A "friendly" and "ever-reliable" basement, off Deansgate; it has
quite a reputation for its "wild and wonderful" Korean dishes.*
/ **Sample dishes:** lemon ribs; soya bean casserole; Korean rice cake with cream.
Details: www.koreana.co.uk; 10.30 pm; closed Sat L & Sun.

Kro Bar £21 Ⓐ
325 Oxford Rd M13 9PG   (0161) 274 3100
*A Scandinavian menu plus "the best full English breakfasts" and
"a good selection of beers" all contribute to the charms of this
"laid-back" café, near the University; it's "always busy".*
/ **Sample dishes:** smoked fish chowder; African-spiced chicken with coconut rice;
hot chocolate fudge cake. **Details:** www.kro.co.uk; 11 pm; no Amex; no smoking
area; children: 18+ only.

Kro2 £24 Ⓐ
Oxford Hs, Oxford Rd M1 7ED   (0161) 236 1048
*This "great all-round" younger member of the Kro empire makes
a perennially "good cheap and cheerful choice", and supporters
say its Danish bar food "is of restaurant standard".*
/ **Sample dishes:** gravadlax plate with sweet mustard sauce & rye bread; haddock
cooked in soy, ginger, garlic & sake. **Details:** www.kro.co.uk/two; 10 pm; no smoking
area.

Lal Haweli £18 ★
68-72 Wilmslow Rd M14   (0161) 248 9700
*"Friendly" and "efficient", this Rusholme Indian is consistently
rated among the best on the Curry Mile.* / **Sample dishes:** king prawn
kebabs; chilli chicken; 'funky pie'. **Details:** 12.30 am, Fri 2 am, Sat 3 am;
no smoking area.

Lead Station £26
99 Beech Rd M21 9EQ   (0161) 881 5559
*"Very good, especially for light meals", this "cheerful" and "lively"
Chorlton café/bar is the sort of place that's "excellent for
breakfast or brunch, or for meeting friends" (especially in
summer); service, however, can be slow.* / **Sample dishes:** baked goats
cheese with honey; Spanish lamb casserole with chorizo & mash; Belgian chocolate
cheesecake. **Details:** 9.30 pm, Thu-Sat 10 pm; no booking.

The Lime Tree   £35   A★

8 Lapwing Ln M20 2WS   (0161) 445 1217
*"A Manchester benchmark" – this "old favourite" Didsbury
brasserie remains the top local destination for "a decent meal
without breaking the bank"; "happy" and "helpful" staff help
create a "lovely" atmosphere in which to enjoy some "well-
prepared and tasty" cooking. / Sample dishes: peppered tuna carpaccio;
fillet steak with black pepper & cream sauce; Baileys cheesecake with honeycomb ice
cream. Details: www.thelimetreerestaurant.com; toward Manchester airport;
10.30 pm; closed Mon L & Sat L; no smoking area.*

Little Yang Sing   £23   ★

17 George St M1 4HE   (0161) 228 7722
*There was an unusually high number of "average" reports this
year on this – usually – "reliable" and affordable Chinatown
fixture; for many people, however, it remains "the best little
restaurant in town". / Details: www.littleyangsing.co.uk; 11.30 pm.*

Livebait   £32

22 Lloyd St M2 5WA   (0161) 817 4110
*This "austere" outpost of the London chain is a top destination for
those seeking "perfect seafood in the heart of Manchester"; by
local standards, however, it can seem "expensive" for what it is.
/ Sample dishes: Mediterranean fish soup; lobster with new potato salad; panna
cotta & strawberries. Details: www.santeonline.co.uk; 10.30 pm, Sat 11 pm;
no smoking area.*

Lounge 10   £48   A

10 Tib Ln M2 4JB
(0161) 839 7222
*"Very sexy", "opulent" and "romantic" – this "OTT" city-centre
venue is hard to beat as a night out destination ("especially if they
have a singer"); there's the odd snipe that the place is "all fur
coat and no knickers", but what's in fact more surprising is how
well – for so trendy a place – the food is rated.
/ Sample dishes: goats cheese with seaweed & chilli dressing; salt & pepper duck
with onion bhaji & plum sauce; white chocolate mousse.
Details: www.lounge10manchester.co.uk; 11 pm; D only, closed Mon & Sun;
children: 18+ only.*

Love Saves The Day   £22   A★

Smithfield Buildings, Tib St M4 1LA   (0161) 832 0777
*"A life-saver in the self-consciously grungy Northern Quarter", this
"hip", "Manhattan-style" deli-diner is "a great place for a coffee
and a chat" ("and the lunch food is pretty cool too"); now also
open on Thu & Fri evenings. / Sample dishes: Cheshire ham & cheeses
with picalilli; sausages with bacon bubble 'n' squeak; sticky toffee pudding.
Details: www.lovesavestheday.co.uk; 7 pm, Thurs & Fri 10 pm; closed Sun;
no smoking.*

The Lowry   £31

Pier 8, Salford Quays M50 3AZ   (0161) 876 2121
*Standards are certainly nothing special, but this "busy" cultural
centre brasserie is still generally thought to be "great for a pre-
performance meal". / Sample dishes: sauteed chicken livers, wholegrain
mustard sauce, warm onion tart; pork & caramelized apple sausages, rosemary and
red onion marmalade, champ, calvados jus; chocolate orange torte with chocolate
Creme Anglaise. Details: www.thelowry.com; 7.45 pm; L only, D on performance
nights only; no smoking.*

The Lowry Hotel £ 45 X
50 Dearmans Pl M3 5LH (0161) 827 4000
"Zero ambience" is just one of the many flaws detected in the
dining room of Rocco Forte's (otherwise quite good) design-hotel;
some reporters fear it suffers from *"delusions of grandeur"*.
/ **Sample dishes:** *pistou soup with scallops; roast duck breast with juniper jus;
praline crème brûlée.* **Details:** *www.thelowryhotel.com; 10.30 pm; no smoking area;
booking: max 8.* **Accommodation:** *165 rooms, from £275.*

Malmaison £ 33
Piccadilly M1 3AQ (0161) 278 1000
"It used to be fun", when it was the hottest hang out in town, but
this central design-hotel dining room can seem a bit *"dull"* these
days; it's still a *"stylish"* and *"professional"* operation, though, if
with rather *"expensive"* food. / **Sample dishes:** *eggs benedict; sea bream
with asparagus; champagne & strawberry jelly.* **Details:** *www.malmaison.com; near
Piccadilly Station; 10.45 pm; no smoking area.* **Accommodation:** *167 rooms,
from £129.*

The Market £ 37 𝔸★
104 High St M4 1HQ (0161) 834 3743
"Eccentric but marvellous" – this retro *"hidden gem"* makes *"a
unique contribution to the Manchester scene"*; extended opening
hours this year coincided with a couple of uncharacteristic duff
reports – hopefully just 'growing pains'. / **Sample dishes:** *potato ravioli
with mint; Parmesan turkey with red pepper confit; banana & passion fruit pavlova.*
Details: *www.market-restaurant.com; 10 pm; closed Sun-Tue & Sat L.*

Metropolitan £ 25
2 Lapwing Ln M20 2WS (0161) 374 9559
"Relentlessly popular" and *"noisy"*, this West Didsbury gastropub
is especially hailed for its *"very good burgers"*, and for its *"great
Sunday lunch"*; *"more adventurous stuff is variable"*.
/ **Sample dishes:** *Stilton fritters with lemongrass dressing; pork & leek sausages
with apple mash; sticky toffee pudding.* **Details:** *near Withington hospital; 9.30 pm;
no smoking.*

Le Mont
Urbis Science Museum £ 48 ★
Cathedral Gdns M4 3BG
(0161) 605 8282
*"The impressive vista reinforces Manchester's image as a
'happening' place"*, says a fan of the city-centre's most ambitious
restaurant – it's on the top floor of a trendy museum (though
much of the view is lost thanks to a bizarre decision to frost much
of the glass); it's *"expensive"* of course, but Robert Kisby's cooking
is *"refined and imaginative"*. / **Sample dishes:** *creamy white onion & cider
soup with cheese croutons; grilled & roast lamb with vegetables; cinnamon poached
pear with ice cream.* **Details:** *www.urbis.org.uk; 10.30 pm; closed Sat L & Sun;
no smoking area.*

Moss Nook £ 53 ★
Ringway Rd M22 5WD (0161) 437 4778
*The determinedly "old-fashioned" décor of this "quiet" and
"comfortable" stalwart strikes some reporters as plain "bizarre" –
its Gallic cuisine is of "unvarying quality", though, and service is
"attentive", too.* / **Sample dishes:** *twice-baked cheese & chive soufflé; beef
with foie gras pâté & rosti; crème brûlée.* **Details:** *on B5166, 1m from Manchester
airport; 9.30 pm; closed Mon, Sat L & Sun; children: 11+.*

Mr Thomas's Chop House £32 𝔸
52 Cross St M2 7AR   (0161) 832 2245
"Wonderful fish 'n' chips with mushy peas" and "steak and kidney puddings" are recommended dishes at this ultra-"traditional" city-centre Victorian institution — a popular business lunch haunt.
/ **Sample dishes:** black pudding, egg & smoked bacon salad; roast cod with bubble 'n' squeak; jam sponge with custard. **Details:** L only.

New Emperor £25
52-56 George St M1 4HF   (0161) 228 2883
This gaudy Chinatown stalwart inspired mixed reports this year, but its "fine" dim sum still won praise. / **Details:** www.newemperor.co.uk; midnight.

Obsidian £41
18-24 Princess St M1 4LY   (0161) 238 4348
An interior by Julian Taylor (who designed London's Hakkasan) has created a fair degree of hype for this basement restaurant of a new hotel; it opened too late for survey feedback, but press commentary has not been encouraging.
/ **Details:** www.obsidianmanchester.co.uk; 10.30 pm; no smoking.

The Ox £26
71 Liverpool Rd M3 4NQ   (0161) 839 7740
A "reliable" Castlefield boozer with an "interesting" (if perhaps "over-long") menu that features "a mixture of dishes, traditional and modern". / **Sample dishes:** teriyaki beef; roast rack of lamb; toffee & pecan cheesecake. **Details:** www.theox.co.uk; 10.30 pm; no smoking area. **Accommodation:** 9 rooms, from £44.95.

Pacific £33 ★
58-60 George St M1 4HF   (0161) 228 6668
This "minimalistic" Chinatown oriental has become a major city-centre destination; opinions divide as to whether the Chinese section (ground floor) or the Thai first floor is better — on balance, the latter narrowly wins (particularly for its "great Sunday buffet").
/ **Sample dishes:** steamed scallops in garlic sauce; sizzling beef in black pepper sauce; toffee banana & ice cream.
Details: www.pacific-restaurant-manchester.co.uk; 10.45 pm; no smoking area; children: 3+.

Palmiro £28 ★
197 Upper Chorlton Rd M16 OBH   (0161) 860 7330
This "honest" but "inconsistent" Whalley Grange four-year-old pleases and infuriates reporters in equal measure — "it keeps trying", though, and on a good day the "different" Italian cooking can be "fantastic". / **Sample dishes:** slow-roast tomato risotto; char-grilled sea bass; poached pears & caramel with polenta. **Details:** www.palmiro.net; 10.30 pm; D only, except Sun open L & D.

Pearl City £21 ★
33 George St M1 4PH   (0161) 228 7683
This Cantonese in Chinatown is the "best everyday Chinese", for some reporters; it spices up its menu with "a few unusual dishes".
/ **Details:** 1.15 am, Fri & Sat 3 am.

Le Petit Blanc £31
55 King St M2 4LQ (0161) 832 1000
*It may be the best-rated member of the five-strong national chain,
but this city-centre Gallic brasserie (largely managed by Loch Fyne
nowadays) – still dishes up "standard" fare in "unatmospheric"
surroundings. / Sample dishes: snail & spinach fricassée; roast chicken with
braised leeks & morels; lemon tart with raspberry sorbet.
Details: www.lepetitblanc.co.uk; 11 pm; no smoking.*

Piccolino £32
8 Clarence St M2 4DW (0161) 835 9860
*This plain but "slick" Italian – with its "really buzzy" ("frantic")
ambience – has "'quickly became an essential central
rendezvous"; the menu offers a "wider-than-average range" –
perhaps explaining why the place is sometimes thought "over-
rated". / Sample dishes: antipasto misto; lamb shank; chocolate nemesis.
Details: www.individualrestaurant.co.uk; 11 pm.*

Punjab Tandoori £17 ★★
177 Wilmslow Rd M14 5AP (0161) 225 2960
*"Possibly the only genuine Indian restaurant in Rusholme", this
"reliable" Punjabi is crowned by reporters as "the best place on
the Curry Mile"; its attractions include a "fantastic choice for
veggies". / Details: 11.45 pm; no Amex.*

The Restaurant Bar & Grill £30
14 John Dalton St M2 6JR
(0161) 839 1999
*"Glam" and "buzzy", this city-centre rendezvous is still something
of "a location to eat and be seen"; service can be "arrogant",
though, and – with the cooking "decidedly average" – the place is
"not the magnet it once was". / Sample dishes: spicy shrimp risotto; crispy
duck with pear & watercress salad; bread & butter pudding.
Details: www.individualrestaurants.co.uk; 11 pm; no smoking area; booking: max 8
at weekends.*

Rhubarb £33 Ⓐ
167 Burton Rd M20 2LN (0161) 448 8887
*"A useful addition to trendy West Didsbury", this "noisy"
newcomer benefits from "exceptionally friendly" service, and
offers quite an "adventurous" menu.
/ Details: www.rhubarbrestaurant.co.uk; 10 pm; D only, closed Mon; no Amex.*

El Rincon £27 Ⓐ
Longworth St, off St John's St M3 4BQ (0161) 839 8819
*"Like being in the backstreets of Madrid, not Manchester", this
"authentic" bar has quite a name for offering a "proper tapas
experience". / Sample dishes: prawns 'pil-pil'; grilled sea bass with lemon;
cheesecake. Details: off Deansgate; 11.30 pm.*

Sam's Chop House £29
Black Pool Fold, Chapel Walks M2 1HN (0161) 834 3210
*This "hidden gem" in a city-centre basement wins rave reviews
from locals as a "convivial" venue for good-value "pure stodge"
(not least "divine steak and kidney pud"); "despite the name, fish
'n' chips is also rather special". / Sample dishes: soup of the day;
home-made corn beef hash; steamed pudding. Details: www.samschophouse.com;
9.30 pm; closed Sun.*

Sangam £15
9-19 Wilmslow Rd M14 5TB (0161) 257 3922
A location "at the beginning of the Curry Mile" helps win attention for this large and "lively" subcontinental; it's not the best, but it is pretty "consistent". / **Details:** www.sangam.co.uk; midnight; no smoking area.

**Second Floor Restaurant
Harvey Nichols** £39
21 New Cathedral St M1 1AD (0161) 828 8898
With its "highly inconsistent" standards, this second-floor newcomer typifies the performance of the other "style-conscious" eateries attached to this department store chain; unlike some of its siblings, though, it lacks views sufficient to provide much in the way of compensation. / **Details:** www.harveynichols.com; 9.45 pm, Fri & Sat 10.15 pm; closed Mon D, Tue D & Sun D; no smoking area.

Shere Khan £18
52 Wilmslow Rd M14 5TQ (0161) 256 2624
For fans, this "busy", brightly-lit fixture is "a reliable option in the often unreliable Curry Mile"; it can "disappoint", though. / **Sample dishes:** chicken tikka; lamb jalfrezi; kulfi. **Details:** www.sherekhan.com; midnight, Fri & Sat 3 am; no smoking area.

Siam Orchid £23
54 Portland St M1 4QU (0161) 236 1388
A "consistent" Thai stand-by, handy for Piccadilly Station. / **Details:** 11.30 pm; closed Sat L & Sun L.

Simply Heathcote's £30 X
Jackson Row, Deansgate M2 5WD (0161) 835 3536
Paul Heathcote seems to have mastered a (rather Conran-style) "production line" approach, exemplified by this "minimalist" city-centre brasserie; reporters frequently damn it as "pretentious", "disappointing" and "overpriced" – only the "good-value lunchtime menu" could really be recommended. / **Sample dishes:** ham hock terrine; roast lamb with couscous; rice pudding with vanilla ice cream. **Details:** www.heathcotes.co.uk; near Opera House; 10 pm, Sat 11 pm; no smoking.

Stock £40
4 Norfolk St M2 1DW (0161) 839 6644
The "uncrowded" quarters of the former stock exchange provide an "impressive" backdrop for this "formal" Italian; it could be a great business restaurant, but some reporters think the prices are "taking the p***". / **Sample dishes:** linguine with crayfish tails; calves liver in balsamic vinegar sauce; caramelised peach tartlet. **Details:** www.stockrestaurant.co.uk; 10.30 pm; closed Sun.

Tai Pan £24 ★
81-97 Upper Brook St M13 9TX (0161) 273 2798
"The best dim sum" is a feature at this warehouse-like Chinese, a little way from the city-centre, which achieved consistently positive reviews this year. / **Sample dishes:** dim sum; king prawns in black bean sauce; mango pudding. **Details:** www.taipanliverpool.com; 11 pm, Sun 9.30 pm.

Tai Wu £24 ★
44 Oxford St M1 5EJ (0161) 236 6557
This vast new Chinese restaurant (an offshoot of the Tai Pan), in a former cinema, is extolled by fans for its "vibrant" and sometimes "outstanding" cooking. / **Details:** www.tai-wu.net.co.uk; 3.15 am; no smoking area.

Tampopo   £ 24   ★
16 Albert Sq M2 5PF   (0161) 819 1966
*"Beating Wagamama hands down" – this "funky" noodle parlour
has established itself as an ever-"bustling" city-centre stand-by;
"for a chain, albeit a small one, it maintains a high standard".
/ **Sample dishes:** honey-marinated ribs; prawns in coconut & basil sauce; ginger
crème brûlée. **Details:** 11 pm; no smoking; need 7+ to book.*

That Café   £ 36   Ⓐ ★
1031-1033 Stockport Rd M19 2TB   (0161) 432 4672
*This "dependable" operation – with its "interesting" cooking and
its "relaxed and friendly" atmosphere – would be "a lovely place"
anywhere; in unsunny Levenshume, it comes as a particularly nice
"surprise". / **Sample dishes:** pan-fried squid & king prawn salad; beef fillet with
celeriac rosti; passion fruit tart. **Details:** www.thatcafe.co.uk; on A6 between
Manchester & Stockport; 10.30 pm; closed Mon, Tue-Sat D only, closed Sun D;
no Amex; no smoking area.*

This & That   £ 5   ★
3 Soap St M4 1EW   (0161) 832 4971
*Mancunians know a bargain when they see it, and this Northern
Quarter fixture – "a very basic Indian café offering astonishing
value-for-money" – attracts "all walks of life"; the 'rice-and-three'
is the top tip. / **Details:** 5 pm; closed Sat; no credit cards.*

Wong Chu   £ 21   ★
63 Faulkner St M1 4FF   (0161) 236 2346
*Even a reporter who scents "an attempt to move upmarket"
prizes the fact that there are "still few concessions to Western
tastes" at this Chinatown stalwart; duck comes especially
recommended. / **Sample dishes:** chicken & sweetcorn soup; roast pork with
fried rice; coconut ice cream. **Details:** midnight.*

Woodstock Tavern   £ 23
139 Barlow Moor Rd M20 2DY   (0161) 448 7951
*Handy if you're in Chorlton-cum-Hardy, this lively boozer – where
the use of exotic ingredients is a feature – is hailed by fans as
"everything a good pub should be". / **Sample dishes:** salt & pepper
chicken wings; kangaroo steak with port & mushroom sauce; strawberry Daiquiri
cheesecake. **Details:** 8 pm; no Amex; no smoking area; no booking; children: before
8.30 pm only.*

Yang Sing   £ 30   ★★
34 Princess St M1 4JY   (0161) 236 2200
*"The finest Chinese in the UK" – this Chinatown linchpin remains
the North's most celebrated restaurant, thanks to Harry Yeung's
"outstanding", "always fresh" and "different" cuisine (with
"astounding banquets" particularly praised). / **Sample dishes:** crispy
spring rolls; pan-fried squid with vegetables; sweet dim sum.
Details: www.yang-sing.com; 11.45 pm, Fri & Sat 12.15 am; no smoking.*

Zinc Bar & Grill   £ 40   X
The Triangle, Hanging Ditch M4 3ES   (0161) 827 4200
*"They carry on getting customers, just because of the location" (in
the 'Triangle') – otherwise, reports suggest this tedious Conran
brasserie concept is too often "an all-round disappointment".
/ **Sample dishes:** fried squid with chilli; lamb kebabs with bulgar wheat salad;
lemon tart. **Details:** www.conran.com; 10 pm; no smoking.*

MANNINGTREE, ESSEX   3–2C

Stour Bay Café   £32
39-43 High St CO11 1AH   (01206) 396687
"Very good fish" is what this *"buzzy"* (and *"closely packed"*) bistro
near the seafront is all about; live music is an occasional
additional attraction. / **Sample dishes:** crab bisque with whisky; seared tuna
with bean & tomato salad; pecan pie. **Details:** www.stourbaycafe.com; 9.30 pm;
closed Mon & Tue; no Amex; no smoking.

MARKET HARBOROUGH, LEICESTERSHIRE   5–4D

Han's   £24
29 St Mary's Rd LE16 7DS   (01858) 462288
A *"very reliable"* town-centre Chinese; it's *"the best in the area"* –
not, admittedly, difficult in this corner of the shires.
/ **Sample dishes:** seafood & lettuce wraps; sizzling beef & black pepper; toffee
apples & banana. **Details:** 11 pm; closed Sat L & Sun.

MARLBOROUGH, WILTSHIRE   2–2C

Coles Bar & Restaurant   £39   Ⓐ
27 , Kingsbury St SN8 1JA   (01672) 515004
It's not a hold-the-front-page kind of place, but this *"warm"* and
"friendly" spot wins praise as *"an ideal venue for an intimate, but
relaxed date"*, and it's applauded by locals for its *"good food"*.
/ **Details:** www.colesrestaurant.co.uk; 10 pm; closed Sun; no Amex; no smoking.

Harrow Inn   £39   ★
Little Bedwyn SN8 3JP   (01672) 870871
It's the wine list – *"the size of a small encyclopaedia"*, and with
many choices *"you wouldn't find in London, let alone in darkest
Wiltshire"* – which singles out this revamped inn, but the cooking
it offers is *"thoroughly enjoyable"*, too. / **Details:** www.harrowinn.co.uk;
9 pm; closed Mon, Tue & Sun D; no smoking area.

MARLOW, BUCKINGHAMSHIRE   3–3A

Compleat Angler   £57   X
Marlow Bridge SL7 1RG   (0870) 400 8100
Macdonald Hotels' management of this famous riverside dining
room is a continuing disgrace – it was again slammed by most
reporters for *"very poor menu execution"*, *"ridiculously small
portions"*, *"inexpert and discourteous service"* or *"unjustifiable
prices"*. / **Sample dishes:** smoked haddock & potato terrine; roast duck with
marinated white cabbage; Baileys & honey parfait.
Details: www.compleatangler-hotel.co.uk; 10 pm; no smoking area.
Accommodation: 64 rooms, from £208.

Danesfield House Hotel   £65   Ⓐ
Henley Rd SL7 2EY   (01628) 891010
*"Both food and service are good, but they're trading on the
ambience and the Thames-side location"* – a repeated view on
this wedding cake-style country house hotel, where the prices give
nothing away. / **Sample dishes:** cauliflower pannacotta with oysters; venison
with artichoke & shallot fricassée; apricot & ginger crème brûlée.
Details: www.danesfieldhouse.co.uk; 3m outside Marlow on the A4155; 9.30 pm;
no smoking. **Accommodation:** 87 rooms, from £230.

Marlow Bar & Grill £34 🅐
92-94 High St SL7 1AQ (01628) 488544
This self-descriptive establishment is "great fun", even if it is
"quite expensive" for what it is; the ambience is "buzzy" or "too
noisy", to taste. / **Sample dishes:** *fried chilli squid with thai noodle salad; grilled
fillet steak; warm chocolate pudding with Malteser ice cream.*
Details: *www.individualrestaurant.co.uk; 11 pm; no smoking area.*

Royal Oak £31
Frieth Rd, Bovingdon Grn SL7 2JF (01628) 488611
"A pub on the outside and a good restaurant on the inside", this
"lovely" venue is located in "glorious countryside"; its "fresh" and
"varied" contemporary fare is "generally reliable".
/ **Details:** *www.royaloakmarlow.co.uk; 10 pm.*

The Vanilla Pod £50
31 West St SL7 2LS
(01628) 898101

"Imaginative and clear-flavoured" cooking quickly made a big
name for Michael Macdonald's "cramped" Gallic two-year-old; it
can seem a very "cold" place, though, and this year a
disappointing number of reports recounted meals "falling far short
of a tour-de-force". / **Sample dishes:** *scallops with vanilla-poached pears; sea
bass with Szechuan sauce; bitter chocolate fondant.*
Details: *www.thevanillapod.co.uk; 10 pm; closed Mon & Sun; no smoking.*

MASHAM, NORTH YORKSHIRE 8–4B

Black Sheep Brewery Bistro £26
Wellgarth HG4 4EN (01765) 680101
"Lovely, simple dishes" ("excellent toad-in-the-hole", for example)
again make this "rustic" restaurant, attached to a brewery, a
"pleasant" destination for all who comment on it.
/ **Sample dishes:** *beaujolais paté with sweet green pickles; lamb shank marinated
in ale served with mash & rosemary jus; treacle tart with ice cream.*
Details: *www.blacksheep.co.uk; 9.30 pm; Mon-Wed L only, closed Sun D; no Amex;
no smoking area.*

Floodlite £34 ★
7 Silver St HG4 4DX (01765) 689000
Charles Flood's wittily-named restaurant – now approaching the
end of its second decade of operation – achieves very "consistent"
results, from a menu featuring local game and other produce.
/ **Sample dishes:** *Arbroath Smokie soufflé; chicken stuffed with banana & curry
sauce; strawberry shortbread.* **Details:** *9 pm; closed Mon, Tue-Thu D only, except
Sun when L only; no Switch; no smoking area.*

MELBOURN, CAMBRIDGESHIRE 3–1B

The Pink Geranium £52
25 Station Rd SG8 6DX (01763) 260215
A well-known "pretty and romantic" thatched cottage, where the
food is consistently thought to be "very good" and "well
presented"; some reporters, though, find it too "pricey".
/ **Sample dishes:** *niçoise vegetable terrine with tapenade dressing; boudin of lobster
with new potatoes; crème brûlée with raspberry coulis.*
Details: *www.pinkgeranium.co.uk; off A10, 2nd exit (opp church); 9.30 pm; closed
Mon & Sun D; no smoking.*

Sheene Mill £ 45   𝔸★

Station Rd SG8 6DX   (01763) 261393

TV-chef Steven Saunders won more consistent praise this year for this 17th-century mill-conversion as a "very good all-rounder", which serves "all fresh and organic" food in a "very romantic, smart and colourful" setting. / **Sample dishes:** crispy duck spring rolls with sweet chilli sauce; wild venison with mushroom risotto; banana tarte Tatin. **Details:** www.sheenemill.co.uk; off A10, 10m S of Cambridge; 10 pm; closed Sun D; no smoking. **Accommodation:** 9 rooms, from £95.

MELBOURNE, DERBYSHIRE   5–3C

Bay Tree £ 39   ★

4 Potter St DE73 1DW   (01332) 863358

"Consistently good food" – and from a "very varied" menu – is the gist of all reports on Rex Howell's former coaching inn; service is "wonderful" too, and wine prices "very fair". / **Sample dishes:** minted melon with lemongrass granita; pork tenderloin with goats cheese gnocchi; Canadian pancakes with maple syrup. **Details:** www.baytreerestaurant.co.uk; 10 pm; closed Mon & Sun D; no smoking area.

MELLOR, CHESHIRE   5–2B

Oddfellows Arms £ 27   𝔸

73 Moor End Rd SK6 5PT   (0161) 449 7826

Fine views across the Peak District help make this atmospheric tavern, housed in ancient cottages, of more than usual note; the food is consistently well rated too. / **Sample dishes:** soused herrings with mustard sour cream; Catalan pork tenderloin with basil ragu; frosted peach schnapps cheesecake. **Details:** 7m S of Stockport; 9.30 pm; closed Mon & Sun D; no Amex; no smoking.

MELMERBY, CUMBRIA   8–3A

Shepherd's Inn £ 23   𝔸★

CA10 1HF   (0870) 745 3383

"Rich food, good ale, spectacular view" – that's the whole story about this "wonderful" dining inn (which is also "a marvellous boozer in its own right"). / **Sample dishes:** dill-marinated herrings; breaded wholetail scampi; lemon cheesecake. **Details:** 9.45 pm weekends 9pm weekdays; no Amex; no smoking area; no booking.

Village Bakery £ 23   ★★

CA10 1HE   (01768) 881811

This "excellent" organic café – part of the famous bakery – is hailed by all reporters as "a marvellous little place", that offers "superlative food", using "the freshest ingredients"; "great breakfasts" are a special hit. / **Sample dishes:** vegetable soup; grilled trout with herb butter; upside down pear & ginger pudding. **Details:** www.village-bakery.com; 10m NE of Penrith on A686; 5 pm; L only; no Amex; no smoking; need 6+ to book.

MERTHYR TYDFIL, MERTHYR TYDFIL   4–4D

Nant Ddu Lodge £ 31   ★

Brecon Rd CF48 2HY   (01685) 379111

This family-run hotel is "the only place worth visiting south of Brecon"; "you can eat in the bar or the bistro", and value is "very good" throughout. / **Sample dishes:** duck mousse with caramelised oranges; ham hock with mustard mash & parsley sauce; plum crumble. **Details:** www.nant-ddu-lodge.co.uk; 6m N of Merthyr on A470; 9.30 pm; no smoking; booking: max 8. **Accommodation:** 28 rooms, from £79.50.

MEVAGISSEY, CORNWALL   1–4B

School House   £ 35   ★
West End PL26 6BX   (01726) 842474
*"Make sure you've parked above the high watermark", when you
visit this re-purposed educational establishment – a "very relaxed"
and "comfy" place, where the "home-cooking" can be "superb".*
/ *Details: www.schoolhouserestaurant.co.uk; 9.30 pm; D only, closed Mon & Sun;
no Amex.*

MICKLEHAM, SURREY   3–3A

King William IV   £ 27   ★
Byttom HI RH5 6EL   (01372) 372590
*"Honest food and excellent beers" are the sort of virtues
commending this popular hillside freehouse; it also has "a good
garden for the summer". / Sample dishes: garlic bread with Mozzarella;
steak & kidney pie; treacle tart. Details: www.king-williamiv.com; off A24; 9.30 pm;
closed Sun D; no Amex; no booking in summer; children: 12+.*

MILTON KEYNES, BUCKINGHAMSHIRE   3–2A

Jaipur   £ 24
599 Grafton Gate East MK9 1AT   (01908) 669796
*This "amazing" and unexpected fixture (claimed as Europe's
largest purpose-built Indian) can serve up some "first-class"
cooking; some locals feel it's "let down by relatively high prices",
though. / Details: www.jaipur.co.uk; 11 pm; no smoking.*

MORSTON, NORFOLK   6–3C

Morston Hall   £ 54   𝔸★★
Main Coast Rd NR25 7AA   (01263) 741041
*Galton Blackiston's cooking at this "lovely" country house hotel
near the coast may be "fairly conservative", but it's also "simply
divine"; with its "welcoming" service and "lack of pretention"
most reporters just "can't find enough nice things to say about the
place". / Sample dishes: Milanese risotto with deep-fried leeks; roast lamb with
buttery mash; sticky toffee pudding with butterscotch sauce.
Details: www.morstonhall.com; between Blakeney & Wells on A149; 8 pm; D only,
except Sun open L & D; no smoking. Accommodation: 7 rooms, from £100.*

MOULSFORD, OXFORDSHIRE   2–2D

Beetle & Wedge   £ 48   𝔸
Ferry Ln OX10 9JF   (01491) 651381
*"The food, service and beautiful riverside location" make this
"idyllic" hotel – on the stretch of the Thames that inspired 'The
Wind in the Willows' – a "consistent favourite", for many
reporters; the "relaxed" Boathouse grill (recently refurbished) is
often preferred to the "placid" dining room. / Sample dishes: onion
tart with foie gras & truffle sauce; monkfish & surf clams in champagne & saffron
sauce; Cointreau soufflé with raspberry coulis. Details: www.beetleandwedge.co.uk;
on A329 between Streatley & Wallingford, take Ferry Lane at crossroads; 9.45 pm;
D only Thu-Sat, closed Sun D, Boathouse open daily; no smoking.
Accommodation: 11 rooms, from £160.*

MOULTON, NORTH YORKSHIRE 8–3B

Black Bull £43 A★
DL10 6QJ (01325) 377289
A "happy" and slightly "old-fashioned" Yorkshire "institution",
where "absolutely fantastic seafood" (in particular) is served in
the "romantic" setting of a former railway carriage (or in an
adjoining conservatory). / *Sample dishes:* shellfish bisque; lemon sole in
prawn, leek & cheese sauce; pancakes with lemon sauce. *Details:* 1m S of Scotch
Corner; 10.15 pm; closed Sun; children: 7+.

MOUSEHOLE, CORNWALL 1–4A

Cornish Range £37 A
6 Chapel St TR19 6SB (01736) 731488
A "good seafood platter" is among the culinary attractions of this
"modern-Mediterranean"-feeling establishment, near the harbour.
/ *Sample dishes:* steamed mussels & clams with creamy saffron broth; roast
monkfish tail with chorizo, razor clams & herbs; trio of mini brûlées.
Details: www.cornishrange.co.uk; on coast road between Penzance & Lands End;
9.30 pm, 9 pm in Winter; D only; no Amex; no smoking. *Accommodation:* 3
rooms, from £65.

MYLOR BRIDGE, CORNWALL 1–4B

Pandora Inn £32 A
Restronguet Creek TR11 5ST (01326) 372678
This rural, "old world" smugglers inn – complete with a pontoon
on a picturesque creek – is "popular with yachtsmen" (who can
even have a shower); thanks to its evident attractions and
popularity, prices give nothing away. / *Sample dishes:* avocado, mango &
smoked salmon salad; turbot with fresh greens; lemon ricotta cheesecake.
Details: signposted off A390, between Truro & Falmouth; 9 pm; no Amex;
no smoking.

NAILSWORTH, GLOUCESTERSHIRE 2–2B

Calcot Manor £38 ★
GL8 8YJ (01666) 890391
Very "sound" cooking – both in the "relaxing" conservatory and
the adjoining gastropub-annexe (the Gumstool Inn) – wins praise
for the "always enjoyable" dining experience at this small country
house hotel. / *Sample dishes:* scallops with spiced couscous; roast pork confit
with lardons & red onion; bread & butter pudding. *Details:* www.calcotmanor.co.uk;
junction of A46 & A4135; 9.30 pm; no smoking area; children: no children at D.
Accommodation: 30 rooms, from £175.

NANT-Y-DERRY, MONMOUTHSHIRE 2–2A

The Foxhunter £39 A★
Abergavenny NP7 9DN (01873) 881101
"A warm and inviting place" in "beautiful countryside", the
Tebbutts' former stationmaster's house is roundly praised for its
"wonderful" food – more than one reporter commented that it
has now "overtaken the nearby Walnut Tree".
/ *Details:* www.thefoxhunter.com; 9.30 pm; closed Mon & Sun; no Amex;
no smoking.

NAYLAND, SUFFOLK   3–2C

White Hart   £36
11 High St C06 4JF (01206) 263382
*Carl Shillingford's cooking is rated "very enjoyable" by all who
comment on this rural pub (owned by Michel Roux); the place has
"loads of potential" – not all reporters are sure it's being fully
realised.* / **Sample dishes:** *rock fish soup; roast suckling pig with sweet potato
purée; ginger & lemon gâteau.* **Details:** *www.whitehart-nayland.co.uk; off A12,
between Colchester & Sudbury; 9.30 pm.* **Accommodation:** *6 rooms, from £90.*

NETHER ALDERLEY, CHESHIRE   5–2B

Wizard   £39   ★
Macclesfield Rd SK10 4UB (01625) 584000
*"A cut above the general standard of the many local eateries" –
reports all confirm that this former-pub restaurant is a
"welcoming" place, where the food is "invariably good".*
/ **Sample dishes:** *baby spinach, avocado & Gorgonzola salad; herb-crusted cod with
pea purée; rice pudding with stem ginger & maple syrup.* **Details:** *from A34, take
B5087; 9.30 pm; closed Mon & Sun D; no smoking area.*

NETHER BROUGHTON, LEICESTERSHIRE   5–3D

Red House   £40
23 Main St LE14 3HB (01664) 822429
*This village pub has recently "gone upmarket", and now offers "a
full restaurant, and high-quality bar meals"; for "casual" dining –
especially in the "relaxed" garden in summer – it already has a
fair local following.* / **Details:** *www.the-redhouse.com; 9.30 pm; closed Sun D.*

NETTLEBED, OXFORDSHIRE   2–2D

White Hart   £47
High St RG9 5DD (01491) 641245
*Reporters aren't wholly convinced that this "busy" hotel restaurant
in a "pretty village" deserves its not-inconsiderable reputation –
the décor is "stark", and the food often no more than
"competent".* / **Sample dishes:** *pan-fried scallops with roast fennel & orange
salad; duck with white bean cassoulet; iced chestnut parfait with rum sauce.*
Details: *www.whitehartnettlebed.com; Between Wallingford & Henley-on-Thames
on the A430; 9 pm; closed Sun-Wed, Thu-Sat for D only (bistro open every day for
L & D); no Amex; no smoking; children: 14+ in dining room.* **Accommodation:** *12
rooms, from £125.*

NEW MILTON, HAMPSHIRE   2–4C

Chewton Glen   £63   Ⓐ
Christchurch Rd BH25 6QS (01425) 275341
*This famously "beautiful" New Forest-fringe hotel (which sells
itself as 'the best in the world') suffered from comings and goings
in the kitchen this year, perhaps explaining some complaints from
reporters about "bland" and "overpriced" cooking; the
"extensive" cellar offers some compensation.* / **Sample dishes:** *tiger
prawn ravioli with white truffle sauce; Angus beef with green pepper hollandaise;
caramelised apples with cinnamon ice cream.* **Details:** *www.chewtonglen.com; on
A337 between New Milton & Highcliffe; 9.30 pm; jacket required at D; no smoking;
children: 5+.* **Accommodation:** *58 rooms, from £290.*

NEWARK, NOTTINGHAMSHIRE   5–3D

Café Bleu   £ 29   𝔸★
14 Castle Gate NG24 1BG   (01636) 610141
*"Very good" food, at "very reasonable" prices and in "smart but
relaxed" surroundings, ensures consistently positive feedback on
this waterside brasserie; weather permitting, you can dine "in the
garden, near the river".* / **Sample dishes:** *sardines with saffron couscous;
braised Aberdeen beef with baby carrots; lemon posset with champagne sorbet.*
Details: *www.cafebleu.co.uk; 9.30 pm; closed Sun D; no Amex; no smoking area.*

NEWBURY, BERKSHIRE   2–2D

The Crab At Chieveley   £ 40   ★
Wantage Rd RG20 8UE
(01635) 247550
*"It may be in the middle of the country", but a "huge range of fish
and seafood" is what this former pub is all about; all reporters
laud its consistently high standards (the bistro being marginally
preferred to the restaurant proper).* / **Details:** *www.crabatchieveley.com;
9 pm; no smoking.* **Accommodation:** *10 rooms, from £140.*

NEWCASTLE UPON TYNE, TYNE & WEAR   8–2B

Given that Newcastle does not have a huge quality dining-out
scene, it manages to a commendable extent to offer
'something for everyone'. It's a famously going-out kind of city
and most of the action is around the Quayside (where Terry
Laybourne's mid-range *Café 21* is of particular note).

The city's top-end restaurant, *Fisherman's Lodge* (actually in leafy
Jesmond Dene), goes from strength to strength under new
ownership. Towards the cheaper end, *Pani's* and *Valley Junction
397* stand out. *McCoys at the Baltic* (in Gateshead) makes a
good 'special occasion' destination, even if it is more notable
for its location than for its cuisine.

Barn @ the Biscuit   £ 37
18 Stoddard St NE2 1AN   (0191) 230 3338
*"Some of the quirkiness has gone", but this re-sited local favourite
– formerly housed in a barn – still makes a "great", if "oddly
decorated", destination; now appended to an art gallery, it
remains extremely popular.* / **Sample dishes:** *wild garlic leaf risotto with
Parmesan; spiced lamb with aubergine & Mozzarella; fallen chocolate soufflé.*
Details: *www.thebiscuitfactory.com; follow Biscuit factory signs; 9.45 pm; closed
Sun D; no smoking.*

Café 21   £ 36   ★
21 Queen St, Princes Whf NE1 3UG   (0191) 222 0755
*"Still a real success story" – Terry Laybourne's landmark
restaurant (once called 21 Queen St) may pitch itself as a
"relatively casual" venue nowadays, but it remains "a good-value
place for a sound meal in the centre of town".*
/ **Sample dishes:** *duck & green peppercorn pâté; sirloin with parsley butter &
chips; crème brûlée.* **Details:** *10.30 pm; closed Sun; no smoking area.*

Café Live   £ 26
27 Broad Chare NE1 3DQ   (0191) 232 1331
*Terry Laybourne's "consistent" culinary standards make this
informal sibling of Café 21 of some note locally; one regular,
though, feels the place "ought to be great", but that it's "let down
by the service – I keep going back expecting it'll improve, but it
doesn't!"* / **Details:** www.live.org.uk/information/CafeLive.php; 10 pm; closed Sun;
no smoking area.

Café Royal   £ 22
8 Nelson St NE1 5AW   (0191) 231 3000
*This "Continental-feeling" grand café is widely tipped for a
"delightful laid-back brunch" (or for breakfast, coffee, lunch or
tea) – "the only downside is the queues".* / **Sample dishes:** crispy
duck & watercress salad; beefburger; Irish chocolate cake. **Details:** www.sjf.co.uk;
6 pm; L only, except Thu open L & D; no smoking.

Fisherman's Lodge   £ 54   ★
Jesmond Dene NE7 7BQ   (0191) 281 3281
*Under new ownership, this long-established restaurant – "the
smartest place in Newcastle" – is really beginning to live up to its
"idyllic" Jesmond Dene location; almost all of the many reports
attest to its "tip-top" cooking (including "fabulous" fish) and its
"attentive" service.* / **Sample dishes:** assiette of crab; trio of salmon with
langoustine sauce; chocolate ganache tart. **Details:** www.fishermanslodge.co.uk; 2m
from city centre on A1058, follow signposts to Jesmond Dene; 10.30 pm; closed Sun;
no smoking; children: 8+.

Francesca's   £ 18   𝔸
Manor House Rd NE2 2NE   (0191) 281 6586
*"Huge helpings" and "hearty service" help define this
"atmospheric" and often "overcrowded" local institution, whose
style is "best described as Geordie-Italian".* / **Sample dishes:** garlic king
prawns; mixed fish grill; tiramisu. **Details:** 9.30 pm; closed Sun; no Amex;
no booking.

Heartbreak Soup   £ 30
77 The Quayside NE1 3DE   (0191) 222 1701
*This "very Quayside" bistro is a "rough and ready" sort of place,
but its quirky appeal charms most reporters.* / **Sample dishes:** Korean
beef skewers; tandoori tempura of monkfish; white chocolate baked cheesecake.
Details: www.heartbreaksoup.com; overlooking the River Tyne; 10 pm, Fri & Sat
11 pm; D only, closed Sun; no Amex or Switch.

King Neptune   £ 33   ★
34-36 Stowell St NE1 4XQ   (0191) 261 6657
*"Always busy, thanks to the quality of the cooking", this
Chinatown favourite is praised by all who comment on it; as you'd
hope, it's "excellent for seafood".* / **Sample dishes:** crispy duck pancakes;
chicken with Szechuan sauce; lemon sorbet. **Details:** 10.45 pm.

Malmaison   £ 33
Quayside NE1 3DX   (0191) 245 5000
*"Wonderful views, but…" – this design-hotel brasserie is too often
criticised for the indifferent standards so typically associated with
rooms-with-a-view; it's quite a "romantic" place nonetheless, and a
recent refurb (that will cut the size of the dining room) may
improve matters.* / **Sample dishes:** artichokes & asparagus with walnut oil;
steamed sea bass with radish & aubergine salad; English cheese platter.
Details: www.malmaison.com; 10.30 pm; no smoking area.
Accommodation: 116 rooms, from £129.

McCoys at the Baltic
Baltic £45 Ⓐ

South Shore Rd NE8 3BA (0191) 440 4949
"Fantastic" views ("especially at night") help make this rooftop
venue atop an arts centre the top "seal-the-deal" location in these
parts; it can seem "very expensive" by local standards, though,
and some reporters feel it's "over-rated" generally.
/ **Sample dishes:** langoustine ravioli with shellfish reduction; braised pork wrapped
in Parma ham with potato rosti; chocolate bread pudding.
Details: www.balticmill.com; 9.45 pm, Sun 1.45 pm; closed Sun D; no smoking
area.

Pani's £21 Ⓐ★

61-65 High Bridge NE1 6BX (0191) 232 4366
"Number one for cheap 'n' cheerful in Newcastle", this "great"
café – with its "homely" Italian cooking and its "quick and
cheery" service – is "always busy". / **Sample dishes:** bruschetta; chicken
stuffed with Dolcelatte; tiramisu. **Details:** www.pani.net; off Gray Street; 10 pm;
closed Sun; no Amex; no booking at L.

Paradiso £26 Ⓐ

1 Market Ln NE1 6QQ (0191) 221 1240
"Modern cooking, sometimes with a north African twist" is the
speciality at this "dark and sultry" local favourite; (kick off with a
drink in the "excellent" new downstairs cocktail bar, Popolo, and
fans say it's "impossible to screw up a date here").
/ **Sample dishes:** goats cheese & courgette lasagne; Indian-spiced cod with
couscous & roast vegetables; egg custard tart. **Details:** www.gustouk.com; opp fire
station; 10.45 pm; closed Sun D; no Amex; no smoking area.

Sachins £27

Forth Banks NE1 3SG (0191) 261 9035
Arguably it's only "the best of a bad bunch" in this part of town,
but this Bangladeshi-Punjabi behind Central Station "ploughs a
different furrow" from most local cuzzas, and offers quite
"authentic" cuisine. / **Details:** www.sachins.co.uk; behind Central Station;
11.15 pm; closed Sun.

Sale Pepe £16 Ⓐ

115 St George's Ter NE2 2DN (0191) 281 1431
A "friendly local Italian with a laid-back feel and relaxed
atmosphere"; praised by all reporters, it offers "especially good
value early in the week". / **Details:** 10.30 pm; closed Sun.

Treacle Moon £50 Ⓐ★

5-7 The Side NE1 3JE (0191) 232 5537
"Without question, one of Newcastle's finest" – that's almost
invariably the view on this small and "opulent" Quayside
Mediterranean (though it can seem "a bit overpriced"); some
reporters don't take to the ambience, but most find it very
"romantic". / **Details:** www.treaclemoonrestaurant.com; beneath Tyne Bridge on
Quayside; 10 pm; D only, closed Sun; no smoking.

Valley Junction 397 £28 Ⓐ★

Old Jesmond Station, Archbold Ter NE2 1DB
(0191) 281 6397
A "novel" location in an old signal box ("with a carriage next door
for aperitifs") isn't the sole attraction at this "consistently high-
quality" operation – it also serves up "great modern Indian
cooking". / **Sample dishes:** kebabs; salmon cooked with fresh herbs; Indian
sweets. **Details:** www.thevalleyrestaurants.co.uk; near Civic Centre, off Sandyford
Rd; 11.15 pm; closed Mon; no smoking area.

Vujon £ 32 ★
29 Queen St NE1 3UG (0191) 221 0601
After a difficult period this Quayside modern Indian is re-establishing itself as "the best in town", with something of a name for its "interesting and different" cooking.
/ **Details:** ww.vujon.demon.co.uk; 11 pm; closed Sun L.

NEWENT, GLOUCESTERSHIRE 2–1B
Three Choirs Vineyards £ 38 Ⓐ
GL18 1LS (01531) 890223
"Stunning views over the vineyards" give many diners "the feeling of being in France", at this well-known estate's simple eatery; the "delicate" cooking plays something of a supporting rôle.
/ **Sample dishes:** seared scallops with pine nut dressing; seared duck breast with confit of butternut squash; sticky pear & ginger pudding with clotted cream & butterscotch. **Details:** www.three-choirs-vineyards.co.uk; 9 pm; closed Mon L; no Amex; no smoking. **Accommodation:** 8 rooms, from £95.

NEWICK, EAST SUSSEX 3–4B
Newick Park Hotel £ 52 Ⓐ
Newick St BN8 4SB (01825) 723633
For "country house-style dining" in a "formal" setting, this "lovely" hotel is consistently approved of; even those who find the food "a touch predictable" concede that it's "well executed" – perhaps new chef Chris Moore will add a dash of zing.
/ **Sample dishes:** scallop, lobster and basil tortellini with crab soup; fillet steak with pommes fondant, foie gras sauce and baby carrots; pain perdu, caramelised apples and pears with vanilla ice cream. **Details:** www.newickpark.co.uk; 9 pm; jacket required at D; no smoking. **Accommodation:** 16 rooms, from £165.

NEWLAND, GLOUCESTERSHIRE 2–2B
Ostrich Inn £ 32 Ⓐ
GL16 8NP (01594) 833260
This "fabulously old-fashioned pub", in the middle of the village, offers "an excellent range of freshly-cooked bar meals", washed down with a list of "first-class real ales and wines".
/ **Sample dishes:** pan-fried goat's cheese; rack of lamb with garlic potato; chocolate amaretti pudding with cream. **Details:** www.theostrichinn.com; 2m SW of Coleford; 9.30 pm; no Amex; no smoking; no booking.

NEWPORT, NEWPORT 2–2A
The Chandlery £ 34
77-78 Lower Dock St NP20 1EH (01633) 256622
As usual, reports on this town-centre restaurant are thin on the ground, but they all confirm its "good standards".
/ **Sample dishes:** tian of Pembrooke crab & mango with red pepper salsa; roast loin of venison with garlic mash, mushy peas & wild mushrooms; hot chocolate fondant with pistachio ice cream. **Details:** www.chandleryrestaurant.co.uk; at the foot of George St bridge on the A48 (hospital side); 10 pm; closed Mon, Sat L & Sun; no Switch; no smoking area.

Junction 28 £ 31
Station Approach NP10 8LD (01633) 891891
A quirky location has helped make something of a name for this venture in a former railway station; fans say it "offers a good choice of fare at reasonable prices (especially for lunch)", but doubters insist it's "consistently over-rated".
/ **Sample dishes:** mushroom & pancetta risotto; Thai red monkfish & prawn curry; chilled melon soup with mint sorbet. **Details:** off M4, J28 towards Caerphilly; 9.30 pm; closed Sun D; no smoking.

NEWTON LONGVILLE, BUCKINGHAMSHIRE   3–2A

Crooked Billet   £38   ★
2 Westbrook End MK17 0DF   (01908) 373936
The "immensely long" wine list – which includes a "massive
selection by the glass" – is "the real star" at this
"unprepossessingly located" gastropub; the cooking is also often
"of a very high standard". / **Sample dishes:** watercress soup with goats
cheese crostini; rack of lamb with coriander couscous & tapenade jus; roasted
peaches with thyme ice cream. **Details:** www.thebillet.co.uk; 10 pm; D only, ex
Sun L only; no smoking.

NEWTON, CAMBRIDGESHIRE   3–1B

Queens Head   £14   𝔸★
Fowlmere Rd CB2 5PG   (01223) 870436
"Fantastic baked potatoes, soup and to-die-for sandwiches" – the
range may be "limited", but quality is "fabulous", at this small,
family-owned boozer (run by the Shorts since the early '70s).
/ **Sample dishes:** pâté; beef sandwiches; chocolate. **Details:** off A10; 9.30 pm;
no credit cards; no booking.

NEWTON-ON-THE-MOOR, NORTHUMBERLAND   8–2B

Cook & Barker   £28
NE65 9JY   (01665) 575234
A "good A1 gastropub"; it's a "cosy" place – offering "a wide
menu range in both bar and restaurant" – which is often "very
busy". / **Sample dishes:** avocado, tandoori chicken & rocket salad; pot-roast lamb
with bubble 'n' squeak; Belgian chocolate truffle cake. **Details:** 12m N of Morpeth,
just off A1; 9 pm. **Accommodation:** 19 rooms, from £65.

NOMANSLAND, WILTSHIRE   2–3C

Les Mirabelles   £31   𝔸★★
Forest Edge Rd SP5 2BN   (01794) 390205
"First-class everything" – not least "genuine" Gallic cuisine –
makes Eric Nicholas and Claude Laage's New Forest ten-year-old
well worth seeking out; despite the "remote" location, fans say
there are "always enough people to create a good atmosphere".
/ **Sample dishes:** smoked salmon mousse; lamb fillet; crème brûlée. **Details:** off
A36 between Southampton & Salisbury; 9.30 pm; closed Mon & Sun D; no smoking.

NORTHALLERTON, NORTH YORKSHIRE   8–4B

Arden Arms   £29   𝔸★
Atley Hill, South Cowton DL7 0JB   (01325) 378678
"Popular" and "unpretentious", this "stylish" boozer – owned by
the former proprietors of Manchester's Take That – is
unanimously tipped for its "well-cooked and tasty food"; it's "good
with children", too. / **Sample dishes:** Scottish salmon with avocado ice cream;
fillet of halibut with artichokes, mushrooms & saffron sauce; cherry clafoutis.
Details: www.ardenarms.co.uk; 9 pm; closed Mon & Sun D; no smoking area.

NORTON, SHROPSHIRE   5–4B

Hundred House   £ 45
Bridgnorth Rd TF11 9EE (01952) 730353
Housed in a "fascinating" ancient building, this "reliable"
gastropub provides "good, solid food, well presented"; on the
drinks front, it offers not only its own beer, but also locally-
produced wine! / **Sample dishes:** shallot, fennel & goats cheese tartlet; wild
boar with white bean casserole & chorizo; raspberry & meringue ice cream.
Details: www.hundredhouse.co.uk; on A442 between Bridgnorth & Telford;
9.30 pm; no Amex; no smoking area. **Accommodation:** 10 rooms, from £99.

NORWICH, NORFOLK   6–4C

Adlards   £ 46   ★
79 Upper Giles St NR2 1AB (01603) 633522
This "almost quaint" townhouse-restaurant has long been a
culinary beacon in East Anglia, and has many fans of its "first-
class" food and "splendid" wines; the occasional reporter, though,
suspects it of being "over-rated". / **Sample dishes:** foie gras in cumin with
toasted brioche; veal with mash & roast parsnips; banana tarte Tatin.
Details: www.adlards.co.uk; near the Roman Catholic Cathedral; 10.30 pm; closed
Mon & Sun; no smoking.

Brummells   £ 43   𝔸★
7 Magdalen St NR3 1LE (01603) 625555
"High-quality seafood" and a "very good wine list" make this
pretty restaurant, which is housed in an interesting 17th-century
building, a thoroughly satisfactory experience for reporters –
"pricey" but "worth it". / **Sample dishes:** seafood pancakes with aniseed
sauce; sea bass & leeks with prawn butter; apple & wild mushroom crumble with
cider sorbet. **Details:** www.brummells.co.uk; 10.30 pm.

By Appointment   £ 40   𝔸
25-29 St George's St NR3 1AB (01603) 630730
The food can be "erratic", but most reporters are of the view that
the "extravagant" and "intimate" atmosphere of this city-centre
restaurant-with-rooms "makes up for it". / **Sample dishes:** tuna
carpaccio with capers; guinea fowl, chorizo & mushrooms with basil sauce; pineapple
tarte Tatin with cardamom ice cream. **Details:** in a courtyard off Colegate; 9 pm;
D only, closed Mon & Sun; no Amex; no smoking; children: 12+.
Accommodation: 4 rooms, from £95.

Tatlers   £ 36   ★
21 Tombland NR3 1RF (01603) 766670
"Good-value" food (making "good use of local ingredients") and a
"buzzy" ambience commend this city-centre bistro to all who
comment on it. / **Sample dishes:** salad Lyonnaise; rib-eye steak with red
wine & mushroom sauce; lemon tart. **Details:** www.tatlers.com; near Cathedral,
next to Erpingham Gate; 10 pm; closed Sun; no smoking area.

The Tree House   £ 22   ★
14-16 Dove St NR2 1DE (01603) 763258
"The vegetarian restaurant of choice in East Anglia"; co-operative-
run, its "imaginative, quirky and wholesome" food continues to
win nothing but praise. / **Sample dishes:** spicy tomato & lentil soup;
potato & cauliflower curry with rice; blueberry tofu cheesecake. **Details:** 9 pm;
L only Mon-Wed, closed Sun; no credit cards; no smoking; no booking at L.

Waffle House   £ 20
39 St Giles St NR2 1JN   (01603) 612790
*For over 20 years, this "slightly Bohemian" city-centre "enclave"
has been popular for its "freshly prepared, deep waffles laden
with sweet or savoury toppings".* / **Sample dishes:** *garlic mushrooms;
ham, cheese & mushroom waffle; banana & butterscotch waffle.* **Details:** *10 pm;
no Amex; no smoking area; need 6+ to book.*

NOTTINGHAM, CITY OF NOTTINGHAM 5–3D

Nottingham makes a perhaps surprisingly solid mid-range
destination, boasting some restaurants of real note. But with
the recent re-opening of *Sonny's* and the ongoing changes at *Sat
Bains*, the scene is in something of a state of transition. *Hart's*
remains by far the best-known local destination by quite a
margin. And though it may not be a great foodie destination,
the continuing success of the trendy *World Service* is impressive.

Atlas   £ 7   𝔸★★
9 Pelham St NG1 2EH   (0115) 950 1295
*"Superb coffee" and "the humble sandwich elevated to another
level" make it well worth seeking out this Mediterranean café/deli.*
/ **Sample dishes:** *ciabatta with tuna, basil & plum tomatoes; Danish pastry.*
Details: *L only; no smoking.*

Broadway Cinema Bar   £ 18   ★
Broadway, Broad St   (0115) 952 1551
*"Tasty and cheap snacks" (including "a good veggie selection")
commend the "buzzing" bar of 'The Home of Independent
Cinema in the East Midlands' to all reporters; for less than a
tenner, the Broadway Bites deal buys your ticket plus a "yummy"
main dish.* / **Details:** *11 pm; no Amex; no smoking area.*

French Living   £ 21
27 King St NG1 2AY   (0115) 958 5885
*"Good-quality, basic fare" ensures the continuing popularity of this
"convincingly Gallic" city-centre fixture.* / **Sample dishes:** *Burgundy snails
with garlic & parsley butter; venison with peppered blueberry sauce; white chocolate
bavarois.* **Details:** *www.frenchliving.co.uk; near Market Square; 10 pm; closed
Mon & Sun; booking: max 10.*

Hart's   £ 44   ★
Standard Ct, Park Row NG1 6GN   (0115) 911 0666
*"Very high standards" – including often "superb" cooking, and
service which is "almost too professional" – have long made Tim
Hart's "sophisticated" city-centre venture a destination of real
note; the "smart" modern setting, though, can seem a touch
"unsympathetic".* / **Sample dishes:** *courgette tart with goats cheese; veal with
spinach & Parmesan risotto; tarte Tatin with caramel ice cream.*
Details: *www.hartsnottingham.co.uk; near Castle; 10.30 pm; no smoking.*
Accommodation: *32 rooms, from £115.*

Mem Saab   £ 26
12-14 Maid Marian Way NG1 6HS   (0115) 957 0009
*"The food is just as good, if not slightly better", says an early
report on the new (spring 2004) régime at this popular curry
house, where "dishes are light, and you can taste the individual
flavours"; service is still "friendly and welcoming", too.*
/ **Sample dishes:** *vegetable pakora; honey & mustard salmon; kulfi.* **Details:** *near
Castle; 10.30 pm, Fri & Sat 11 pm; D only, closed Sun; no smoking area; children:
5+.*

Merchants
Lace Market Hotel　　　　£ 37
29-31 High Pavement NG1 1HE   (0115) 958 9898
This potentially "cosy" design-hotel dining room was relaunched after an expensive refit in early 2004; feedback remains limited, but suggests the place may – finally! – be settling into a more consistent and satisfactory rhythm. / Sample dishes: aubergine, smoked Mozzarella & chorizo tart; tuna steak with cherry tomato salad; vanilla & blackcurrant bavarois. Details: www.merchantsnottingham.co.uk; 10.30 pm; no smoking; children: 18+ only. Accommodation: 42 rooms, from £110.

Mr Man's　　　　£ 26　　★
Wollaton Park NG8 2AD   (0115) 928 7788
By Wollaton Park, it's a bit of a surprise to encounter this "vast" restaurant, which has "the feel of one of the large Hong Kong places"; "hard-to-fault" food is one of the features making it "popular for family celebrations". / Details: 11 pm.

Petit Paris　　　　£ 27
2 Kings Walk NG1 2AE   (0115) 947 3767
"Busy and easy-going", this "Continental" brasserie remains a "reliable" stand-by. / Sample dishes: smoked chicken & mushroom pancake; veal with mushroom & brandy flambé; profiteroles with hot chocolate sauce. Details: www.petit-paris.co.uk; near Theatre Royal; 10.30 pm; closed Sun; no smoking area.

Pretty Orchid　　　　£ 29
12 Pepper Street NG1 2GH   (0115) 958 8344
"Good set menus" and "fast service" (from the "chatty" owner) are the sort of virtues which commend this well-established city-centre Thai; "it's in an interesting building, too". / Sample dishes: chicken yakitori; stir-fried seafood with Thai chilli oil; sticky rice & mango. Details: 11 pm; no Amex; no smoking.

Restaurant Sat Bains　　　　£ 61
Old Lenton Ln NG7 2SA
(0115) 986 6566
Hotel des Clos – a former farmhouse a little way from the centre of town – was finally sold to its award-winning chef in late 2004; reports for the period ranged from "exciting" to "pretentious" – lets hope Mr B (who plans an adjoining cookery school) can now re-establish his former consistency. / Sample dishes: roast scallops with Indian-spiced cauliflower; duck with apple & foie gras; apple tart with Granny Smith sorbet. Details: www.hoteldesclos.com; 9.30 pm; closed Mon, Sat L & Sun; no smoking; children: 8+. Accommodation: 9 rooms, from £109.50.

Royal Thai　　　　£ 23
189 Mansfield Rd NG1 3FS   (0115) 948 3001
"Good-value" lunches remain a highlight, but the professional standards of this Mansfield Road Thai make it a handy stand-by at any time. / Details: 11 pm; closed Sun L; no smoking.

Saagar　　　　£ 28　　★
473 Mansfield Rd NG5 2DR   (0115) 962 2014
"Large portions" of "lovely fresh food" ensure that this Sherwood Indian is "always packed". / Details: 1.5m from city centre; midnight; closed Sun L; no smoking area; children: 5+.

Siam Thani   £ 26
16-20 Carlton St NG1 1NN   (0115) 958 2222
"Consistent standards" make this large Lace Market Thai a top
local stand-by. / **Details:** www.siamthani.co.uk; 10.30 pm; closed Sun L;
no smoking area.

Sonny's   £ 34
3 Carlton St NG1 1NL   (0115) 947 3041
This *"classic"* modern brasserie re-opened after a major (post-fire)
renovation in mid-2004; before the revamp, its *"fairly standard"*
cooking had increasingly struck some reporters as *"very
expensive"* for what it was. / **Sample dishes:** tomato linguine with roast
peppers; roast lamb; blueberry & almond tart. **Details:** near Victoria Centre;
10.30 pm, Fri & Sat 11 pm; no smoking area.

La Toque   £ 38   ★
61 Wollaton Rd NG9 2NG   (0115) 922 2268
Swede Mattias Karlsson's *"delightful"* and *"seriously good"* Gallic
cooking – plus *"very professional and pleasant service"* – is hailed
by all who comment on this Beeston venture. / **Sample dishes:** quail
consommé & toasted brioche; lemon sole with green bean fricassée; baked prune
soufflé. **Details:** off A52 towards Beeston; 9.30 pm; closed Mon, Sat L & Sun;
no smoking area; children: 6+.

Victoria Hotel   £ 20   ★
Dovecote Ln NG9 1JG   (0115) 925 4049
You get *"very good home-cooked food and excellent real ales"*, at
this *"well-priced"* pub – a former railway hotel by Beeston station.
/ **Sample dishes:** spinach & apple soup; herb-crusted rack of lamb; Mars bar
cheesecake. **Details:** www.tynemill.co.uk/nottm/vic.htm; by Beeston railway station;
8.45 pm, Sun 7.45 pm; no Amex; no smoking; need 6+ to book; children: before
8 pm only.

World Service   £ 39   Ⓐ
Newdigate Hs, Castle Gate NG1 6AF   (0115) 847 5587
This *"slick"* operation may appear to be a *"hidden gem"* to first-
time visitors, but it's a *"bustling"* place with a very big name in
these parts – not least with *"the local beautiful people"*; the
"cool" setting is (almost) matched by some surprisingly
"imaginative" food. / **Sample dishes:** salt & pepper squid with orange salad;
roast lamb with braised fennel & crispy garlic; pear & cinnamon tarte Tatin.
Details: www.worldservicerestaurant.com; 10 pm; no smoking.

NUTFIELD, SURREY   3–3B

Nutfield Priory (The Cloisters)   £ 54   Ⓐ
RH1 4EL   (01737) 824400
This *"delightful"* restaurant has a setting *"just right for romance"*
(which comes as *"a surprise"* in this *"gloomy"* hotel); its
"beautifully presented" food was only modestly commented on by
reporters, but always positively. / **Sample dishes:** home-cured gravadlax;
poached fillet of beef with vegetables; glazed apple tart with caramel ice cream.
Details: www.nutfield-priory.com; M25 from E: J6 to Redhill. from W: J8, signs to
Reigate and Redhill; 9.30 pm; closed Sat L; no smoking. **Accommodation:** 60
rooms, from £135.

OAKHAM, RUTLAND   5–4D

Nicks
Lord Nelson's House   £ 38   ★
11 Marketplace LE15 6DT   (01572) 723199
*"Consistently very good food in a quirky hotel at the corner of the
market square" – that's still the summary on Nick Healey's
handily located and "homely" venture, in a medieval timber-
framed building. / **Sample dishes:** roast goats cheese with poached pears;
steak with rosti & caramelised onions; walnut & ginger steamed pudding.
Details: www.nelsons-house.com; 9.30 pm; closed Mon & Sun; no Amex;
no smoking. **Accommodation:** 4 rooms, from £80.*

OBAN, ARGYLL & BUTE   9–3B

Ee-Usk (Fish Café)   £ 35   ★★
North Pier PA35 5QD
(01631) 565666
*For "fish as it should be", Callum McLeod's striking-looking new
venture overlooking Mull and Kerrara is – like his former premises
– "well worth a lengthy detour". / **Sample dishes:** mussels with garlic
butter; monkfish with mornay sauce & savory mash; bread & butter pudding with
Irish cream. **Details:** 10 pm; no Amex; no smoking area.*

OCKLEY, SURREY   3–4A

Bryce's at the Old School House   £ 37   ★
RH5 5TH   (01306) 627430
*The appearance may be, well, "a bit old school", but the ratings
awarded by reporters at this pre-Victorian house tend to support
those who claim that this is "the best fish restaurant in Surrey".
/ **Sample dishes:** coconut crab cakes with sweet & sour scallops; plaice with
brioche herb crust; butterscotch & honeycomb cheesecake.
Details: www.bryces.co.uk; 8m S of Dorking on A29; 9.30 pm; closed Sun D in Nov,
Jan & Feb; no Amex; no smoking.*

ONGAR, ESSEX   3–2B

Smiths Brasserie   £ 40
Fyfield Rd CM5 0AL   (01277) 365578
*A "smart and reliable" (if sometimes "loud") modern brasserie,
with a big name locally for its "beautiful fish"; even fans, though,
concede it's "a bit unimaginative". / **Sample dishes:** asparagus
hollandaise; salmon fillet cake with parsley; roasted pineapple with butterscotch
sauce. **Details:** www.smithsbrasserie.co.uk; left off A414 towards Fyfield; 10.30 pm;
closed Mon; no Amex; children: 12+.*

ORFORD, SUFFOLK   3–1D

Butley Orford Oysterage   £ 31   ★
Market Hill IP12 2LH   (01394) 450277
*"It's simple and Spartan, but the fish is always excellent" at this
"great", if "squashed", seafood café; it's remained pretty much
unchanged these last 30 years (though the younger generation of
the Pinney family recently took over at the stoves).
/ **Sample dishes:** smoked salmon pâté; hot smoked mackerel with mustard sauce;
rum baba. **Details:** 9 pm; Mon-Thu L only, closed Sun D in winter; no Amex;
no smoking.*

The Crown & Castle   £35
IP12 2LJ   (01394) 450205
*"Good food, but not up to all the hype" – fairly typical feedback
on this attractively-located hotel, where "erratic" service is a
recurrent issue. / **Sample dishes:** cockle, bacon & endive salad; crispy pork
with spiced lentils & gingered greens; hot bitter chocolate mousse.
Details: www.crownandcastle.co.uk; 9 pm; closed Sun D in winter; no Amex;
no smoking; booking: max 8; children: under 8s in Parlour only.
Accommodation: 18 rooms, from £75.*

ORKNEY ISLANDS, ORKNEY ISLANDS

The Creel   £41   A★
Front Rd, St Margaret's Hope, South Ronaldsay KW17 2SL
(01856) 831311
*Go for the fish – "they can tell you who caught it, and where" –
at Allan Craigie's "excellent" seafront restaurant-with-rooms; it
offers "fantastic food" and "friendly and professional" service, and
"what a view!" / **Sample dishes:** crab bisque; supreme of cod; Drambuie
panna cotta. **Details:** www.thecreel.co.uk; off A961 S of town, across Churchill
barriers; 9 pm; D only; closed Jan-Mar; no Amex; no smoking. **Accommodation:** 3
rooms, from £80.*

ORPINGTON, KENT   3–3B

Xian   £23   ★
324 High St BR6 0NG   (01689) 871881
*"A really good Chinese that can compete with anywhere in
London" – that's how Kentish folk have long thought of this
"reliable" family-run fixture, for which "you need to book well in
advance". / **Details:** 11.15 pm, Fri & Sat 11.45 pm; closed Sun L.*

OSMOTHERLEY, NORTH YORKSHIRE   8–4C

Golden Lion   £30
6 West End DL6 3AA   (01609) 883526
*An "atmospheric" rural pub, where even some of those who say
the "menu could use a revamp" still rate the food as "very good"
for what it is. / **Sample dishes:** spaghetti with clams; pork & Parma ham with
sage mash; lemon & passion fruit pavlova. **Details:** 10.30 pm; no Amex;
no smoking area.*

Three Tuns   £38
9 South End DL6 3BN   (01609) 883301
*"A very nice place, in the middle of nowhere" – this modernised
inn is decorated in a style that "seems very 'now', for a small
village", and it offers cooking that's "quite pricey, but generally
worth it". / **Sample dishes:** crab & salmon fishcakes; Dover sole with lemon &
chive butter; mini croque-en-bouche. **Details:** www.the3tuns.net; 6m NE of
Northallerton; 9.30 pm; no smoking. **Accommodation:** 7 rooms, from £75.*

OSWESTRY, SHROPSHIRE   5–3A

Sebastian's   £ 42   ★

45 Willow St SY11 1AQ   (01691) 655444

"Perfectionism plus originality" makes Mark Sebastian Fisher's
restaurant with rooms a destination of some note; sadly it's
currently open one night a week only (usually Sat), Mr F having
secured a major contract to make puddings for the Orient
Express! / **Sample dishes:** seafood cassoulet with bacon & cannellini beans; roast
duck with caramelised apples & sage sauce; cinnamon cream with spiced rhubarb.
Details: www.sebastians-hotel.co.uk; near town centre, follow signs towards Selattyn;
9.45 pm; D only, closed Mon & Sun; no smoking. **Accommodation:** 8 rooms,
from £65.

OTLEY, WEST YORKSHIRE   5–1C

Korks   £ 30   Ⓐ

40 Bondgate LS21 1AD   (01943) 462020

"A top-class range of wines, from Spain and the Rhone" (and with
"good bottle-age") is the headline attraction at this *"astonishing"*
wine bar, but the food and the atmosphere are *"pretty good"*, too.
/ **Sample dishes:** tandoori chicken with coriander noodles; pork with cauliflower &
turmeric jus; summer berry pavlova. **Details:** www.korks.com; 10 pm, Fri & Sat
11 pm; closed Sat L & Sun.

OUNDLE, NORTHAMPTONSHIRE   3–1A

Falcon Inn   £ 34

Fotheringay PE8 5HZ   (01832) 226254

"An excellent view of the local church" figures largely in reports on
this old stone hostelry – it's *"well supported by locals"* and
consistently rated by reporters. / **Sample dishes:** pea & mint soup with
Parma ham; curried pork with fruity rice & poppadums; sticky toffee pudding.
Details: www.huntsbridge.co.uk; just off A605; 9.30 pm; no smoking.

OVINGTON, HAMPSHIRE   2–3D

The Bush Inn   £ 30

SO24 0RE   (01962) 732764

A *"good atmosphere"* helps make this Wadworth's pub,
attractively located near the River Itchen, a popular local
destination, despite a menu that strikes some as rather *"limited"*.
/ **Sample dishes:** chicken liver pâté with brandy & port; spinach & wild mushroom
lasagne; chocolate & black cherry bread & butter pudding.
Details: www.wadworth.co.uk; just off A31 between Winchester & Alresford;
9.30 pm; closed Sun D; no smoking area.

OXFORD, OXFORDSHIRE   2–2D

Especially for a city of such beauty and affluence, Oxford's
restaurants are woeful. Some of them – such as *Gee's* and, in a
different way, the recently re-opened *Lemon Tree* – have notably
attractive settings, but otherwise none of the European
establishments is of any note whatsoever, and many of the city's
best-known places would deserve a place in any 'rogues'
gallery' of underperformers. Those wishing to eat well will
generally do best if they eat Thai or Indian.

Al Shami £ 24
25 Walton Cr OX1 2JG (01865) 310066
*An "ever-popular" and "cosmopolitan" Jericho Lebanese – even
those who feel "it's welcome in Oxford, but not of any special
note" admit that "you could never complain about its prices".*
/ **Sample dishes:** *falafel; mixed grill; Lebanese sweets.*
Details: *www.al-shami.co.uk; 11.45 pm; no Amex; no smoking area.*
Accommodation: *12 rooms, from £45.*

Aziz £ 30
228-230 Cowley Rd OX4 1UH (01865) 794945
*A "popular" east-Oxford curry house that some think is the "best
in town"; there were gripes this year, though about "clueless"
service and "OK but unremarkable" food. / **Details:** www.aziz.uk.com;
10.45 pm; closed Fri L; no smoking area.*

Bangkok House £ 24 A★
42a High Bridge St OX1 2EP (01865) 200705
*Reporters tend to agree that this "good all-rounder" – decoratively
distinguished by "masses of intricately-carved wood" – is "one of
the best" of Oxford's (quite numerous) Thais. / **Details:** 10.45 pm;
closed Sun; no smoking.*

Bombay £ 18
82 Walton St OX2 6EA (01865) 511188
*For "Jericho's best curry" seek out this "consistent" operation;
"BYO increases its appeal". / **Details:** 11.15 pm; closed Fri L; no Amex.*

Branca £ 33
111 Walton St OX2 6AJ (01865) 556111
*"A buzzy neighbourhood feeling" has established this "eclectic"
Jericho Italian as one of the most popular destinations in town; it
serves a "limited" menu of "basics", at "competitive" prices.
/ **Sample dishes:** summer minestrone soup; linguine with tiger prawns & chilli;
tiramisu.* **Details:** *www.branca-restaurants.com; 11 pm; no smoking urea.*

Browns £ 28 X
5-11 Woodstock Rd OX2 6HA (01865) 511995
*Run into the ground by its owners (Bass, sorry Mitchells & Butler),
this "faded" brasserie favourite – once such a destination – is now
just thoroughly "institutional". / **Sample dishes:** grilled goats cheese salad;
confit duck with plum relish; bread & butter pudding.*
Details: *www.browns-restaurants.com; 11.30 pm; no smoking area; need 5+ to
book.*

Café Coco £ 25 A
23 Cowley Rd OX4 1HP (01865) 200232
*"Trendy", "friendly", "cool" and "unpretentious", this "consistently
buzzy", "Continental-style" café/bar is an all-day destination that
attracts unanimous praise from reporters.
/ **Sample dishes:** houmous & garlic bread; Greek wine, sausage & ham pizza;
tiramisu.* **Details:** *11 pm; no Amex; no booking.*

Cherwell Boathouse £ 30 X
Bardwell Rd OX2 6ST (01865) 552746
*"A great wine list" and an "excellent location" ("it's fun watching
people try to punt") are the only reasons to seek out this riverside
fixture; otherwise, as one reporter succinctly put it: the place
"needs a kick up the backside". / **Sample dishes:** sweetcorn & spring
onion risotto; chicken in bacon with cranberry confit; lime pie.*
Details: *www.cherwellboathouse.co.uk; 10 pm; no smoking.*

Chiang Mai £ 28 A ★
Kemp Hall Passage, 130a High St OX1 4DH
(01865) 202233
"*Extraordinary*" *surroundings help make this* "*very atmospheric*"
Tudor house – tucked away down an alley off the High Street –
"*comfortably Oxford's best restaurant*"; *the Thai cuisine is*
"*admirable*", *too, but did not quite achieve the* "*superb*" *ratings of*
some previous years. / **Details:** *www.chiangmaikitchen.co.uk; 10.30 pm;*
no smoking area.

Chutney's £ 27 ★
36 St Michael's St OX1 2EB (01865) 724241
Near the city-centre, this is "*an Indian with a difference*", *not least*
for its "*good veggie choice*". / **Details:** *www.chutneysoxford.co.uk; 11 pm;*
closed Sun.

Edamame £ 18 ★
15 Holywell St OX1 3SA (01865) 246916
"*A tiny, no-frills, but authentic-feeling Japanese eatery*" *that*
makes a "*welcoming and affordable*" *pit stop; it serves* "*excellent*"
oriental "*home cooking*" *(and sushi).* / **Details:** *www.edamame.co.uk; opp*
New College; 8.30 pm; L only, except Fri & Sat when L & D, closed Mon; no Amex;
no cards at L; no smoking; no booking.

Fishers £ 33
36-37 St Clements OX4 1AB (01865) 243003
Some liken it to "*a glorified chippie*", *but this* "*buzzy*" *fish bistro*
remains a popular destination (not least because it is, of its type,
pretty much the only show in town). / **Sample dishes:** *king prawns with*
garlic mayonnaise; seared tuna with aubergine salsa & herb oil; sticky toffee pudding.
Details: *www.fishers-restaurant.com; by Magdalen Bridge; 10.30 pm; closed*
Mon L & Tue L; no Amex; no smoking.

Gee's £ 40 A
61 Banbury Rd OX2 6PE (01865) 553540
A "*great ambience*" – *especially for romance* – *is the special*
strength of this restaurant in a "*delightful*" *conservatory; some*
claim the cooking is "*the best in Oxford*" – *however, as one such*
reporter notes, that's "*not saying much*". / **Sample dishes:** *king scallops*
with leeks; roast lamb with borlotti beans & tapenade; chocolate soufflé with
pistachio sauce. **Details:** *www.gees-restaurant.co.uk; 10.30 pm, Fri & Sat 11 pm;*
no smoking.

Jamals £ 21 ★
108 Walton St OX2 6AJ (01865) 310102
This "*efficient*" *curry house near the Phoenix Cinema is tipped as*
"*the best Indian in Oxford*" *by some reporters, not least for its*
"*slick*" *service and* "*generous and delicious*" *cuisine.*
/ **Details:** *www.jamals.co.uk; 11 pm; no smoking area.*

Kazbah £ 21 A
25-27 Cowley Rd OX4 1HP (01865) 202920
Near the city-centre, this "*atmospheric*" *Spanish bar makes a very*
handy stand-by, thanks not least to its "*inventive*" *tapas and*
"*friendly*" *service.* / **Sample dishes:** *anchovies cured in vinegar; chicken & olive*
tajine with preserved lemon; baklava. **Details:** *11 pm; no Amex; no booking.*

The Lemon Tree   £38   Ⓐ
268 Woodstock Rd OX2 7NW   (01865) 311936
*"The ambience is there but, like so many Oxford restaurants, the
food and service were not particularly impressive, given the
prices"* – the definitive review of this *"idyllic"* North Oxford villa;
now bought back by its original owners, it *"still has a way to go to
recapture its glory days"*. / **Details:** *1.5m N of city centre; 11 pm;
Mon-Thu D only, Fri-Sun open L & D; no Amex.*

Loch Fyne   £34
55 Walton St OX2 6AE (01865) 292510
"Reliable but nothing special" – it speaks volumes for the quality
of Oxford's restaurants that this *"competent-enough"* branch of
the national fish chain is one of the most commented-on places in
town. / **Sample dishes:** *lobster bisque with garlic rouille; rosemary-infused bream
with tomatoes & black olives; lemon sorbet.* **Details:** *www.loch-fyne.com; 10 pm;
no smoking.*

The Old Parsonage   £37   Ⓐ
1 Banbury Rd OX2 6NN   (01865) 310210
Standards seem to be improving at this *"lovely"* and
"atmospheric" medieval city-centre townhouse hotel, where the
food was generally *"good"* this year – if still a bit *"pricey"* and
"standard". / **Sample dishes:** *seared smoked salmon; rare marinated beef &
salad; cheesecake.* **Details:** *www.oxford-hotels-restaurants.co.uk; 0.5m N of city
centre; 10.30 pm; no smoking.* **Accommodation:** *30 rooms, from £155.*

Le Petit Blanc   £31   X
71-72 Walton St OX2 6AG (01865) 510999
"Arrogant and inefficient service" and utterly *"mediocre"* food too
often spoil a visit to this *"over-rated"* Gallic bistro; though largely
run by Loch Fyne these days, Raymond Blanc (of 'Manoir' fame)
retains an interest – isn't it time he made his name 'mean'
something? / **Sample dishes:** *foie gras & chicken liver pâté; confit of guinea fowl
with wild mushrooms; 'floating island' dessert.* **Details:** *www.lepetitblanc.co.uk;
11 pm; no smoking.*

Quod
Old Bank Hotel   £31   X
92-94 High Street OX1 4BN   (01865) 799599
"They spent the money on the interior not the chef", at this
"noisy" Italianate outfit (the latest creation from Brown's-founder
Jeremy Mogford); ratings for its *"formulaic"* and *"boring"* offering
went from bad to worse this year. / **Sample dishes:** *crab salad with sweet
chilli; confit duck with caramelised prunes & lardons; chocolate marble brownie.*
Details: *www.oldbank-hotel.co.uk; opp All Souls College; 11 pm; no smoking area;
no booking, Sun L.* **Accommodation:** *42 rooms, from £165.*

Radcliffe Arms   £13
67 Cranham St OX2 6DE   (01865) 514762
"At prices this low, how do they manage to stay in business" – the
question's the same as ever at this Jericho pub, where the fare is
"wholesome" and *"cheap"*. / **Sample dishes:** *tomato soup; lasagne &
salad; chocolate fudge cake.* **Details:** *9 pm; no Amex; no booking.*

Randolph £ 45 X
Beaumont St OX1 2LN (0870) 400 8200
*This famous Macdonald hotel remains "stuck in a very
disappointing time warp", and incites too many reports of
"dreadful" experiences.* / **Sample dishes:** clam chowder; spiced duck with
red cabbage; walnut tart with maple syrup ice cream.
Details: www.macdonaldhotels.com; opp Ashmolean Museum; 10 pm; no smoking.
Accommodation: 151 rooms, from £140.

Saffron £ 25
204-206 Banbury Rd OX2 7BY (01865) 512211
*"Indian-French fusion cooking" (largely the former) makes this
Summertown spot something of a "stand-out in a gastronomic
desert"; critics can find the approach "bizarre", but low prices
help disarm criticism.* / **Details:** www.saffronoxford.com; 11.30 pm;
no smoking area.

Thai Orchid £ 25 ★
58a St Clements St OX4 1AH (01865) 798044
*"Lovely food" makes this east-Oxford outfit – for some reporters –
"the best Thai in town".* / **Details:** nr Headington Park; 10.30 pm; closed
Sat L & Sun L; no smoking area.

The Ebb £ 38 A★★
1a The Strand PL28 8BS
(01841) 532565
*Karen Scott's "light, low-fat and clean-tasting cuisine" helps win
unmitigated rave reviews for this year-old seafood specialist; it
benefits from "a wonderful chic ambience" and offers "very good
value", too ("especially compared to the Stein empire").*
/ **Details:** 10 pm; D only, closed Tue; no Amex; no smoking; children: 14+.

Margot's £ 34 ★
11 Duke St PL28 8AB (01841) 533441
*"Why bother with Rick Stein?" – Adrian Oliver's tiny and
"friendly", "feel-good" restaurant offers some "superb" (mainly
fish) dishes, and at very reasonable prices; it is "deservedly busy"
– a High Street offshoot is planned.* / **Sample dishes:** sardines with
watercress & radish salad; rack of lamb with spring onion crust; saffron poached
pears with shortbread. **Details:** www.margots.co.uk; 9.30 pm; closed Mon L & Tue;
closed Jan; no smoking.

Rick Stein's Café £ 33 ★
10 Middle St PL28 8AP (01841) 532700
*"A good, cheaper alternative to the Seafood Restaurant" – the
cooking here may be "less complex" than at its famed sibling, but
the "good value" on offer at this "cosy" café makes it far from
being a second-best choice.* / **Sample dishes:** Thai fishcakes with sweet &
sour cucumber dressing; char-grilled steak with tomato & red onion salad; lime
posset with balsamic strawberries. **Details:** www.rickstein.com; 9.30 pm;
no smoking. **Accommodation:** 3 rooms, from £60.

The Seafood Restaurant £65 ★
Riverside PL28 8BY (01841) 532700
*"Seafood doesn't get any fresher or any better", says one of the many fans of this "superb" harboursider; thanks to the TV fame of proprietor Rick Stein, it has long been a place of culinary pilgrimage (and is able to charge accordingly), and it was on top form this past year. / **Sample dishes:** cuttlefish salad; shark & Dover sole vindaloo; panna cotta with stewed rhubarb. **Details:** www.rickstein.com; 10 pm; no Amex; no smoking; booking: max 14; children: 3+. **Accommodation:** 13 rooms, from £85.*

St Petroc's House Bistro £43
4 New St PL28 8EA (01841) 532700
*Last year, Rick Stein's 'No. 2' venture was easier to recommend than the Seafood Restaurant; this year, however, the position is reversed – commentary, especially on the service at this hotel bistro, notably lacked the consistency you might hope for. / **Sample dishes:** poached egg, bacon & crouton salad; lemon sole with sea salt & lemon; Gorgonzola with honey & walnuts. **Details:** www.rickstein.com; 9.30 pm; no smoking. **Accommodation:** 10 rooms, from £110.*

Stein's Fish & Chips £18 A★
South Quay PL28 8BY (01841) 532700
*Rick goes chippy – "upmarket", naturally; his new operation is unanimously praised in early reports, not least for its "huge array of fresh fish" and its "lovely" atmosphere. / **Details:** 9 pm; no smoking.*

PAINSWICK, GLOUCESTERSHIRE 2–2B

Painswick Hotel £51 A
Kemps Ln GL6 6YB (01452) 812160
*A "lovely" dining room is a highlight at this grand Cotswold hotel, where "delicious" dishes come at prices which are "reasonable, considering the setting". / **Sample dishes:** smoked quail ravioli; monkfish wrapped in Parma ham & basil; rhubarb & custard upside-down crème brûlée. **Details:** www.painswickhotel.com; 9.30 pm; no smoking. **Accommodation:** 19 rooms, from £125.*

PARK GATE, HAMPSHIRE 2–4D

Kam's Palace £32 A★
1 Bridge Rd SO31 7GD (01489) 583328
*"A real Chinese feel about the place" sets the tone at this ever-popular, pagoda-style oriental, where there's "no sign of MSG". / **Details:** 11 pm.*

PARKGATE, CHESHIRE 5–2A

Marsh Cat £26 A
1 Mostyn Sq CH64 6SL (0151) 336 1963
*"Great views over the River Dee are a bonus", say fans of this popular bistro, which benefits from a strong local reputation for "value for money". / **Sample dishes:** crab claws & monkfish in Thai coconut sauce; Cajun blackened swordfish & catfish; nutty torte with raspberries. **Details:** www.marshcat.com; 10 pm, Fri & Sat 10.30 pm; no smoking.*

PAXFORD, GLOUCESTERSHIRE 2–1C
Churchill Arms £32
GL55 6XH (01386) 594000
"Arrive very early", if you want a table at this "unpretentious" but locally celebrated gastropub, where the food is "interesting, but not OTT". / **Sample dishes:** duck with grapefruit & fennel salad; guinea fowl in Madeira & mushroom cream sauce; sticky toffee pudding.
Details: www.thechurchillarms.com; off Fosse Way; 9 pm; no Amex; no booking.
Accommodation: 4 rooms, from £70.

PENSHURST, KENT 3–3B
Spotted Dog £33
Smarts Hill TN11 8EP (01892) 870253
"A menu of high quality that's fairly priced" plus "fantastic views over the Kent countryside" ensure consistent popularity for this pretty old pub – it's "always busy at weekends".
/ **Sample dishes:** crispy seafood platter; chicken in tarragon & garlic sauce; chocolate Bailey's mousse. **Details:** near Penshurst Place; 9.30 pm, 6 pm Sun; closed Sun D; no Amex; no smoking area; children: 10+ after 7 pm.

PERTH, PERTH & KINROSS 9–3C
Let's Eat £34   Ⓐ★★
77-79 Kinnoull St PH1 5EZ (01738) 643377
"Excellent Scottish produce, simply cooked" – but not without the odd "eclectic" influence – has helped create a formidable reputation for Tony Heath's "cosy", "friendly" and "efficient" bistro; "booking is essential". / **Sample dishes:** smoked salmon with spiced prawns & avocado; herb-crusted lamb with rosemary jus; steamed ginger pudding with rhubarb. **Details:** www.letseatperth.co.uk; opp North Inch Park; 9.45 pm; closed Mon & Sun; no smoking area.

63 Tay Street £37   ★
63 Tay St PH2 8NN (01738) 441451
"Scottish restaurants, please take note – this is how it should be done!"; "Jeremy and Shona Wares go from strength to strength", and continue to bring some "superb" cooking to the "eating-out desert" that is central Perth. / **Sample dishes:** smoked trout salad with lardons; Angus beef with spring onion mash; date & fig pudding.
Details: www.63taystreet.co.uk; on city side of River Tay, 1m from Dundee Rd; 9 pm; closed Mon & Sun; no smoking; children: 10+ at D.

PETERSFIELD, HAMPSHIRE 2–3D
JSW £46   ★★
1 Heath Rd GU31 4JE (01730) 262030
"Small and sophisticated, but without pretensions", this "friendly" family-run restaurant inspires a hymn of praise for its "excellent" service and "perfect food, beautifully presented"; by some accounts, though, "the décor still needs a make-over".
/ **Sample dishes:** roast foie gras with shallot tarte Tatin; wild salmon with summer vegetables; milk chocolate fondant. **Details:** 9.30 pm; closed Mon & Sun; no Amex; no smoking; children: 8+.

River Kwai £26   ★
16-18 Dragon St GU31 4JJ (01730) 267077
"Consistent standards over many years" distinguish this quite opulent Thai – a real oddity in these parts.
/ **Details:** www.riverkwaipetersfield.co.uk; 10.30 pm; closed Mon L & Sun L; no smoking.

PETWORTH, WEST SUSSEX   3–4A

Well Diggers Arms   £ 35
Pulborough Rd GU28 0HG   (01798) 342287
This beautifully-located Georgian inn is this year celebrating half a century in the ownership of the Whitcomb family; it lives up to its name – "make sure you go with a hearty appetite".
/ **Sample dishes:** French onion soup; roast duck; crème brûlée. **Details:** 1m out of town on Pulborough Road; 9.30 pm; closed Mon, Tue D, Wed D & Sun D.

PHILLEIGH, CORNWALL   1–4B

Roseland Inn   £ 33   𝔸★
TR2 5NB   (01872) 580254
"Beautiful food" is not the only attraction of this "darling" old pub; it's acclaimed by all reporters for its "helpful" staff and its sheer "charm". / **Sample dishes:** duck liver pâté; rump steak with potatoes & salad; chocolate bread & butter pudding. **Details:** www.roseland-inn.co.uk; near King Harry ferry; 9 pm; no Amex; no smoking area.

PICKERING, NORTH YORKSHIRE   8–4C

White Swan   £ 35   ★
Market Pl YO18 7AA   (01751) 472288
The "excellent quiet bar" ("separate from the main restaurant") is the top tip, especially at lunchtime, if you're visiting this ancient town-centre coaching inn; its selection of "many and varied" wines is also appreciated. / **Sample dishes:** chicken liver & foie gras terrine; rack of lamb with aubergine & tomato caviar; grilled figs & Amaretto cream. **Details:** www.white-swan.co.uk; 9 pm; no smoking. **Accommodation:** 12 rooms, from £130.

PINNER, GREATER LONDON   3–3A

Friends   £ 36   ★
11 High St HA5 5PJ   (020) 8866 0286
This Gallic fixture (occupying a Tudor building) remains "a continued and deserved local favourite", thanks to its "quaint" and "cosy" ambience and its "really well done modern dishes". / **Sample dishes:** leek & goats cheese strudel; lamb steak with bubble 'n' squeak; Bramley apple crumble. **Details:** www.friendsrestaurant.co.uk; near Pinner Underground station; 10 pm; closed Mon & Sun D; no smoking.

La Giralda   £ 20
66-68 Pinner Grn HA5 2AB   (020) 8868 3429
"In an ill-served part of the suburbs", this "well-run" Spanish establishment of long standing continues to provide a "reliable and cheerful" venue, at "reasonable" prices. / **Sample dishes:** melon with Serrano ham; pink trout with nut butter; poached pears with syrup. **Details:** A404 to Cuckoo Hill Junction; 10 pm; closed Mon & Sun D.

L'Orient   £ 26   𝔸
58 High St HA5 5PZ   (020) 8429 8488
Offering "a fusion of all oriental cuisines", this is a "stylish" and "interesting" suburban spot, which delivers "excellent quality"; prices are "a bit on the ambitious side", though. / **Sample dishes:** miso soup; duck green curry; glazed pineapple. **Details:** www.lorientcuisine.com; 11 pm; no smoking.

PLOCKTON, HIGHLAND   9–2B

Plockton Inn   £25   ★
Innes St IV52 8TU   (01599) 544222
"Wonderful seafood in a picturesque village" (including *"the best
langoustines and prawns"*) draws fans from far and wide to this
rural inn. / **Sample dishes:** smoked seafood platter; salmon with orange
vinaigrette; sorbet. **Details:** www.plocktoninn.co.uk; 9 pm; no Amex; no smoking.
Accommodation: 14 rooms, from £36.

PLUMTREE, NOTTINGHAMSHIRE   5–3D

Perkins   £31
Old Railway Station NG12 5NA   (0115) 937 3695
*The second generation nowadays runs the show at this "friendly"
and long-established bistro in a former railway station; even a
reporter who finds it's "trying harder" as a result finds results still
a fraction "variable".* / **Sample dishes:** spicy tomato & oatmeal soup; fillet
steak with pickled walnut sauce; lime torte with dark chocolate pastry.
Details: www.perkinsrestaurant.co.uk; off A606 between Nottingham & Melton
Mowbray; 9.45 pm; closed Mon & Sun D; no smoking area; children: 10+.

PLYMOUTH, DEVON   1–3C

Thai Palace   £26
3 Elliot St, The Hoe PL1 2PP   (01752) 255770
*All reporters agree that this is "one of the few good places in
town"; applying national standards, though, some say the place is
"excellent", while others find it "ordinary".* / **Sample dishes:** chicken
satay; green beef curry; raspberry pavlova. **Details:** www.thaipalace.co.uk; 11 pm;
D only, closed Sun.

PONTELAND, NORTHUMBERLAND   8–2B

The Smithy   £31
3 Bell Villas NE20 9BD   (01661) 820020
"Good food" makes this *"cheerful"* village bistro a continuingly
"popular" destination hereabouts, even if it's *"a bit pricey"* for
what it is. / **Sample dishes:** seared scallops in leek & ginger broth; duck confit &
puy lentils with blackberry jus; roast peaches with nougatine. **Details:** 10 pm; closed
Sat L & Sun D; no smoking.

POOLE, DORSET   2–4C

Mansion House   £36   🅐★
Thames St BH15 1JN   (01202) 685666
"Staff try hard" in the *"panelled"* dining room of this *"wonderful
secluded Georgian house"*, which is lauded for the *"high
standard"* of its cuisine and its *"very reasonable prices"*.
/ **Sample dishes:** mackerel terrine; scallops with lentils & Indian spices; bread &
butter pudding. **Details:** www.themansionhouse.co.uk; follow signs for Ferry, turn left
onto quayside; 9.30 pm; closed Sat L & Sun D; no smoking; children: 5+ at D.
Accommodation: 32 rooms, from £130.

PORT APPIN, ARGYLL & BUTE   9–3B

Pier House Hotel   £36   A★★
PA38 4DE   (01631) 730302
As you'd expect, "superb fresh fish" is the menu highlight at this
beautifully-located hotel dining room, on the shore of Loch Linnhe;
it continues to inspire only the most complimentary of reports.
/ *Sample dishes: scallops with rice; beef Stroganoff; death by chocolate.*
Details: *www.pierhousehotel.co.uk; just off A828 by pier; 9.30 pm; no Amex;
no smoking.* **Accommodation:** *12 rooms, from £65.*

PORTAFERRY, COUNTY DOWN   10–2D

Portaferry Hotel   £37   A★
10 The Strand BT22 1PE   (028) 4272 8231
"An excellent, friendly hotel restaurant" – overlooking Strangford
Loch – which is unanimously applauded for its "superb seafood at
amazingly low prices". / *Sample dishes: warm goats cheese, Parma ham &
fig salad; salmon & champ with prawn cream; double chocolate torte with coconut
ice cream.* **Details:** *www.portaferryhotel.com, on shore front, opposite ferry slipway;
9 pm.* **Accommodation:** *14 rooms, from £95.*

PORTHMADOG, GWYNEDD   4–2C

Yr Hen Fecws   £30   A★
16 Lombard St LL49 9AP   (01766) 514625
The word on the "top-rate food" at this "cosy" and "friendly"
former bakery, now a restaurant-with-rooms, is well and truly out
nowadays – it can be "difficult to get reservations in summer".
/ *Details: www.henfecws.com; 10 pm; closed Sun; no Amex; no smoking.*
Accommodation: *7 rooms, from £55.*

PORTMEIRION, GWYNEDD   4–2C

Portmeirion Hotel   £45   A★
LL48 6ET   (01766) 770000
"The view over the estuary really makes the atmosphere", at this
"amazing", "romantic" dining room in the heart of the famous
fantasy-Mediterranean village; fans say it's "first class in every
way", with the "excellent-value lunch" particularly commended.
/ *Sample dishes: crab & smoked salmon potato cake; chicken & pancetta with wild
mushroom tartlet; bara brith bread & butter pudding.*
Details: *www.portmeirion-village.com; off A487 at Minffordd; 9 pm; no jeans or
trainers; no smoking.* **Accommodation:** *14 rooms, from £160.*

PORTRUSH, COUNTY ANTRIM   10–1C

Ramore   £25   A★
The Harbour BT56 8D3   (028) 7082 4313
"Still outstanding, and always busy with locals and passing trade";
this "old-favourite", "great-value" seaside Mediterranean
bar/bistro offers a "fabulous menu" in "enormous portions".
/ *Sample dishes: tortilla chips with guacamole; pizza with spicy meatballs &
peppers; tiramisu.* **Details:** *10 pm; no Amex; need 10+ to book; children: before
8 pm only.*

PORTSMOUTH, HAMPSHIRE   2–4D
Lemon Sole   £ 32
123 High St PO1 2HW (023) 9281 1303
There's "a great array of fresh fish" on offer at this "simple"
eatery – you point out your selection and it's prepared "any way
you like"; a "friendly" place, it offers fair "value-for-money".
/ *Sample dishes:* pan-fried scallops in garlic; grilled sea bass with home made
chips; lemon & lime mousse. *Details:* www.lemonsole.co.uk; 10 pm; closed Sun;
no smoking area; booking: max 10 at Sat D.

POULTON, GLOUCESTERSHIRE   2–2C
The Falcon Inn   £ 32   A ★
London Rd GL7 5HN
(01285) 850844
This stylish new gastropub is praised by all reporters for its "good
and consistent" cooking, from seasonal menus that manage to be
interesting (but without trying too hard).
/ *Details:* www.thefalconpoulton.co.uk; on A417 between Cirencester and Fairford;
9 pm; no Amex; no smoking area.

PRESTBURY, CHESHIRE   5–2B
White House   £ 40   ★
New Rd SK10 4DG (01625) 829376
"Great food and service" is the gist of all commentary on the
Wakehams' long-established restaurant-with-rooms, in the heart
of this pretty, if chichi, village. / *Sample dishes:* Caesar salad with sautéed
tiger prawns; Dover sole with sea salt & lime; strawberry brûlée with roast rhubarb.
Details: www.thewhitehouse.uk.com; 2m N of Macclesfield on A538; 10 pm; closed
Mon L & Sun D. *Accommodation:* 11 rooms, from £110.

PRESTEIGNE, POWYS   5–4A
Hat Shop   £ 26
7 High St LD8 2BA (01544) 260017
A "great all-women band" cooks at this cosy bistro, creating
"simple" food from "excellent local sources".
/ *Sample dishes:* aubergine & sweet potato samosas; chicken with bacon & walnut
stuffing; chocolate charlotte. *Details:* 9 pm; closed Sun; no credit cards; no smoking.

PRESTON BAGOT, WARWICKSHIRE   5–4C
The Crabmill   £ 33   A
B95 5DR (01926) 843342
"A terrific place to find in the middle of the country", this
"wonderful" modern pub "in an old timbered barn-type building"
is quite a local hotspot; the food may not have great aspirations,
but it's "always reliable". / *Sample dishes:* roast veal with tuna confit &
lemon mayonnaise; char-grilled pork with sage & lemon polenta; pannacotta with
honeycomb biscuits. *Details:* www.thecrabmill.co.uk; on main road between
Warwick & Henley; 9.30 pm; closed Sun D; no smoking.

PRESTON, LANCASHIRE   5–1A
Simply Heathcote's   £ 34
23 Winckley Sq PR1 3JJ (01772) 252732
The "original and best branch" of Paul Heathcote's brasserie
chain; the food is generally "reliable", but even supporters can
find the setting "dreary". / *Sample dishes:* grilled mackerel with sour cream;
wild mushroom linguine with Parmesan & basil; rum & raisin parfait.
Details: www.heathcotes.co.uk; 10 pm, Sat 11 pm; no smoking.

PRESTWOOD, BUCKINGHAMSHIRE 3–2A

Polecat £ 27

170 Wycombe Rd HB16 0HJ (01494) 862253

"The best pub food in the area" and a "nice garden in summer" make this roadside inn a popular destination – the pressure can sometimes make service "chaotic", though. / **Sample dishes:** baked field mushrooms with melted cheese; walnut-crusted pork with spring onion salsa; coconut meringues with mango syllabub. **Details:** on A4128 between Great Missenden & High Wycombe; 9 pm; closed Sun D; no credit cards; no smoking area; need 8+ to book.

PRIORS HARDWICK, WARWICKSHIRE 2–1D

Butchers Arms £ 40 ★

Church End CV47 7SN (01327) 260504

"The food is traditional but excellent", says one of the fans of this "olde English pub" that's "now been in the hands of the same Portuguese family for forty years" (and benefits from "warm" and "entertaining" service); there is also a good wine list. / **Sample dishes:** mushroom & Stilton tart; beef Stroganoff; profiteroles. **Details:** www.thebutchersarms.com; 9.30 pm; closed Sat L & Sun D; no smoking.

PURTON, WILTSHIRE 2–2C

Pear Tree at Purton £ 40 ★

SN5 4ED (01793) 772100

"What a find" – a large fan club sings the praises of this "great gastropub", in a "delightful" village setting; there is some feeling, though, that "simple dishes are best". / **Sample dishes:** creamed leek & smoked haddock broth; roast lamb with olive mash & pesto gravy; pear & hazelnut tart with fudge ice cream. **Details:** www.peartreepurton.co.uk; 9.15 pm; closed Sat L. **Accommodation:** 17 rooms, from £110.

PWLLHELI, GWYNEDD 4–2C

Plas Bodegroes £ 42 🄰★

Nefyn Rd LL53 5TH (01758) 612363

"A delightful countryside setting" and "great" cooking commend the Chowns' "idyllic" country house to nearly all reporters (even if there is the odd gripe that it's getting "a bit pleased with itself"). / **Sample dishes:** cod with Carmarthen ham & laver bread; roast spiced lamb with couscous; cardamom crème brûlée. **Details:** www.bodegroes.co.uk; on A497 1m W of Pwllheli; 9.30 pm; closed Mon, Tue-Sat D only, closed Sun D; closed Dec-mid Feb; no Amex; no smoking. **Accommodation:** 11 rooms, from £80.

RAMSBOTTOM, LANCASHIRE 5–1B

Ramsons £ 34 ★

18 Market Pl BL0 9HT (01706) 825070

"Imaginative dishes, exquisitely cooked and presented by enthusiasts" – that is the hallmark of this "idiosyncratic" establishment, where "proper" Italian cuisine is prepared according to the principles of 'Slow Food'. / **Sample dishes:** loin of tuna with cucumber spaghetti; loin of lamb & baby potatoes; panna cotta. **Details:** www.ramsons.org.uk; 9.30 pm; closed Mon, Tue & Sun D; no Amex; no smoking; booking: max 10.

RAMSGATE, KENT   3–3D

Surin   £ 26   ★
30 Harbour St CT11 8HA   (01843) 592001
*"The best Thai in the county" – this small, family-run venture,
near the harbour, offers "genuine cooking" from "fresh
ingredients". / **Details:** www.surinrestaurant.co.uk; 11 pm; closed Mon L & Sun.*

RAMSGILL-IN-NIDDERDALE, N YORKS   8–4B

Yorke Arms   £ 47   🇦★
HG3 5RL   (01423) 755243
*Some would say that "the best food in Yorkshire" is to be had at
Frances Atkins's "stylish and upmarket country inn", in the heart
of the Dales (which real devotees hail as "almost a mini-
Winteringham Fields"). / **Sample dishes:** lobster ravioli; lamb in parsley
crust; warm pear & butterscotch tart. **Details:** www.yorke-arms.co.uk; 4m W of
Pateley Bridge; 9 pm; no smoking; booking: max 6. **Accommodation:** 14 rooms,
from £105.*

READING, BERKSHIRE   2–2D

London Street Brasserie   £ 39
2-4 London St RG1 4SE   (0118) 950 5036
*Those who had despaired of discovering a decent place to eat in
Reading account this "enviably located" riverside brasserie "a real
find"; its menu – if not inexpensive – is generally "well executed".
/ **Sample dishes:** foie gras & duck terrine with raisin toast; sea bass with baby
squid & saffron dressing; Bakewell tart & custard.
Details: www.londonstbrasserie.co.uk; 10.30 pm.*

Old Siam   £ 25
Kings Wk, Kings St RG1 2HG   (0118) 951 2600
*Even those who feel it has a "poor location in a small shopping
centre", approve of the "good and reliable food" and the
"obliging" service at this well-established Thai – still one of the
best eating options in town. / **Details:** www.oldsiam.co.uk; 10 pm; closed
Sun; no smoking.*

REIGATE, SURREY   3–3B

La Barbe   £ 43   🇦
71 Bell St RH2 7AN   (01737) 241966
*"Charming" service and an "unforced" ambience help make this
"relaxed" local favourite an "outstanding" fixture for some
reporters, and "romantic", too; its Gallic fare is "honest".
/ **Sample dishes:** Roquefort mousse with poached pears; chicken, apple & cider
casserole; iced coffee mousse with lavender sauce. **Details:** www.labarbe.co.uk;
9.30 pm; closed Sat L & Sun; no smoking area.*

Tony Tobin @ The Dining Room   £ 47
59a High St RH2 9AE   (01737) 226650
*"Why trek to London, when perfection is on your doorstep", says
one of the many fans of TV-chef Toby Tobin's town-centre
restaurant; it doesn't please everyone, though, particularly on the
ambience front – "like some sort of '70s-throwback".
/ **Sample dishes:** crispy squid with fried green tomatoes; crispy duck with melted
onions; banana tart with vanilla ice cream. **Details:** www.tonytobinrestaurants.co.uk;
10 pm; closed Sat L & Sun D; no smoking; booking: max 8, Fri & Sat.*

REYNOLDSTON, SWANSEA   1–1C

Fairyhill   £43   A★★
SA3 1BS   (01792) 390139
"Very good food, making the best of local produce" has created a
formidable reputation for this "relaxing" country house hotel, in a
"remote" and hard-to-find corner of the Gower Peninsula; "allow
plenty of time to study the extensive wine list". / **Sample dishes:** crab
bisque; chicken supreme with mustard risotto cake; banana soufflé pancakes with
fudge sauce. **Details:** www.fairyhill.net; 20 mins from M4, J47 off B4295; 9 pm;
no Amex; no smoking area; children: 8+. **Accommodation:** 8 rooms, from £140.

RIPLEY, SURREY   3–3A

Drakes   £47   ★
The Clock Hs, High St GU23 6AQ   (01483) 224777
"Newly opened but showing great promise" – in 2004, chef
Steven Drake left nearby Drakes on the Pond for this grandly-
housed site on a cobbled street (previously Michel's); service is
"excellent" and all reporters say the food is "good" (or better),
but there's a feeling "the ambience needs greater attention".
/ **Details:** www.drakesrestaurant.co.uk; 9.30 pm; closed Mon, Sat L & Sun;
no Amex; no smoking; booking: max 6.

ROADE, NORTHAMPTONSHIRE   3–1A

Roade House   £39   ★
16 High St NN7 2NW   (01604) 863372
Chris & Sue Kewley's "reliably good" restaurant-with-rooms
continues to please all reporters, in particular for its "very well-
prepared" cooking. / **Sample dishes:** tomato & basil tartlet with prosciutto;
sea bass with ginger & lime sauce; apple & blackcurrant crumble.
Details: www.roadehousehotel.co.uk; 9.30 pm; closed Mon L, Sat L & Sun;
no smoking. **Accommodation:** 10 rooms, from £67.

ROCK, CORNWALL   1–3B

Black Pig   £47   ★
Rock Rd PL27 6LQ   (01208) 862622
Nathan Outlaw's "very proficient and precise cooking" making
much use of local ingredients has won instant acclaim (and foodie
gongs) for this year-old venture; atmosphere, however, is decidedly
not a key strength. / **Details:** www.blackpigrestaurant.co.uk; 9.30 pm; closed
Sun; no smoking; children: 12+.

ROCKBEARE, DEVON   1–3D

Jack in the Green Inn   £32   ★
London Rd EX5 2EE   (01404) 822240
Just off the A30, this is "an impressive operation with a wide
range and ambition"; the menus offer "very good value" in both
the bar and the restaurant. / **Sample dishes:** smoked seafood mousse;
roast pigeon with salsify & pink peppercorns; rice pudding with pralines.
Details: www.jackinthegreen.uk.com; 9.30 pm; no smoking.

ROMALDKIRK, COUNTY DURHAM 8–3B

The Rose & Crown £34
DL12 9EB (01833) 650213
The sort of "cosy" old coaching inn (on a village green) that's
"good for Sunday lunch"; otherwise – though some reports say it's
"excellent" – its repertoire can seem a bit "uninspired".
/ *Sample dishes:* Cotherstone cheese fritters with sweet & sour aubergines; roast
lamb with puy lentils & pesto; baked chocolate cheesecake.
Details: www.rose-and-crown.co.uk; 6m NW of Barnard Castle on B6277; 9 pm;
D only, except Sun open L & D; no Amex; no smoking; children: 6+.
Accommodation: 12 rooms, from £110.

ROSEVINE, CORNWALL 1–4B

Driftwood £40 ★
TR2 5EW (01872) 580644
"A fantastic clifftop spot" with "marvellous sea views" set the
scene at this hotel that opened a couple of years ago; Rory
Duncan's "really good" cooking includes the "wonderful" fish
dishes you'd hope for. / *Sample dishes:* cured salmon vinaigrette; braised
Cornish cod filet; lemon tart with rasberry sorbet. *Details:* 9.30 pm; D only;
no smoking; children: 2+. *Accommodation:* 11 rooms, from £150.

ROWDE, WILTSHIRE 2–2C

George & Dragon £37 ★
High St SN10 2PN (01380) 723053
"The best fish you'll find inland" makes this "friendly" gastropub
"oasis" in Wiltshire – "a land-locked county!" – popular with all
who comment on it. / *Sample dishes:* spinach & watercress soup; curried
smoked haddock pancakes; baked orange custard. *Details:* on A342 between
Devizes & Chippenham; 9 pm; closed Mon & Sun; no Amex; no smoking; booking:
max 8.

ROYAL LEAMINGTON SPA, WARWICKSHIRE 5–4C

Emperors £28 🅐
Bath Pl CV31 3BP (01926) 313666
"Always reliable in quality of food and service", this "classy"
Chinese has a setting that's quite "impressive", too, especially
considering the prices. / *Details:* 10.45 pm; closed Sun.

Loves £40 ★
15 Dormer Pl CV32 5AA (01926) 315522
"Complex, but always delicious" – Stephen Love's deft cooking
continues to win high praise from reporters, despite the rather
"unprepossessing" feel of his basement premises.
/ *Sample dishes:* meli melo of salmon caviar & rock oyster; saddle of lamb with
garlic purée & red wine jus; chocolate pudding. *Details:* 9.45 pm; closed Mon &
Sun; no smoking; no booking, Sat; children: 10+.

Thai Elephant £32
20 Regent St CV32 5HQ (01926) 886882
An "elegant" oriental, with "attentive" service and "good" cooking;
even some fans, though, consider it "pretty expensive" for what it
is. / *Details:* 10.30 pm; closed Sat L.

RYE, EAST SUSSEX   3–4C

Landgate Bistro   £ 27   ★
5-6 Landgate TN31 7LH   (01797) 222829
*"No pretensions, but food quality is right on the button", at this
long-established bistro; ambience, however, is "lacking".*
/ **Sample dishes:** *broad bean & pecorino tart; lambs kidneys with grain mustard
sauce; Jamaican chocolate cream.* **Details:** *www.landgatebistro.co.uk; 9.30 pm, Sat
10 pm; D only, closed Mon & Sun; no Amex; no smoking.*

Mermaid   £ 51
Mermaid St TN31 7EY   (01797) 223065
*Until recently, the grand Tudor-style dining room of "England's
oldest inn" had managed to avoid undue reliance on its 'heritage'
charms – no longer, it seems, and some "extremely disappointing"
meals were reported this year.* / **Sample dishes:** *pan-fried scallops &
langoustines; lobster thermidor; crème brûlée.* **Details:** *www.mermaidinn.com;
9.30 pm; no jeans; no smoking.* **Accommodation:** *31 rooms, from £160.*

SALISBURY, WILTSHIRE   2–3C

Jade   £ 28   ★
109a Exeter St SP1 2SF   (01722) 333355
*This "friendly" Chinese "may look as if it's just stepped out of the
'70s", but fans say "you can't beat it"; seafood is a highlight.*
/ **Sample dishes:** *spare ribs; lobster with ginger & spring onion; banana split.*
Details: *www.jaderestaurant.co.uk; near the Cathedral; 11.30 pm; closed Sun;
no Amex.*

LXIX   £ 29
69 New St SP1 2PH   (01722) 340000
*"The welcome is warm", at this "good, basic, reasonably-priced
bistro" (there's no longer a restaurant), which makes a handy
rendezvous, near the Cathedral.* / **Sample dishes:** *blue fin tuna with chilli
salsa; roast cod with lime oil & noisette butter; chocolate marquise.*
Details: *adjacent to Cathedral Close; 9.30 pm; closed Sun; no smoking area;
children: 12+.*

SALTAIRE, WEST YORKSHIRE   5–1C

Salts Diner   £ 23   Ⓐ
Salts Mill, Victoria Rd BD18 3LB   (01274) 530533
*A "busy" arts centre restaurant, in an old mill, which serves a
"limited" menu of "home-cooked" and "consistently good" fare.*
/ **Sample dishes:** *garlic bread; confit duck leg; sticky toffee pudding.* **Details:** *2m
from Bradford on A650; L & afternoon tea only; L only; no Amex; no smoking area.*

SAPPERTON, GLOUCESTERSHIRE   2–2C

The Bell At Sapperton   £ 36   Ⓐ
GL7 6LE   (01285) 760298
*A "superb" setting has helped this "above-average" Cotswold
gastropub make quite a name for itself, and it's often "busy"; the
food, though, can seem "dear for what it is".*
/ **Sample dishes:** *pan-fried scallops; local fish.* **Details:** *www.foodatthebell.co.uk;
9.30 pm; no Amex; no smoking area; no booking at L; children: 10+ at D.*

SARK, CHANNEL ISLANDS

La Sablonnerie Hotel   £ 33   A ★
GY9 0SD   (01481) 832061
*Fans say this cottagey restaurant-with-rooms (which is remote
even by the standards of this mile-square island) repays the
dramatic carriage ride across the bridge to reach it; it certainly
offers a culinary pilgrimage that's "so different".*
/ **Sample dishes:** *smoked salmon roulard with citrus dressing; fillet steak with
casserole of wild mushrooms; rum & chocolate pot with orange syrup.*
Details: *www.lasablonnerie.com; 8.45 pm; no Switch; no smoking area.*
Accommodation: *20 rooms, from £120.*

SAWLEY, LANCASHIRE   5–1B

Spread Eagle   £ 28   A
BB7 4NH   (01200) 441202
*"A lovely setting by the River Ribble" contributes to the "very
enjoyable old-fashioned experience" of visiting this "attractive" inn,
which serves "consistently good" and "unpretentious" fare.*
/ **Sample dishes:** *fish hors d'oeuvres; braised lamb with root vegetable sauce; tarte
Tatin.* **Details:** *www.the-spreadeagle.co.uk; NE of Clitheroe off A59; 9 pm; closed
Mon & Sun D; no Amex; no smoking.*

SAWSTON, CAMBRIDGESHIRE   3–1B

Jade Fountain   £ 23
42-46 High St CB2 4BG   (01223) 836100
*It might be unremarkable elsewhere, but "good" Chinese fodder is
hard to find in this part of the world – "booking is essential".*
/ **Details:** *1m from M11, J10; 9.30 pm.*

SAXMUNDHAM, SUFFOLK   3–1D

Bell Hotel   £ 26   ★
31 High St IP17 1AF   (01728) 602331
*"Sleepy Saxmundham", says one reporter, "is the last place you'd
expect to find such decent grub", but this recently revamped "old
market town hotel" is applauded for its "interesting" and "varied"
menu, and its "short but excellent" wine list.* / **Details:** *9 pm; closed
Mon & Sun; no Amex; no smoking.* **Accommodation:** *10 rooms, from £65.*

SCARBOROUGH, NORTH YORKSHIRE   8–4D

Lanterna   £ 35
33 Queen St   (01723) 363616
*"We've not had a bad meal in 30 years", thus speaks one
satisfied customer of this "delightful", "old-favourite" Italian,
where the "quality" ingredients ("especially the local fish") are
particularly praised.* / **Details:** *www.lanterna-ristorante.co.uk; 10 pm; D only,
closed Sun; no Amex; children: 2+.*

SCAWTON, NORTH YORKSHIRE   8–4C

Hare Inn   £ 30   A
YO7 2HG   (01845) 597289
*"A homely country pub, with food to match"; the location is
isolated, so it's certainly safest to book ahead.* / **Sample dishes:** *warm
smoked duck & bacon salad; deep-fried Whitby haddock; strawberry pavlova.*
Details: *www.thehareinn.com; off A170; 8.30 pm; closed Mon; no smoking area.*

SEAHAM, COUNTY DURHAM   8–3C

Seaham Hall   £ 70   A

Lord Byron's Walk SR7 7AG
(0191) 516 1400

*Especially by North Eastern standards, a visit to this "elegant"
and "romantic" country house hotel (now famous for its spa) is
"an experience to dent the deepest wallet"; the cooking generally
– but not invariably – measures up. / **Sample dishes:** assiette of foie
gras; venison with chocolate & coffee jus; chocolate & orange tart with citrus confit.
Details: www.seaham-hall.com; 9.30 pm; no smoking. **Accommodation:** 19
rooms, from £175.*

SEAVIEW, ISLE OF WIGHT   2–4D

Seaview Hotel   £ 36   A ★

High St PO34 5EX   (01983) 612711

*This "personal" and traditional "family-friendly" hotel is
consistently praised by reporters, not least for its "great food" and
its "wonderful", "cosy" setting. / **Sample dishes:** hot crab ramekin;
monkfish wrapped in Parma ham with crab bisque; blackcurrant sorbet with forest
fruits. **Details:** www.seaviewhotel.co.uk; 9.30 pm, closed Sun D; no smoking area;
children: 5+ at D. **Accommodation:** 16 rooms, from £105.*

SELLACK, HEREFORDSHIRE   2–1B

The Lough Pool Inn   £ 36

HR9 6LX   (01989) 730236

*"London's loss was Herefordshire's gain", say fans of Stephen
Bull's rural inn, praised by many reporters for its "beautiful" and
"distinctive" cooking; rising prices, however, are disenchanting
some former devotees, and some accounts this year have been of
"forgettable" meals. / **Sample dishes:** butternut squash risotto; roast
monkfish with curried red lentil salsa; warm ginger cake with brown bread ice cream.
Details: 9.30 pm; no Amex; no smoking; booking: max 8 at weekends.*

SELLING, KENT   3–3C

White Lion   £ 35   ★

The St ME13 9RQ   (01227) 752211

*After an 'escape' to France that didn't work out, the former
owners of local favourite, the Albion Tavern, have now returned to
run this rural gastropub; their "interesting" cooking is praised by
all reporters. / **Details:** 9.30 pm; no Amex; no smoking.*

SHEFFIELD, SOUTH YORKSHIRE   5–2C

Bahn Nah   £ 26

19-21 Nile St S10 2PN   (0114) 268 4900

*The odd misfire notwithstanding, a reputation for cooking of
"unwavering quality" ensures that this local-favourite Thai can get
pretty crowded. / **Details:** www.bahnnah.co.uk; on A57 from Sheffield to
Manchester; 10.30 pm; D only, closed Sun; no smoking.*

Blue Room Brasserie   £ 36   A ★

798 Chesterfield Rd S8 0SG   (0114) 255 2004

*Especially "for business entertainment", this "spacious"
Woodseats spot is a consistent tip from local reporters; the
volume of commentary isn't huge, but all say the food is "a treat".
/ **Details:** 10 pm; D only, closed Mon & Sun; no Amex; no smoking area.*

Candy Town Chinese   £ 20   ★
27 London Rd S2 4LA   (0114) 272 5315
*"A proper oriental buzz" helps make this a "top" local Chinese;
its "very good-value set meals" help make it "ideal for large
parties".* / **Details:** *11 pm; no smoking area.*

Kashmir Curry Centre   £ 13
123 Spital Hill S4 7LD   (0114) 272 6253
*"It does exactly what it says on the tin" – this "dreary"-looking
Indian has a big name locally as a "cheap and cheerful"
destination, and gets pretty "crowded" as a result.* / **Details:** *midnight;
D only, closed Sun; no credit cards; no smoking area.*

Marco @ Milano   £ 30   ⒶÐ★
Archer Rd S8 0LA   (0114) 235 3080
*"At last, a restaurant Sheffield can be proud of", says one of the
many fans of this "authentic" Italian (in a former police station),
where "the freshest food is cooked simply and with care".*
/ **Sample dishes:** *spicy mussel & cannelloni bean soup; lamb with Gorgonzola
polenta; chocolate fudge cake with raspberry sorbet.*
Details: *www.marco@milano.co.uk; 11.30 pm; D only, closed Mon & Sun;
no Amex; no smoking.*

Nirmals   £ 24
189-193 Glossop Rd S10 2GW   (0114) 272 4054
*Fans still applaud Mrs Nirmal Gupta's "extremely good, freshly-
cooked Indian cuisine", at this institution of over two decades'
standing; critics, however, say it's "getting to feel down-at-heel"
nowadays, and is "becoming predictable".* / **Details:** *near West St;
midnight, Fri & Sat 1 am; closed Sun L; no smoking area.*

Nonna's   £ 33   Ⓐ★
539-541 Eccleshall Rd S11 8PR   (0114) 268 6166
*With its "noisy and busy ambience, strong fresh coffee and Italian
TV in the background" – this "buzzing" café/restaurant still
captures local hearts and minds; all Italian eating options are
catered for, be it an espresso, antipasti or a full meal.*
/ **Sample dishes:** *chilli tuna carpaccio with rocket; polenta with Italian sausage &
roast tomatoes; vanilla & lemon cream with plums.* **Details:** *www.nonnas.co.uk; M1,
J33 towards Bakewell; 9.45 pm; no Amex; no smoking area.*

Rafters   £ 36   ★
220 Oakbrook Rd, Nether Green S11 7ED
(0114) 230 4819
*A strong local fan club proclaims Marcus Lane's "special" cooking
– at his intimate and brightly-decorated modern venture – simply
a "gastronomic delight".* / **Sample dishes:** *twice-baked Cheddar soufflé; rack
of lamb with smoked aubergine caviar; baked apple bread & butter pudding.*
Details: *www.raftersrestaurant.co.uk; 10 pm; D only, closed Tue & Sun; children:
7+.*

Richard Smith at Thyme   £ 36
32-34 Sandygate Rd S10 5RY   (0114) 266 6096
*When it comes to modern bistro-style dining, Richard Smith is
something of a local hero, and supporters say his main operation
is "still excellent"; however, the pressures of opening a (generally
well-received) café offshoot (at 490-492 Glossop Rd, Broomhill)
seem to have dented ratings.* / **Sample dishes:** *smoked salmon & haddock
with cucumber gazpacho; Tuscan veal casserole with polenta mash; sticky toffee
pudding & toffee sauce.* **Details:** *www.thymeforfood.co.uk; 9.30 pm; no smoking.*

Zing Vaa £28
55 The Moor S1 4PF (0114) 275 6633
A "reliable" Chinese that's "jammed full" for Sunday dim sum,
attracting an encouraging proportion of oriental customers.
/ **Details:** www.freespace.virgin.net/zingvaa.rest; 11.30 pm; no smoking area.

SHELLEY, WEST YORKSHIRE 5–2C

Three Acres £38 🅐★★
Roydhouse HD8 8LR (01484) 602606
"The only problem is its deserved popularity!" – this "welcoming"
gastropub, near the Emley Moor TV mast, is always "very busy" –
you "need to book" to enjoy its "exceedingly good" cooking (with
fish a highlight); the "attractive adjacent deli" is also something of
a local institution. / **Sample dishes:** oxtail & spring vegetable terrine; chicken
with pak choy in sweet & sour sauce; meringue with muscat poached fruits.
Details: www.3acres.com; near Emley Moor TV tower; 9.45 pm; closed Sat L.
Accommodation: 20 rooms, from £75.

SHEPPERTON, SURREY 3–3A

Edwinns £36
Church Rd TW17 9JT (01932) 223543
"Reliable Anglo-French cooking" – "well cooked and presented",
and in "large portions" – makes this "well run" modern bistro a
"consistent" choice. / **Sample dishes:** char-grilled artichoke with Parmesan
crisps; crispy duck with Thai vegetables; lemon & ginger steamed sponge.
Details: www.edwinns.co.uk; opp church & Anchor Hotel; 9.50 pm, Fri & Sat
10.30 pm; closed Sat L & Sun D; no smoking area.

SHEPTON MALLET, SOMERSET 2–3B

Charlton House £62
Charlton Rd BA4 4PR (01749) 342008
This "Mulberry-owned and -decorated" country house hotel dining
room continues to inspire rather mixed reports, ranging from
"very pleasing" (the majority view) to "hyped" and "ordinary" (a
not insignificant minority). / **Sample dishes:** salt beef terrine with cumin
seed bread; bream with smoked salmon & leek tart; raspberry tart with spicy praline
mousse. **Details:** www.charltonhouse.com; on A361 towards Frome; 9.30 pm;
no smoking. **Accommodation:** 17 rooms, from £155.

SHERE, SURREY 3–3A

Kinghams £38 🅐★
Gomshall Ln GU5 9HE (01483) 202168
A "good-quality country restaurant" that wins consistent praise
across the board – for its "lovely 16th-century setting", for its
"obliging" service, and (last but not least) its "fabulous" modern
British cooking. / **Sample dishes:** seared scallops with pea & bacon patties;
roast lamb with sweet potato mash; chocolate pudding with espresso sauce.
Details: www.kinghams-restaurant.co.uk; off A25 between Dorking & Guildford;
9 pm; closed Mon & Sun D; no smoking.

SHINFIELD, BERKSHIRE   2–2D
L'Ortolan   £ 84

Church Ln RG2 9BY
(0118) 988 8500
*Would he, wouldn't he?…; after much vacillation (and an abortive
spell at Chewton Glen), Alan Murchison finally returned to help re-
open this famed site in a former rectory in late-2004; let's hope
he can maintain the "exceptional" standard that he previously
achieved here.* / **Sample dishes:** crab blinis & caviar; roast sea bass with Thai
shellfish; passion fruit tart with mango sorbet. **Details:** www.lortolan.com; 9.30 pm;
closed Mon & Sun; no smoking.

SHIPLEY, WEST YORKSHIRE   5–1C
Aagrah   £ 22   ★

4 Saltaire Rd BD18 3HN   (01274) 530880
*A top outlet of this "upmarket" and "excellent" Yorkshire curry-
house chain; "children are always made very welcome".*
/ **Details:** www.aagrah.com; 11 pm; no smoking area.

SHREWSBURY, SHROPSHIRE   5–3A
Cromwells Hotel   £ 30

11 Dogpole SY1 1EN   (01743) 361440
*"Fun", "simple", "intimate", "varied" – this town-centre inn has
no great pretensions, but its individualistic style helps it stand out
in a too thinly provided for town.* / **Sample dishes:** baked aubergine &
goats cheese; Cajun seafood sausages; rhubarb tart with ginger custard.
Details: www.cromwellsinn.com; opp Guildhall; 10 pm; no smoking.
Accommodation: 6 rooms, from £60.

SIDMOUTH, DEVON   2–4A
Swan Inn   £ 20

37 York St EX10 8BY   (01395) 512849
"A value-for-money pub", where "good seafood" is a highlight.
/ **Details:** 8.45 pm; no credit cards.

SKENFRITH, MONMOUTHSHIRE   2–1B
Bell   £ 41   𝔸★

NP7 8UH   (01600) 750235
*"Fresh food from local ingredients" helps make this riverside inn –
"superbly sited by a ruined castle" – "a real find"; it has "a very
good location for gentle and not-so-gentle walks".*
/ **Sample dishes:** whole globe artichoke with hollandaise; pork tenderloin with
shallot mash; cherry & cashew frangipane tart. **Details:** www.skenfrith.co.uk; on
B4521, 10m NE of Abergavenny; 9.30 pm; closed Mon (Nov-Mar only); no smoking.
Accommodation: 8 rooms, from £95.

SLEAT, ISLE OF SKYE   9–2A
Kinloch Lodge   £ 52

IV43 8QY   (01471) 833333
*Fans say it's "always unforgettable" to dine at Lord Macdonald
of Macdonald's former hunting lodge, and to be cooked for by
Lady M herself; others, though, have found it "slightly below its
reputation", or even simply "ordinary".* / **Sample dishes:** smoked Skye
salmon with lime & cucumber; roast rack of lamb with oatmeal stuffing; ginger
steamed sponge. **Details:** www.kinloch-lodge.co.uk; D only (closed weekdays in
winter); no smoking. **Accommodation:** 14 rooms, from £50.

SNAPE, SUFFOLK   3–1D

The Crown Inn   £30
Bridge Rd IP17 1SL   (01728) 688324
*There were rather up-and-down reports this year on this "lively"
rural inn – on most accounts, it serves "reliable" scoff, but there
were also those finding it "missed the mark".* / **Sample dishes:** coarse
game pâté with chutney; scallops with lemon couscous & spiced sauce; sticky toffee
pudding. **Details:** off A12 towards Aldeburgh; 9 pm; no Amex; no smoking; children:
14+. **Accommodation:** 3 rooms, from £70.

SNETTISHAM, NORFOLK   6–4B

Rose & Crown   £35
Old Church Rd PE31 7LX   (01485) 541382
*It looks good – a thatched tavern, part of which dates from the
13th century – but the occasional reporter feels let down by the
interior of this dining pub; even doubters, though, commend the
"delicious" cooking, with "fresh fish" a highlight.*
/ **Sample dishes:** grilled smoked salmon in vinaigrette; fillet of bream & mussels jus;
almond tart. **Details:** www.roseandcrownsnettisham.co.uk; 9.30 pm; no Amex;
no smoking area. **Accommodation:** 11 rooms, from £90.

SOLIHULL, WEST MIDLANDS   5–4C

Beau Thai   £28   ★
761 Old Lode Ln B92 8JE   (0121) 743 5355
*"One of the longest-established Thais in the West Midlands, and
still the best"; its "freshly-cooked" fare is heartily praised by all
reporters, and its "recent make-over" has "improved the
atmosphere tremendously".* / **Details:** www.beauthai.co.uk; 10 pm; closed
Mon L, Sat L & Sun; no smoking area.

SONNING ON THAMES, WOKINGHAM   2–2D

The French Horn   £71
RG4 6TN   (0118) 969 2204
*It exudes a certain "old-school" charm and – with its "stunning"
riverside location – this "relaxed" and "elegant" fixture is still
hailed by many as "tops for romance" (or "for the impressive wine
list"); doubters, however, say: "prices seem elevated just for the
sake of it".* / **Sample dishes:** scallops in bacon with creamed pea soup; rack of
lamb with olive jus; poached pear with chocolate sorbet.
Details: www.thefrenchhorn.co.uk; M4, J8 or J9, then A4; 9.30 pm; booking:
max 10. **Accommodation:** 21 rooms, from £140.

SOUTH SHIELDS, TYNE & WEAR   8–2B

Marsden Grotto   £36   Ⓐ
Coast Rd NE34 7BS   (0191) 455 6060
*This "amazing seafood restaurant overlooking Marsden Beach"
has an outstanding location; "the food is very average, though,
despite the not-so-average prices".* / **Sample dishes:** pan-fried scallops
with lemon, mint & toasted pine nut salad; wild salmon with samphire fresh pasta &
tomato sauce; toasted brioche with summer berries. **Details:** 11.30 pm; closed
Mon & Sun in Summer, open only Fri & Sat D in Winter.

SOUTHALL, GREATER LONDON   3–3A
Gifto's Lahore Karahi   £ 17   ★
162-164 The Broadway, UB1 1NN   (020) 8813 8669
*Though refurbished last year, this "vast" and "always bustling"
fixture is still largely "devoid of style or ambience"; no one seems
to care, though, when it serves such "excellent grilled and
tandoori dishes and breads", and at "very low prices".*
/ **Details:** www.gifto.com; 11.45 pm.

SOUTHAMPTON, SOUTHAMPTON   2–3D
Kuti's   £ 28
37-39 Oxford St SO14 3DP   (023) 8022 1585
*"Kuti's deserves its reputation as a fine Indian, or, to be more
accurate, Bangladeshi": this popular spot remains "as reliable as
ever" and one of the best options in this direly-served city.*
/ **Details:** www.kutis.co.uk; near Ocean Village; midnight.

SOUTHEND-ON-SEA, ESSEX   3–3C
Pipe of Port   £ 25
84 High St SS1 1JN   (01702) 614606
*"No-nonsense" food (with "great wines") commends this '70s
wine bar to most, if not quite all, reporters.* / **Sample dishes:** herrings
with creamed Stilton dressing; pork, plum & celery pie; ginger cheesecake with
orange syrup. **Details:** www.pipeofport.com; Basement just off High Street;
10.15 pm; closed Sun; no Amex; no smoking area; children: 16+.

SOUTHPORT, MERSEYSIDE   5–1A
Auberge Brasserie   £ 32
1b Seabank Rd PR9 0EW   (01704) 530671
*It doesn't please all reporters, but this "buzzing" "French-biased"
venture has expanded in recent times (so presumably must be
getting something right).* / **Sample dishes:** hot duck & apple salad; lemon
sole with prawn & dill mousse; chocolate & basil marquise.
Details: www.auberge-brasserie.com; 10.30 pm; no smoking area.

Warehouse Brasserie   £ 32
30 West St PR8 1QN   (01704) 544662
*A "popular" and "modern" destination that's "easily the best
place in town"; "friendly" staff deliver "reliably good" fare.*
/ **Sample dishes:** Lebanese mezze; grilled chicken with smoked cheese & leek
risotto; chocolate & honeycomb torte. **Details:** www.warehouse-brasserie.co.uk;
10.15 pm; closed Sun.

SOUTHWOLD, SUFFOLK   3–1D
The Crown   £ 32
High Street IP18 6DP   (01502) 722275
*"It needs a bomb under it to get it back to where it was" –
reports on this "crowded" Adnams-owned tavern continue to
decline; there are some suggestions that a new chef is helping get
things back on track, however, and you can always seek
consolation in the "excellent selection of fairly-priced wines".*
/ **Sample dishes:** Norfolk crab with potato salad; cod tempura with sweet potato
chips; apple & cinnamon tart. **Details:** www.adnams.co.uk; 9.30 pm, Fri & Sat
10 pm; no Amex; no smoking; children: 5+ after 7 pm. **Accommodation:** 14
rooms, from £116.

The Swan   £36   🄰
The Market Pl IP18 6EG   (01502) 722186
Reporters prize the slightly "formal" style of this "old-fashioned" grand hotel dining room; these days, the cooking contains "no surprises", but is generally "well done" and there's also the indubitable attraction of "that great Adnams wine list".
/ **Sample dishes:** seared tuna with Niçoise style salad; roast lemon chicken; caramelised lemon tart. **Details:** www.adnams.co.uk; 9 pm; no Amex; no smoking; children: 5+ at D. **Accommodation:** 42 rooms, from £130.

SOWERBY BRIDGE, WEST YORKSHIRE   5–1C

Gimbals   £32   🄰★
Wharf St HX6 2AF   (01422) 839329
This "small bistro" has a big name locally, and all reports are a hymn of praise to its "superb" food, its "very accommodating" service and its "relaxed" atmosphere. / **Sample dishes:** Dolcelatte & mushroom open lasagne; mustard-glazed pork with parsnip mash; bread & butter pudding. **Details:** 9.15 pm; D only, closed Tue; no Amex; no smoking.

The Millbank   £35   ★
Millbank HX6 3DY   (01422) 825588
"Delicious food", "decent ale" and a "pleasant ambience" make it well worth braving the "perilous" approach to this Pennine gastropub. / **Sample dishes:** pea soup with potato & ham dumplings; lamb with artichoke & chestnuts in pastry; Yorkshire parkin with toffee apple mousse. **Details:** www.themillbank.com; 9.30 pm; closed Mon & Sun D; no Amex; no smoking.

SPARSHOLT, HAMPSHIRE   2–3D

Plough Inn   £32
SO21 2NW   (01962) 776353
It's "a pity you have to book, even for a Monday lunchtime", but that's the worst anyone has to say against this "beautifully-located" inn. / **Sample dishes:** grilled goats cheese with herb croutons; roast pork in smoked bacon, apricot & ginger sauce; pear Condé with chocolate sauce. **Details:** 9 pm, Fri & Sat 9.30 pm; no Amex; no smoking area.

SPEEN, BUCKINGHAMSHIRE   3–2A

Old Plow   £40
Flowers Bottom Ln HP27 0PZ   (01494) 488300
"Charming" service wins particular praise for this family-run bistro and restaurant, in a converted pub; the food is often "nice" too, though its style can seem a bit "dated". / **Sample dishes:** game terrine with redcurrant & beetroot preserve; goats cheese, leek & Stilton tart; caramel tart with coffee sauce. **Details:** www.yeoldplough.co.uk; 20 mins from M40, J4 towards Princes Risborough; 8.45 pm; closed Mon, Sat L & Sun D; no smoking.

ST ALBANS, HERTFORDSHIRE   3–2A

Claude's Crêperie   £22   ★
15 Holywell Hill   (01727) 846424
"Worth a special trip if you're a pancake-lover", this "dark" little place is also hailed as quite a "romantic" destination (and with "excellent" wines). / **Details:** 9.30 pm; closed Mon, Tue-Fri D only, Sat & Sun open L & D; no Amex.

La Cosa Nostra £22

62 Lattimore Rd AL1 3XR (01727) 832658
*"Good Italian food" and reasonable prices makes this jolly local a handy stand-by. / **Sample dishes:** grilled aubergine salad; spaghetti with garlic & parsley; tiramisu. **Details:** near railway station; 11 pm; closed Sat L & Sun.*

Darcy's £38 ★

2 Hatfield Rd AL1 3RP (01727) 730777
*"A very good, two-year-old all-rounder", which is already widely hailed as "St Albans's best", thanks to its "interesting and well-executed food" and its "friendly service". / **Sample dishes:** duck spring roll with sweet chilli sauce & cucumber salad; chicken breast with Mozzarella & pesto wrapped in Prosciutto; Amaretti baked peaches & vanilla bean ice cream. **Details:** www.darcysrestaurant.co.uk; 9.30 pm; no smoking.*

St Michael's Manor £46 🄰

Fishpool St AL3 4RY (01727) 864444
*A "good, if pricey" hotel restaurant, where the "lovely" conservatory – "looking down over gardens to the river" – is the top place to dine. / **Sample dishes:** marinated saffron noodles with crayfish, asparagus & mango lime coulis; red mullet & ham with cous cous; blackberry & almond tart. **Details:** www.stmichaelsmanor.com; nr Cathedral; 9 pm; no smoking. **Accommodation:** 22 rooms, from £170.*

Sukiyaki £23

6 Spencer St AL3 5EG (01727) 865009
*An "attentive" owner breathes life into this "minimalist" (going on "sterile") Japanese of ten years' standing, where the cooking is "consistent" and "inexpensive". / **Details:** 10 pm; closed Mon & Sun; children: no babies, no children after 7.30 pm.*

The Waffle House
Kingsbury Water Mill £20 🄰

St Michael's St AL3 4SJ (01727) 853502
*"A fun place for brunch, if you're feeling greedy and especially if you have children in tow" – this self-explanatory joint is prettily located, in an old mill overlooking the river. / **Sample dishes:** chunky vegetable soup; ham, cheese & mushroom waffle; banana & butterscotch waffle. **Details:** near Roman Museum; L only; no Amex; no smoking; no booking.*

ST ANDREWS, FIFE 9–3D

Seafood Restaurant £47 🄰★

The Scores KY16 9AB
(01334) 479475
*This "very modern sparkling glass box, hidden in the dunes right across from the Royal & Ancient" is one of the most striking restaurants to have opened in Britain in recent years (and it has "fantastic sea views", too); on most reports, the "outstanding" cooking matches up. / **Details:** www.theseafoodrestaurant.com; 9.30 pm; no smoking.*

Vine Leaf Garden £36 ★

131 South St KY16 9UN (01334) 477497
*"Booking is always essential", at the Hamilton family's popular "Scottish-Mediterranean" (!), where Mrs H's "rich" cuisine is complemented by mein host's "good and personal" wine list. / **Sample dishes:** Indian-spiced prawns with mini poppadoms; venison with mushroom, brandy & peppercorn soup; brown sugar pavlova with strawberries. **Details:** www.vineleafstandrews.co.uk; 9.30 pm; D only, closed Mon & Sun; no smoking. **Accommodation:** 2 rooms, from £80.*

ST HELENS, ISLE OF WIGHT   2–4D

Baywatch On The Beach   £ 29   A
The Waterfront PO33 IXX   (01983) 873259
*A beach café by day, this becomes "a top-class seafood restaurant
by night"; it offers "nothing special… apart from its location and
its food!" / Details: www.bay-watch.co.uk; 8.45 pm; closed Sun D; no Amex;
no smoking; children: no children after 7.30 pm.*

ST IVES, CORNWALL   1–4A

Blue Fish   £ 38   A★
Norway Ln TR26 ILZ   (01736) 794204
*"Interesting" cooking (with "good seafood" a highlight) and a
"pleasant" setting make this arts-centre restaurant an "excellent"
destination for all who comment on it. / Sample dishes: shrimps in
garlic; chicken & goats cheese salad; chocolate ganache. Details: behind the Sloop
Inn; 9.30 pm; no Amex; no smoking.*

Pedn Olva Hotel   £ 42   A
The Warren, Porthminster Beach TR26 2EA 2EA
(01736) 796222
*A "fine location", with "stunning" sea views, is the star attraction
of this waterside hotel – dining is also "fine", though, with the
menu usually "interesting" and "well prepared". / Details: 8.45 pm;
no smoking; children: 8+ after 7 pm. Accommodation: 30 rooms, from £136.*

Porthgwidden Beach Café   £ 29   A★
TR26 ISL   (01736) 796791
*The more informal sister establishment of the Porthminster Café,
"overlooking a small and attractive beach"; "very good
breakfasts" are a star feature. / Details: www.restaurantsstives.co.uk;
10 pm; closed in Winter; no Amex; no smoking; booking: max 10.*

Porthminster Café   £ 35   A★
Porthminster Beach TR26 2EB   (01736) 795352
*A "perfect" setting "right on the beach" – and with a "well-
designed terrace" – helps win numerous rave reviews for this
seaside fixture; "helpful" staff and "fine" fish complete a winning
package. / Sample dishes: grilled scallops & goats cheese; turbot with braised
leeks; chocolate pudding with orange ice cream.
Details: www.porthminstercafe.co.uk; near railway station; 10 pm; closed Nov-Mar;
no Amex; no smoking.*

The Seafood Café   £ 32   ★
45 Fore St TR26 IHE
(01736) 794004
*It offers "no frills", but this "modern, light and vibrant" venture –
where you "view your fish at the counter, and choose the
accompanying sauce" – is widely hailed by reporters as a "top
concept". / Sample dishes: Cornish shellfish; catch of the day with seasonal
vegetables; sticky toffee pudding. Details: www.seafoodcafe.co.uk; map on website;
10.30 pm; no Amex; no smoking area.*

ST KEYNE, CORNWALL   1–3C

The Well House   £46   🄰★
PL14 4RN   (01579) 342001
*It may be "in the middle of nowhere", but it's worth seeking out
this "quiet" country house hotel dining room – it's just "very good
all round".* / **Sample dishes:** *ham terrine with pineapple tart; vanilla-seared
bream with Swiss chard; pecan tart with coffee bean ice cream.*
Details: *www.wellhouse.co.uk; half way between Liskeard & Looe off the B3254;
8.30 pm; no Amex; no smoking; booking essential at L; children: 8+ at D.*
Accommodation: *9 rooms, from £115.*

ST MARGARETS AT CLIFFE, KENT   3–3D

Walletts Court   £50
Westcliffe CT15 6EW   (01304) 852424
*"Near the edge of the cliffs", "lovely" gardens are an undoubted
plus of this "upmarket" country house hotel; views on the food are
split, though – from "superb" to "mediocre".* / **Sample dishes:** *grilled
squid with blackened green peppers; partridge stuffed with game parfait; crème
brûlée with raspberries.* **Details:** *www.wallettscourt.com; on B2058 towards Deal,
3m NE of Dover; 9 pm; closed Mon L & Sat L; no smoking; children: 8+, no children
after 8 pm.* **Accommodation:** *16 rooms, from £90.*

ST MAWES, CORNWALL   1–4B

Hotel Tresanton   £45   🄰
27 Lower Castle Rd TR2 5DR   (01326) 270055
*"Great views" help make this fashionable hotel restaurant (and
especially its terrace) "the best place to eat on the south Cornish
coast", for some reporters (and certainly the trendiest); "ordinary"
meals, however, are not unknown.* / **Sample dishes:** *Gorgonzola &
spinach tart; roast John Dory with saffron gnocchi; honey fritters with lemon ricotta.*
Details: *www.tresanton.com; near Castle; 9.30 pm; no smoking area; booking:
max 10; children: 8+.* **Accommodation:** *29 rooms, from £165.*

Rising Sun   £38
The Square TR2 5DJ   (01326) 270233
*"A good gastropub-with-rooms", where you can dine at the bar or
more formally in the restaurant; it numbers among its attractions
"attentive" service and "a wide range of reasonably priced wines".*
/ **Sample dishes:** *smoked salmon kedgeree & quails egg; ballotine of duck;
raspberry oatmeal meringue.* **Details:** *www.risingsunstmawes.com; 8.30 pm; D only,
except Sun open L & D; no Amex; no smoking.* **Accommodation:** *8 rooms,
from £130.*

ST MERRYN, CORNWALL   1–3B

Ripleys   £50   ★
PL28 8NQ   (01841) 520179
*"Simple, beautifully-cooked food" (with fish a speciality) is the
theme of most feedback on Paul Ripley's ambitious three-year-old
near Newquay Airport; some reporters, however, find the
ambience "lacking".* / **Sample dishes:** *twice-baked goat cheese soufflé; roast
monkfish with mussels & clam chowder; hot chocolate fondant with banana ice
cream.* **Details:** *9.30 pm; closed Sun & Mon, D only Tue-Sat; no Amex; no smoking;
booking: max 8.*

ST MONANS, FIFE   9–4D
Seafood Restaurant   **£38**   A★
16 West End KY10 2BX   (01333) 730327
*You get "great food, great views, and a great time", at this seaside
venture (which now has a sibling in St Andrews); even those who
gripe that the menu is a bit "static" admit that "you get the
freshest fish".* / **Sample dishes:** *seared sea bass with truffle & herb risotto;
roast cod fillet with bacon mash, spinach, onion ice cream & garlic sauce; pineapple
tarte Tatin with coconut sorbet.* **Details:** *www.theseafoodrestaurant.com; 9.30 pm;
closed Mon & Sun D in Winter; no smoking.*

STADDLEBRIDGE, NORTH YORKSHIRE   8–4C
McCoys at the Tontine   **£38**
DL6 3JB   (01609) 882671
*They're still "packing 'em in" ("especially in the downstairs
bistro"), but quite a few reporters feel this local institution of a
quarter century's standing is "going downhill", and note
"indifferent" service and "complacent" standards generally.*
/ **Sample dishes:** *grilled black pudding with beetroot sauce; salmon & mussels with
langoustine butter; sticky toffee pudding.* **Details:** *www.mccoysatthetontine.co.uk;
junction of A19 & A172; 10 pm; bistro L & D every day, restaurant Sat D only.*
Accommodation: *6 rooms, from £100.*

STADHAMPTON, OXFORDSHIRE   2–2D
Crazy Bear   **£47**   A
Bear Ln OX44 7UR   (01865) 890714
*If you're looking for "martini, oysters, champagne, strawberries,
candlelight…" – well, you get the picture – this "secret hide-
away" inn may be just the place; even non-romantics may delight
in its eccentric charms, and "the choice of English or Thai menus
adds interest".* / **Sample dishes:** *Roquefort soufflé with pears & walnuts; roast
duck with cider braised potatoes; warm chocolate cake.*
Details: *www.crazybearhotel.co.uk; 10 pm.* **Accommodation:** *12 rooms,
from £110.*

STAITHES, NORTH YORKSHIRE   8–3C
Endeavour   **£35**   A★★
1 High St TS13 5BH
(01947) 840825
*"Fantastic fish", "wonderful seafood" and "sublime puddings"
again win consistent praise for Brian Kay & Charlotte Willoughby's
former fisherman's cottage; service, however, can be rather
variable.* / **Sample dishes:** *parsnip & orange soup; fillet steak with foie gras
butter; iced Drambuie mousse.* **Details:** *www.endeavour-restaurant.co.uk; 10m N of
Whitby, off A174; 9 pm; D only, closed Mon & Sun; no smoking.*
Accommodation: *3 rooms, from £65.*

STAMFORD, LINCOLNSHIRE   6–4A
The George Hotel   **£44**   A
St Martins PE9 2LB   (01780) 750750
*"A most welcome halt on the long road north"; this grand and
famous coaching inn offers a "smooth" and "amazingly
atmospheric" setting (in either the panelled dining room or in the
courtyard summer brasserie); the food is "sound" rather than
spectacular, and the wine "well priced".* / **Sample dishes:** *chicken &
wild mushroom sausage with lentils; pork & tarragon mustard in filo pastry; British
cheeses.* **Details:** *www.georgehotelofstamford.com; off A1, 14m N of Peterborough,
onto B1081; 10.30 pm; jacket & tie required; no smoking; children: 7+ at D.*
Accommodation: *47 rooms, from £110.*

STANTON, SUFFOLK   3–1C

Leaping Hare Vineyard   £38
Wyken Vineyards IP31 2DW   (01359) 250287
*It has a "fantastic location in an ancient barn", so it's a great
shame that this once-admirable country restaurant at a well-
known winery continues to decline – the "expensive" dishes are
sometimes "poorly cooked", and service can be "very slow";
perhaps the new chef (June 2004) will buck things up.*
/ **Sample dishes:** *tempura courgette flowers stuffed with Thai crab; vine-smoked
guinea fowl with bacon mash; apricot sorbet.* **Details:** *9m NE of Bury St Edmunds;
follow tourist signs off A143; 9 pm; L only, except Fri & Sat when L & D; no Amex;
no smoking.*

STATHERN, LEICESTERSHIRE   5–3D

Red Lion Inn   £29   ★
2 Red Lion St LE14 4HS
(01949) 860868
*The ambience can "vary" (as can the service), but this village inn
near Belvoir Castle has rapidly – like its sibling the Olive Branch at
Clipsham – carved out a strong reputation for "above-average"
cuisine; there's also an "excellent choice of wines".*
/ **Sample dishes:** *peppered beef salsa with rocket & Stilton; Lincolnshire sausages
with sage mash & onion gravy; apple pie with cream.*
Details: *www.theredlioninn.co.uk; 9.30 pm; closed Sun D; no Amex; no smoking.*

STOCKBRIDGE, HAMPSHIRE   2–3D

Greyhound   £42   ★
31 High St SO20 6EY   (01264) 810833
*This "modern rustic" boozer has made quite a name, but even
fans concede it has been through a "rocky patch" of late; the food
is still generally hailed as "interesting" (if "pricey"), but service can
be "amateurish", and the décor strikes some as "disappointing".*
/ **Details:** *10 pm; closed Sun D; no Amex; no smoking area; booking: max 12.*
Accommodation: *8 rooms, from £70.*

STOCKCROSS, BERKSHIRE   2–2D

Vineyard at Stockcross   £75
RG20 8JU   (01635) 528770
*"You need the manager, just to get you to the right page on the
list", at this ambitious Californian-style restaurant-with-rooms,
where œnophile owner Sir Peter Michael's "stunning" wine
selection (especially US) is of real note; the cuisine is "not
exceptional", though, and service can be "awful".*
/ **Sample dishes:** *pressed chicken & foie gras terrine; roast sea bass with butter
bean purée; warm chocolate fondant.* **Details:** *www.the-vineyard.co.uk; from M4,
J13 take A34 towards Hungerford; 9 pm; no smoking.* **Accommodation:** *49 rooms,
from £200.*

STOCKLAND, DEVON   2–4A

Kings Arms Inn   £28   ★
EX14 9BS   (01404) 881361
*"John the manager is a perfect host", and he crops up quite
frequently in reports on this thatched former coaching inn; fans
say the cooking is "excellent", too.* / **Details:** *www.kingsarms.net; 9 pm;
no Amex.* **Accommodation:** *3 rooms, from £60.*

STOKE BRUERNE, NORTHAMPTONSHIRE   2–1D

Bruerne's Lock   £ 39   🅐
5 The Canalside NN12 7SB   (01604) 863654
The appeal of this canalside venture goes beyond its "romantic"
potential – though it induces only limited feedback, its cooking is
consistently praised for its "good value". / *Sample dishes:* deep-fried
quails eggs with pancetta; beef Wellington with port jus; apple & cinnamon crumble.
Details: www.bruerneslock.co.uk; 0.5m off A508 between Northampton & Milton
Keynes; 9 pm; closed Mon & Tue; no smoking; children: no babies Sat D.

STOKE BY NAYLAND, ESSEX   3–2C

Crown   £ 26   🅐★
Pank St CO6 4SE   (01206) 262346
"A bar/pub/restaurant which combines all three functions
effectively" – this "cheerful" venture has "fabulous" décor that
helps create "a sense of occasion"; its cooking is very consistently
praised, too. / *Details:* 9.30 pm, no Amex; no smoking area.

STOKE BY NAYLAND, ESSEX   3–2C

Angel Inn   £ 34
Polstead St CO6 4SA   (01206) 263245
This "nice", "well-run" gastropub generates few complaints…
apart, that is, from the fact that "if you arrive late, it can get too
busy for a comfortable seat". / *Sample dishes:* mushroom & pistachio
pâté; roast pork with apple mousse & red cabbage; raspberry bavarois. *Details:* 5m
W of A12, on B1068; 9.30 pm; no Amex; no smoking area; children: 14+.
Accommodation: 6 rooms, from £67.50.

STOKE HOLY CROSS, NORFOLK   6–4C

Wildebeest Arms   £ 34
Norwich Rd NR14 8QJ   (01508) 492497
"Great food in an unprepossessing location" remains the general
drift of the good number of reports on this "friendly" pub-cum-
restaurant, in a small village. / *Sample dishes:* sautéed calamari with squid
ink risotto; roast lemon & thyme pork fillet; passion fruit tart & rhubarb sorbet.
Details: from A140, turn left at Dunston Hall, left at T-junction; 10 pm; no smoking
area.

STOKE ROW, OXFORDSHIRE   2–2D

The Crooked Billet   £ 38   🅐★
Newlands Ln RG9 5PU   (01491) 681048
It's hidden away "down a potholed track", but it's "worth the
effort" of seeking out this "outstanding" former boozer, which
offers "haute cuisine-style appetisers and hearty main dishes",
plus "a good selection of wines". / *Sample dishes:* onion & pepper tartlet
with Roquefort glaze; gammon hock with Polish sausage & sauerkraut; Bakewell
tart & custard. *Details:* www.thecrookedbillet.co.uk; on A4130; 10 pm; no Amex or
Switch.

STONEHAVEN, ABERDEEN   9–3D
Lairhillock Inn   £ 27   ★
Netherley AB39 3QS   (01569) 730001
*This "culinary oasis in the foodie desert of north east Scotland"
was back on steadier form this year; a cosy pub and (pricier)
dining room, it "can source some of the finest meat anywhere in
the UK", and there's "good local fish", too. / Sample dishes: chunky
seafood chowder; wild boar sausage with mustard mash; sticky toffee pudding.
Details: www.lairhillock.co.uk; 7m S of Aberdeen; 9.30 pm; no smoking area.*

STOURBRIDGE, WORCESTERSHIRE   5–4B
French Connection   £ 31   𝔸★
3 Coventry St DY8 1EP   (01384) 390940
*As the name hints, there's a "very French" feel to this family-run
venture, whose cosy charms make it well worth knowing about in
a thin area. / Sample dishes: chicken liver, brandy & garlic pâté; baked
pesto-crusted cod; brioche bread & butter pudding.
Details: www.frenchconnectionbistro.co.uk; 9.30 pm; closed Mon, Tue D & Sun;
no smoking.*

STOW ON THE WOLD, GLOUCESTERSHIRE   2–1C
The Royalist (947AD)
Eagle & Child   £ 42
Digbeth St GL54 1BN   (01451) 830670
*The surroundings of this Cotswold inn may be certified ancient
(Guinness Book of Records), but it offers a surprisingly "plain" and
"modern" menu. / Sample dishes: avocado & pine nut salad; crab & cod
cakes with tomato & ginger sauce; caramelised orange & pineapple pancake.
Details: www.theroyalisthotel.co.uk; 9 pm; closed Mon & Sun; no Amex;
no smoking; need 6+ to book; children: 6+. Accommodation: 8 rooms, from £90.*

STRATFORD UPON AVON, WARWICKSHIRE   2–1C
Lambs   £ 34   𝔸
12 Sheep St CV37 6EF   (01789) 292554
*"Popular with tourists and locals alike", this "comfortable" and
"atmospheric" bistro is the best-known place in town, thanks not
least to its "very good-value pre-theatre menu".
/ Sample dishes: crispy duck & watercress salad; roast chicken & mango in lime
butter; banoffi pie. Details: www.lambsrestaurant.co.uk; 10 pm; no Amex; booking:
max 12.*

The Oppo   £ 30
13 Sheep St CV37 6EF   (01789) 269980
*A "reliable", "efficient", and "buzzy" wine bar that makes a
dependable pre-theatre destination. / Sample dishes: Greek salad with
deep-fried halloumi; chorizo & red pepper pizza; tiramisu.
Details: www.theoppo.co.uk; 10.30 pm; no Amex; booking: max 12.*

Russons   £ 32
8 Church St CV37 6HB   (01789) 268822
*As ever, "friendly and reliable" is the gist of commentary on this
town-centre restaurant; as you'd hope, "very good pre-theatre
meals" are a highlight. / Sample dishes: snails in garlic butter with spiced
croutons; monkfish, salmon & bacon brochettes; sticky toffee cheesecake.
Details: 9.30 pm; closed Mon & Sun; no smoking area; booking: max 8; children:
8+ after 7 pm.*

Thai Kingdom £ 28
11 Warwick Rd CV37 6YW (01789) 261103
Even those who say the selection of dishes is "standard", can find the results at this consistent oriental "very good".
/ **Details:** 10.45 pm; no smoking area.

STUCKTON, HAMPSHIRE 2–3C

Three Lions £ 42 ★
Stuckton Rd SP6 2HF (01425) 652489
"The Womersleys' kitchen consistently hits the high notes" at this "high-quality restaurant", in a former inn in the New Forest; the "grannyish" décor, though, strikes some reporters as plain "terrible". / **Sample dishes:** *crab bisque with shrimps; roast roe buck with ceps; hot chocolate pudding.* **Details:** *www.thethreelionsrestaurant.co.uk; 1m E of Fordingbridge off B3078; 9.30 pm; closed Mon & Sun D; no smoking.* **Accommodation:** *4 rooms, from £95.*

STUDLAND, DORSET 2–4C

Shell Bay Seafood £ 38 𝔸★
Ferry Rd BH19 3BA (01929) 450363
"The only thing better than the food is the view"; this unpretentious operation, "right by the lapping waters of Poole Harbour", serves "superb" fresh fish – you "always need to book". / **Sample dishes:** *seared tuna loin with peppercorn crust; grilled sea bass with garlic & rosemary; raspberry & vanilla panna cotta.* **Details:** *www.shellbayrestaurant.co.uk; 9 pm; no smoking; children: 12+ at D.*

STURMINSTER NEWTON, DORSET 2–3B

Plumber Manor £ 38 𝔸
DT10 2AF (01258) 472507
This "imposing country house in lovely grounds" (family-owned for over 30 years) offers "consistent" standards, including a "well-cooked" menu in fairly "traditional" style. / **Sample dishes:** *wild mushroom millefeuille with brandy cream; peppered sirloin steak with mustard sauce; lemon meringue pie.* **Details:** *www.plumbermanor.com; off A357 towards Hazelbury Bryan; 9.30 pm; D only, except Sun open L & D; no smoking.* **Accommodation:** *16 rooms, from £110.*

SUNDERLAND, TYNE & WEAR 8–2C

throwingstones
National Glass Centre £ 25
Liberty Way SR6 0GL (0191) 565 3939
If only all museum cafés offered the "bright and shining experience" of this airy venue, on the banks of the River Wear; its "pleasant" menu offers "a good mix of fare for adults and children". / **Sample dishes:** *roast pepper & Mozzarella salad; salmon with rocket & orange salad; brandy snap with toffee ice cream.* **Details:** *www.nationalglasscentre.com; A19 to Sunderland, follow signs for National Glass Centre; Mon-Thu L only, closed Sun D; no Amex; no smoking.*

SURBITON, SURREY   3–3B

The French Table   £41   ★

85 Maple Rd KT6 4AW   (020) 8399 2365
"A bit of France, in Surrey"; this "buzzy", "classy" and "good-value" venue is consistently praised for its "interesting" cuisine ("well up to London standards"); the only real downside? – the tables are "too close". / **Sample dishes:** mushroom cannelloni with truffle oil; pork stuffed with chorizo mousse & endive; lemon curd ice cream. **Details:** www.thefrenchtable.co.uk; 10.30 pm; closed Mon, Tue-Sat D only, closed Sun D; no Amex; no smoking area; booking: max 10, Fri & Sat.

Joy   £24   ★

37 Brighton Rd KT6 5LR   (020) 8390 3988
"Unusual", "refreshing" and "harmonious" regional Indian cuisine makes this "friendly" two-year-old of more than usual note. / **Details:** www.joy-restaurant.co.uk; 11.30 pm.

SUTTON COLDFIELD, WEST MIDLANDS   5–4C

Boathouse At Bracebridge   £28   A

Bracebridge Pool B74 2YR   (0121) 308 8890
It "overlooks one of the prettiest lakes in this 2,400-acre park", but fortunately this waterside dining room doesn't just rely on its location – it also serves up "quality cooking", with fish a speciality. / **Details:** 10 pm.

SUTTON GAULT, CAMBRIDGESHIRE   3–1B

Anchor   £36   A★

Bury Ln CB6 2BD   (01353) 778537
This "lovely gastropub in a beautiful riverbank spot" is again almost unanimously hailed as "a winner"; service which is "always great" plays its part. / **Sample dishes:** Cornish crab salad with baby leeks; calves liver with Bayonne ham on bacon mushroom mash; warm chocolate mousse. **Details:** www.anchor-inn-restaurant.co.uk; 7m W of Ely, signposted off B1381 in Sutton; 9pm, Sat 9.30 pm; no smoking area. **Accommodation:** 2 rooms, from £62.

SWANSEA, SWANSEA   1–1D

La Braseria   £32

28 Wind St SA1 1DZ   (01792) 469683
This basic Spanish venue (once related to the similarly named Cardiff fixture, and with a similar choose-at-the-counter philosophy) remains a useful stand-by; "now that they have an adjacent wine bar and extension, you don't have to get drunk waiting in the cramped entrance". / **Sample dishes:** devilled chicken livers; halibut Mornay; crème caramel. **Details:** www.labraseria.com; 11.30 pm; closed Sun; need 6+ to book; children: 6+.

Morgans Hotel   £36   ★

Somerset Pl SA1 1RR   (01792) 484848
The "beautifully renovated" former Associated Ports building provides the setting for this ambitious dining room; the place would benefit from "more staff training", but Chris Keenan's "delicious" cooking still generally satisfies nonetheless. / **Sample dishes:** salmon & crab potato cakes with garlic saffron sauce; roast tenderloin of pork bubble with bubble & squeak; pot au chocolat with ice cream. **Details:** www.morganshotel.co.uk; 9.30 pm; no Amex; no smoking. **Accommodation:** 20 rooms, from £100.

PA's Wine Bar £ 30 ★
95 Newton Rd SA3 4BN (01792) 367723
"Fantastic non-fussy cooking at a good price" – with *"excellent fish"* a highlight – wins only praise for this *"real treat"* of a small, traditional wine bar, in the Mumbles. / **Sample dishes:** crispy king prawn won tons; fillet of ostrich served with duo of sauces; banoffi pie. **Details:** www.paswinebar.co.uk; 9.30 pm; closed Sun D.

Patricks £ 35
638 Mumbles Rd SA3 4EA (01792) 360199
Locals still rate this seafront brasserie-with-rooms, on the Mumbles, for its "good, and well-sourced" grub. / **Sample dishes:** feta sorbet with char-grilled watermelon; sesame-crusted pork with satay sauce; cappuccino & chocolate terrine. **Details:** www.patricks-restaurant.co.uk; in Mumbles, 1m before pier; 9.45 pm; closed Sun D; no smoking. **Accommodation:** 8 rooms, from £105.

SWINTON, SCOTTISH BORDERS 8–1A

Wheatsheaf Inn £ 36
Main St TD11 3JJ (01890) 860257
"A delightful and busy pub in the middle of nowhere", where cooking has generally proved *"plain but tasty"*; owners and chef changed this year, though, and reports for the period are very up-and-down. / **Sample dishes:** chicken, spring vegetable & herb broth; beef in claret & cep oil sauce; iced Drambuie parfait. **Details:** www.wheatsheaf-swinton.co.uk; between Kelso & Berwick-upon-Tweed, by village green; 9 pm; closed Mon & Sun D (to non-residents); no Amex; no smoking. **Accommodation:** 7 rooms, from £95.

TADCASTER, NORTH YORKSHIRE 5–1D

Aagrah £ 23 ★
York Rd LS24 8EG (01937) 530888
"Really good Indian food" wins continuing popularity for this busy branch of the eminent Yorkshire subcontinental chain.
/ **Details:** www.aagrah.com; 7m from York on A64; 11.30 pm; D only; no smoking area.

TAPLOW, BERKSHIRE 3–3A

Waldo's
Cliveden House £ 85 Ⓐ
Berry Hl SL6 0JF (01628) 668561
It's no great surprise that a meal at the Astors' "incredible" Thames-side palazzo (now a National Trust property) is a touch "overpriced"; most reporters, however, find a visit to the basement dining room (the grander of its two restaurants) an "unforgettable" experience, with "unobtrusive" service and "simple but exceptionally well-prepared" food. / **Sample dishes:** sea bass poached in champagne; roast partridge with blackcurrant vinegar; fig tartlet with honey ice cream. **Details:** www.clivedenhouse.co.uk; M4, J7 then follow National Trust signs; 9.30 pm; D only, closed Mon & Sun; jacket & tie required; no smoking; booking: max 6; children: 12+. **Accommodation:** 39 rooms, from £190.

TARPORLEY, CHESHIRE   5–2B

Swan   £30   ★
50 High St CW6 0AG   (01829) 733838
*A recent revamp seems to have brushed up more than the décor
at this former coaching inn in a "lovely village", and it offers
"interesting" food and "good" wines. / **Sample dishes:** scallops on puff
pastry; sirloin steak; caramelised rice pudding.
Details: www.theswanhotel-tarporley.co.uk; 9.30 pm; no smoking.
Accommodation: 16 rooms, from £77.*

TAUNTON, SOMERSET   2–3A

Brazz
Castle Hotel   £32   X
Castle Bow TA1 3NF   (01823) 252000
*Some like it as "a place to see and be seen", but most reporters
are harsh in their views on this "slow", "unreliable" and
"unappealing" branch of a small south western chain; it needs to
buck up its ideas, or it's going to follow its Bristol sibling into
oblivion... / **Sample dishes:** walnut & blue cheese salad; sirloin steak with sauce
béarnaise; Eton Mess. **Details:** www.brazz.co.uk; 10.30 pm; no smoking.*

The Castle Hotel   £52
Castle Grn TA1 1NF   (01823) 272671
*"Really good English cooking at reasonable prices" – with
"superior service" too – is lauded by fans of the dining room of
this wisteria-clad landmark hotel; for a place with a rare history as
a culinary 'destination', though, it inspires very few reports these
days and some are of the "faintly disappointing" variety.
/ **Sample dishes:** rabbit pie with mustard dressing; sea bass with truffled macaroni
cheese; golden raisin soufflé. **Details:** www.the-castle-hotel.com; follow tourist
information signs; 9.45 pm; closed Sun D; no smoking. **Accommodation:** 44
rooms, from £165.*

Sanctuary Wine Bar   £29
Middle St TA1 1SJ   (01823) 257788
*"Decent quality, but expensive" – a pretty fair view (from a
London reporter), on this "excellent wine bar/restaurant" (where
some of the dishes are surprisingly ambitious).
/ **Sample dishes:** lemon chicken with veggie crisps & rocket salad; Thai crab cakes
with chilli salsa; chocolate terrine with honey-roasted oranges.
Details: www.sanctuarywinebar.co.uk; 9.30 pm; closed Sat L & Sun; no Amex;
no smoking area.*

Willow Tree   £40   𝔸★
3 Tower Ln TA1 4AR
(01823) 352835
*The "gorgeous" food is "obviously a labour of love for the chef"
(Darren Sherlock), at this "lovely", "tucked-away" yearling; it
comes at very "reasonable" prices, too. / **Sample dishes:** roast pigeon
breaded with bacon & chestnut mushrooms in red wine sauce; sauteed medalions of
monkfish with spaghetti of celeriac carrot; hot mango soufflé with a pricot sauce.
Details: 10 pm; D only, closed Sun & Mon; no Amex; no smoking.*

TETBURY, GLOUCESTERSHIRE   2–2B

Trouble House Inn   £ 40
Cirencester Rd GL8 8SG (01666) 502206
A "proper pub-like ambience" can make this popular
gastroboozer a "lovely" destination; as last year, though, there are
a few too many reports of "bland" or "disappointing" meals for
comfort. / *Sample dishes:* wild mushroom casserole; lemon sole with braised
leeks & mussels; white chocolate cheesecake with lemon ice cream.
Details: www.troublehouse.co.uk; 1.5m from Tetbury on A433 towards Cirencester;
9.30 pm; closed Mon; closed 2 weeks in Jan; no smoking area; booking: max 8;
children: 14+ in bar.

THORNBURY, GLOUCESTERSHIRE   2–2B

Thornbury Castle   £ 57   A★
Castle St BS35 1HH (01454) 281182
A "beautiful" setting and a "fascinating" history add lustre to a
visit to this Tudor landmark hotel; as at a number of other
properties under the same ownership (Von Essen hotels), the food
is "really first-class", too. / *Sample dishes:* pan-fried French quail with
tomato confit; grilled halibut with tomato fondue & caviar cream; pecan & maple
chocolate brownie. *Details:* www.thornburycastle.co.uk; near intersection of M4 &
M5; 9.30 pm, Sat 10 pm; no smoking. *Accommodation:* 25 rooms, from £130.

THORNHAM, NORFOLK   6–3B

Lifeboat Inn   £ 31   A
PE36 6LT (01485) 512236
"Best out-of-season" – it can be "too crowded" otherwise – this
"fine", old worlde inn near the harbour and beach has a name for
its "good fresh food". / *Sample dishes:* Thai crab cakes with capsicum
chutney; lemon sole with crisp capers & prawns; fruit crumble.
Details: www.lifeboatinn.co.uk; 20m from Kings Lynn on A149 coast road; 9.30 pm;
D only, except Sun L only; no Amex; no smoking. *Accommodation:* 14 rooms,
from £76.

THORPE LANGTON, LEICESTERSHIRE   5–4D

Bakers Arms   £ 32   A
Main St LE16 7TS (01858) 545201
This "lovely village pub" maintains a high local profile for its
cuisine; the occasional reporter finds its food in a bit of "a rut",
but most say it's "consistently good". / *Sample dishes:* fresh mussels; sea
bass with sweet potato mash; chocolate tart with caramelised bananas.
Details: near Market Harborough off the A6; 9.30 pm; open only Tue-Fri D, all day
Sat & Sun L; no Amex; no smoking area; children: 12+.

TITLEY, HEREFORDSHIRE   2–1A

Stagg Inn   £ 35   A★★
HR5 3RL (01544) 230221
"This is the stuff that all country pubs should be made of: local
produce, a beautiful setting and a wonderful welcoming
atmosphere"; ex-Gavroche chef Stephen Reynolds's
"unremarkable-looking" boozer seems finally to be living up to the
Michelin-inspired hype that has long surrounded it.
/ *Sample dishes:* mussel & saffron risotto; braised lamb with tomato & tarragon
gravy; treacle tart with clotted cream. *Details:* www.thestagg.co.uk; on B4355, NE
of Kington; 9.30 pm; closed Mon & Sun D; closed 2 weeks in Nov; no Amex;
no smoking area. *Accommodation:* 5 rooms, from £70.

TODMORDEN, WEST YORKSHIRE   5–1B

The Old Hall Restaurant   £ 35   Ⓐ
Hall St OL14 7AD   (01706) 815998
A *"beautiful"* 17th-century (and earlier) building sets the tone at
the Hoyles' town-centre venture; it offers *"good food"* and
"excellent" service, and reporters are unanimous that the place
"deserves more support". / **Sample dishes:** grilled mackerel with potato
cakes; crispy duck & watercress salad; winter berry pavlova. **Details:** 15 mins from
M62; 9 pm, Sat 9.30 pm; closed Mon & Sun D; no Amex; no smoking.

TOPSHAM, DEVON   1–3D

The Galley   £ 47   ★
41 Fore St EX3 0HU   (01392) 876078
It's clearly not inexpensive, but (limited) reports consistently speak
of a *"great experience"* – *"good food in a beautiful setting"* – at
this quirky fish restaurant, overlooking an estuary.
/ **Sample dishes:** deep-fried Thai fishcakes; roast salmon with blinis & mango;
meringues with iced Turkish Delight. **Details:** www.galleyrestaurant.co.uk; 11 pm;
closed Mon & Sun; no smoking; children: 12+. **Accommodation:** 4 rooms,
from £50.

La Petite Maison   £ 37   ★
35 Fore St EX3 0HR   (01392) 873660
"Quality" dishes (albeit from a *"limited"* menu) make this
"stylish", "informal" and *"relaxed"* establishment unanimously
popular with local reporters. / **Sample dishes:** goats cheese soufflé;
medallions of pork; classic crème brûlée. **Details:** 10 pm; closed Mon & Sun;
no Amex; no smoking.

TORCROSS, DEVON   1–4D

Start Bay Inn   £ 22   ★
TQ7 2TQ   (01548) 580553
On a fine day, you get a *"priceless"* experience at this popular
pub – *"sitting on the quay, eating your excellent fish 'n' chips, with
your drink in hand, watching the catches being landed on the
beach in front of you"*; it's always packed – *"with tourists in the
holidays, and locals off-season".* / **Sample dishes:** scallops pan-fried in
garlic; pan-fried monkfish in garlic; treacle tart. **Details:** www.startbayinn.co.uk;
10 pm; no Amex; no smoking area; no booking.

TORQUAY, DEVON   1–3D

No 7 Fish Bistro   £ 35   ★
Beacon Ter TQ1 2BH   (01803) 295055
This family-run bistro is *"as good as ever"*, offering *"consistently
high standards"* of *"freshly-caught fish"*, and also *"friendly"*
service; *"you need to book".* / **Sample dishes:** hot shellfish platter; tempura
special; brandy snap basket topped with amaretti. **Details:** www.no7-fish.com;
9.30 pm; closed Sun & Mon in Winter.

Orestone Manor   £ 48   ★
Rockhouse Ln TQ1 4SX   (01803) 328098
A pleasant country house hotel, overlooking the sea, and tipped
for its *"surprisingly good food".* / **Sample dishes:** crab consommé; roast
lamb; soufflé with loganberry sorbet. **Details:** 9 pm; no smoking.
Accommodation: 12 rooms, from £119.

TREEN, CORNWALL   1–4A

Gurnards Head   £ 29
TR26 3DE   (01736) 796928
*With its spectacular and "lovely" coastal position, this "friendly"
boozer has long been a popular destination; it moved into new
ownership as the survey was drawing to a close, however, so we've
left it unrated until next year.* / **Sample dishes:** Cornish seafood broth;
seared pigeon with bacon & mushrooms; bread & butter pudding.
Details: www.ccinns.com; on coastal road between Land's End & St Ives, near
Zennor B3306; 9.15 pm; no smoking. **Accommodation:** 7 rooms, from £55.

TROON, SOUTH AYRSHIRE   9–4B

Lochgreen House   £ 43
Lochgreen Hs, Monktonhill Rd KA10 7EN   (01292) 313343
*"A good meal is assured", at this Edwardian golf-hotel – as long,
that is, as you can stomach all that tartan.* / **Sample dishes:** scallops
with celeriac & mustard oil; horseradish-crusted lamb with rosemary noodles; hot
chocolate & cherry pudding. **Details:** www.costleyhotels.co.uk; 9 pm; no smoking.
Accommodation: 40 rooms, from £205.

The Oyster Bar   £ 33   𝔸★
The Harbour, Harbour Rd KA10 6DH   (01292) 319339
*"For the freshest of fish, simply cooked to perfection" (plus, of
course, "stunning seafood"), this "welcoming" and "relaxing"
family-run outfit has long been a popular destination.*
/ **Sample dishes:** roast scallops & tomatoes with Prosciutto; baked turbot with
mushrooms, leeks & truffles; lemon Mascarpone with blueberry coulis.
Details: follow signs for Sea Cat Ferry Terminal, past shipyard; 9.30 pm; closed
Mon & Sun D; no Amex.

TROUTBECK, CUMBRIA   7–3D

Queen's Head   £ 26   𝔸★
Townhead LA23 1PW   (01539) 432174
*A "magnificent" Lakeland coaching inn, with a "wonderful menu",
an "attractive" setting and "lively" atmosphere; there's also a
"good selection of locally-brewed beers" and a "fairly priced wine
list", so it's no surprise that it can get "very busy".*
/ **Sample dishes:** wild mushroom, Stilton & black olive terrine; supreme of chicken
with mash; bread & butter pudding. **Details:** www.queensheadhotel.com; A592 on
Kirkstone Pass; 9 pm; no Amex; no smoking area; booking: max 8, Fri & Sat.
Accommodation: 14 rooms, from £75.

TRURO, CORNWALL   1–4B

Idle Rocks Hotel   £ 43   𝔸★
Harbourside TR2 5AN   (01326) 270771
*As the name hints, it's the "great sea view" which is the special
feature of this pretty hotel, but its "good cooking" (and "beautiful
presentation") are also uniformly commended.*
/ **Details:** www.idlerocks.co.uk; 9 pm; no jeans or trainers; no smoking.
Accommodation: 33 rooms, from £130.

TUNBRIDGE WELLS, KENT 3–4B

Hotel du Vin et Bistro £39 A
Crescent Rd TN1 2LY (01892) 526455
The "Gallic bistro fare" has "slightly gone off the boil again", at
this boutique hotel brasserie; the "lovely" setting and the
"excellent" wine list remain. / **Sample dishes:** salt cod brandade with
peppers; chicken with creamed leeks & black pudding; pineapple crème brûlée.
Details: www.hotelduvin.com; 9.45 pm; booking: max 10. **Accommodation:** 36
rooms, from £89.

Sankey's Cellar Bar £32
39 Mount Ephraim TN4 8AA (01892) 511422
A smart little garden is a top attraction at this bar-cum-brasserie,
in the heart of the town; the menu majors in fish and seafood and
its local fan club proclaims "delicious" results.
/ **Sample dishes:** moules marinière; cod & chips; crème brûlée.
Details: www.sankeys.co.uk; A26 on it, almost opposite Kent and Sussex hospital;
9.30 pm; no Amex; no smoking area.

Thackeray's House £50 A★
85 London Rd TN1 1EA (01892) 511921
Richard Phillips's well-known, "classy" venture – occupying a
modern makeover of a period townhouse – is particularly tipped
for "a romantic treat", and rising ratings support those who say
his modern French cuisine is "getting better every year".
/ **Sample dishes:** roast quail salad; grilled tuna with potatoes; banana tarte Tatin.
Details: www.thackerays-restaurant.co.uk; 10 pm; closed Mon & Sun D; no smoking
area.

TUNSTALL, LANCASHIRE 7–4D

Lunesdale Arms £27 A
LA6 2QN (01524) 274203
Emma Gillibrand's "very relaxed" and "reliable" gastropub –
complete with "interesting art on the walls" – maintains its
'destination' status hereabouts. / **Sample dishes:** tomato bruschetta with
pesto; lime & lemongrass chicken with rice; cappuccino mousse.
Details: www.thelunesdale.com; 15 min from J34 on M6 onto A683; 9 pm; closed
Mon; no Amex.

TURNBERRY, SOUTH AYRSHIRE 7–1A

Westin Turnberry Resort £63 A
KA26 9LT (01655) 331000
This grand and famous golfing hotel offers "fantastic views from
the dining room windows"; standards are pretty good across the
board, but it's the "knowledgeable" service and the "extensive"
wine list which attracted particular praise this year.
/ **Sample dishes:** oak-smoked Scottish salmon; seared monkfish with basil polenta;
raspberries & mango. **Details:** www.turnberry.co.uk; A77, 2m after Kirkswald turn
right, then right again after 0.5m; 10 pm; closed Sun L; no smoking.
Accommodation: 221 rooms, from £220.

TURNERS HILL, WEST SUSSEX 3–4B

Alexander House £58 A

East St RH10 4QD (01342) 714914

*Most reports do find the "excellent contemporary cuisine" you might hope for at this grand country house hotel, which is set in extensive grounds; some reporters do feel, however, that prices are excessive. / **Sample dishes:** warm goats cheese ballotine with curry lentils; braised shank of lamb with cream potatoes & ratatouille sauce; glazed coconut custard served on warm macoroon with caramel sauce.*
Details: *www.alexanderhouse.co.uk; off the M23 J10, follow signs to E. Grinstead and Turners Hill, on the B2110; 9 pm; no jeans; no smoking; children: 7+.*
Accommodation: *18 rooms, from £145.*

TYN-Y-GROES, CONWY 4–1D

Groes Inn £32 A

LL32 8TN (01492) 650545

*Characterful décor and a rural location add a certain amount of "wow factor" to a visit to this "reliable" family-run inn (16th-century in origin and "probably the oldest in North Wales"); it serves "good home-cooking". / **Sample dishes:** crispy black pudding, bacon & red onion salad; braised knuckle of lamb; bread & butter pudding.*
Details: *www.groesinn.com; on B5106 between Conwy & Betws-y-coed, 2m from Conwy; 9 pm; no jeans; no smoking area.* ***Accommodation:*** *14 rooms, from £95.*

TYNEMOUTH, TYNE & WEAR 8–2B

Sidney's £27 A★

3-5 Percy Park Rd NE30 4LZ (0191) 257 8500

*"A great little bistro", with "very friendly" service, and offering "a well-priced and varied wine selection"; it's "especially good for lunch". / **Sample dishes:** honey-roast duck with noodles & plum salad; Moroccan-braised lamb with couscous; chocolate-stuffed prune tart.*
Details: *www.sidneys.co.uk; 10 pm; closed Sun; no smoking.*

ULLINGSWICK, HEREFORDSHIRE 2–1B

The Three Crowns Inn £32

HR1 3JQ (01432) 820279

*A welcoming, half-timbered inn which attracts relatively few but unanimously satisfactory reports; "a good-value set lunch" is a highlight. / **Sample dishes:** smoked salmon with cucumber & lovage vinaigrette; rack of lamb with shallots & spinach; chocolate tart.*
Details: *www.threecrownsinn.com; 1.5m from A417; 9.30 pm; closed Mon; no Amex; no smoking area.*

ULLSWATER, CUMBRIA 7–3D

Sharrow Bay £59 A★

CA10 2LZ (01768) 486301

"The most beautifully-located hotel in England" (with "stunning views") is surprisingly "unaltered" in the ownership of Von Essen Hotels; it still offers a "gold standard" (old-style) country house dining experience – combining "copious and tasty" cuisine with "outstanding" service and a "beautifully chosen" wine list.
*/ **Sample dishes:** crab & scallop pancake with crayfish oil; lamb with herb brioche crust & thyme jus; syllabub.* ***Details:*** *www.sharrowbay.co.uk; on Pooley Bridge Rd towards Howtown; 8 pm; jacket & tie required; no smoking; children: 13+.*
Accommodation: *26 rooms, from £320.*

ULVERSTON, CUMBRIA   7–4D

Bay Horse   **£ 40**
Canal Foot LA12 9EL   (01229) 583972
An "interesting" location with "a conservatory overlooking
Morecambe Bay" helps make this ancient coaching inn of more
than usual note; feedback on the cooking improved this year, and
some reporters rated it "very good". / *Sample dishes: chilled tomato &
redcurrant soup; guinea fowl with grape & chestnut stuffing; Irish coffee meringues.*
*Details: www.thebayhorsehotel.co.uk; after Canal Foot sign, turn left & pass Glaxo
factory; 7.30 pm; closed Mon L; no smoking; children: 12+.* **Accommodation:** *9
rooms, from £180.*

UPPER SLAUGHTER, GLOUCESTERSHIRE   2–1C

Lords of the Manor   **£ 75**
GL54 2JD   (01451) 820243
As the survey year was drawing to a close, yet another new chef –
Les Rennie – took over at this "formal but relaxing" country house
hotel, which benefits from a "super situation" in the Cotswolds; in
the circumstances, we've left it unrated. / *Sample dishes: quail ravioli
with morels; roast John Dory with Parma ham & foie gras; pistachio soufflé.*
*Details: www.lordsofthemanor.com; 2m W of Stow on the Wold; 9.30 pm; no jeans
or trainers; no smoking; children: 7+ at D.* **Accommodation:** *27 rooms,
from £160.*

UPPINGHAM, RUTLAND   5–4D

The Lake Isle   **£ 34**
16 High Street East LE15 9PZ   (01572) 822951
"Consistent" standards were more in evidence this year, at this
cosy dining room of a small hotel, near the market square; the
cooking uses "good ingredients" to sometimes "interesting" effect.
/ *Sample dishes: asparagus & Parmesan tart; chicken with tarragon & cranberry
risotto; bread & butter pudding with cherry custard.* **Details:** *www.lakeislehotel.com;
9.30 pm; closed Mon L & Sun D; no smoking.* **Accommodation:** *13 rooms,
from £70.*

USK, MONMOUTHSHIRE   2–2A

Royal Hotel   **£ 26**   𝔸 ★
26 New Market St NP15 1AT   (01291) 672931
"The best food in Monmouthshire"? – that's the claim of fans of
this long-established, "eclectic" pub-cum-restaurant, where "the
best steaks ever" are a leading attraction. / *Details: 9.30 pm; closed
Mon; booking: max 10.*

WADDESDON, BUCKINGHAMSHIRE   3–2A

Five Arrows   **£ 37**
High St HP18 0JE   (01296) 651727
As you'd hope, an "extensive" wine list is a feature of this grand
Rothschild-estate inn (near the family seat, Waddesdon Manor);
even fans, though, can find it "a bit pricey" for what is.
/ *Sample dishes: beetroot & cumin soup; Moroccan lamb stew with cardamom
rice; bourbon mousse with mango & raspberry coulis.*
Details: www.waddesdon.org.uk; on A41; 9.30 pm; no smoking.
Accommodation: *11 rooms, from £85.*

WAKEFIELD, WEST YORKSHIRE 5–1C
Aagrah £22 ★
Barnsley Rd WF1 5NX   (01924) 242222
As so often with outposts of this "excellent chain of Yorkshire Indians", the worst thing anyone can say is that it "can get a little too crowded"; the food, from a "massive" selection, is "fresh and plentiful". / **Details:** www.aagrah.com; from M1, J39 follow Denby Dale Rd to A61; 11.30 pm; D only; no smoking area. **Accommodation:** 13 rooms, from £40.

WAREHAM, DORSET 2–4C
Priory £43 A
Church Grn BH20 4ND   (01929) 551666
At lunch, there are "great views" from the open terrace of this prettily-located and "comfortable" hotel by the River Frome ; the food, however, is "good" at any time. / **Sample dishes:** seared scallops with rhubarb butter; lamb with herb polenta & roast garlic jus; ginger crème brûlée. **Details:** www.theprioryhotel.co.uk; 10 pm; no Amex; no smoking; children: 8+. **Accommodation:** 18 rooms, from £140.

WARHAM ALL SAINTS, NORFOLK 6–3C
Three Horseshoes £20 A
Bridge St NR23 1NL   (01328) 710547
Heading for two decades in the same ownership, this traditional boozer offers "a step back in time"; its cooking is "wholesome" and "generous". / **Sample dishes:** shellfish & cheese bake; Norfolk beef pie; ice cream & sorbet. **Details:** 1m off A148; 8.30 pm; no credit cards; no smoking area; no booking. **Accommodation:** 4 rooms, from £48.

WARWICK, WARWICKSHIRE 5–4C
Saffron £25
Unit 1 Westgate Hs, Market St CV34 4DE   (01926) 402061
"Why is it not in your guide, it's absolutely the best?"; fans of this local Indian concede that "it might look a bit strange, being in a shopping precinct next to Boots", but say it's "much better than many so-called front-runners in Brum". / **Details:** www.saffronwarwick.co.uk.

WATERMILLOCK, CUMBRIA 7–3D
Leeming House Hotel £46 A★
CA11 0JJ   (01768) 486622
"A delightful location" – a 19th-century house with lake and hill views – provides "the ideal venue" for "a relaxing meal in elegant surroundings"; the "well-presented and delicious" food rarely lets it down. / **Sample dishes:** smoked salmon; guinea fowl; chocolate extreme mousse. **Details:** www.macdonald-hotels.co.uk; near A592; 9 pm; jacket required at L, jacket & tie at D; no smoking. **Accommodation:** 41 rooms, from £180.

Rampsbeck Hotel £35 A
CA11 0LP   (01768) 486442
"Grand and tranquil, but not stuffy" – this "beautiful" country house hotel, by Ullswater, has much to commend it; on the food front, though, some reporters continue to find a tendency to "pomposity and over-complication". / **Sample dishes:** baked goat cheese with roast beetroot; roast fillet of beef with veal sweetbread; hot blackberry soufflé with toffee apple ice cream. **Details:** www.hotel-lakedistrict.com; next to Lake Ullswater, J40 on M6, take A592 to Ullswater; 8.30 pm; no Amex; no smoking; children: 8+. **Accommodation:** 19 rooms, from £110.

WATH-IN-NIDDERDALE, NORTH YORKSHIRE 8–4B

Sportsman's Arms £34
HG3 5PP (01423) 711306
*If you like a pretty traditional style (with "well-cooked game" a speciality), Ray Carter's 25-year-old Dales fixture can offer "a beautiful location for a gourmet weekend away"; "the food in the bar is virtually the same as the restaurant". / **Sample dishes:** goats cheese with caramelised red onions; duck with rosti, prunes & oranges; summer pudding. **Details:** www.sportsmans-arms.co.uk; take Wath Road from Pateley Bridge; 9 pm; no Amex; no smoking. **Accommodation:** 11 rooms, from £80.*

WATLINGTON, OXFORDSHIRE 2–2D

Fox And Hounds £32
Christmas Common OX49 5HL (01491) 612599
*New tenants moved in to this "small and cosy" pub shortly before this guide went to press; we hope it will return, fully rated, next year. / **Details:** 9.30 pm; no Amex; no smoking.*

WATTON AT STONE, HERTFORDSHIRE 3–2B

George & Dragon £28
82 High St SG14 3TA (01920) 830285
*This "friendly hostelry in a pretty village" has quite a name locally as a top dining pub; many reporters feel it lives up to its billing, but there are others who fear "the food has deteriorated" in recent times. / **Sample dishes:** potted crab with ginger; fillet steak stuffed with oysters; lemon & passion fruit tart. **Details:** www.georgeanddragon-watton.co.uk; A602 from Stevenage; 10 pm; closed Sun D; no smoking; children: before 9 pm only.*

WEST HALLAM, DERBYSHIRE 5–3C

The Bottle Kiln £17   Ⓐ
High Lane West DE7 6HP (0115) 932 9442
*"Proper home cooking" (including "appealing quiches and salads") makes this "lovely" and "old-fashioned" art gallery annexe an ever-useful stand-by. / **Sample dishes:** tomato and pepper; Stilton and apricot quiche; rum and apple cake. **Details:** L & afternoon tea only; L only, closed Mon; no smoking; no booking; children: not permitted in garden.*

WEST MALLING, KENT 3–3C

Swan £33   ★
35 Swan St ME19 6JU (01732) 521910
*It doesn't induce a huge wave of feedback, but this reasonably-priced gastropub is highly rated by its supporters for its "delicious" cooking and "very good" service. / **Sample dishes:** seared scallops; smoked haddock; chocolate fondue. **Details:** www.theswanwestmalling.co.uk; 10.30 pm; no smoking.*

WEST MERSEA, ESSEX 3–2C

The Company Shed £12   Ⓐ★★
129 Coast Rd CO5 8PA (01206) 382700
*For "smoked and fresh seafood at its best", this small and basic seaside shack is hard to beat; "BYO (bread as well as wine), and come early". / **Sample dishes:** fish platter. **Details:** L only, closed Mon; no credit cards.*

WESTERHAM, KENT   3–3B
Tulsi   £ 25   ★
20 London Rd TN16 1BD   (01959) 563397
"Great food" and (relatively) *"trendy"* décor make this popular
curry-house a *"splendid place to eat"*. / **Details:** 11.30 pm.

WESTFIELD, EAST SUSSEX   3–4C
Wild Mushroom   £ 34
Westfield Ln TN35 4SB   (01424) 751137
*There's nothing remarkable about the style, but "good food"
makes this restaurant in a former boozer a handy stand-by.*
/ **Sample dishes:** red pepper & tomato soup; chicken with mushrooms, capers &
mash; tropical fruit sorbets with jasmine syrup. **Details:** www.wildmushroom.co.uk;
9.30 pm; closed Mon & Sun D; closed 3 weeks in Jan; no smoking; children: 8+ at
D.

WETHERBY, WEST YORKSHIRE   5–1C
La Locanda   £ 30
Wetherby Rd LS22 5AY   (01937) 579797
"Very good for what it is, and always reliable", this *"great family
restaurant"* serves *"authentic"* Italian food (including *"particularly
good"* pizzas); *"get there early"*. / **Sample dishes:** fried calamari with
salad; beef Stroganoff; chocolate fudge cake. **Details:** www.lalocanda.co.uk; 11 pm.

WEYBRIDGE, SURREY   3–3A
Colony   £ 30
3 Balfour Rd KT13 8HE   (01932) 842766
*This "old favourite" of 20 years' standing is "a good, high-class
Chinese, with a touch more elegance than most"; its "good-value"
cooking was more consistently favourably rated by reporters this
year.* / **Sample dishes:** spring rolls & crispy seaweed; sizzling beef; toffee apples.
Details: on A317; 10.30 pm.

WEYMOUTH, DORSET   2–4B
Perry's   £ 35   ★
4 Trinity Rd, The Old Harbour DT4 8TJ   (01305) 785799
"Lots of very fresh fish" are the highlight you'd hope for at this
quayside spot; its *"high-quality and attentive"* service also receives
special praise. / **Sample dishes:** chicken & bacon terrine with apple chutney;
fillet steak with tarragon cream sauce; pear sorbet & brandy snaps.
Details: www.perrysrestaurant.co.uk; 9.30 pm; closed Mon L & Sat L; closed Sun D
in Winter; no smoking area; children: 5+.

WHITBY, NORTH YORKSHIRE   8–3D
Magpie Café   £ 26   ★★
14 Pier Rd YO21 3PU   (01947) 602058
"The best fish 'n' chips in the world" make this unpretentious café
the North East's most talked-about place to eat; *"you'll almost
certainly have to queue, but it's totally worth it"*.
/ **Sample dishes:** grilled tuna with courgette fritters; cod & chips; sticky sultana
loaf. **Details:** www.magpiecafe.co.uk; opp Fish Market; 9 pm; no Amex; no smoking;
no booking at L.

Trenchers £18 ★
New Quay Rd YO21 1DH (01947) 603212
"An excellent posh seaside fish 'n' chip shop"; overall, its scoff may be rated fractionally below its more famous rival, the Magpie, but even reporters averse to queuing say: "the food's definitely worth the wait". / Details: opp railway station, nr marina; 9 pm; no smoking; need 7+ to book.

The White Horse & Griffin £38 A
Church St YO22 4BH (01947) 604857
"A lovely little bistro, tucked away at the back of an hotel"; most – if not quite all – reporters say it's "a real find", offering "good food and wine and an enjoyable all-round experience". / **Sample dishes:** *Caesar salad; char-grilled steak & chips; plum & almond pizza.* **Details:** *www.whitehorseandgriffin.co.uk; centre of old town, on Abbey side of river; 9.30 pm; no Amex; no smoking area.* **Accommodation:** *10 rooms, from £90.*

WHITCHURCH, HAMPSHIRE 2–3D
Red House Inn £33 A★
21 London St RG28 7LH (01256) 895558
"Superb" pub fare ("with a few nice twists") helps distinguish this "friendly and relaxed", ancient inn – now owned by Californian chef Shannon Wells; it has a garden, too, which is "ideal for kids". / **Sample dishes:** *Parmesan-crusted langoustine; fillet steak in bacon with Stilton sauce; lemon tart & strawberry coulis.* **Details:** *9.30 pm; no Amex; no smoking; children: 12+ at D.*

WHITEHAVEN, CUMBRIA 7–3C
Zest £32 ★
Low Rd CA28 9HS (01946) 692848
"Superb food in an unlikely location" is the gist of most reports on this "stark" and "minimalist" brasserie; its new offshoot, Zest Waterside, is a casual, tapas-style operation, already tipped for "a reasonably-priced bite by the pretty harbour". / **Sample dishes:** *chicken liver & whisky cream pâté; spice-coated chicken with curried new potatoes; apple tarte Tatin with green apple sorbet.* **Details:** *9.30 pm; D only, closed Sun-Tue; no Amex; no smoking.*

WHITLEY, WILTSHIRE 2–2B
The Pear Tree Inn £34 A
Top Ln SN12 8QX (01225) 709131
*For its fans, this is simply "a great gastropub in a delightful setting" (and with "excellent wine", too) – for maximum satisfaction, though, the occasional reporter thinks it "best to stick to the simple dishes". / **Sample dishes:** *wild mushroom & tarragon risotto; lamb cutlets with creamed leeks & caper jus; green fig tarte Tatin with panna cotta.* **Details:** *9.30 pm; no Amex; no smoking.* **Accommodation:** *8 rooms, from £90.*

WHITSTABLE, KENT 3–3C
Crab & Winkle £32 ★
South Quay, Whitstable Harbour CT5 1AB
(01227) 779377
"Simple fish cooking" from a "hugely diverse menu" is "well executed" at this straightforward "harbour fish restaurant"; planning permitting, they hope to double in size. / **Sample dishes:** *oysters; baked crab with garlic butter & Cheddar; treacle sponge & custard.* **Details:** *www.crab-winkle.co.uk; 9.45 pm; no Amex.*

Sportsman £ 34 ★
Faversham Rd, Seasalter CT5 4BP (01227) 273370
"Superb" cooking features in most, if not quite all, reports on this
"formerly truly horrible pub", which is now praised for its
"excellent quality and value"; "amazing" seafood is a highlight.
/ **Sample dishes:** marinated salmon; baked cod with cockle sauce; rhubarb sorbet
and burnt cream. **Details:** 8.45 pm; closed Mon & Sun D; no Amex; no smoking
area.

Wheeler's Oyster Bar £ 30 ★★
8 High St CT5 1BQ (01227) 273311
"A quirky delight" – this tiny "gem" at the back of a family-run
Victorian fish shop (the original of what went on to be the chain)
is universally hailed for its "stunning" fish and seafood at
"remarkably good prices"; "remember to book a few days
ahead". / **Sample dishes:** skate ravioli; baked cod with spinach & curried
mussels; date & chocolate sponge. **Details:** 7.30 pm; closed Wed; no credit cards.

Whitstable Oyster Fishery Co. £ 45
Horsebridge CT5 1BU (01227) 276856
A reputation as "a lovely day-trip from London" is the curse of this
"over-publicised" beach-side destination; though generally (rightly)
reputed for fish "of a high standard", the place is "let down by its
high prices", and by "incompetent" and "surly" staff.
/ **Sample dishes:** rock oysters; char-grilled mackerel with roast tomato sauce;
chocolate truffle cake with raspberries. **Details:** www.oysterfishery.co.uk; 9 pm, Sat
10 pm; closed Mon (& Sun D Sep-May). **Accommodation:** 32 rooms, from £55.

WILMINGTON, EAST SUSSEX 3–4B
Giant's Rest £ 27
The Street BN26 5SQ (01323) 870207
"A lovely pub for lunch after a stroll across the Downs" – this
popular inn is no foodie hotspot, but it's a congenial place with a
handy location if you find yourself in this part of the world.
/ **Sample dishes:** avacado & prawns; home-made fish cakes; fruit crumble.
Details: www.giantsrest.co.uk; from A22 at Polegate take A27 towards Lewes, after
2m left at crossroads; 9 pm; no Amex; no smoking; booking: max 12.
Accommodation: 2 rooms, from £50-60.

WILMSLOW, CHESHIRE 5–2B
Chilli Banana
Kings Arms Hotel £ 27
Alderley Rd SK9 1PZ (01625) 539100
The relaxed air of this Thai-behind-a-pub is such as to make it "a
good Sunday lunch venue"; fans say the food is "excellent", too.
/ **Details:** www.chillibanana.co.uk; 11 pm; closed Mon, Tue-Thu D only.

WINCHCOMBE, GLOUCS. 2–1C
5 North Street £ 40 ★
5 North St GL54 5LH
(01242) 604566
Marcus Ashenford's "extremely good" cuisine has won a
formidable reputation for his ambitious, but small and simply-
decorated yearling; reporters were generally more guarded in their
praise this year, though, with "very slow" service a repeated
criticism. / **Sample dishes:** roast scallop with sautéed foie gras & cauliflower
purée; chump of lamb with haggis & baby vegetables; chocolate brownie with vanilla
ice cream & butterscotch sauce. **Details:** 9 pm; closed Mon, Tue L & Sun D;
no smoking.

Wesley House £42 A★
High St GL54 5LJ (01242) 602366
A "beautiful" half-timbered inn, where the "friendly" staff, "relaxing" setting and "superb" food can combine to make for a "memorable" meal. / **Sample dishes:** red snapper terrine with saffron potatoes; seared duck with pickled apples & Calvados cream; iced toffee & pistachio parfait. **Details:** www.wesleyhouse.co.uk; next to Sudeley Castle; 9 pm; closed Sun D; no smoking. **Accommodation:** 5 rooms, from £140.

WINCHELSEA, EAST SUSSEX 3–4C

Queen's Head £23 ★
Parsonage Ln TN36 4BL (01424) 814552
Praise abounds for this "lovely olde worlde country pub", where "the great food matches the setting on the edge of the Downs" (and there's "a fab beer garden", too). / **Details:** www.queenshead.com; 9.45 pm; no Amex; no smoking.

WINCHESTER, HAMPSHIRE 2–3D

Chestnut Horse £36 ★
Easton Village SO21 1EG (01962) 779257
First-timers proclaim this pretty and upmarket boozer "a real find" – a "very friendly" place, where the food can be "excellent". / **Sample dishes:** fresh crab; rack of lamb; sticky toffee pudding. **Details:** 9.30 pm; no Amex; no smoking; children: 14+.

Hotel du Vin et Bistro £41 A★
14 Southgate St SO23 9EF (01962) 841414
The original member of the now-national boutique-hotel chain is "still the best" according to reporters, combining "refreshing modern cooking" with an "extensive and reasonably-priced wine list" in a "classy", but relaxed setting. / **Sample dishes:** moules marinière; salmon pavé with mussel ragoût; lime panna cotta with melon. **Details:** www.hotelduvin.com; 9.45 pm; no smoking; booking: max 10. **Accommodation:** 23 rooms, from £109.

Old Chesil Rectory £52
1 Chesil St SO23 0HU (01962) 851555
The year which saw the sale of this once-exemplary venture in an historic Tudor building has seen very mixed reviews – a definitive rating for the new régime will unfortunately have to wait until the next edition. / **Sample dishes:** twice-baked Roquefort soufflé; duck with parsnip purée & lime vanilla sauce; melon sorbet with ginger shortbread. **Details:** 8.45 pm; closed Mon & Sun; no smoking area.

Wykeham Arms £34 A
75 Kingsgate St SO23 9PE (01962) 853834
This "bustling" boozer – "beautifully located" by the College (and with old desks for tables) – is often hailed as "one of the nicest pubs in the country"; for "traditional food and surroundings" – and an "interesting" wine list, too – it's hard to beat. / **Sample dishes:** mushroom, walnut & Stilton pâté; roast monkfish with red onion & cherry tomato salad; orange & maple cheesecake. **Details:** between Cathedral and College; 8.45 pm; closed Sun D; no smoking area; booking: max 8; children: 14+. **Accommodation:** 14 rooms, from £90.

WINCHMORE HILL, BUCKINGHAMSHIRE 3–2A

Plough £29 A★

The Hill HP7 0PA (01494) 721001

A "surprising" gastropub near Amersham, which wins enthusiastic reviews for its "gourmet" cooking and stylish setting.
/ **Sample dishes:** risotto of Cornish crab; roasted pork with foie gras; pineapple rice pudding. **Details:** www.theploughrestaurant.com; 10 pm; no smoking area.

WINDERMERE, CUMBRIA 7–3D

Gilpin Lodge £55 A★

Crook Rd LA23 3NE (01539) 488818

"Beautifully situated", this Edwardian house offers a "pampering" experience that combines "marvellous" service with "consistently high-quality cuisine". / **Sample dishes:** smoked haddock pavé; roast lamb with truffled potato & garlic sauce; Greek yoghurt sorbet. **Details:** www.gilpinlodge.com; 9.15 pm; no smoking; children: 7+. **Accommodation:** 14 rooms, from £220.

Holbeck Ghyll £58 A★★

Holbeck Ln LA23 1LU (01539) 432375

"It's surprising just how excellent David McLaughlin's food is" ("well up with the Ramsays of the world"), at this "very superior" but "relaxed" Lakeland hotel; it enjoys an "idyllic" setting, in a "beautiful" former hunting lodge, with "wonderful views" of Windermere. / **Sample dishes:** veal ravioli with morels; salmon with tomato fondue; pear & praline parfait. **Details:** www.holbeckghyll.com; 3m N of Windermere, towards Troutbeck; 9.30 pm; no smoking; children: 8+. **Accommodation:** 20 rooms, from £190.

Jerichos £40 ★

Birch St LA23 1EG (01539) 442522

"Very good" (if occasionally "over-complicated") cooking makes this "reliable" and "consistent" town-centre spot worth seeking out; the wine list is "intelligent", too, and "not overpriced".
/ **Sample dishes:** smoked haddock, spring onion & Cheddar risotto; pork tenderloin with roast parsnips & Madeira jus; butterscotch toffee crème brûlée. **Details:** 9.30 pm; D only, closed Mon; no Amex; no smoking; children: 12+.

Samling £60 ★★

Ambleside Rd LA23 1LR (015394) 31922

The style of this "secluded" and "sophisticated" hillside hotel overlooking Windermere – Wordsworth woz 'ere – can sometimes seem just a touch "pretentious", but almost all reporters find its cooking nothing short of "superb".
/ **Details:** www.thesamling.com; 9.30 pm. **Accommodation:** 11 rooms, from £175.

WINDSOR, WINDSOR & MAIDENHEAD 3–3A

Al Fassia £26 ★

27 St Leonards Rd SL4 3BP (01753) 855370

This "friendly" and "excellent" Moroccan wins rave reviews from those who report on it; the only problem is that it's now "the worst-kept secret in town" – "booking's difficult, even during the week". / **Sample dishes:** chicken & almond filo parcels; lamb stew with sweet prunes; Moroccan desserts. **Details:** 10.30 pm, Fri & Sat 11 pm; closed Sun; no smoking area.

Pophams £34 A★

Castle St EX19 8HQ (01837)s83767

It may only rarely be open – and have only ten seats when it is! – but this 'one-off' of 20 years' standing offers "a complete dining experience", including "great" cooking and "very friendly" service. /s**Sampledishes:**sbaked goats cheese with spicy chutney; lamb in puff pastry with mushroom pâté; orange tart with apricot sauce. **Details:**soff A377 between Exeters& Barnstaple; open only Thus& FrisL; closed Feb; noscredit cards; nossmoking; children: 16+.

WINTERINGHAM, N LINCS 5–1D

Winteringham Fields £72 A★★

DN15 9PF (01724)s733096

Annie and Germain Schwab's "absolutely amazing" 16th-century manor house retreat vies closely for reporters' top-rated experience in the UK; thankfully, new head chef Robert Thompson's "brilliant" and "original" cuisine is fully a match for his boss's, and the service manages to be both "slick" and "friendly". /s**Samplesdishes:**span-fried langoustines; veal with wild mushroomss& veal jus; chocolates& macadamia nut mousse.
Details:swww.winteringhamfields.com; 4m SW of Humber Bridge; 9.30spm; closed Mons& Sun; nossmoking; booking: maxs8. **Accommodation:**s10 rooms, froms£115.

WITHERSLACK, CUMBRIA 7–4D

Old Vicarage £42 A★

Church Ln LA11 6RS (01539)s552381

This country house hotel only inspires modest commentary, but, as per usual, it's to the effect that it's a "friendly" and "intimate" destination, with "great food and atmosphere". /s**Samplesdishes:**soyster tempura with horseradish cream; seared smoked venison with sweet potato purée; star anise syrup sponge. **Details:**swww.oldvicarage.com; from M6, J36 follow signs to Barrow on A590; 9spm; Dsonly, except Sun open Ls& D; noscredit cards; nossmoking.

WOBURN, BEDFORDSHIRE 3–2A

Market Place £32 A

19 Market Pl MK17 9PZ (01525)s290877

"Stylish" and "buzzy", this "California-style" eatery offers a "quirky menu focused on fresh and organic produce" – a pleasant surprise in sleepy old Woburn. /s**Samplesdishes:**sasparagus tempura; organic beef fillet topped with mushrooms; Marco's classic cheesecake with mangos& passion fruit. **Details:**swww.marketplacewoburn.co.uk; 9.30spm; closed Mons& SunsD; nosAmex; nossmoking.

WOLVERHAMPTON, WEST MIDLANDS 5–4B

Bilash £36 ★

2 Cheapside WV1 1TU (01902)s427762

"Our local Indian will never seem the same again", bemoans a visiting Surrey reporter, who was impressed by the "fascinating" (if not particularly cheap) cuisine at Sitab Khan's "friendly" town-centre Bangladeshi. /s**Details:**swww.bilash-tandoori.co.uk; opp Civic Centre; 11spm; closed Sun; nossmoking.

WOODBRIDGE, SUFFOLK   3–1D
Captain's Table   £27
3 Quay St IP12 1BX   (01394)s383145
This popular local destination (where fish is, in fact, no particular speciality) wins praise as a "pleasant" and "reliable" spot; it gets "crowded", though, and service can be "amateurish". /s**Samplesdishes:**twice-baked spinach soufflé; slow-roast duck with red wine sauce; hot toffee pudding. **Details:**www.captainstable.co.uk; 100 yds from theatre; 9.30spm, Fris& Sat 10spm; closed Mons& SunsD; closed 2 weeks in Jan; nosAmex; nossmoking.

Riverside   £33   A★
Quayside IP12 1BH   (01394)s382587
With its "nice and quiet, but stylish location, on the edge of the water", this interesting restaurant and theatre venture is noted for its "simple" but "excellent" dishes, often from local organic ingredients. /s**Details:**www.theriverside.co.uk; 9.15spm, Sat 10spm; closed SunsD; nossmoking.

Seckford Hall Hotel   £31   A★
IP13 6NU   (01394)s385678
If you're in search of "a haven of olde worlde peace" – at a reasonable price – this "lovely" Elizabethan house in Constable Country (run by the Bunn family for over 50 years) has much to commend it, not least some "well-presented" modern cooking. /s**Samplesdishes:**salmon roulade; monkfish with pastas& wilted greens; champagne mousse with strawberries. **Details:**www.seckford.co.uk; 9.30spm; closed MonsL; nossmoking; children: 6+ after 7spm. **Accommodation:**s32 rooms, froms£140.

WOODSTOCK, OXFORDSHIRE   2–1D
The Feathers Hotel   £49   A
Market St OX20 1SX   (01993)s812291
This "lovely" and "historic"-feeling venue (converted from a run of townhouses) is praised by most reporters for offering a "great" overall experience; doubters say: "the premium prices have more to do with the setting than the food". /s**Samplesdishes:**confit chicken with fig marmalade; lemon sole with rocket soufflé; nougat glacé with mangos& chocolate sauce. **Details:**www.feathers.co.uk; 8m N of Oxford on A44; 9.15spm; nosjeans or trainers; nossmoking. **Accommodation:**s20 rooms, froms£135.

WORCESTER, WORCESTERSHIRE   2–1B
Angel Chef   £17
Angel Mall, Angel St WR1 3QT   (01905)s731131
"For streetwise cool types" – in Worcester? – locals tip this "exciting" new buffet-oriental, and laud food "of surprisingly good quality". /s**Details:**s11spm; nosAmex.

Brown's   £49   A★
24 Quay St WR1 2JJ   (01905)s26263
"A former pump house, with lovely views" provides the "great setting" for this ultra-consistent riversider (which has no relation to the crummy national chain); Garry Phipps's cooking is "delicious" and "well presented". /s**Samplesdishes:**devilled lambs kidneys with polenta; roast duck with minted pea mousseline; bitter chocolate ice cream. **Details:**near the Cathedral on riverside; 9.45spm; closed Mon, SatsLs& SunsD; nosAmex; nossmoking; children: 8+.

WREXHAM, WREXHAM   5–3A

Pant Yr Ochan   £ 27   Ⓐ
Old Wrexham Rd LL12 8TY   (01978)s853525
"About the closest thing to a gastropub on the North Wales border", this former farmhouse has the particular benefit of a "lovely setting, by a lake" – it is "a wonderful place to eat alfresco on a sunny day". /s**Samplesdishes:**smushroom ravioli; red breams& olive potatoes with asparagus; apple tart with cider custard.
Details:www.brunningandprice.co.uk; 1m N of Wrexham; 9.30spm; nossmoking area; booking: maxs14; children: before 6spm only.

WRIGHTINGTON BAR, LANCASHIRE   5–1A

High Moor   £ 35   Ⓐ
8 High Moor Ln WN6 9PS   (01257)s252364
"Lovely views across the Lancashire Plain" married with "good food and service" make this restaurant in a 17th-century building very popular locally. /s**Details:**s9.30spm; closed Mon; nossmoking.

Mulberry Tree   £ 37
9 Wrightington Bar WN6 9SE   (01257)s451400
"Just off the M6", this "busy" and rather "cavernous" former boozer – where you can eat in the restaurant, or the cheaper bar – certainly makes a very "useful" stop-off; dishes come in "large portions" and – despite the ex-Gavroche chef – "are not too high-brow". /s**Samplesdishes:**speas& ham soup with Parmesan croutons; baked cod with cheeses& basil crust; rice pudding with apricots. **Details:**s2m along Mossy Lea Rd, off M6, J27; 9.30spm; nosAmex; nossmoking; children: 15+.

WYTHAM, OXFORDSHIRE   2–2D

White Hart   £ 34   Ⓐ
OX2 8QA   (01865)s244372
"Excellent" (if possibly "slightly fussy") pub food and a "divine" garden are making this recently revamped boozer a very popular destination for Oxford folk. /s**Details:**s10spm; nosAmex; nossmoking area.

YARM, CLEVELAND   8–3C

D P Chadwicks   £ 35
104b High St TS15 9AU   (01642)s788558
"Still the best in the area" – "good" and "consistent" standards, help revamp this modern brasserie (specialising in "delicious pizza and pasta") is "always busy". /s**Samplesdishes:**sCatalan seafood salad; calves livers& bacon with onion rings; baked cherry cheesecake.
Details:swww.chadwicksrestaurant.com; just after Yarm Bridge; 9.30spm; closed Mons& Sun; nosAmex; nossmoking area; booking: maxs12.

McCoys in Yarm   £ 34
44 High St TS15 9AE   (01642)s791234
The McCoys, of Tontine fame, are behind this "all-day venue" ("above a small department store"), which goes upmarket at night; the food is somewhere between "not bad" and "well prepared". /s**Samplesdishes:**sssmoked haddock fishcake with French bean salad, poached eggs& hollandaise; braised lamb shank with Spanish black pudding, roast tomatoess& wet polenta; Eton mess. **Details:**swww.mccoysinyarm.co.uk; 9.30spm; closed Sun; nossmoking at L.

YARMOUTH, ISLE OF WIGHT   2–4D
George Hotel   £ 45   ★
Quay St PO41 0PE   (01983)s760331
*"Wonderful food, either in the brasserie (nicest in summer) or in
the plush restaurant" – that's the theme of almost all
commentary on the "best place to eat on the island" (even if its
cuisine can seem a touch "complicated" for some tastes).*
/s**Samplesdishes:**strio of duck starters; braised pork with Morteau sausages&
parsnip purée; rum baba with Earl Grey syrup. **Details:**swww.thegeorge.co.uk;
10spm; Dsonly, closed Mons& Sun; nosAmex; children: 12+ in restaurant.
Accommodation:s17 rooms, froms£175.

YATTENDON, BERKSHIRE   2–2D
Royal Oak Hotel   £ 39
The Square RG18 0UG   (01635)s201325
*It's still early-ish days, but the survey gives cause to hope that this
grand and "attractive" inn – once quite a well-known destination
– is returning to form under its new (private) owners.*
/s**Samplesdishes:**slobster ravioli on seasoned spinach; roast lamb with celeriac
gratin; praline soufflé. **Details:**swww.royaloakyattendon.com; 5m W of Pangbourne,
off B4009; 10spm; nossmoking; children: 6+. **Accommodation:**s5 rooms,
froms£130.

YORK, CITY OF YORK   5–1D
Abbey Inn   £ 33   Ⓐ
Byland Abbey YO61 4BD   (01347)s868204
*"Very atmospheric, especially at night when Byland Abbey is
floodlit", this "pleasant" gastropub benefits from a "beautiful"
setting – the "hearty" food can seem a touch "ordinary" by
comparison.* /s**Details:**swww.bylandabbeyinn.co.uk; 9spm; closed MonsLs&
SunsD; nosAmex; nossmoking area. **Accommodation:**s3 rooms, froms£95.

Bettys   £ 28
6-8 St Helen's Sq YO1 8QP   (01904)s659142
*"Increasingly a far-too-pricey tourist-trap" – reporters have a
growing feeling that this famous tea-room (once Taylor's) is
becoming "a place to be seen, not to enjoy good food"; if you
must go, breakfast is best.* /s**Samplesdishes:**sSwiss rosti with bacons&
cheese; Yorkshire rarebit with apple chutney; Yorkshire curd tart.
Details:swww.bettysandtaylors.com; down Blake St from York Minster; 9spm;
nosAmex; nossmoking; nosbooking

Blue Bicycle   £ 40
34 Fossgate YO1 9TA   (01904)s673990
*Reports are still relatively thin on the ground, but they suggest
that the new (Anthony Stephenson) régime at this once-celebrated
bistro is "both better and more consistent than the old".*
/s**Samplesdishes:**sspicy salmon hash with lime salsa; Aberdeen Angus beef with
green bean stir-fry; passion fruits& Campari rice pudding.
Details:swww.thebluebicycle.com; 9.30spm; nosAmex; nossmoking; booking: maxs8.
Accommodation:s1 room, at abouts£150.

Café Concerto   £ 32   Ⓐ★
21 High Petergate YO1 7EN   (01904)s610478
*"There's always a queue, but when you do get a table it's worth
the wait" – this "reliable" and "good-value" café/bistro, near the
Minster, inspires general satisfaction.* /s**Samplesdishes:**sgrilled halloumi
with pomegranate molasses; pork chops with root vegetable mash; Irish coffee jelly
withsamaretti biscuits. **Details:**swww.cafeconcerto.biz; by the W entrance of York
Minster; 9.30spm, Fris& Sat 10spm; nosAmex; nossmoking; nosbooking at L.

City Screen Café Bar £ 22 A★
Coney St YO1 9QL (01904)s541144
This cinema-café with "beautiful views" over the River Ouse does what it does very well – "loads of small-bite meals", served "quickly and cheaply". /s**Samplesdishes:**sParma hams& Mozzarella salad; smoked salmons& scrambled eggs; lemon cheesecake. **Details:**swww.picturehouses.co.uk; 9spm; nosAmex; nossmoking area; nosbooking; children: before 7spm only.

Masons Bistro £ 36
13 Fossgate YO1 9TA (01904)s611919
"Modern but rustic" bistro consistently praised for its "sound, if not spectacular" Mediterranean fare. /s**Samplesdishes:**svine leaves stuffed with feta, spinach, and pine leaves; pan-fried red snapper; cherry and kirsh clafoutis. **Details:**s9.15spm; closed MonsDs& SunsD; nossmoking; booking: maxs8.

Melton's £ 38 ★
7 Scarcroft Rd YO23 1ND (01904)s634341
"In the unlikely surroundings of a terrace house", just outside the city walls, this "unprepossessing" café/bistro remains the most popular place in town, thanks to its "interesting" food and "well-chosen" wine, and its "well meaning" approach generally. /s**Samplesdishes:**sJerusalem artichoke soup; braised oxtail with chervil mash; apple crêpes with cider sorbet. **Details:**swww.meltonsrestaurant.co.uk; 10 mins walk from Castle Museum; 10spm; closed MonsLs& Sun; nosAmex; nossmoking area.

Melton's Too £ 26 X
25 Walmgate YO1 9TX (01904)s629222
"Disappointing, given its parentage" – this "popular" and "buzzy" bistro-style café undoubtedly "has potential", but food that's too often "dull" can "let it down". /s**Samplesdishes:**spork rillettes with Cumberland sauce; Merguez sausage with couscouss& lemon oil; Yorkshire curd tart. **Details:**www.meltonstoo.co.uk; 10.30spm; nosAmex; nossmoking.

Middlethorpe Hall £ 45
Bishopthorpe Rd YO23 2GB (01904)s641241
The "beautiful building and gardens" are the highlight at this country house hotel, in a 200-acre estate on the fringe of the city; the cooking is "good", but plays something of a supporting role. /s**Samplesdishes:**ssoxtail terrine with horseradish cream; pike fillet with Bayonne ham; aniseed parfait with roast pears. **Details:**swww.middlethorpe.com; next to racecourse; 9.45spm; nosAmex; jacket required; nossmoking; children: 8+. **Accommodation:**s29 rooms, froms£165.

Rish £ 44 X
7 Fossgate YO1 9TA (01904)s622688
"They are trying hard, but even with an ex-Winteringham Fields chef, and charging £20 for a main course, it still doesn't quite hit the mark" – there is a marked feeling among reporters that this Edwardian shop-conversion has "prices and pretensions well above what it delivers". /s**Samplesdishes:**sbeetroot-scented gravadlax; roast lamb with olive mashs& salsify; pear Bakewell tart with Calvados sorbet. **Details:**swww.rish-york.co.uk; 10spm; nossmoking.

Tasting Room £ 34
13 Swinegate Court East YO1 8AJ (01904)s627879
Off a small courtyard in the centre of town, this new venture wins a consistent thumbs-up from locals for its "good" contemporary cooking; it must be doing something right, as it's already expanding. /s**Samplesdishes:**sYorkshire blue cheese tart; rump of lamb with thyme potatoes; citrus posset with gooseberries. **Details:**swww.thetastingroom.co.uk; 9.30spm; closed MonsDs& SunsD; nosAmex; nossmoking.

sign up for the survey at www.hardens.com

UK MAPS

10

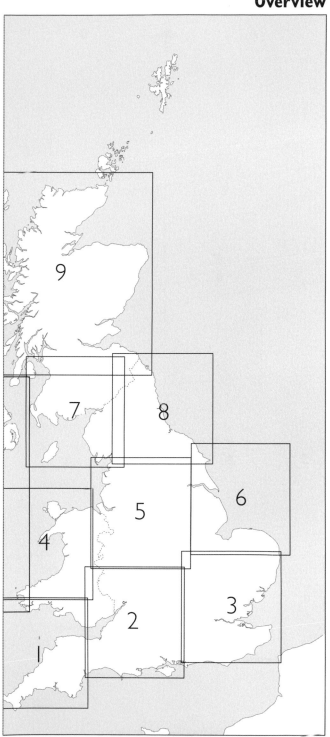

Map 1

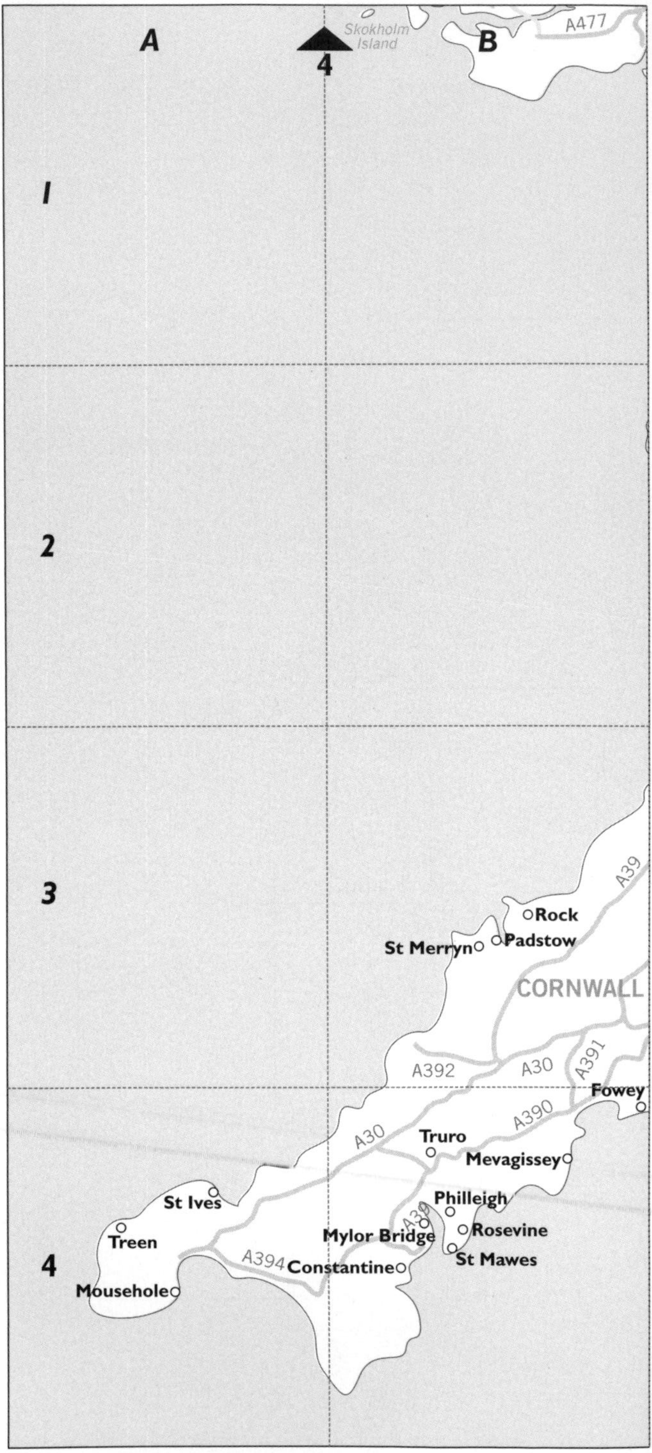

A   Skokholm Island   B   A477

4

1

2

3

○Rock

St Merryn○ ○Padstow

CORNWALL

A39

A392   A30   A391

A30   A390   **Fowey**○

Truro○

Mevagissey○

St Ives○

Treen○   **Philleigh**○

A3○ **Rosevine**○

Mylor Bridge○

A394   **Constantine**○   **St Mawes**

4

Mousehole○

Map 1

Map 2

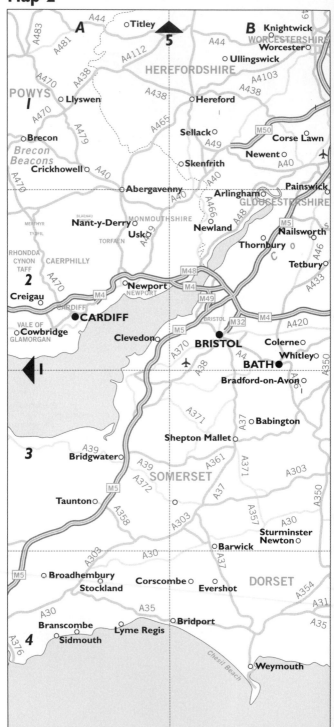

Map 2

Map 3

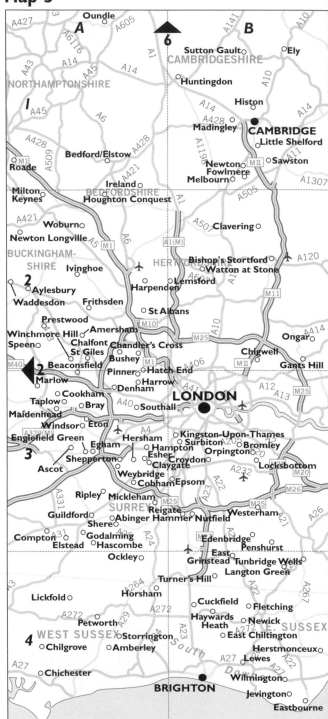

A **B**

Oundle

6

Sutton Gault○ ○ Ely

CAMBRIDGESHIRE

○ Huntingdon

Histon

NORTHAMPTONSHIRE

1

A428
Madingley ○ **CAMBRIDGE** ●
○ Little Shelford

Bedford/Elstow

Roade ○

Newton ○ ○ Sawston
Fowlmere
Melbourn

Milton
Keynes
Ireland ○ **BEDFORDSHIRE**
Houghton Conquest

Woburn ○
Newton Longville ○
Clavering ○

**BUCKINGHAM-
SHIRE**
Ivinghoe ○ **HERTFORDSHIRE**
Bishop's Stortford ○
Watton at Stone ○

2
○ Aylesbury
Lemsford ○
Waddesdon ○
Harpenden ○

Prestwood ○
○ St Albans
Winchmore Hill ○ Amersham
Speen ○ Chalfont Chandler's Cross
St Giles
Ongar ○

Chigwell ○

Beaconsfield ○ Bushey
2
Pinner ○ ○ Hatch End
Gants Hill
Marlow
Harrow ○
Taplow ○ Cookham ○
Denham ○ **LONDON** ●
Maidenhead ○ Bray
Southall ○
Windsor ○ Eton ○

Engglefield Green ○
Hersham ○
Kingston-Upon-Thames ○
3
Egham ○ Hampton ○ Surbiton ○ Bromley ○
Shepperton ○ Esher ○ Croydon ○ Orpington ○
Ascot ○ Claygate ○
Locksbottom ○
Weybridge ○
Cobham ○ Epsom ○

Ripley ○ Mickleham ○

Guildford ○ **SURREY**
Reigate ○ Westerham ○
Shere ○ Abinger Hammer ○ Nutfield ○

Compton ○ Godalming ○
Edenbridge ○ Penshurst ○
Elstead ○ Hascombe ○
Ockley ○ East
Grinstead ○ Tunbridge Wells ○
Langton Green ○

Turner's Hill ○

Lickfold ○
Horsham ○

Cuckfield ○ ○ Fletching
A272
Haywards ○ Newick ○
Petworth ○ Heath **E. SUSSEX**
4 **WEST SUSSEX** Storrington ○ ○ East Chiltington
○ Chilgrove ○ Amberley
Herstmonceux ○
Lewes ○
○ Chichester Wilmington ○
BRIGHTON ●
Jevington ○
Eastbourne ○

Map 3

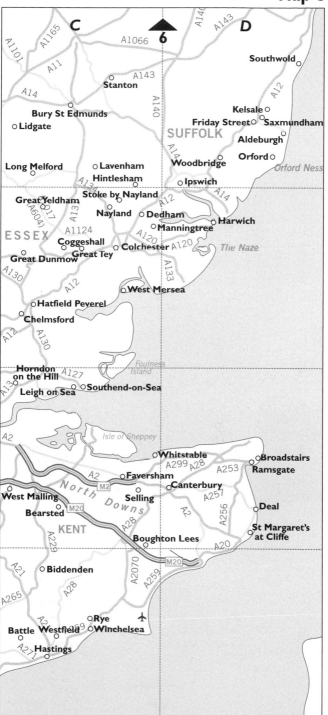

Map 4

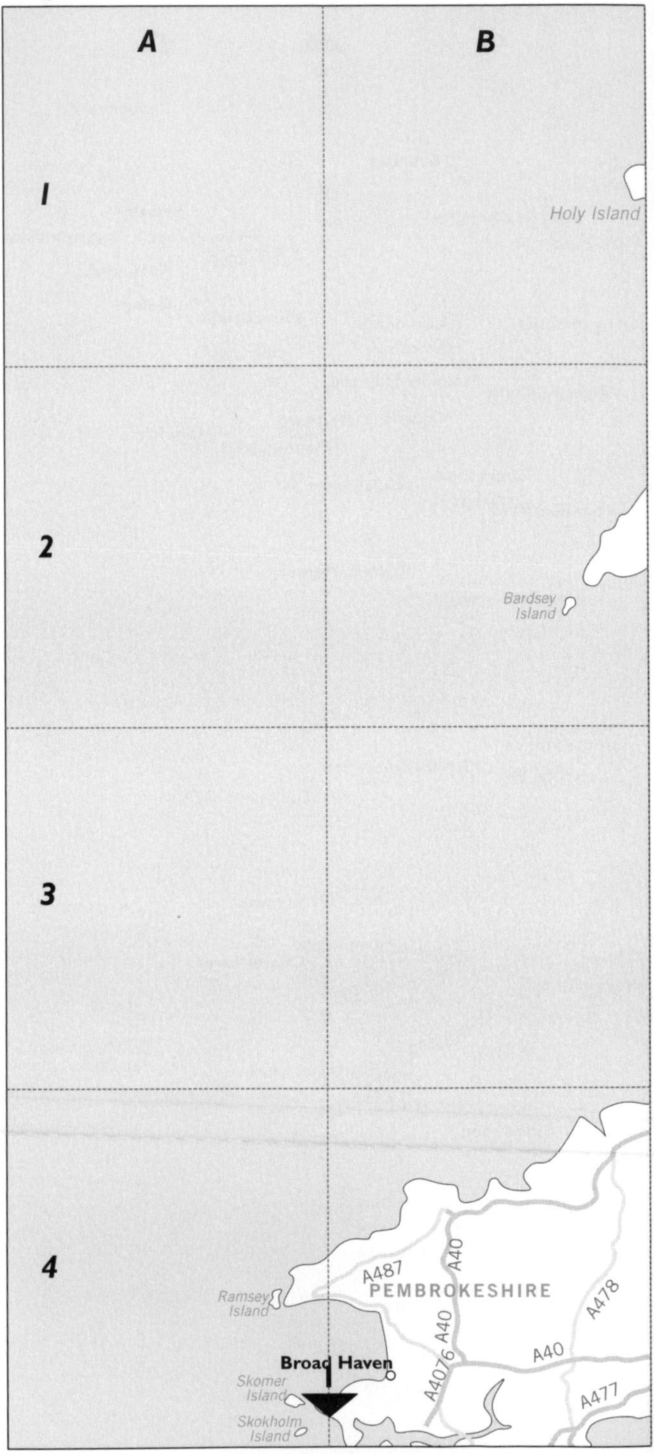

	A	B
1		Holy Island
2		Bardsey Island
3		
4	Ramsey Island / Skomer Island / Skokholm Island	A487 A40 PEMBROKESHIRE A4076 A40 A478 A40 A477 Broad Haven

Map 4

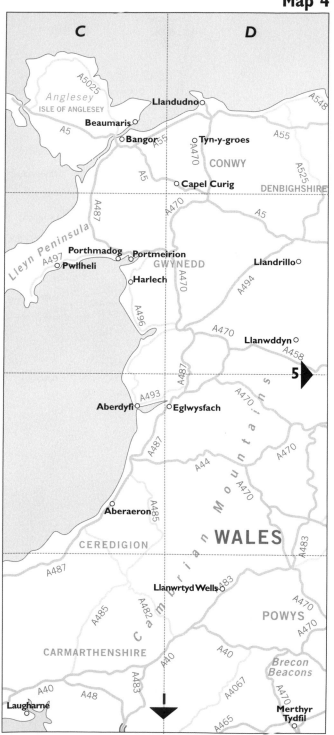

C

D

A5025

Anglesey
ISLE OF ANGLESEY

A5

Llandudno ○

A548

Beaumaris ○

A55

A470

Tyn-y-groes ○

A55

Bangor ○

A5

CONWY

A525

DENBIGHSHIRE

Capel Curig ○

A5

A487

A470

Lleyn Peninsula

A497

Porthmadog ○ **Portmeirion** ○

GWYNEDD

A494

Llandrillo ○

○ **Pwllheli**

Harlech ○

A470

A496

A470

Llanwddyn ○

A458

5 ▶

A487

A493

Aberdyfi ○ **Eglwysfach** ○

A470

Cambrian Mountains

A470

A487

A44

A470

A485

WALES

Aberaeron ○

A483

CEREDIGION

A487

Llanwrtyd Wells ○ A483

A470

POWYS

A485

A482

A470

A483

▼

Brecon Beacons

CARMARTHENSHIRE

A40

A40

A470

A40

A48

A483

A4067

A470

Laugharne ○

A4065

Merthyr Tydfil ○

Map 5

A

B

Lancaster

Hetton

LANCASHIRE

Sawley

Clitheroe

Cowling

1 Blackpool

Longridge

Langho

Kirkham

Lytham

Preston

Todmorden

Southport

Bispham Green

Ramsbottom

Cheesden

Wrightington Bar

Lydgate

MANCHESTER

LIVERPOOL

2 Hoylake

Mellor

Wilmslow

Nether Alderley

Parkgate

Knutsford

Prestbury

FLINTSHIRE

CHESHIRE

Chester

Great Barrow

Tarporley

Cotebrook

4 Astbury

Aldford

Crewe

Llandegla

Wrexham

WREXHAM

3 Llangollen

Oswestry

STAFFORDSHIRE

Shrewsbury

SHROPSHIRE

Norton

Wolverhampton

4 Stourbridge

Clent

Leintwardine

Holy Cross

Ludlow

Cleobury Mortimer

Chaddesley Corbett

Presteigne

2 Brimfield

Map 5

C   **8**   **D**

A59
A166
A19
Harrogate
York
EAST RIDING
OF YORKSHIRE
A59
A65 Burley in
Ilkley Wharfedale
Wetherby
Boston Spa
Otley
A58
A61
Tadcaster
A19
Escrick
A163
Saltaire
Shipley
Haworth
Aberford
Lund
A63
A614
Bradford
LEEDS
A1
Sowerby
Bridge
M621
WEST YORKSHIRE
M62
Halifax
Elland
A63
M62
Huddersfield
Wakefield
Winteringham
Golcar
Grange Moor
M18
A62
A61
Shelley
M1
SOUTH
M180
M181
A628
A629
YORKSHIRE
A616
A1(M)
A159
Bawtry
A57
Sheffield
A57
A631
A156
A6
Peak
M1
A1
A57
District
A619
Hassop
Baslow
A60
A614
Bakewell
A619
DERBYSHIRE
A53
A515
Caunton
A617
6
Birchover
NOTTINGHAM-
A6
SHIRE
Newark-
on-Trent
A17
Ashbourne
A38
A46
A1
A52
Hazlewood
A52
West Hallam
A52
NOTTINGHAM
Great
Gonerby
A50
Derby
A52
A516
A6
Plumtree
Langar
Stathern
A518
Colston Bassett
A606
A607
Melbourne
A515
A444
A38
Nether Broughton
Loughborough
A46
A607
RUTLAND
A50
M42
Oakham
LEICESTERSHIRE
Hambleton
Leicester
Uppingham
A47
M6
Sutton Coldfield
M69
Thorpe Langton
A6003
WEST
M1
Kibworth Beaucham
BIRMINGHAM
A5
Market Harborough
A427
MIDLANDS
M42
A45
A4304
A14
A508
A43
Solihull
Coventry
Hockley
Lapworth
M6
Heath
Kenilworth
NORTHAMPTONSHIRE
M42
M40
2
Henley-in-Arden Warwick
A46
Royal Leamington Spa
A45
Preston Bagot
Bishops Tachbrook

Map 6

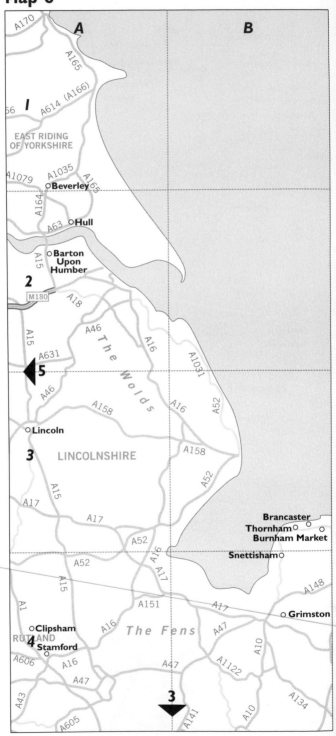

Map 6

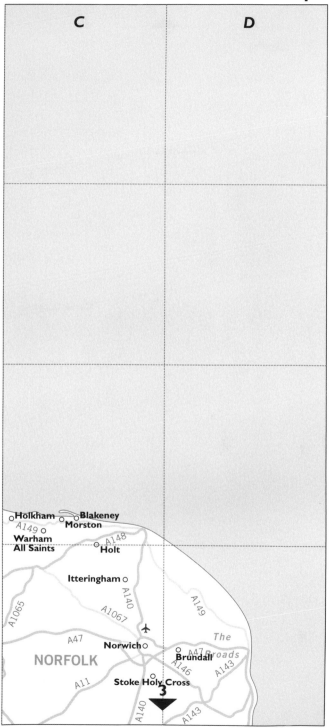

Map 7

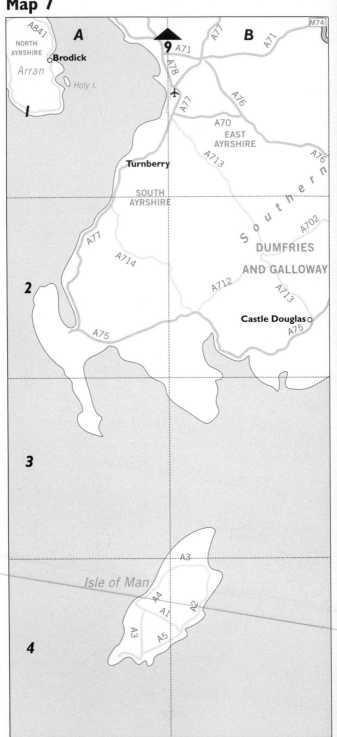

A841
A
NORTH
AYRSHIRE
○**Brodick**
Arran
Holy I.
M74
9 A71
B
A77
A71
A78
A77
A76
A70
EAST
AYRSHIRE
A76
Turnberry
A713
SOUTH
AYRSHIRE
Southern
A702
A77
DUMFRIES
A714
AND GALLOWAY
A712
A713
Castle Douglas○
A75
A75
A3
Isle of Man
A4
A2
A1
A3
A5

Map 7

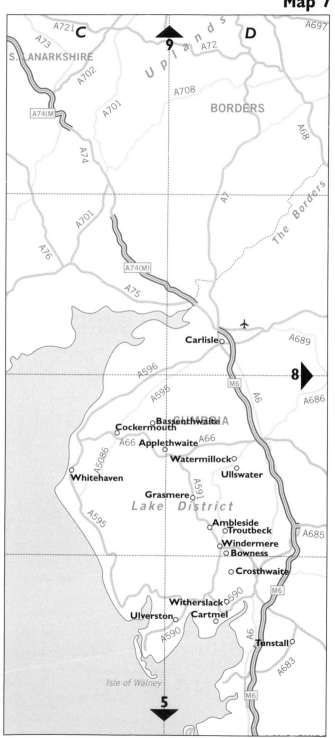

C

9

D

A721

A73

A697

A72

S. LANARKSHIRE

A702

Uplands

A708

BORDERS

A74(M)

A701

A701

A68

A74

The Borders

A7

A76

A74(M)

A75

✈

Carlisle

A689

A596

8▶

A596

M6

A6

A686

Bassenthwaite

CUMBRIA

Cockermouth

Applethwaite

A66

A66

A5086

Watermillock

Ullswater

Whitehaven

A591

Grasmere

Lake District

A595

Ambleside
Troutbeck

A685

Windermere
Bowness

Crosthwaite

M6

Witherslack

A590

Ulverston

Cartmel

Tunstall

A590

A6

A683

Isle of Walney

M6

5

Map 8

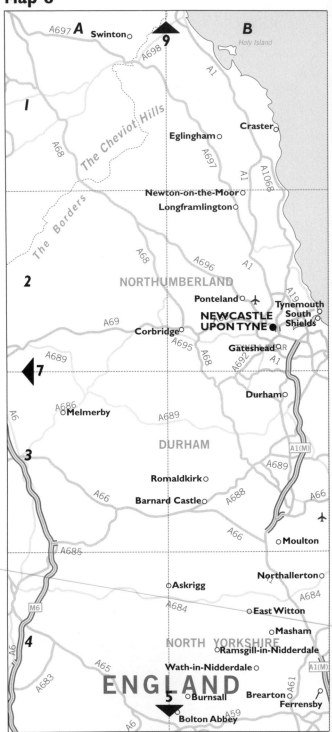

A697 **A** Swinton○

A698 **9**

B *Holy Island*

I *The Cheviot Hills*

A68

A1

Eglingham○ **Craster**○

A697

The Borders

A1 A1068

Newton-on-the-Moor○

Longframlington○

A68 A696 A1

2 **NORTHUMBERLAND**

Ponteland○ ✈ **Tynemouth**

A19 **South Shields**

A69 **NEWCASTLE**

Corbridge○ **UPON TYNE**●

A695 A68 **Gateshead**○ OR

A692 A1

7 A689

A1(M)

A686 A689

○**Melmerby**

A6

3 **DURHAM**

Romaldkirk○

A66 Barnard Castle○ A688 A66

A689

A66 ○**Moulton** ✈

A685 **Northallerton**○

A1

M6 ○**Askrigg** A684

A684 ○**East Witton**

○**Masham**

A6 **4** **NORTH YORKSHIRE**

A61 A1(M)

○Ramsgill-in-Nidderdale

A683 A65 Wath-in-Nidderdale○

ENGLAND

A6 **5** ○Burnsall **Brearton**○

A59 **Ferrensby**

Bolton Abbey

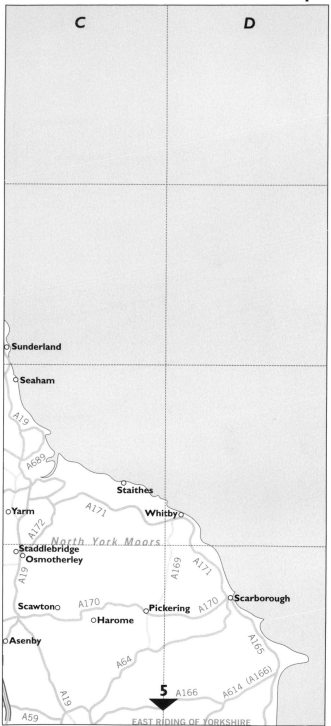

Map 8

C

D

Sunderland

Seaham

A19

A689

Staithes

Yarm

A171

Whitby

A172

North York Moors

Staddlebridge

Osmotherley

A169

A171

A19

Scawton

A170

A170

Scarborough

Pickering

Harome

A165

Asenby

A64

A614 (A166)

5 A166

A19

A59

EAST RIDING OF YORKSHIRE

Map 9

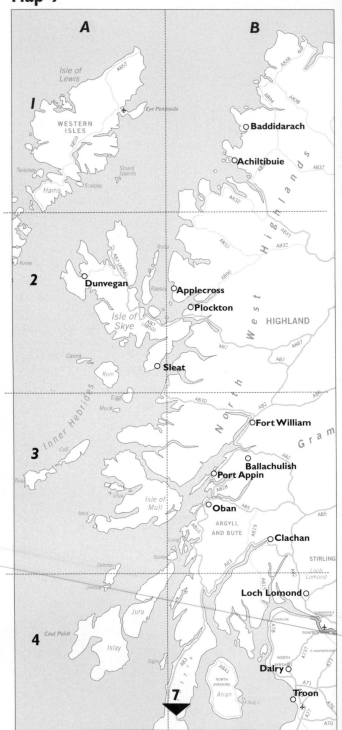

A

B

I

Isle of Lewis

A857

WESTERN
ISLES

Eye Peninsula

A859

Taransay

Shiant
Islands

Harris

Scalpay

○ **Baddidarach**

○ **Achiltibuie**

A837

A838

A835

A832

A890

HIGHLAND

N
o
r
t
h

W
e
s
t

Highlands

2

Ronay

○ **Dunvegan**

A87 (A850)

Rona

Raasay

○ **Applecross**

○ **Plockton**

Isle of
Skye

A87
(A850)

A87

A87

A87

Canna

Rum

○ **Sleat**

Eigg

Muck

A830

A82

A887

3

Inner Hebrides

Coll

Tiree

Iona

Ulva

Isle of
Mull

N
o
r
t
h

W
e
s
t

○ **Fort William**

A82

○ **Ballachulish**

○ **Port Appin**

A828

○ **Oban**

A85

○ **Clachan**

A819

ARGYLL
AND BUTE

G r a m

A85

STIRLING

Loch
Lomond

4

Coul Point

Colonsay

Oronsay

Islay

Jura

Scarba

A816

A83

Gigha

A815

Loch Lomond ○

DUMBARTON &
CLYDEBANK

INVERCLYDE

RENFREW AIRPORT

A78

NORTH
AYRSHIRE

7

A841

NORTH
AYRSHIRE

Arran

Holy I.

Dalry ○

A737

A71

Troon ○

A76

A77

A70

Map 9

C

D

Island of Stroma

MORAY

ABERDEENSHIRE

Monadhliath
Mountains

Kingussie Cairngorm Mountains

Ballater

Aberdeen

Stonehaven

pian   Mountains

Killiecrankie

PERTH
AND KINROSS

ANGUS

Blairgowrie

Dunkeld

Kinclaven

Perth

SCOTLAND

Auchterarder

St Andrews

Balquhidder

Cupar

Anstruther

St Monans

FIFE

Gullane

FALKIRK

EDINBURGH

Linlithgow

East Linton

W. LOTHIAN

E. LOTHIAN

GLASGOW

MIDLOTHIAN

Lammermuir Hills

Holy Island

S. LANARKSHIRE

Upland

7

BORDERS

Cheviot Hills

Map 10

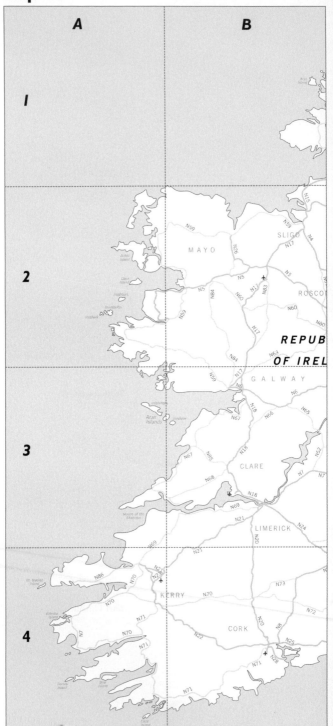

	A	B
I		
2		
3		
4		

MAYO

SLIGO

ROSCO

REPUB
OF IREL

GALWAY

CLARE

LIMERICK

KERRY

CORK

Aran
Islands

Mouth of the Shannon

N59
N59
N4
N26
N17
N5
N5
N83
N84
N60
N17
N60
N60
N59
N63
N84
N59
N17
N6
N6
N18
N65
N67
N66
N67
N85
N18
N52
N68
N7
N7
N69
N18
N21
N24
N20
N69
N21
N21
N86
N70
N21
N22
N70
N73
N70
N71
N20
N8
N72
N7
N70
N22
N25
N71
N71
N71

Map 10

ALPHABETICAL INDEX

NOTES

NOTES